Student Solutions Manual

to Accompany

Statistics for Management and Economics

NINTH EDITION

© 2012 Cengage Learning. All Rights Reserved. May not be scanned, copied or duplicated, or posted to a publicly accessible website, in whole or in part.

Student Solutions Manual

to Accompany

Statistics for Management and Economics

Ninth Edition

Gerald Keller
Wilfrid Laurier University

Australia • Brazil • Japan • Korea • Mexico • Singapore • Spain • United Kingdom • United States

© 2012 Cengage Learning. All Rights Reserved. May not be scanned, copied or duplicated, or posted to a publicly accessible website, in whole or in part.

© 2012, 2009 South-Western, Cengage Learning

ALL RIGHTS RESERVED. No part of this work covered by the copyright herein may be reproduced, transmitted, stored, or used in any form or by any means graphic, electronic, or mechanical, including but not limited to photocopying, recording, scanning, digitizing, taping, Web distribution, information networks, or information storage and retrieval systems, except as permitted under Section 107 or 108 of the 1976 United States Copyright Act, without the prior written permission of the publisher except as may be permitted by the license terms below.

For product information and technology assistance, contact us at **Cengage Learning Academic Resource Center, 1-800-423-0563**.

For permission to use material from this text or product, submit all requests online at **www.cengage.com/permissions**. Further permissions questions can be emailed to **permissionrequest@cengage.com**.

ISBN-13: 978-1-111-53188-1
ISBN-10: 1-111-53188-9

South-Western Cengage Learning
5191 Natorp Boulevard
Mason, OH 45040
USA

Cengage Learning is a leading provider of customized learning solutions with office locations around the globe, including Singapore, the United Kingdom, Australia, Mexico, Brazil, and Japan. Locate your local office at: **international.cengage.com/region**.

Cengage Learning products are represented in Canada by Nelson Education, Ltd.

For your course and learning solutions, visit **www.cengage.com**.

Purchase any of our products at your local college store or at our preferred online store **www.CengageBrain.com**.

Printed in the United States of America
1 2 3 4 5 6 7 16 15 14 13 12

© 2012 Cengage Learning. All Rights Reserved. May not be scanned, copied or duplicated, or posted to a publicly accessible website, in whole or in part.

TABLE OF CONTENTS

© 2012 Cengage Learning. All Rights Reserved. May not be scanned, copied or duplicated, or posted to a publicly accessible website, in whole or in part.

How the Solutions Were Produced

All answers have been-double-checked for accuracy. However, we cannot be absolutely certain that there are no errors. When and if we discover mistakes we will post corrected answers on our web page. (See page 8 in the textbook for the address.) If you find any errors, please email the author (address on web page). We will be happy to acknowledge you with the discovery.

Chapter 2
Excel was employed to draw the histograms, bar charts, pie charts, line charts, and scatter diagrams.

Chapter 4
Excel was used to draw box plots and compute the descriptive statistics for exercises with data sets.

Chapters 6 through 9

Probabilities were computed manually. Probability trees were used where possible.

Chapters 10 through 19 and 21

Calculations for exercises that provided statistics either in the exercise itself or in Appendix A were completed manually. The solutions to exercises requiring the use of a computer were produced using Excel. Confidence interval estimates used critical values obtained from the tables in Appendix B. In some cases we were required to use approximations. As a consequence some confidence interval estimates will differ slightly from those produced by computer. In tests of hypothesis where the sampling distribution is normal, p-values were computed manually using Table 3. Excel was employed to calculate the p-value for all other tests.

© 2012 Cengage Learning. All Rights Reserved. May not be scanned, copied or duplicated, or posted to a publicly accessible website, in whole or in part.

Chapters 13, and Appendixes 13 to 17, and 19

We employed the F-test of two variances at the 5% significance level to decide which one of the equal-variances or unequal-variances t-test and estimator of the difference between two means to use to solve the problem. Additionally, for exercises that compare two populations and are accompanied by data files, our answers were derived by defining the sample from population 1 as the data stored in the first column (often column A in Excel and column 1 in Minitab). The data stored in the second column represent the sample from population 2. Paired differences were defined as the difference between the variable in the first column minus the variable in the second column.

Chapter 19 and Appendix 19

In the exercises whose datasets contained interval data we used a nonparametric technique after examining the relevant histograms and subjectively judging the variable to be "extremely nonnormal."

Chapters 17 and 18

Excel produced all the solutions to these exercises.

Chapter 20

Most solutions were produced manually. Excel solved the more time-consuming exercises.

Chapter 21

All control charts were produced by Excel.

Chapter 22

Solutions to these exercises were completed manually.

© 2012 Cengage Learning. All Rights Reserved. May not be scanned, copied or duplicated, or posted to a publicly accessible website, in whole or in part.

Chapter 1

1.2 Descriptive statistics summarizes a set of data. Inferential statistics makes inferences about populations from samples.

1.4a The complete production run

b 1000 chips

c Proportion of the production run that is defective

d Proportion of sample chips that are defective (7.5%)

e Parameter

f Statistic

g Because the sample proportion is less than 10%, we can conclude that the claim is true.

1.6a Flip the coin 100 times and count the number of heads and tails

b Outcomes of flips

c Outcomes of the 100 flips

d Proportion of heads

e Proportion of heads in the 100 flips

1.8a The population consists of the fuel mileage of all the taxis in the fleet.

b The owner would like to know the mean mileage.

c The sample consists of the 50 observations.

d The statistic the owner would use is the mean of the 50 observations.

e The statistic would be used to estimate the parameter from which the owner can calculate total costs. We computed the sample mean to be 19.8 mpg.

© 2012 Cengage Learning. All Rights Reserved. May not be scanned, copied or duplicated, or posted to a publicly accessible website, in whole or in part.

Chapter 2

2.2 a Interval

b Interval

c Nominal

d Ordinal

2.4 a Nominal

b Interval

c Nominal

d Interval

e Ordinal

2.6 a Interval

b Interval

c Nominal

d Ordinal

e Interval

2.8 a Interval

b Ordinal

c Nominal

d Ordinal

2.10 a Ordinal

b Ordinal

c Ordinal

© 2012 Cengage Learning. All Rights Reserved. May not be scanned, copied or duplicated, or posted to a publicly accessible website, in whole or in part.

2.12

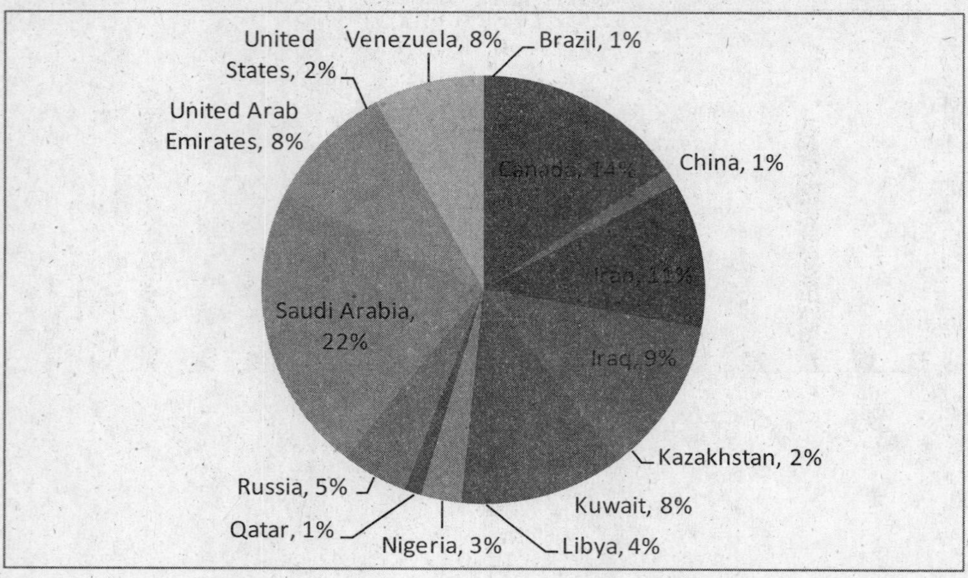

2.14

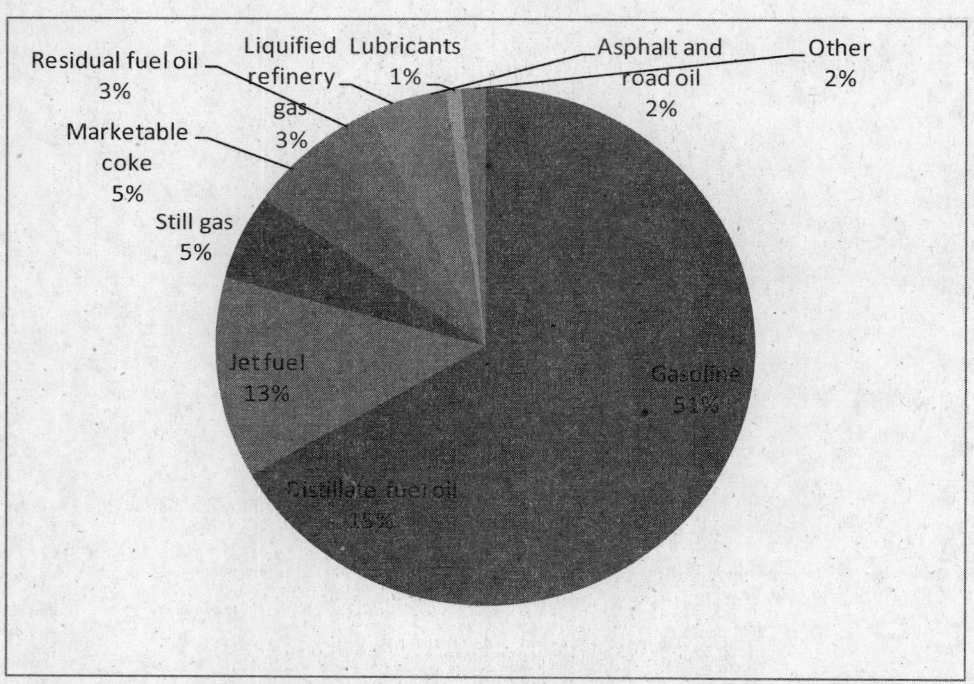

© 2012 Cengage Learning. All Rights Reserved. May not be scanned, copied or duplicated, or posted to a publicly accessible website, in whole or in part.

2.16

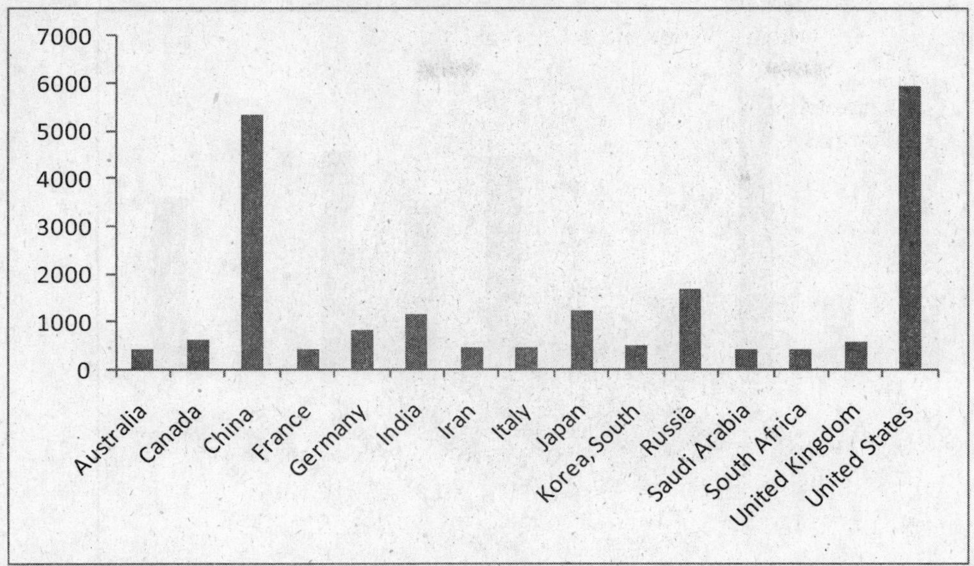

2.18

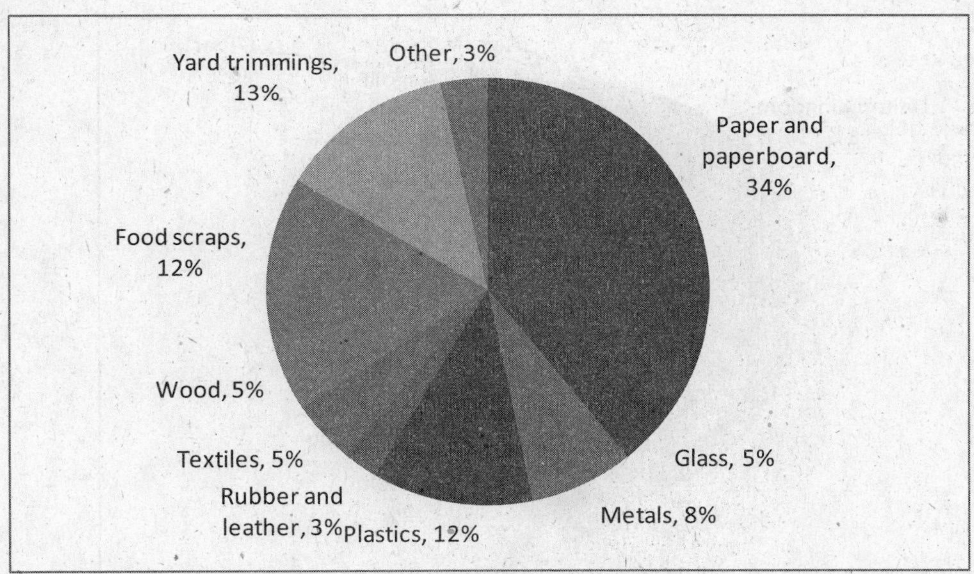

© 2012 Cengage Learning. All Rights Reserved. May not be scanned, copied or duplicated, or posted to a publicly accessible website, in whole or in part.

2.20 a.

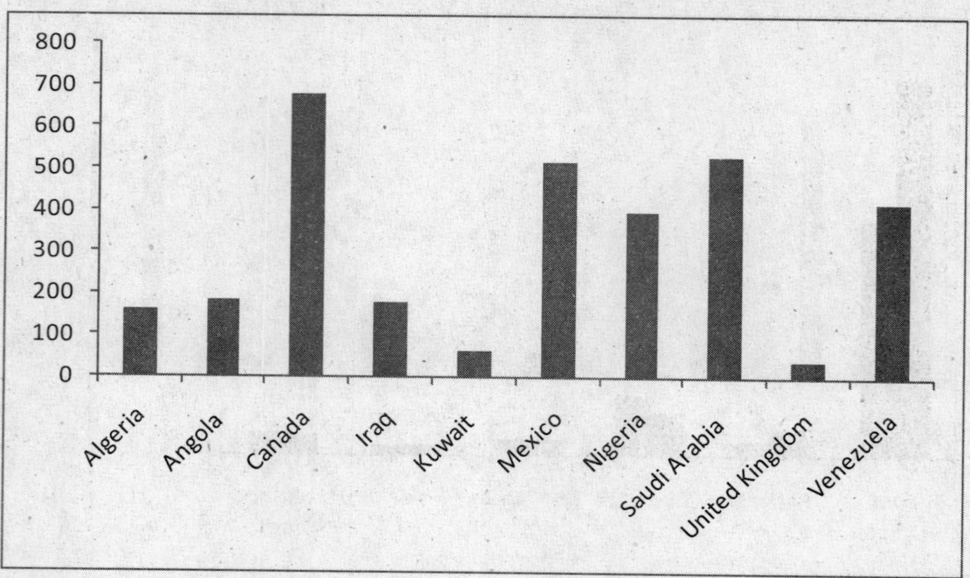

b.

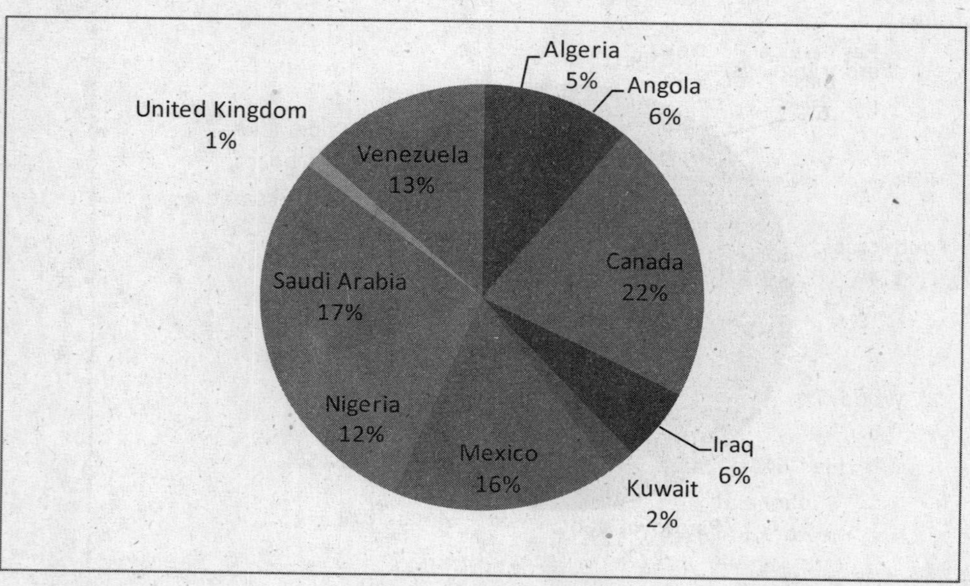

The bar chart provides the frequencies and the pie chart displays the relative frequencies.

© 2012 Cengage Learning. All Rights Reserved. May not be scanned, copied or duplicated, or posted to a publicly accessible website, in whole or in part.

2.22

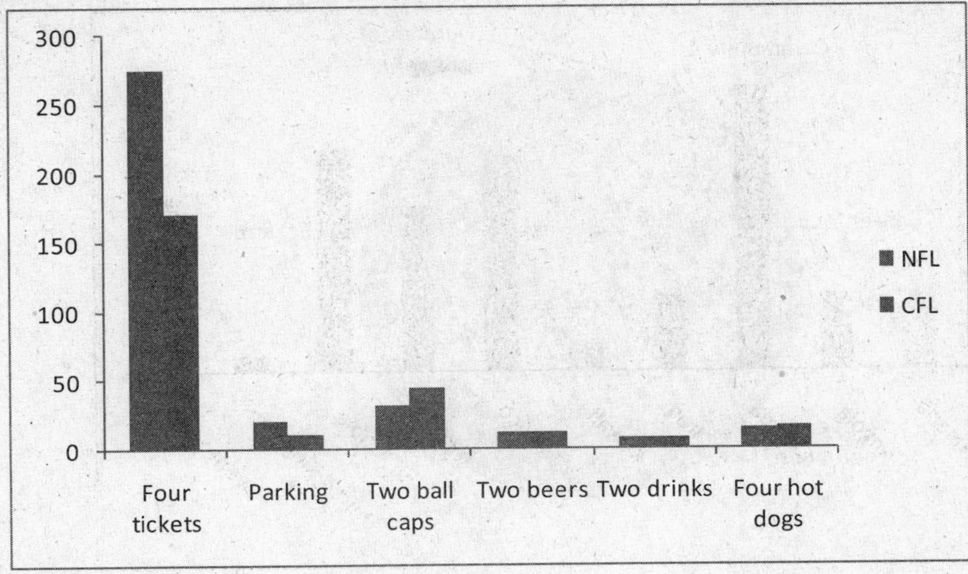

2.24

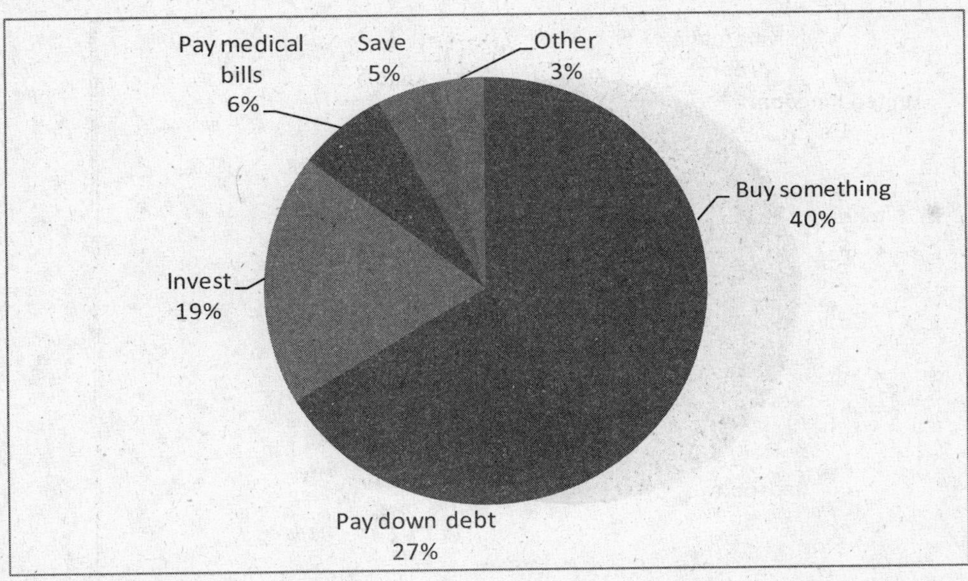

© 2012 Cengage Learning. All Rights Reserved. May not be scanned, copied or duplicated, or posted to a publicly accessible website, in whole or in part.

2.26

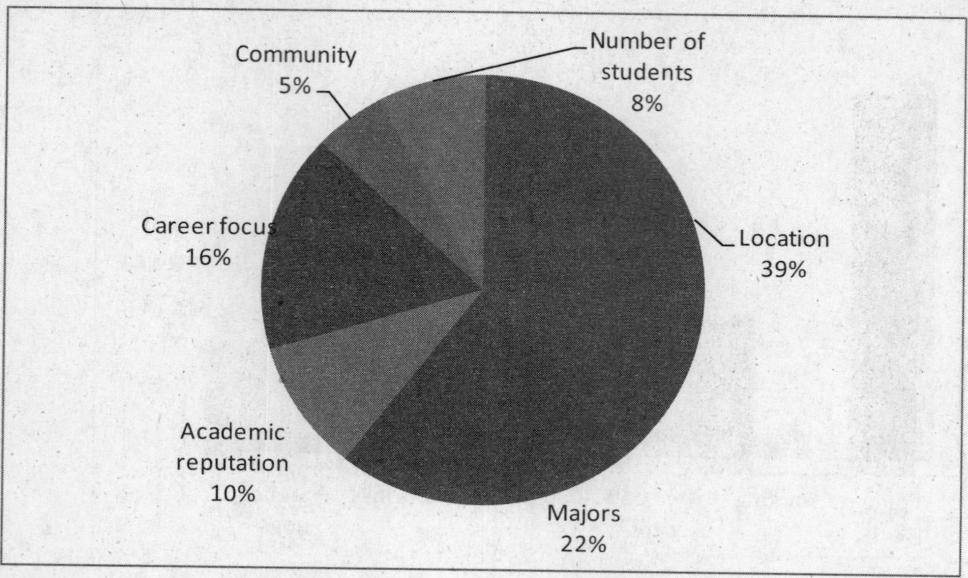

2.28

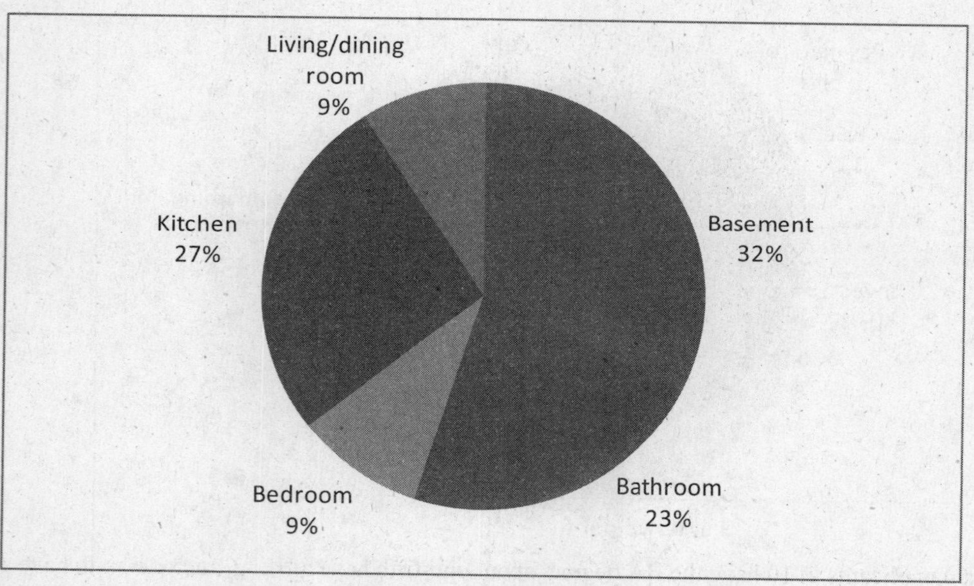

2.30a

Degree	Frequency
BA	88
BBA	37
B Eng	51
B Sc	24
Other	30

© 2012 Cengage Learning. All Rights Reserved. May not be scanned, copied or duplicated, or posted to a publicly accessible website, in whole or in part.

b.

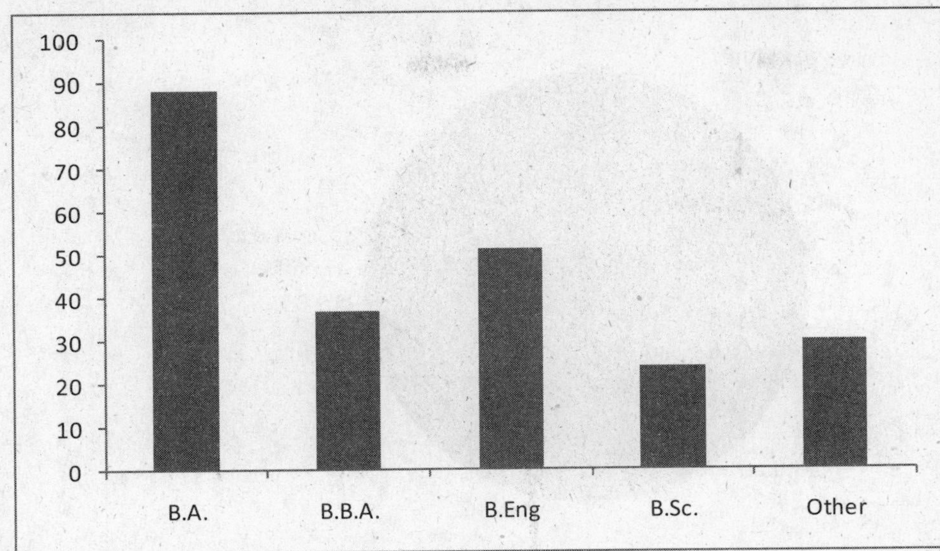

c

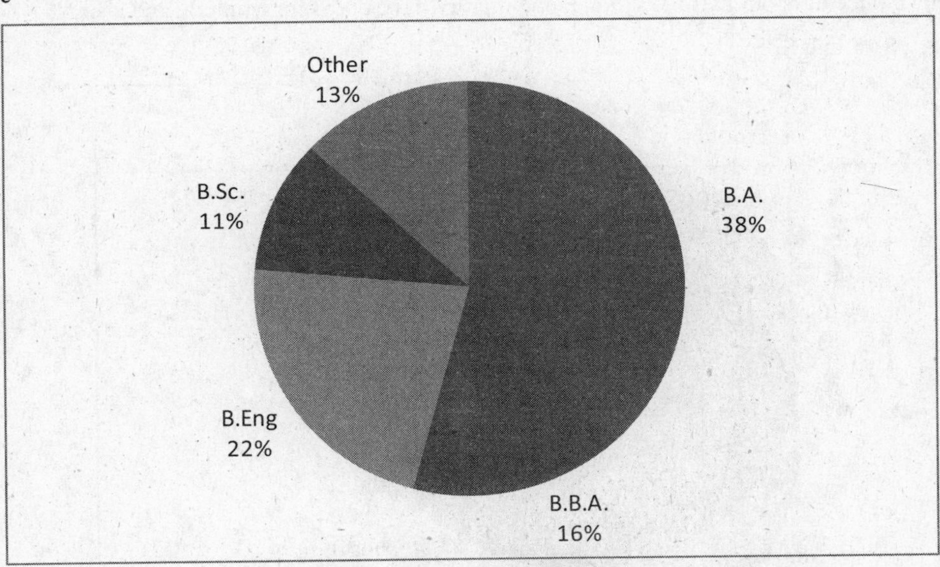

d. About 4 applicants in 10 have the BA degree, about one-fifth have a BEng. and one-sixth have a BBA.

2.32 a

Software	Frequency
Excel	34
Minitab	17
SAS	3
SPSS	4
Other	12

© 2012 Cengage Learning. All Rights Reserved. May not be scanned, copied or duplicated, or posted to a publicly accessible website, in whole or in part.

b

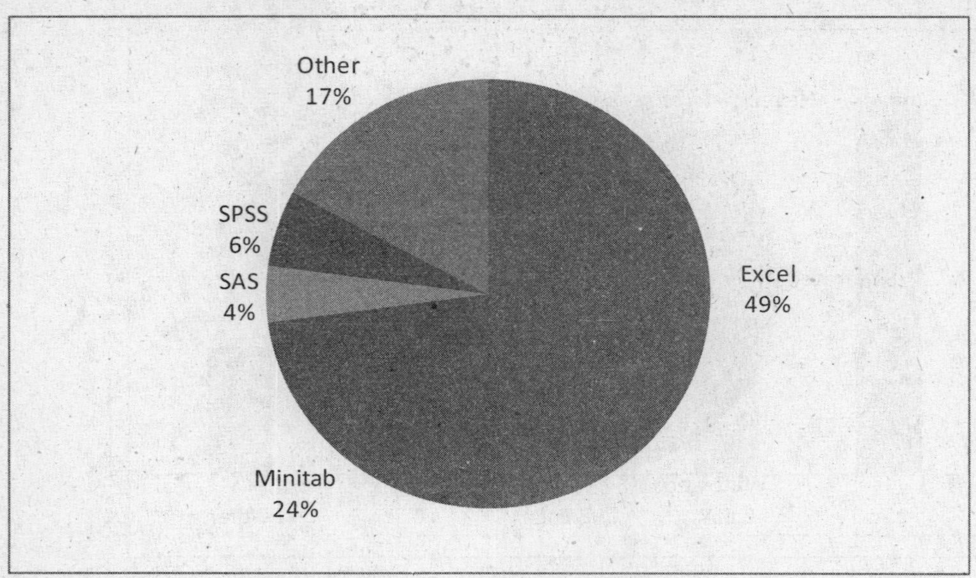

c Excel is the choice of about half the sample, one-quarter have opted for Minitab, and a small fraction chose SAS and SPSS.

2.34

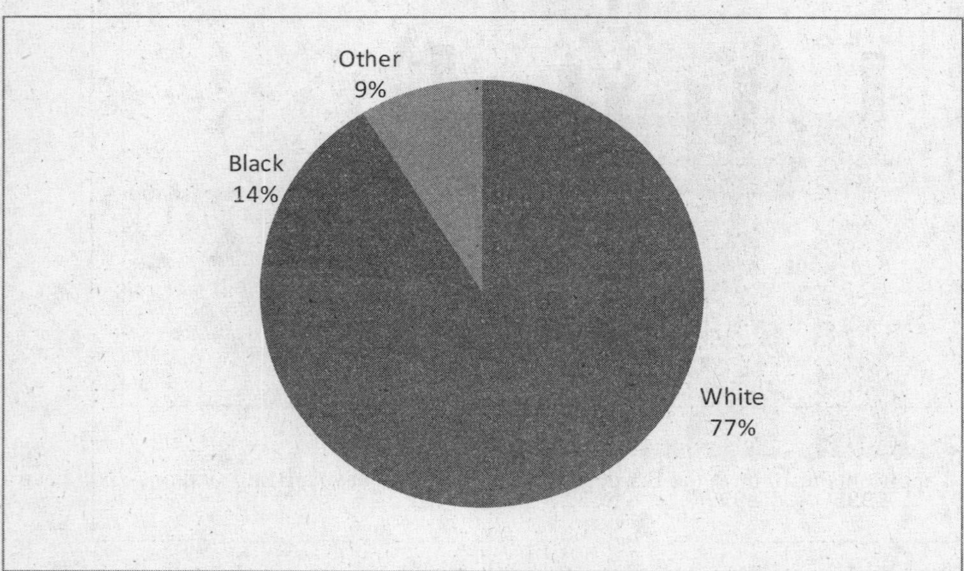

Three out of four Americans are White. Note that the survey did not separate Hispanics.

© 2012 Cengage Learning. All Rights Reserved. May not be scanned, copied or duplicated, or posted to a publicly accessible website, in whole or in part.

2.36

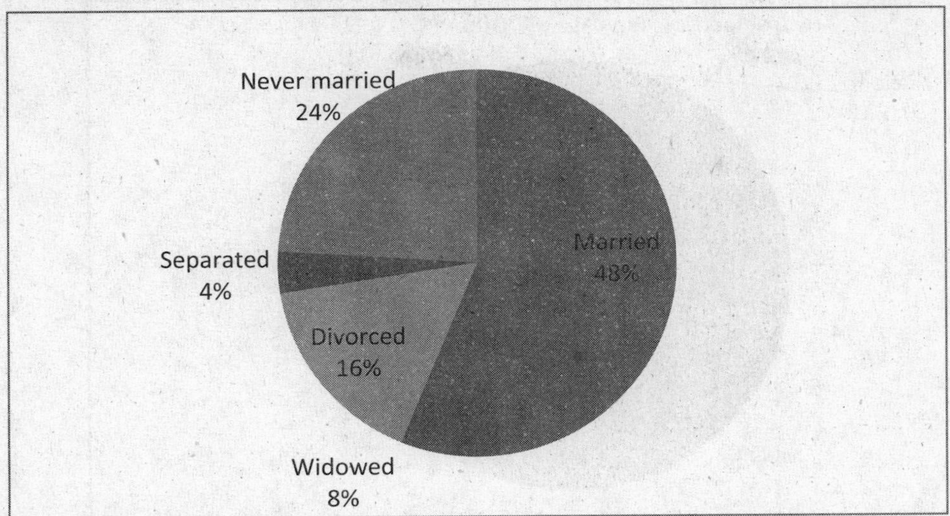

Almost half the sample is married and about one out of four were never married.

2.38

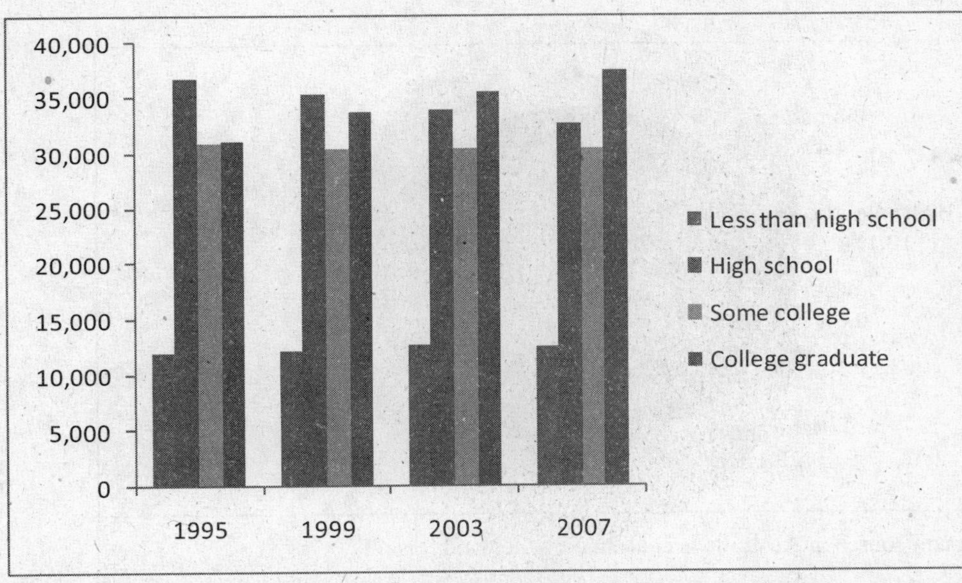

The "Less than high school" category has remained constant, while the number of college graduates has increased.

© 2012 Cengage Learning. All Rights Reserved. May not be scanned, copied or duplicated, or posted to a publicly accessible website, in whole or in part.

2.40 Australian Energy Sources

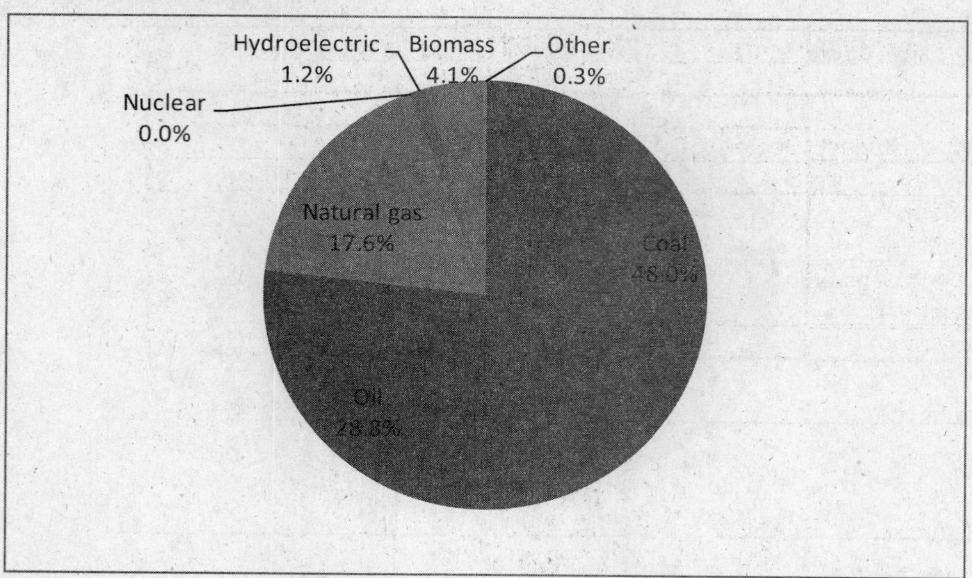

New Zealand Energy Sources

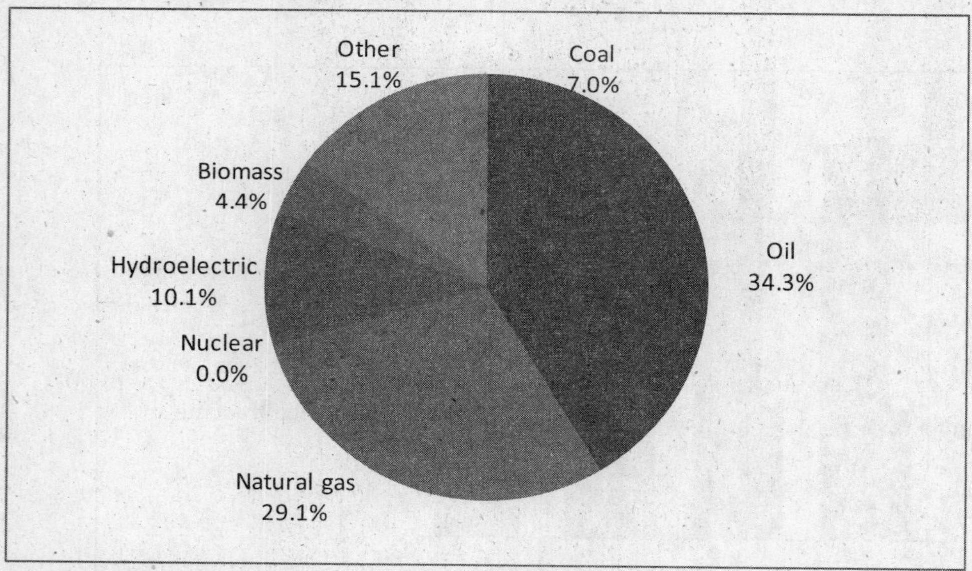

The dominant source in Australia is coal. In New Zealand it is oil.

© 2012 Cengage Learning. All Rights Reserved. May not be scanned, copied or duplicated, or posted to a publicly accessible website, in whole or in part.

2.42

	A	B	C	D	E	F
1	Drop Page Fields Here					
2						
3	Count of Student	Degree				
4	University	B.A.	B.Eng	B.B.A.	Other	Grand Total
5	University 1	44	11	34	11	100
6	University 2	52	14	27	7	100
7	University 3	31	27	18	24	100
8	University 4	40	12	42	6	100
9	Grand Total	167	64	121	48	400

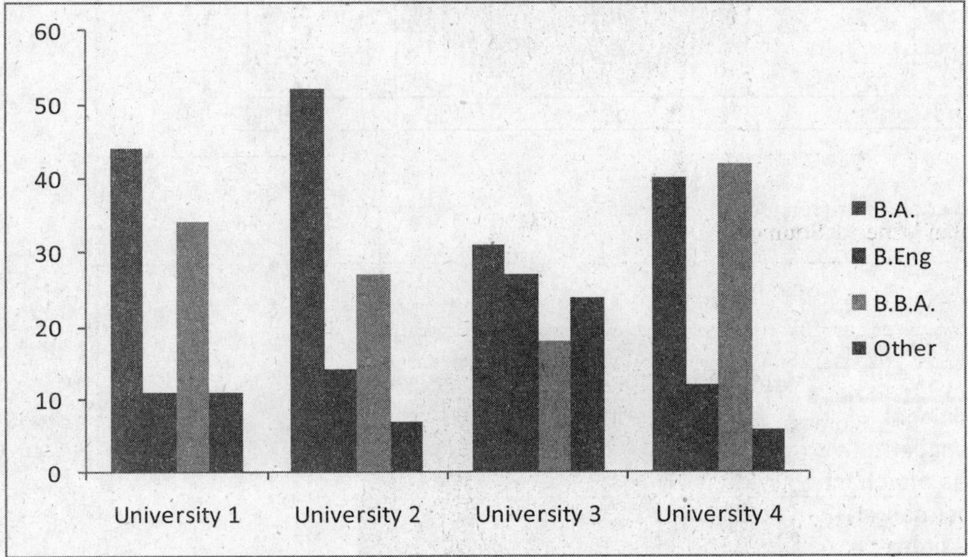

Universities 1 and 2 are similar and quite dissimilar from universities 3 and 4, which also differ. The two nominal variables appear to be related.

© 2012 Cengage Learning. All Rights Reserved. May not be scanned, copied or duplicated, or posted to a publicly accessible website, in whole or in part.

2.44

	Count of Respondent	Smoke?		
4	Parent	Smoke?	Do not smo	Grand Total
5	Neither	73	14	87
6	Father	26	12	38
7	Mother	31	18	49
8	Both	10	41	51
9	Grand Total	140	85	225

3	Count of Respondent	Smoke?		
4	Parent	Smoke?	Do not smoke	Grand Total
5	Neither	52%	16%	39%
6	Father	19%	14%	17%
7	Mother	22%	21%	22%
8	Both	7%	48%	23%
9	Grand Total	100%	100%	100%

The two variables are related.

2.46 Counts

	A	B	C	D
1		Year: 1995	Year: 2000	Year: 2007
2	Traditional	91	134	166
3	Indpendent	67	70	75
4	Mass merchant	24	29	39
5	Supermarket	22	39	48
6	Mail order	9	15	24

Column percent

	A	B	C	D
1		Year: 1995	Year: 2000	Year: 2007
2	Traditional	43%	47%	47%
3	Indpendent	31%	24%	21%
4	Mass merchant	11%	10%	11%
5	Supermarket	10%	14%	14%
6	Mail order	4%	5%	7%

© 2012 Cengage Learning. All Rights Reserved. May not be scanned, copied or duplicated, or posted to a publicly accessible website, in whole or in part.

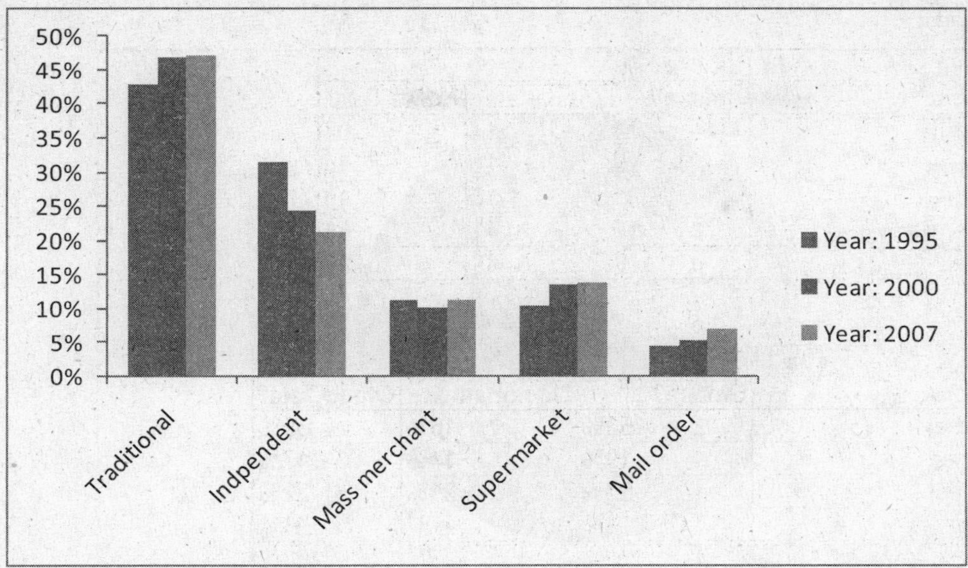

The number of prescriptions filled by independent drug stores has decreased while the others remained constant or increased slightly.

2.48

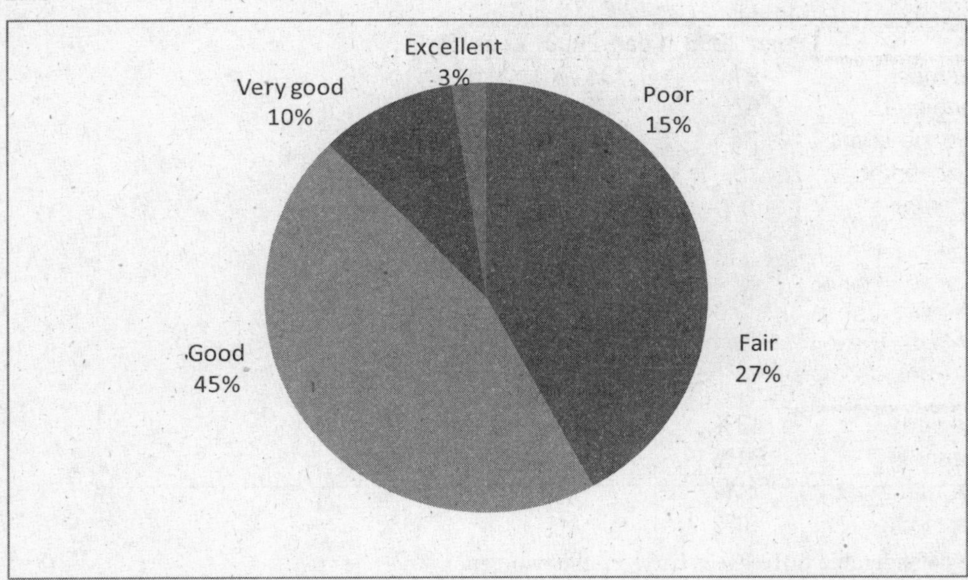

More than 40% rate the food as less than good.

© 2012 Cengage Learning. All Rights Reserved. May not be scanned, copied or duplicated, or posted to a publicly accessible website, in whole or in part.

2.50 Canada

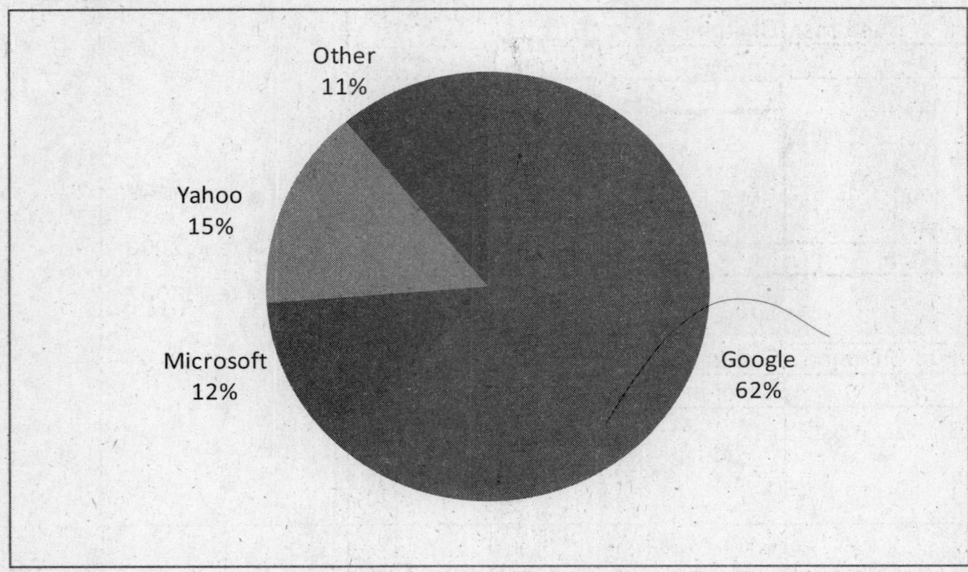

United States

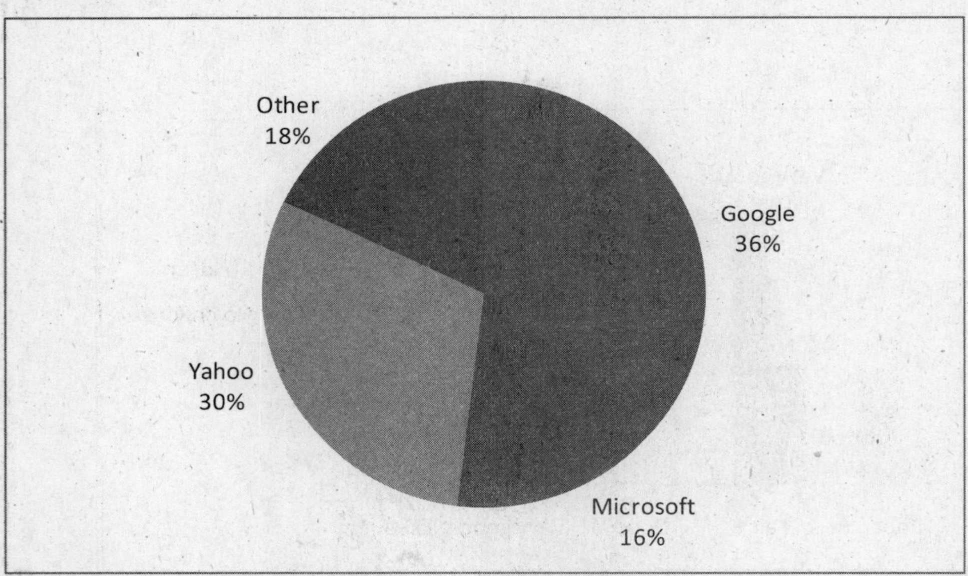

There are considerable differences between the two countries.

© 2012 Cengage Learning. All Rights Reserved. May not be scanned, copied or duplicated, or posted to a publicly accessible website, in whole or in part.

2.52

3	Count of Customer	Children		
4	Rate	Children	No children	Grand Total
5	Poor	4	13	17
6	Fair	13	30	43
7	Good	28	40	68
8	Very good	43	25	68
9	Excellent	20	4	24
10	Grand Total	108	112	220

3	Count of Customer	Children		
4	Rate	Children	No children	Grand Total
5	Poor	4%	12%	8%
6	Fair	12%	27%	20%
7	Good	26%	36%	31%
8	Very good	40%	22%	31%
9	Excellent	19%	4%	11%
10	Grand Total	100%	100%	100%

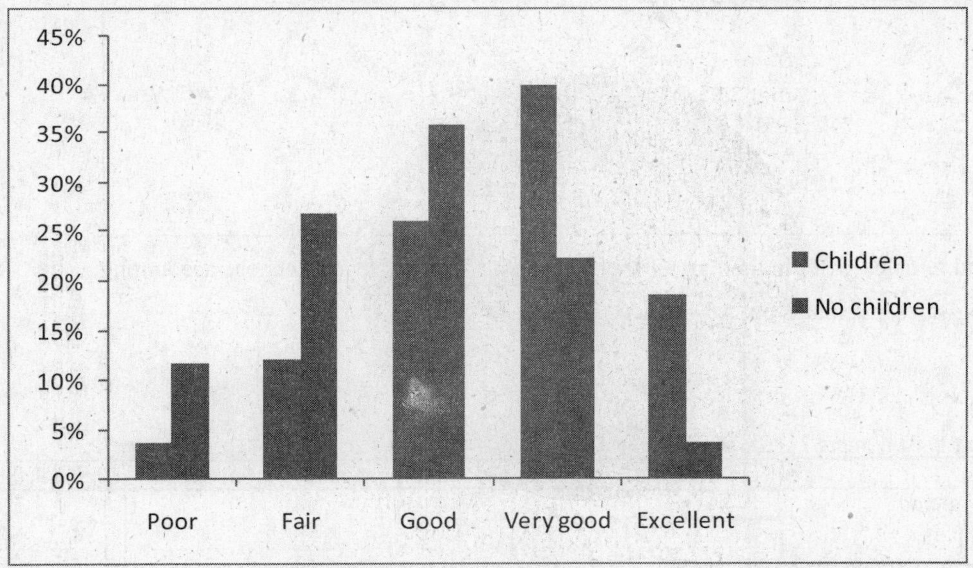

Customers with children rated the restaurant more highly than did customers with no children.

© 2012 Cengage Learning. All Rights Reserved. May not be scanned, copied or duplicated, or posted to a publicly accessible website, in whole or in part.

2.54

3	Count of ID number	Gender		
4	Area	Female	Male	Grand Total
5	Accounting	40	33	73
6	Finance	21	31	52
7	General management	18	18	36
8	Marketing/sales	39	25	64
9	Other	13	15	28
10	Grand Total	131	122	253

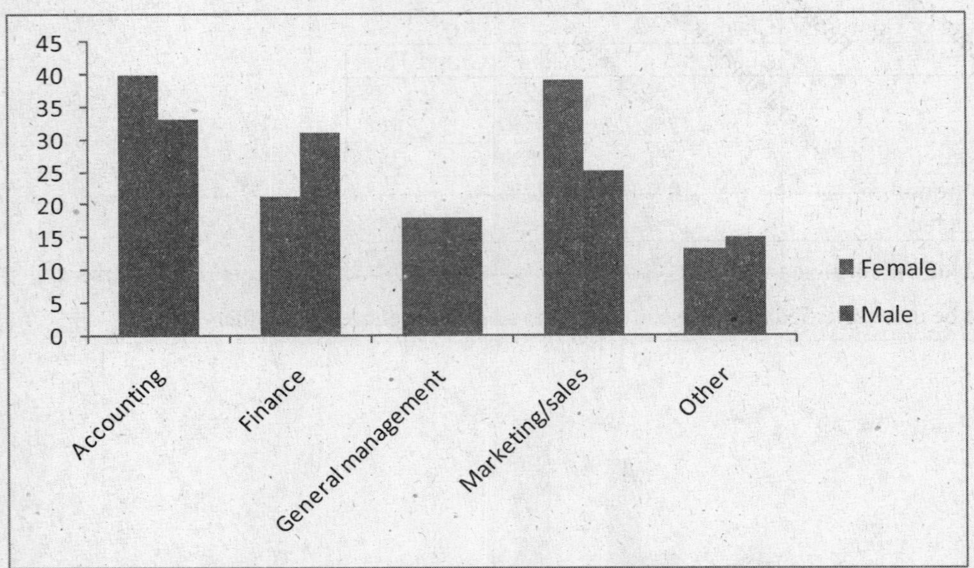

Males and females differ in their areas of employment. Females tend to choose accounting marketing/sales and males opt for finance.

b

3	Count of ID number	Satisfaction				
4	Area	Very satisfied	Quite satisfied	Little satisfied	Not satisfied	Grand Total
5	Accounting	18	36	18	1	73
6	Finance	24	19	9		52
7	General management	[illegible]	11	8	1	36
8	Marketing/sales	[illegible]	21	18	6	64
9	Other	[illegible]	15	7	2	28
10	Grand Total	[illegible]	102	60	10	253

Count of ID number
Value: 16
Row: General management
Column: Very satisfied

© 2012 Cengage Learning. All Rights Reserved. May not be scanned, copied or duplicated, or posted to a publicly accessible website, in whole or in part.

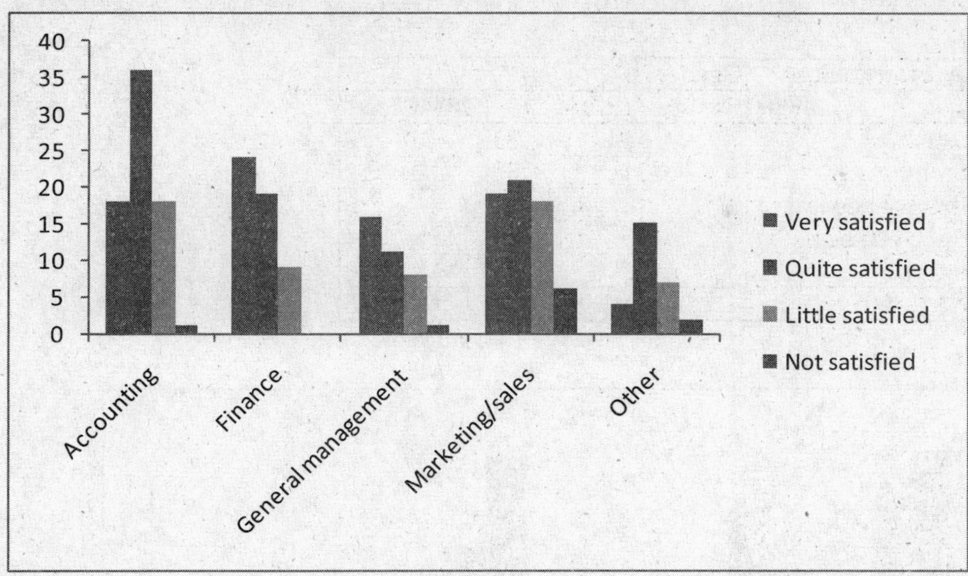

Area and job satisfaction are related. Graduates who work in finance and general management appear to be more satisfied than those in accounting, marketing/sales, and others.

© 2012 Cengage Learning. All Rights Reserved. May not be scanned, copied or duplicated, or posted to a publicly accessible website, in whole or in part.

Chapter 3

3.2 10 or 11

3.4 a 7 to 9

b Interval width $\approx \frac{6.1-5.2}{7}$ = .13 (rounded to .15); upper limits: 5.25, 5.40, 5.55, 5.70, 5.85, 6.00, 6.15

3.6 a

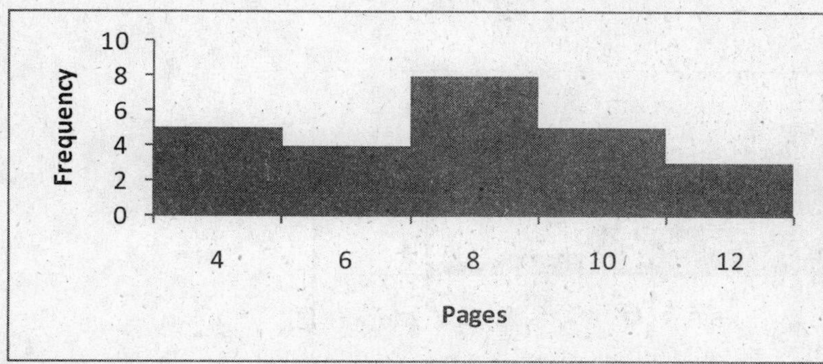

b

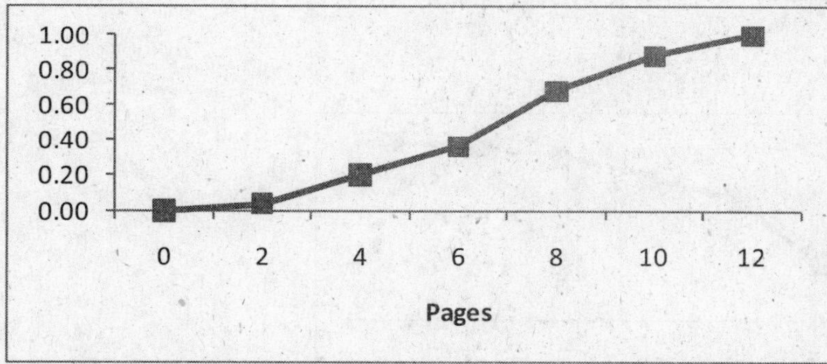

c The number of pages is bimodal and slightly positively skewed.

© 2012 Cengage Learning. All Rights Reserved. May not be scanned, copied or duplicated, or posted to a publicly accessible website, in whole or in part.

3.8

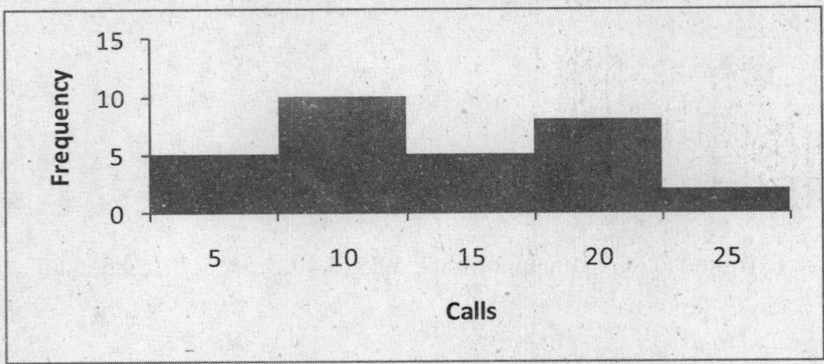

The histogram is bimodal.

3.10 a

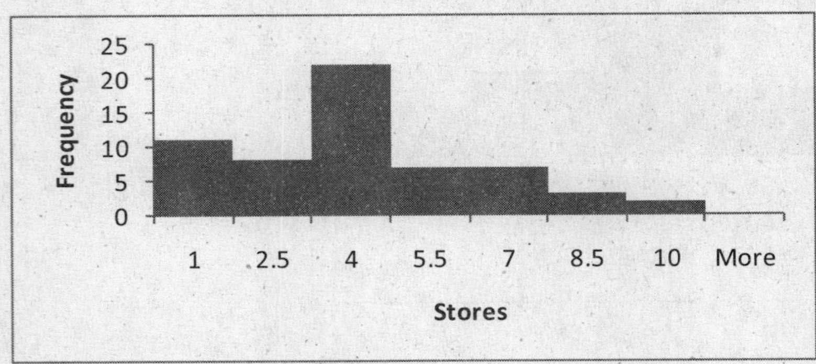

b

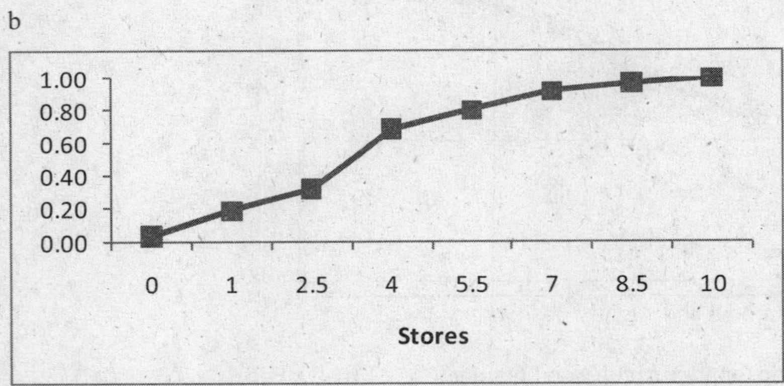

c The number of stores is bimodal and positively skewed.

© 2012 Cengage Learning. All Rights Reserved. May not be scanned, copied or duplicated, or posted to a publicly accessible website, in whole or in part.

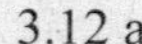

3.12 a

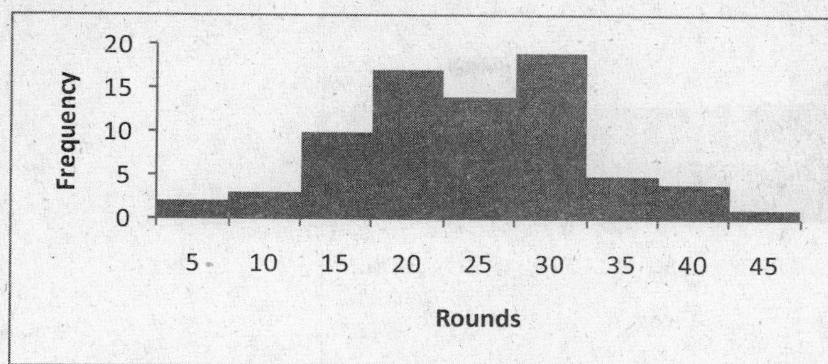

b

	A	B	C	D	E	F
1	Stem & Leaf Display					
2						
3	Stems		Leaves			
4	0		->359			
5	1		->0023334445556677888888899			
6	2		->00001223334444455566667888889999			
7	3		->00000112556668			
8	4		->2			

c

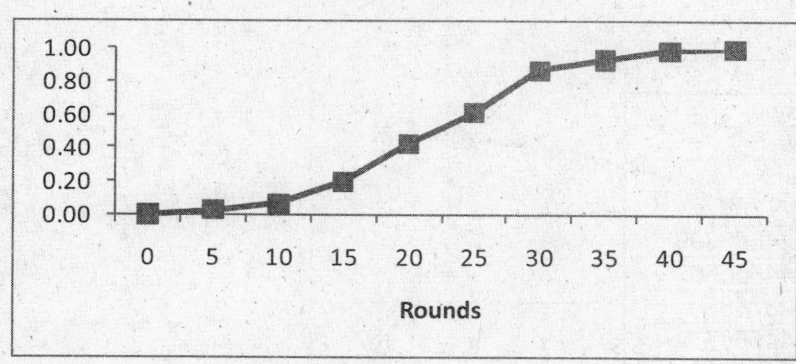

d The histogram is symmetric (approximately) and bimodal.

© 2012 Cengage Learning. All Rights Reserved. May not be scanned, copied or duplicated, or posted to a publicly accessible website, in whole or in part.

3.14 a

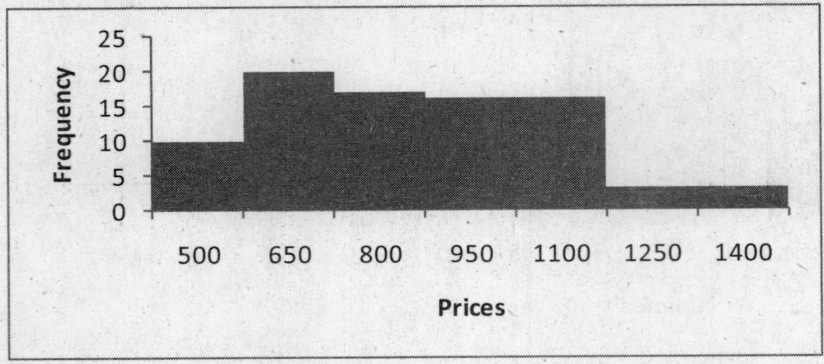

b

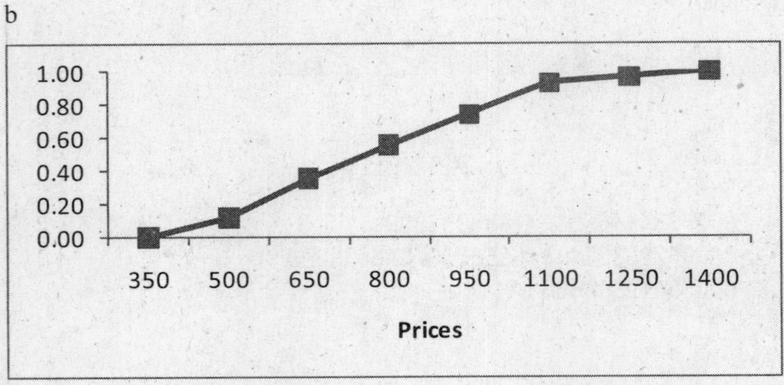

c

	A	B	C
1	**Stem & Leaf Display**		
2			
3	**Stems**	**Leaves**	
4	4	->2445677789	
5	5	->0122224668899	
6	6	->0001244555667	
7	7	->00022237889	
8	8	->01333445667	
9	9	->012246667788	
10	10	->00233788	
11	11	->015	
12	12	->18	
13	13	->23	

d The histogram is slightly positively skewed, unimodal, and not bell-shaped.

3.16 a The histogram should contain 9 or 10 bins. We chose 10.

© 2012 Cengage Learning. All Rights Reserved. May not be scanned, copied or duplicated, or posted to a publicly accessible website, in whole or in part.

b

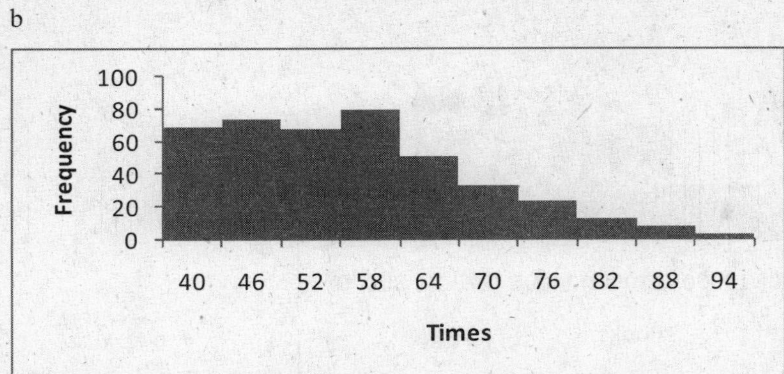

c The histogram is positively skewed.

d The histogram is not bell-shaped.

3.18

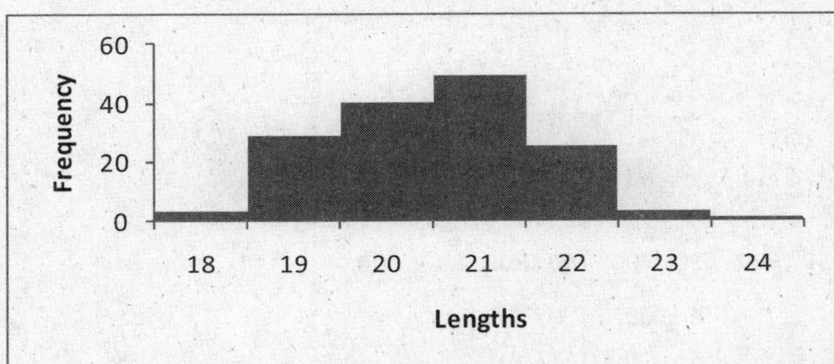

The histogram is unimodal, bell-shaped and roughly symmetric. Most of the lengths lie between 18 and 23 inches.

3.20

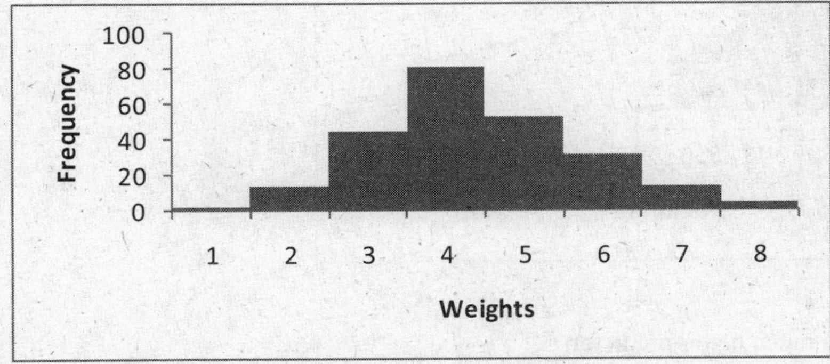

The histogram is unimodal, symmetric and bell-shaped. Most tomatoes weigh between 2 and 7 ounces with a small fraction weighing less than 2 ounces or more than 7 ounces.

© 2012 Cengage Learning. All Rights Reserved. May not be scanned, copied or duplicated, or posted to a publicly accessible website, in whole or in part.

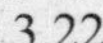

3.22

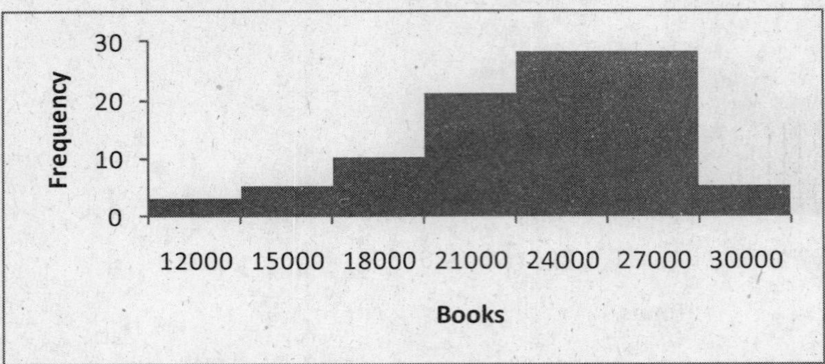

The histogram of the number of books shipped daily is negatively skewed. It appears that there is a maximum number that the company can ship.

3.24 a

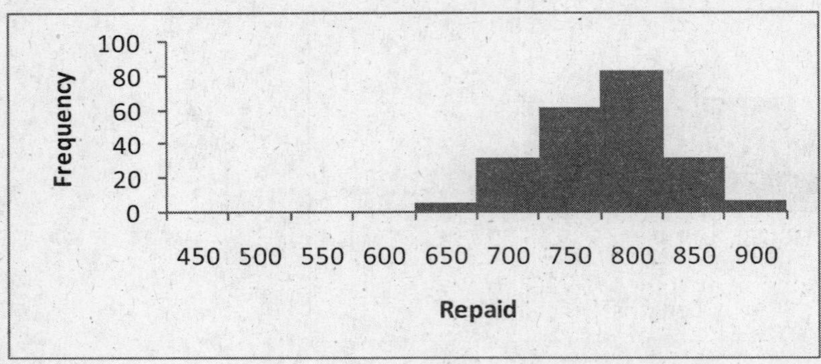

b

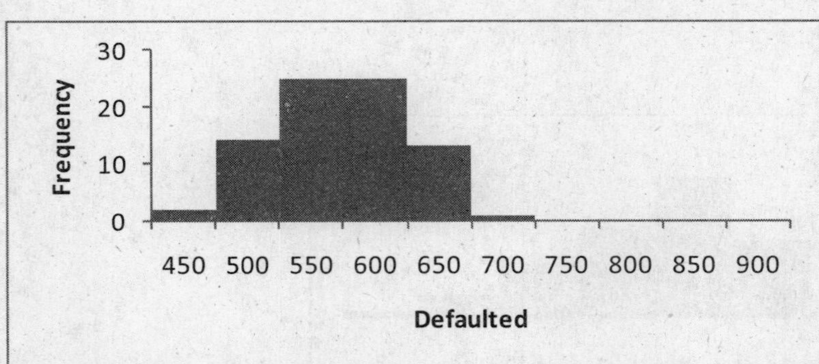

c. and d. This scorecard is a much better predictor.

© 2012 Cengage Learning. All Rights Reserved. May not be scanned, copied or duplicated, or posted to a publicly accessible website, in whole or in part.

3.26

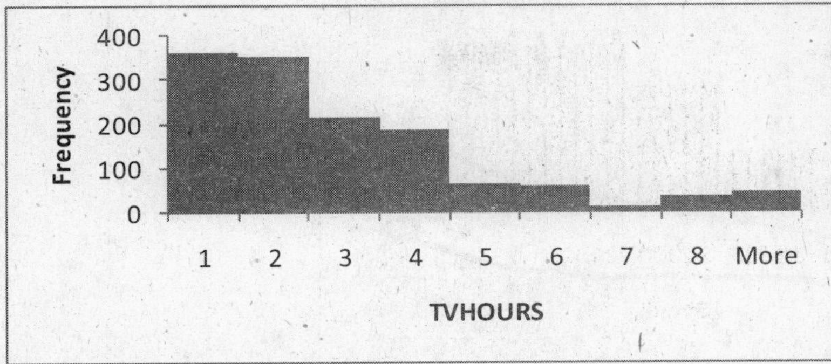

The histogram is highly positively skewed indicating that most people watch 4 or less hours per day with some watching considerably more.

3.28

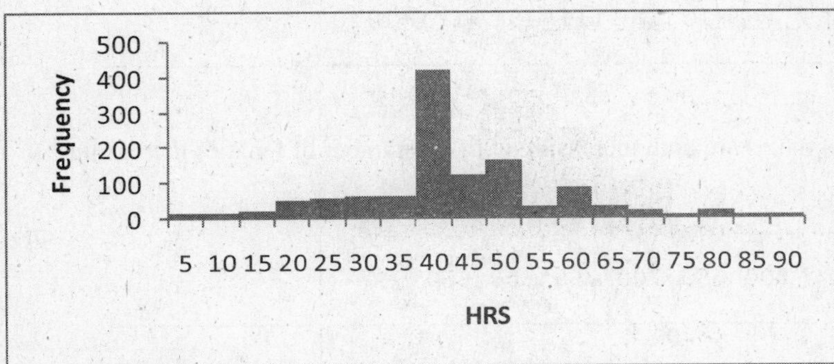

Many people work more than 40 hours per week.

3.30

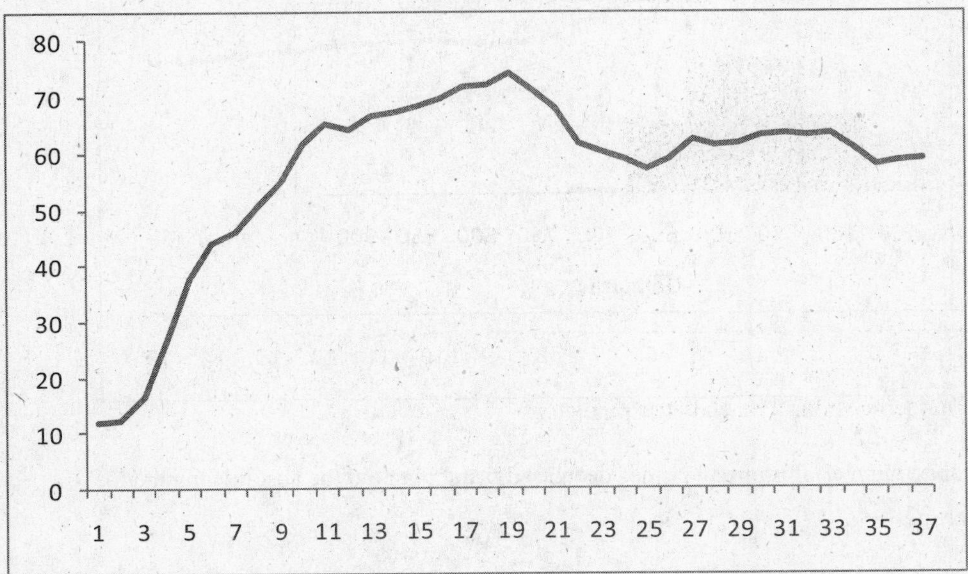

After a rapid increase the numbers have leveled off.

© 2012 Cengage Learning. All Rights Reserved. May not be scanned, copied or duplicated, or posted to a publicly accessible website, in whole or in part.

3.32

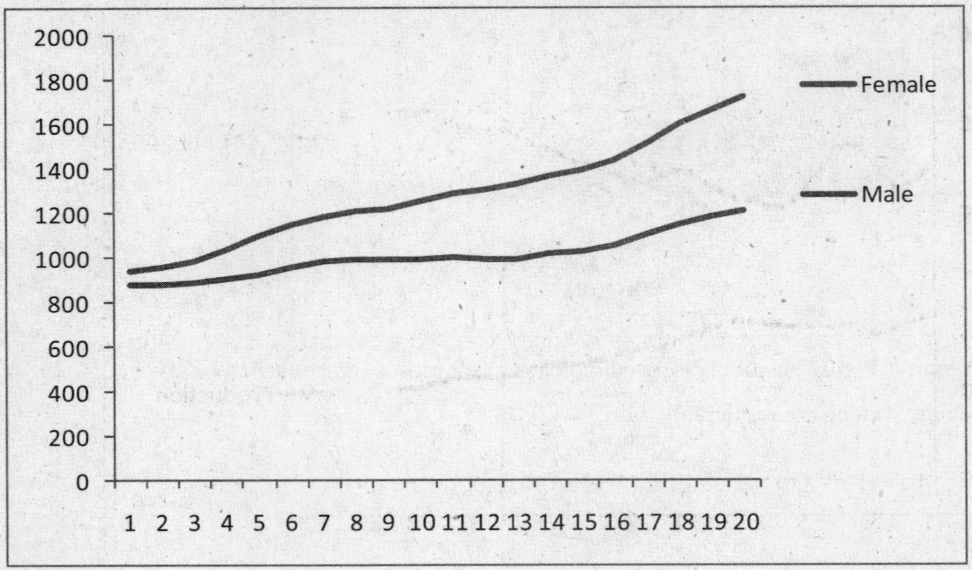

The numbers of females and males are both increasing with the number of females increasing faster.

3.34

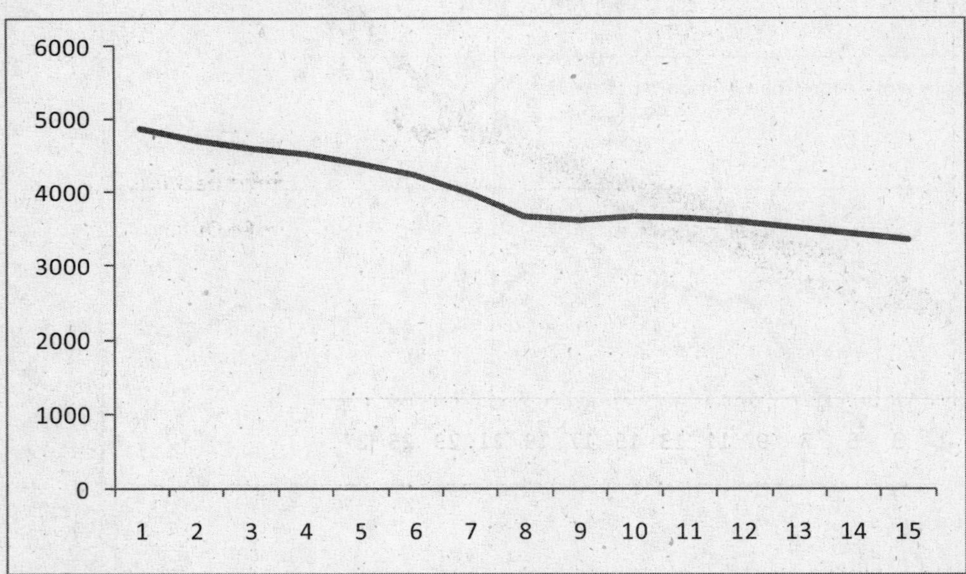

The per capita number of property crimes decreased faster than did the absolute number of property crimes.

© 2012 Cengage Learning. All Rights Reserved. May not be scanned, copied or duplicated, or posted to a publicly accessible website, in whole or in part.

3.36

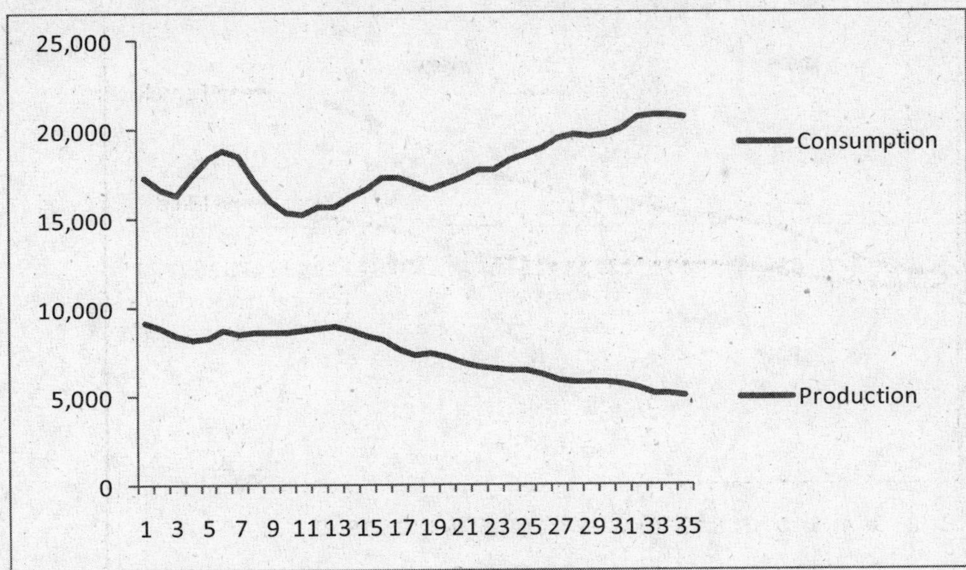

Consumption is increasing and production is falling.

3.38

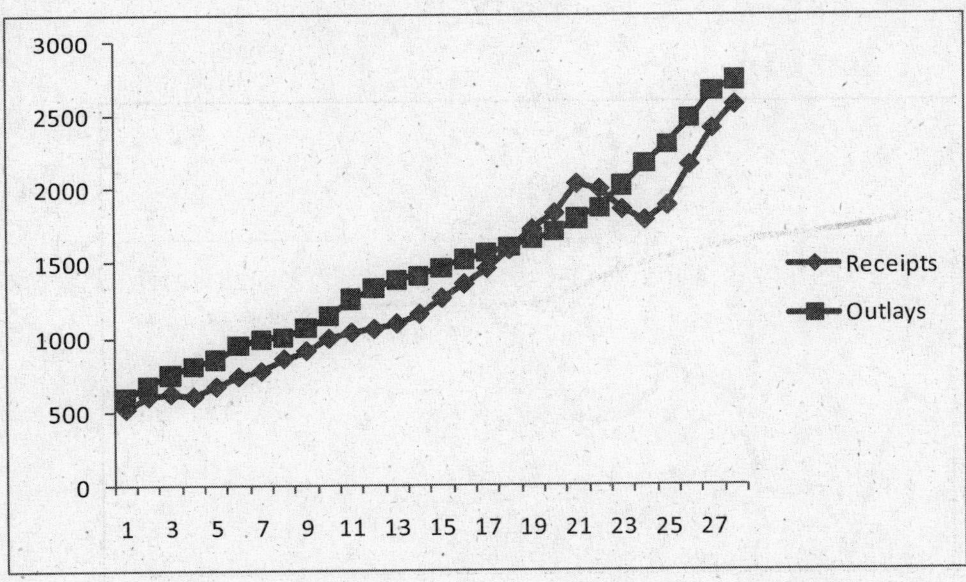

© 2012 Cengage Learning. All Rights Reserved. May not be scanned, copied or duplicated, or posted to a publicly accessible website, in whole or in part.

b

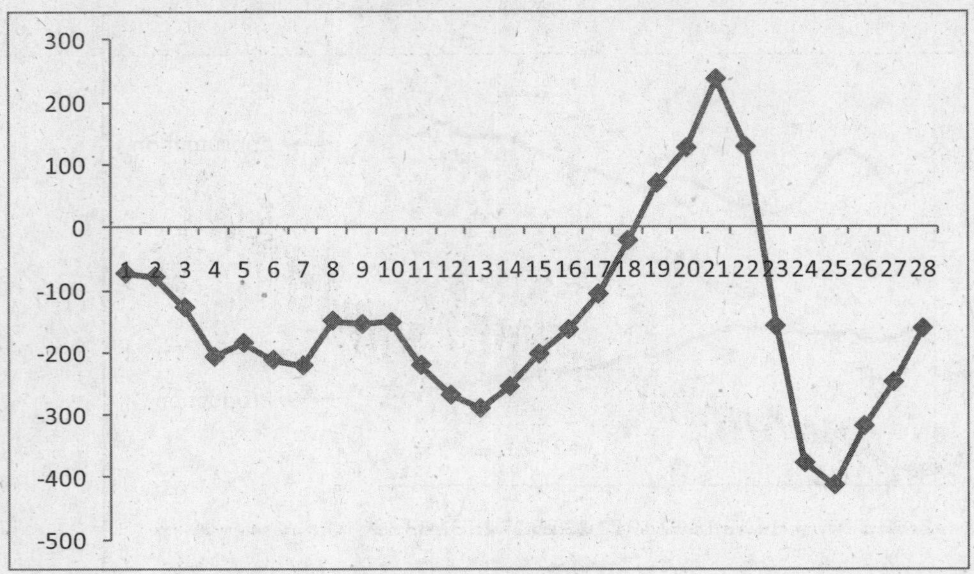

Over the last 28 years both receipts and outlays increased rapidly. There was a five-year period where receipts were higher than outlays. Between 2004 and 2007 the deficit has decreased.

3.40

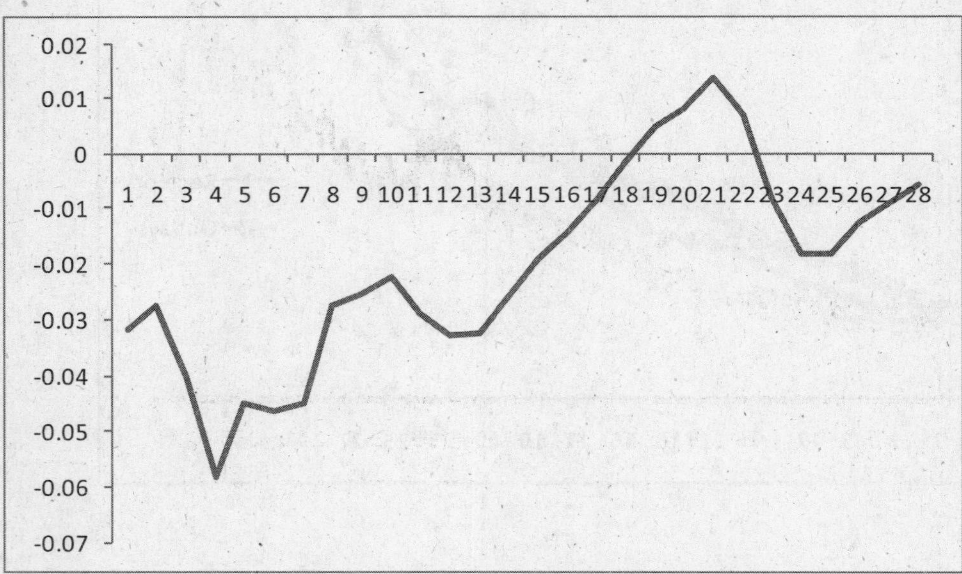

The inflation adjusted deficits are not large.

© 2012 Cengage Learning. All Rights Reserved. May not be scanned, copied or duplicated, or posted to a publicly accessible website, in whole or in part.

3.42 Exports to Canada

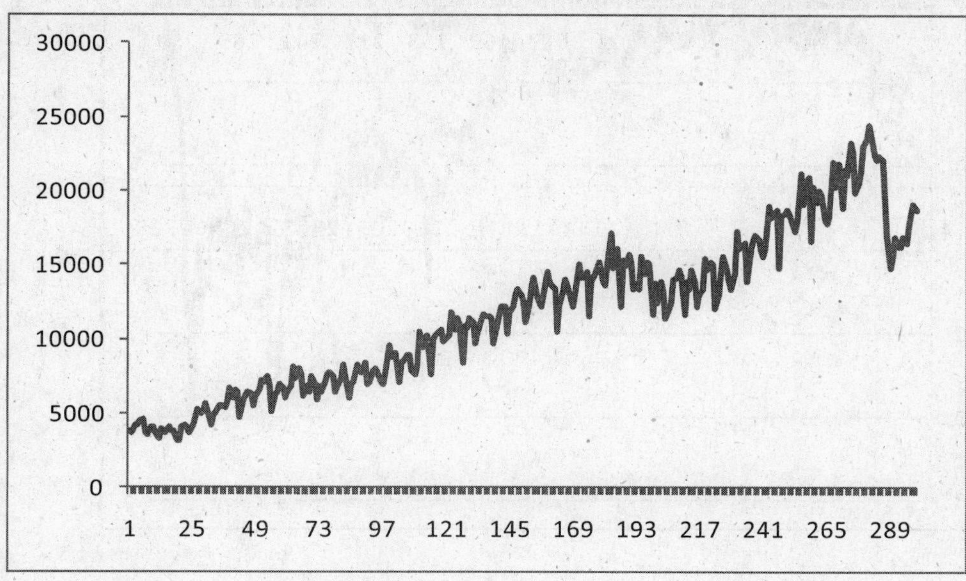

Imports from Canada

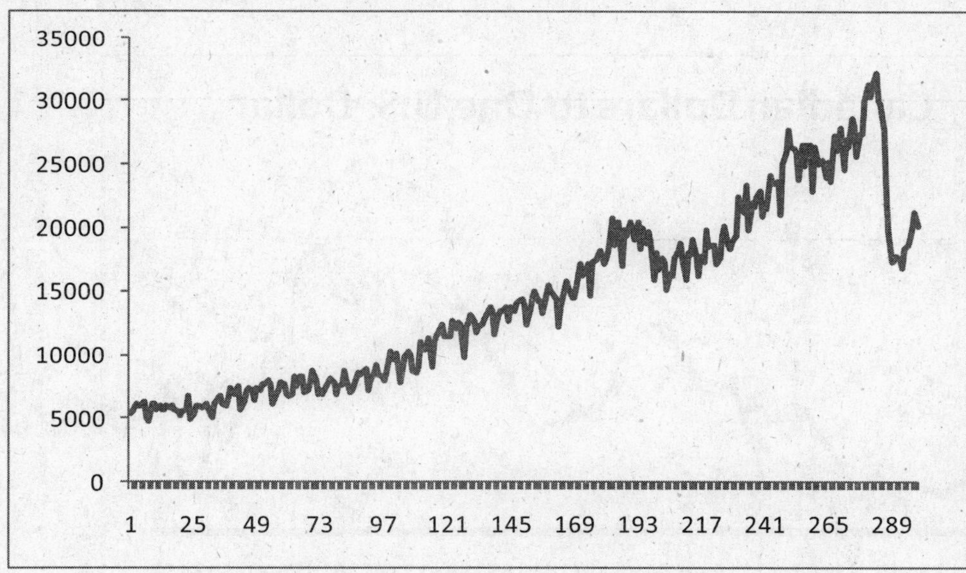

© 2012 Cengage Learning. All Rights Reserved. May not be scanned, copied or duplicated, or posted to a publicly accessible website, in whole or in part.

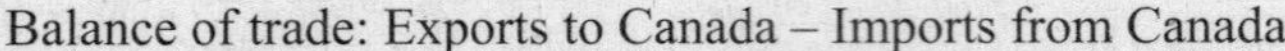

Balance of trade: Exports to Canada – Imports from Canada

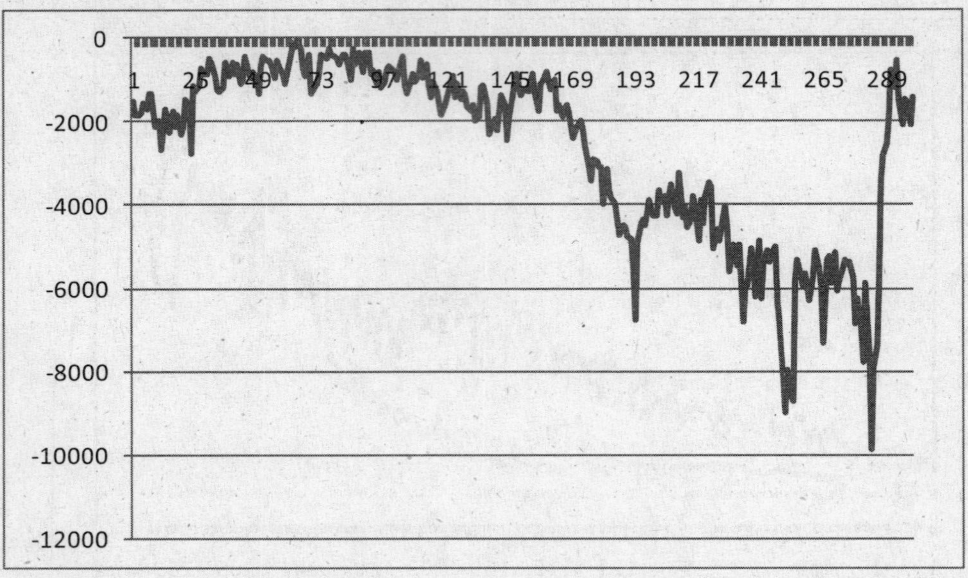

Imports from Canada have greatly exceeded exports to Canada.

3.44

In the early seventies the Canadian dollar was worth more than the U.S. dollar. By the late seventies the Canadian lost ground but has recently recovered.

© 2012 Cengage Learning. All Rights Reserved. May not be scanned, copied or duplicated, or posted to a publicly accessible website, in whole or in part.

3.46

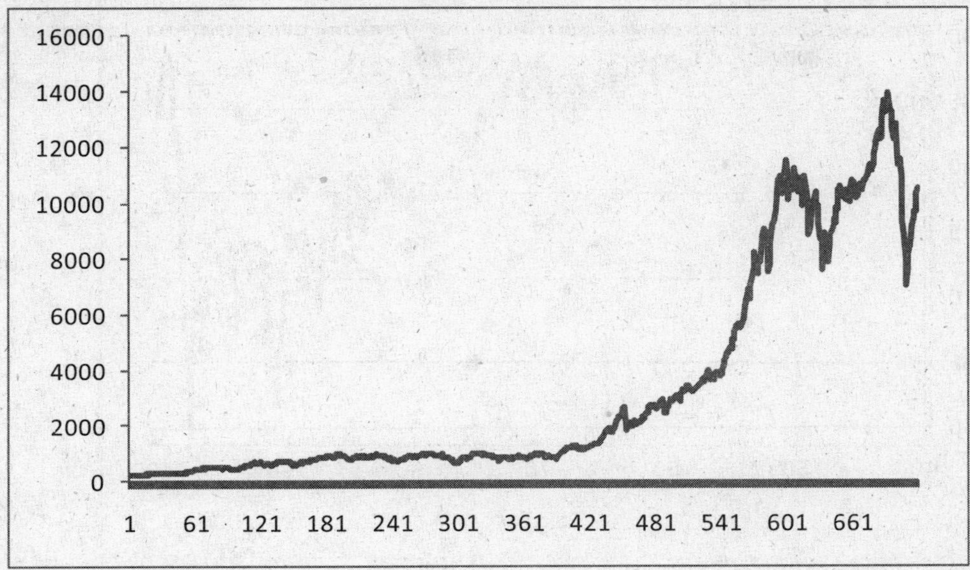

The index grew slowly until month 400 and then grew quickly until month 600. It then fell sharply and recently recovered.

3.48

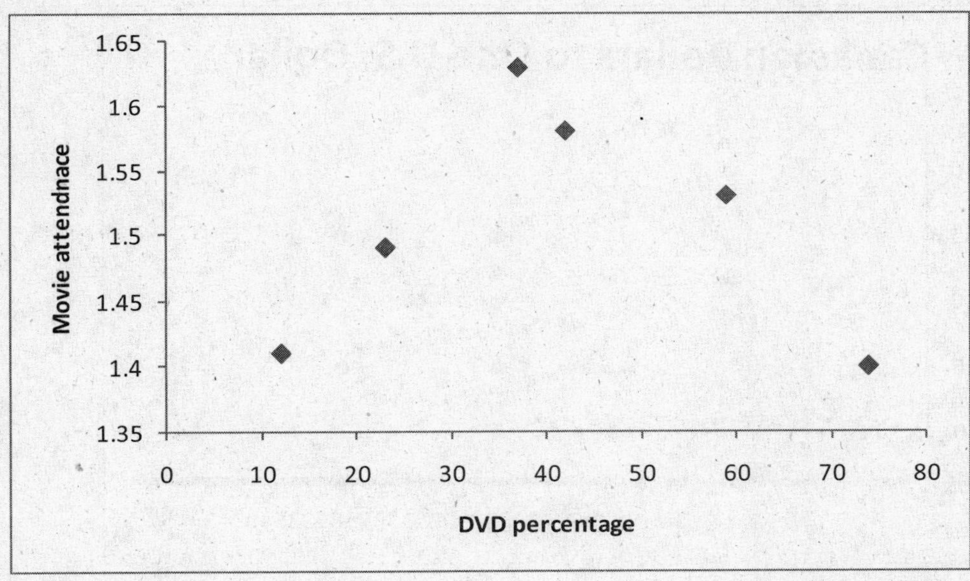

There does not appear to be a linear relationship between the two variables.

© 2012 Cengage Learning. All Rights Reserved. May not be scanned, copied or duplicated, or posted to a publicly accessible website, in whole or in part.

3.50a

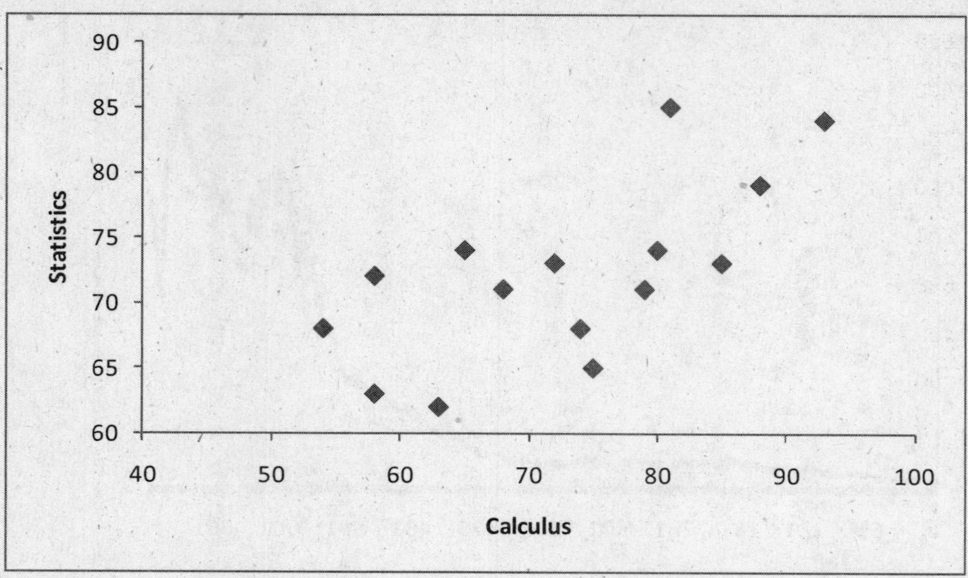

b. There is a positive linear relationship between calculus and statistics marks.

3.52a

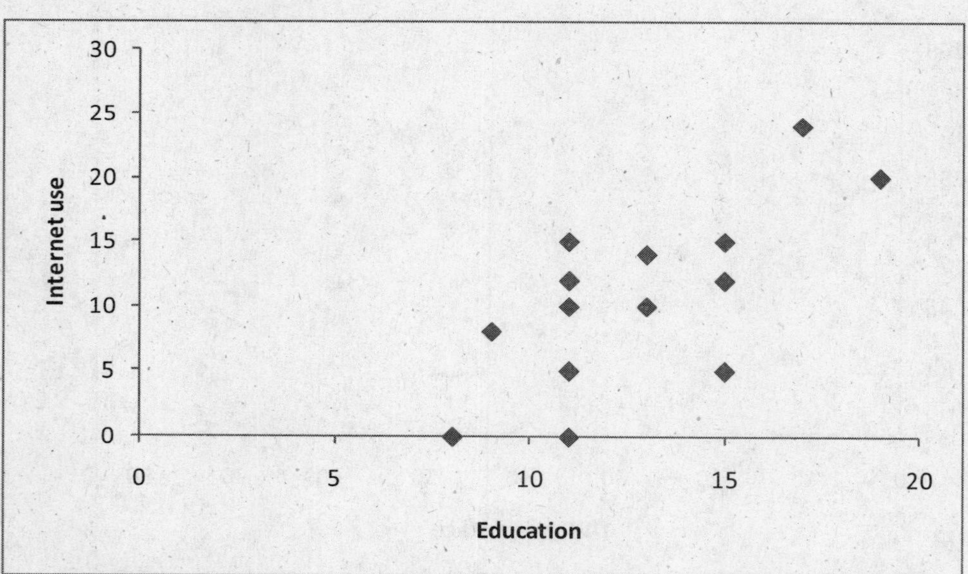

b. There is a moderately strong positive linear relationship. In general those with more education use the Internet more frequently.

© 2012 Cengage Learning. All Rights Reserved. May not be scanned, copied or duplicated, or posted to a publicly accessible website, in whole or in part.

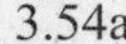

3.54a

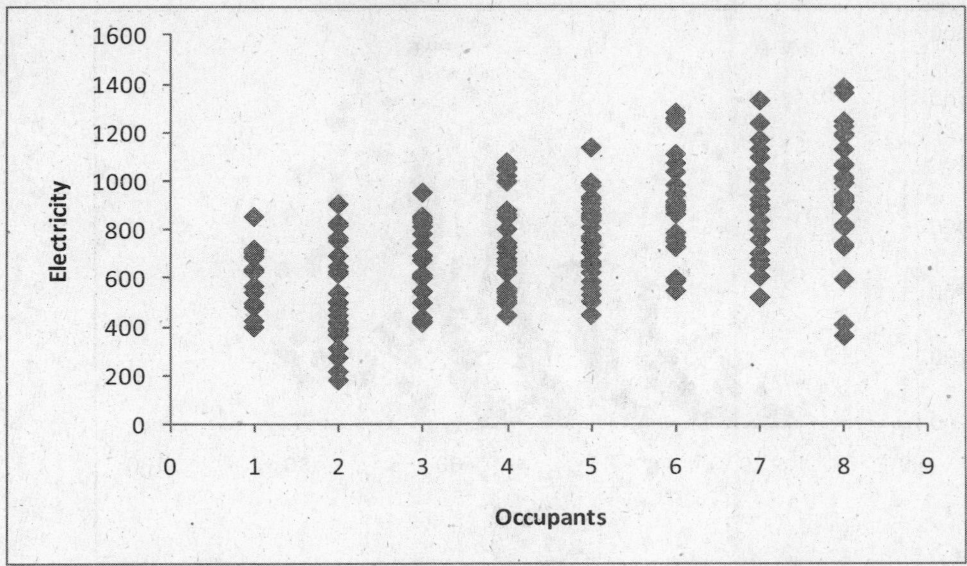

b. There is a moderately strong positive linear relationship.

3.56a

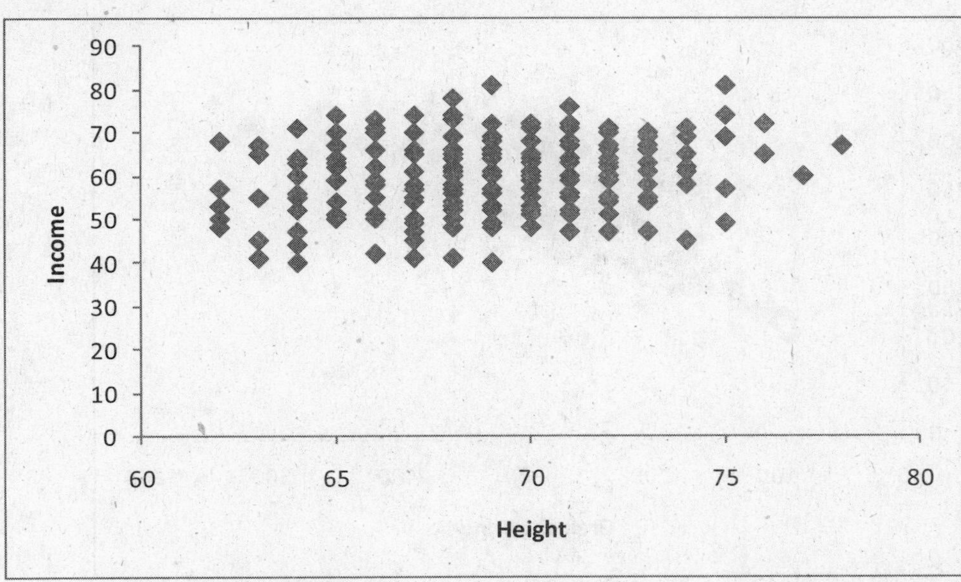

b. There is a very weak positive linear relationship.

© 2012 Cengage Learning. All Rights Reserved. May not be scanned, copied or duplicated, or posted to a publicly accessible website, in whole or in part.

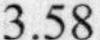

3.58

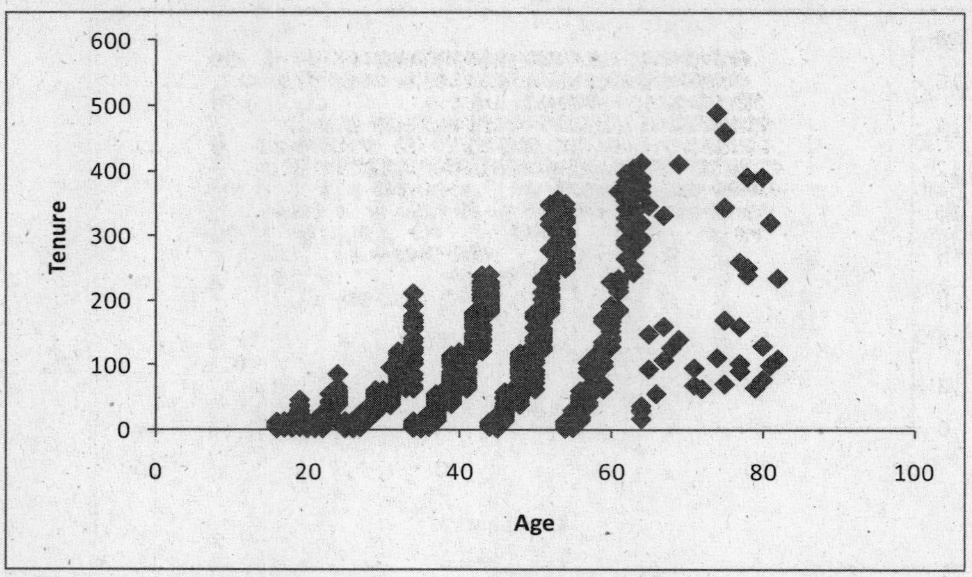

There is a moderately strong positive linear relationship.

3.60

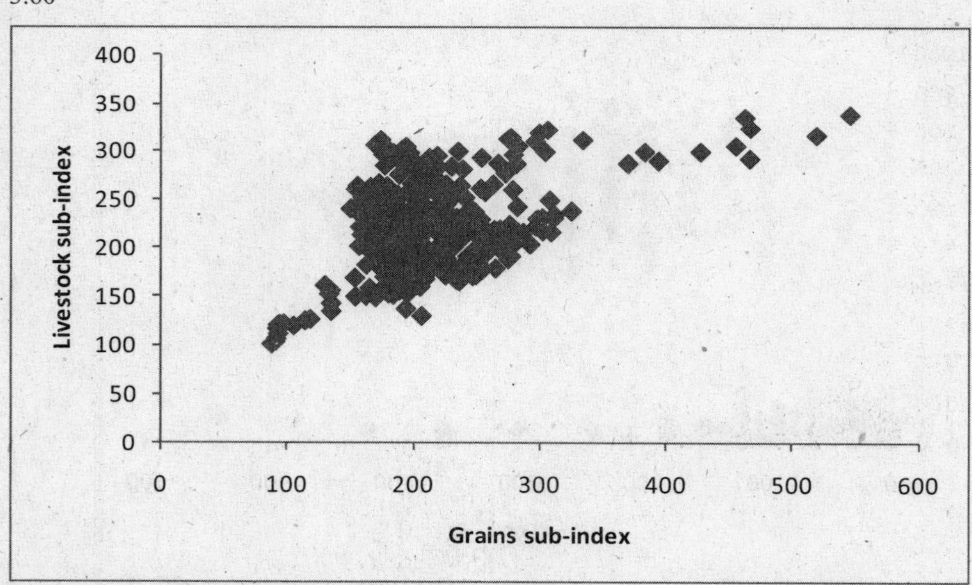

There is moderately strong positive linear relationship.

© 2012 Cengage Learning. All Rights Reserved. May not be scanned, copied or duplicated, or posted to a publicly accessible website, in whole or in part.

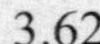

3.62

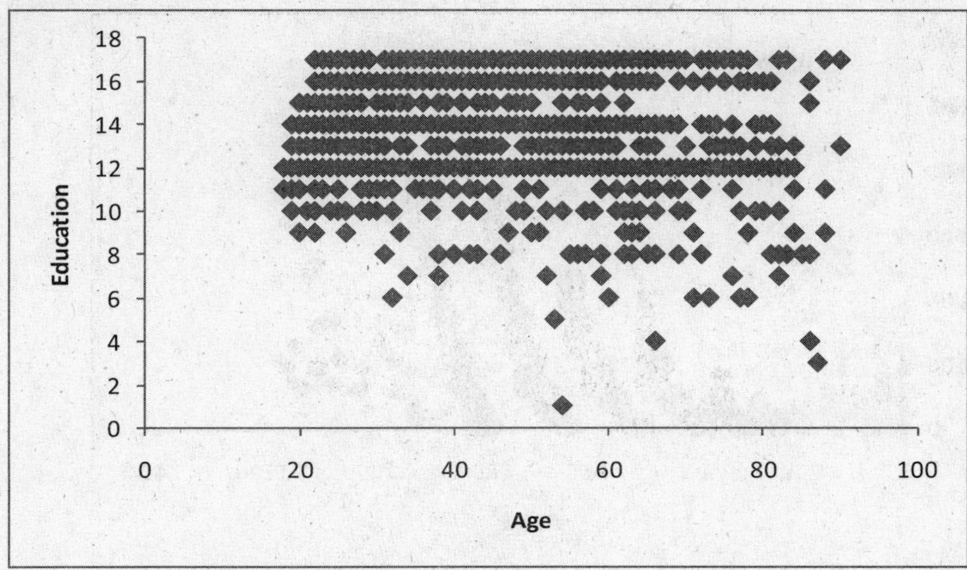

There does not appear to be any relationship between the two variables.

3.64

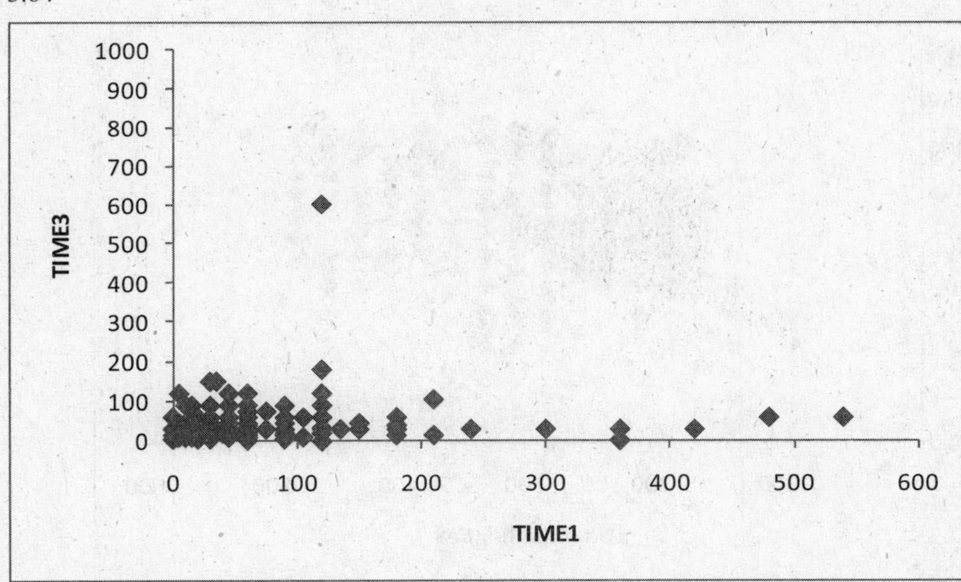

There does not appear to be a linear relationship.

© 2012 Cengage Learning. All Rights Reserved. May not be scanned, copied or duplicated, or posted to a publicly accessible website, in whole or in part.

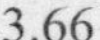

3.66

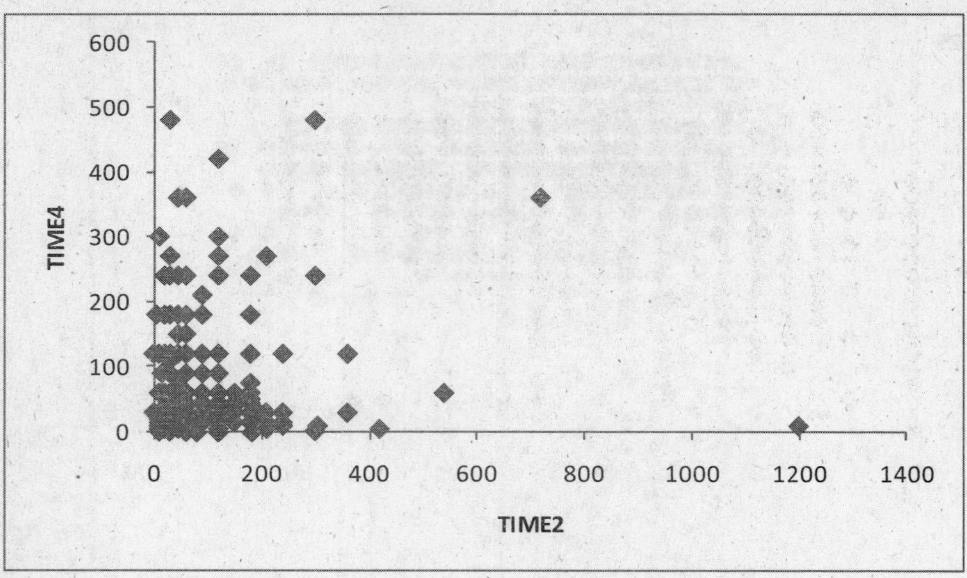

There does not appear to be a linear relationship between the two variables.

3.68

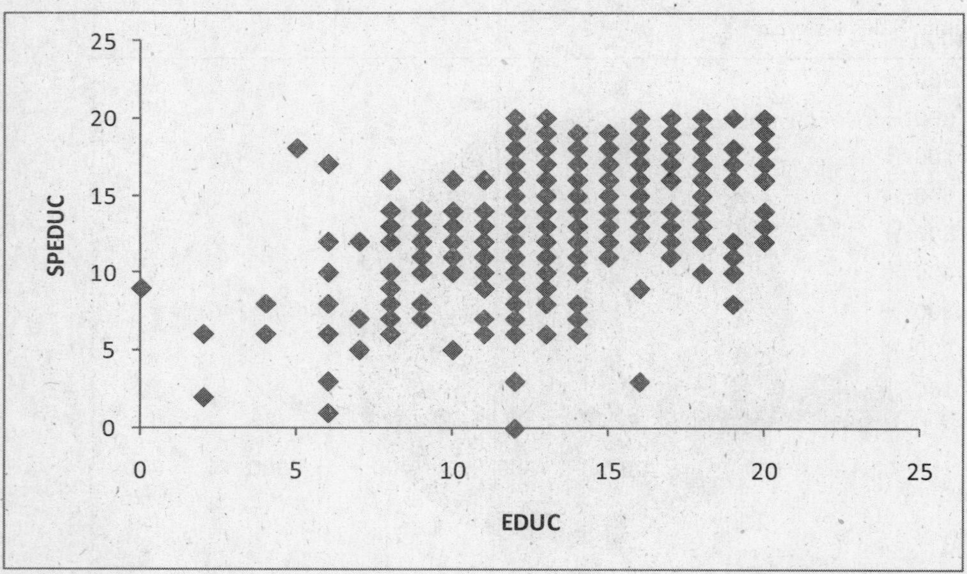

There is a moderately strong positive linear relationship between the education levels of spouses.

© 2012 Cengage Learning. All Rights Reserved. May not be scanned, copied or duplicated, or posted to a publicly accessible website, in whole or in part.

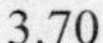

3.70

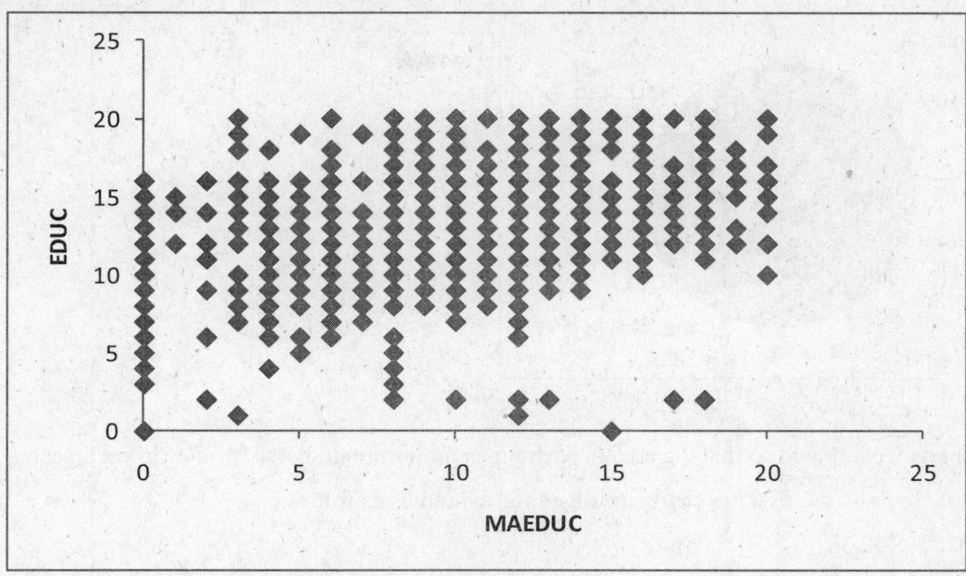

There is a weak positive linear relationship between the amount of education of mothers and their children.

3.72 Region: Sales last year

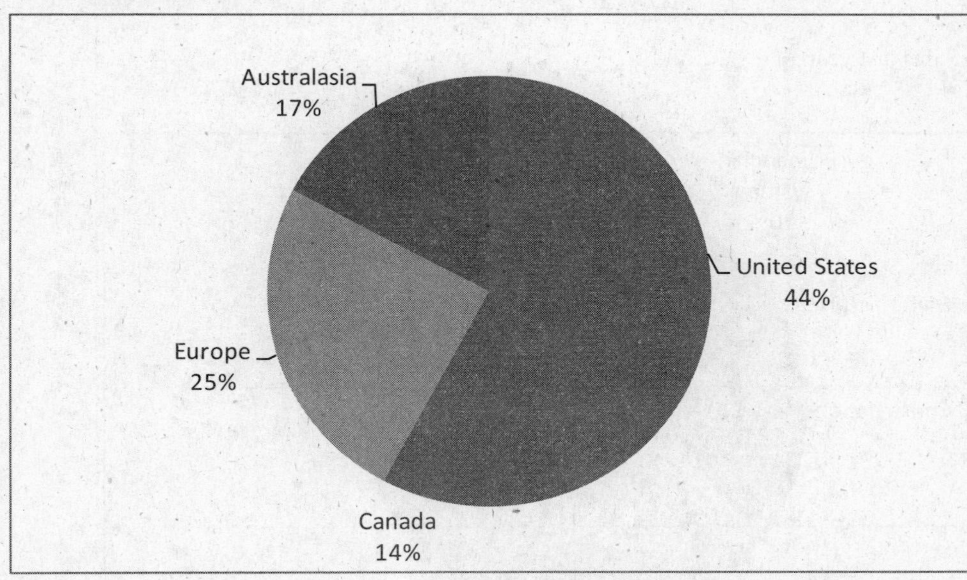

© 2012 Cengage Learning. All Rights Reserved. May not be scanned, copied or duplicated, or posted to a publicly accessible website, in whole or in part.

Region: Sales previous year

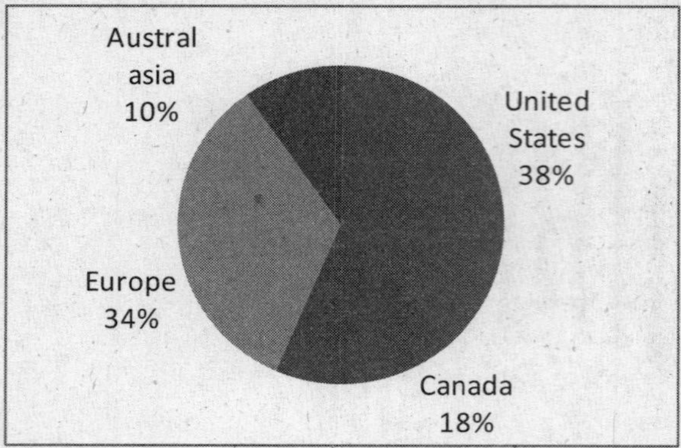

The pie charts were drawn so that the area in each pie is proportion to the total sales in each year. For example to draw the first pie chart we solved for the radius as follows.

$\Pi r^2 = 152.3$

Solving for r we find

$r = 6.96$

For the second pie chart we find $r = 5.78$.

We draw the pie charts for the divisions in each year in the same way.

Division: Sales last year

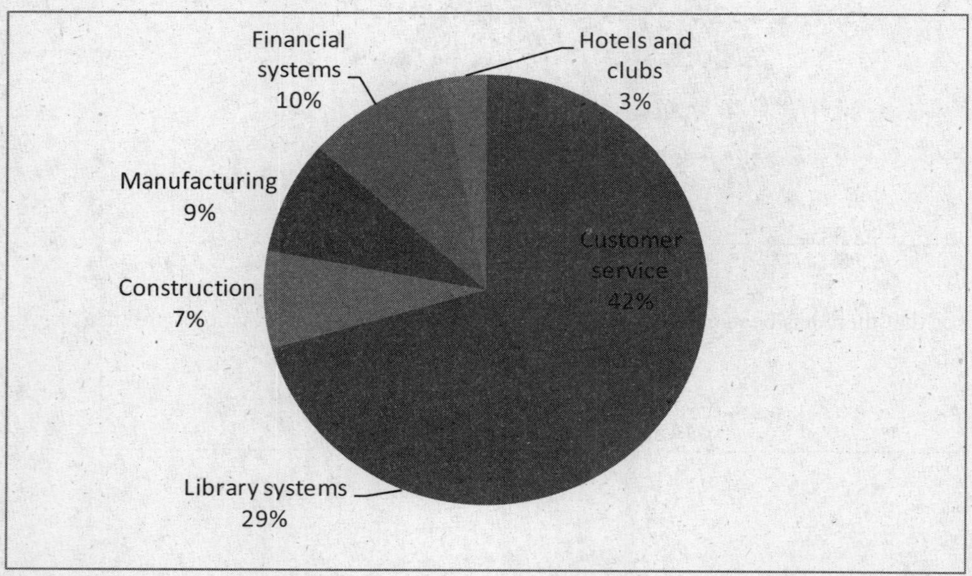

© 2012 Cengage Learning. All Rights Reserved. May not be scanned, copied or duplicated, or posted to a publicly accessible website, in whole or in part.

Division: Sales previous year

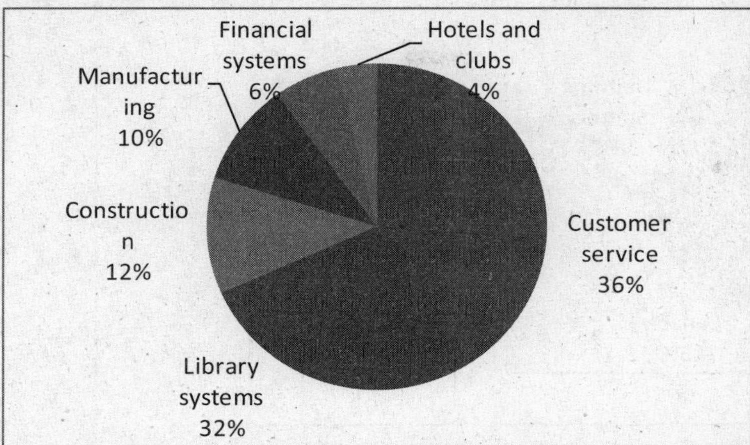

3.74 We divided the number of crimes by the population and multiplied by 1,000. The result is the number of crimes per thousand of population.

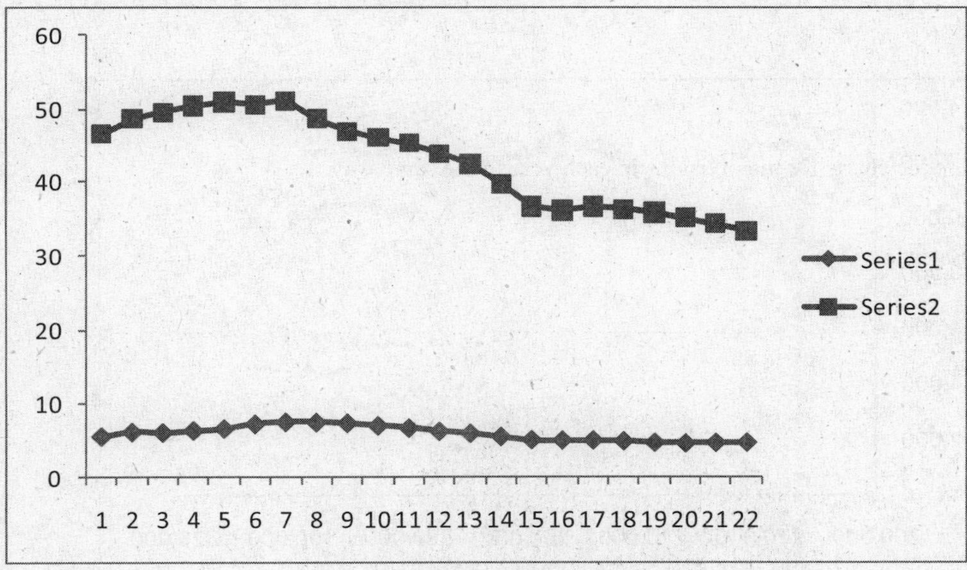

b We can see that there has been a decrease in the number of crimes per thousand of population

c Another possible chart is a scatter diagram of the number of crimes and population.

© 2012 Cengage Learning. All Rights Reserved. May not be scanned, copied or duplicated, or posted to a publicly accessible website, in whole or in part.

Violent crimes

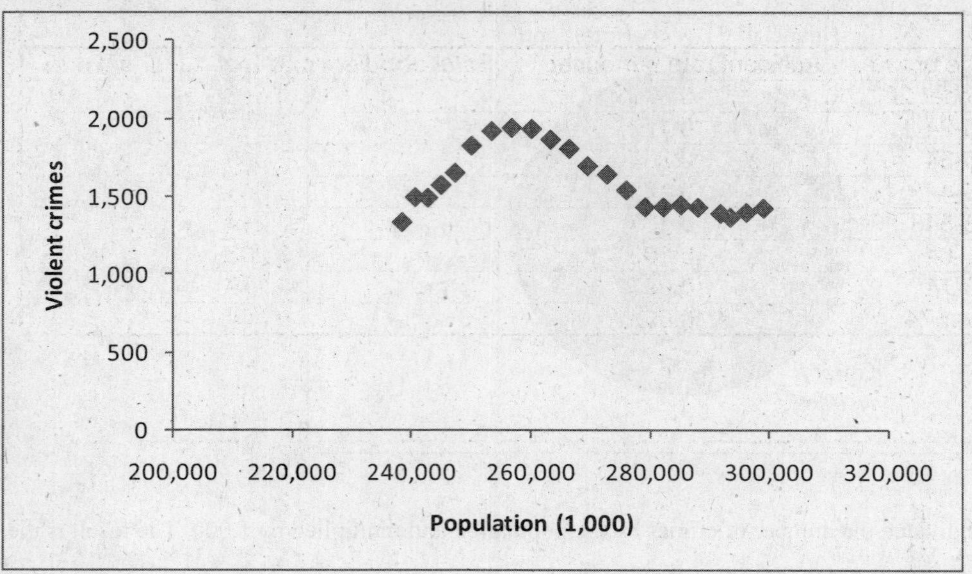

Property crimes

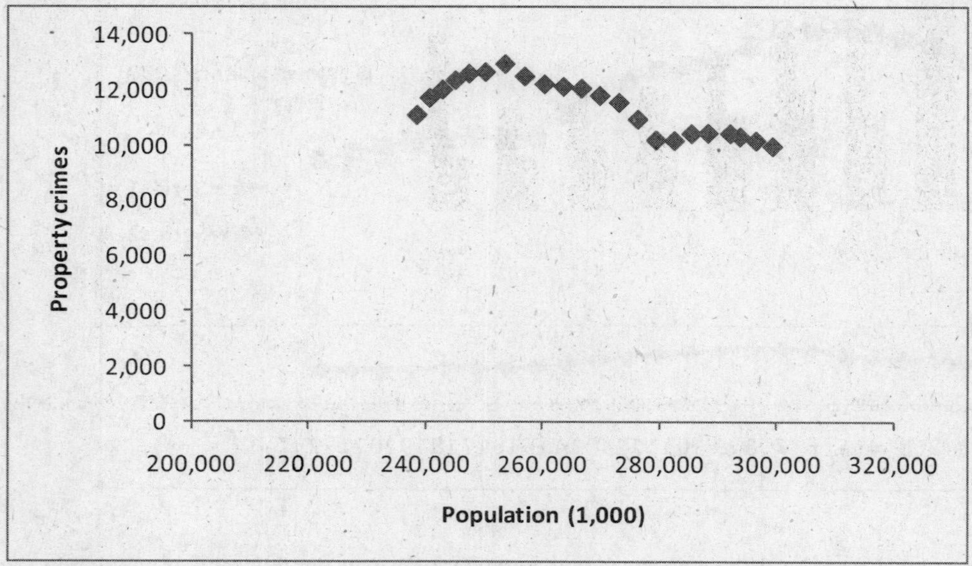

The unusual shapes of the scatter diagram are difficult to explain. Both charts are quadratic rather than linear. They suggest that when the population was less than 255 million the population and the number of crimes were positively linear related, whereas when the population was more than 255 million the relationship was negative.

© 2012 Cengage Learning. All Rights Reserved. May not be scanned, copied or duplicated, or posted to a publicly accessible website, in whole or in part.

3.76 a We convert the numbers to accident rate and fatal accident rate.

	A	B	C
1	Age group	Accident rate per driver	Fatal accidient rate (per 1,000 drivers)
2	Under 20	0.373	0.643
3	20-24	0.173	0.352
4	25-34	0.209	0.305
5	35-44	0.162	0.251
6	45-54	0.133	0.214
7	55-64	0.108	0.208
8	65-74	0.095	0.177
9	Over 74	0.093	0.304

b

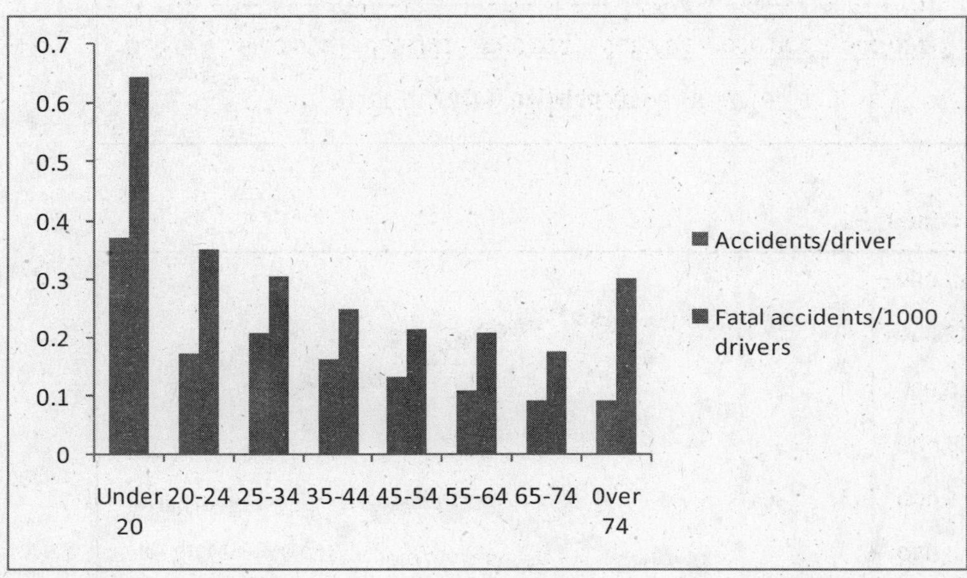

c. The accident rate generally decreases as the ages increase. The fatal accident rate decreases until the over 64 age category where there is an increase.

© 2012 Cengage Learning. All Rights Reserved. May not be scanned, copied or duplicated, or posted to a publicly accessible website, in whole or in part.

3.78a

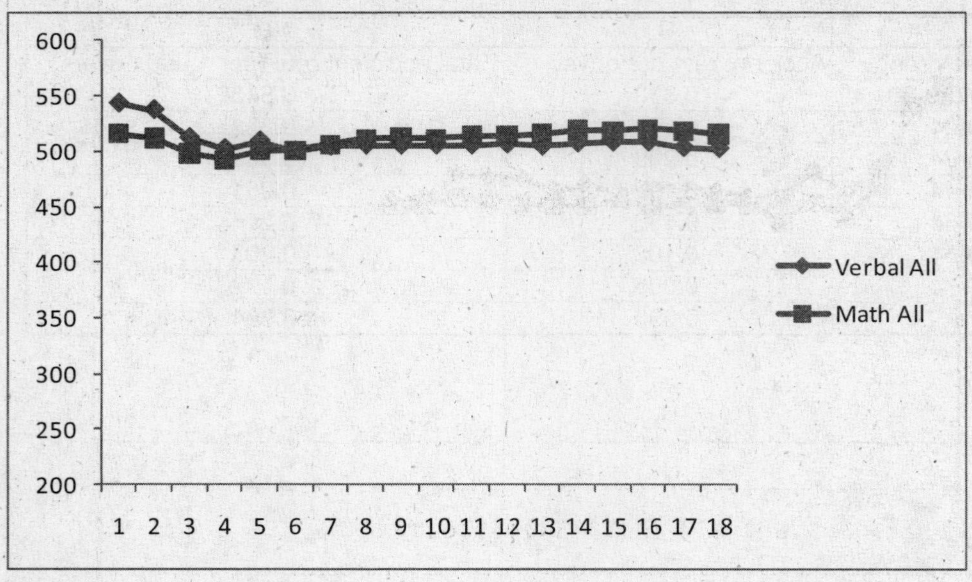

b

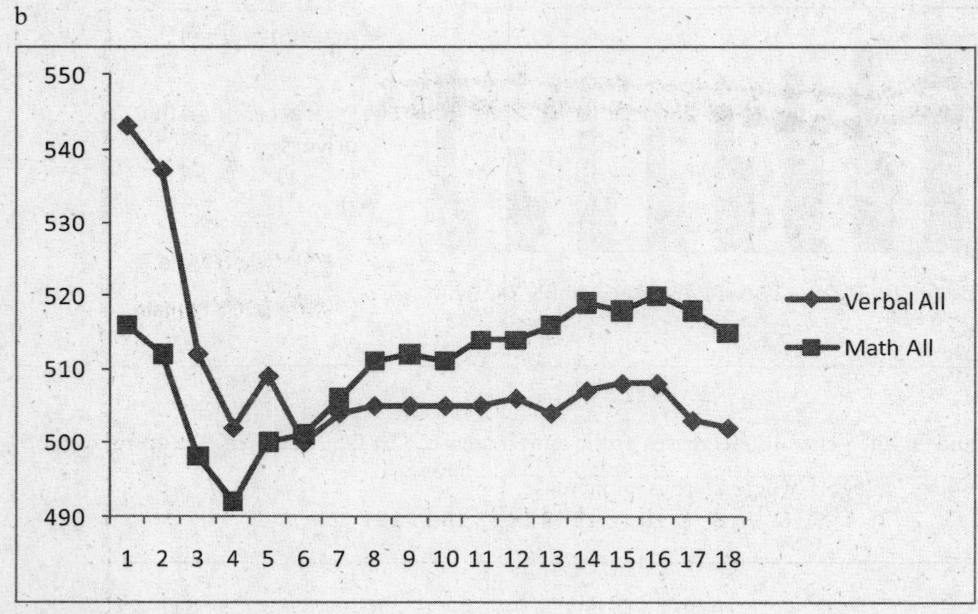

© 2012 Cengage Learning. All Rights Reserved. May not be scanned, copied or duplicated, or posted to a publicly accessible website, in whole or in part.

c

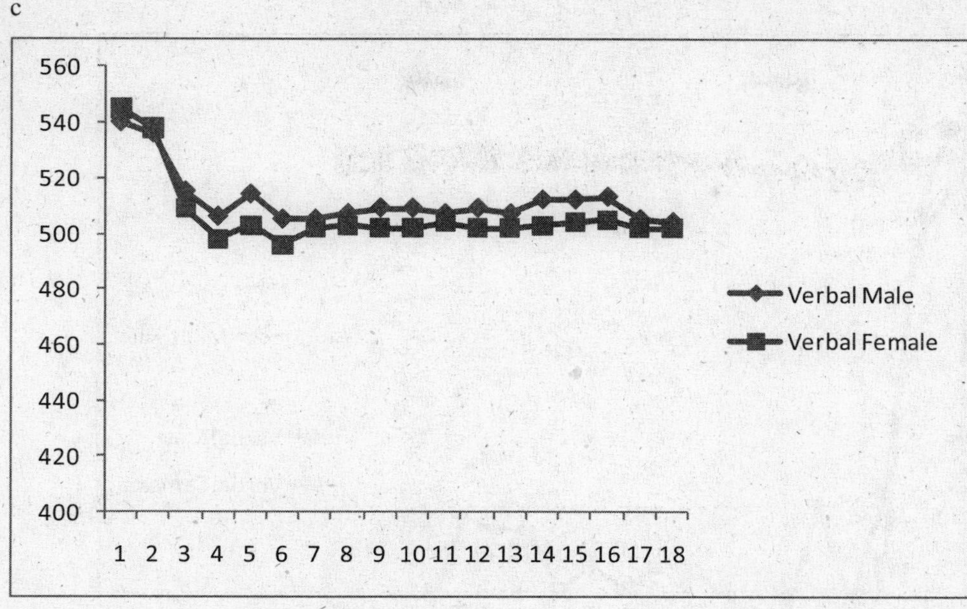

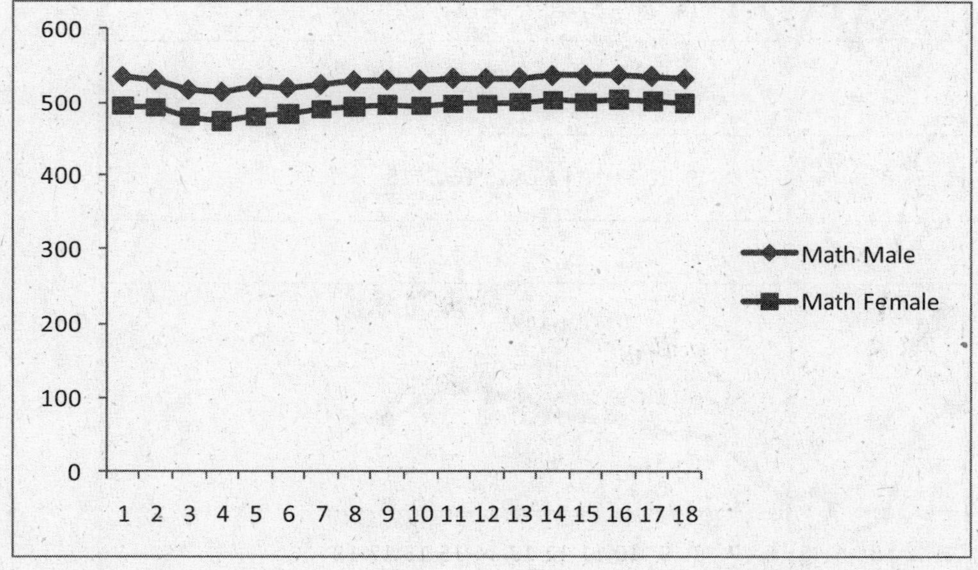

© 2012 Cengage Learning. All Rights Reserved. May not be scanned, copied or duplicated, or posted to a publicly accessible website, in whole or in part.

d

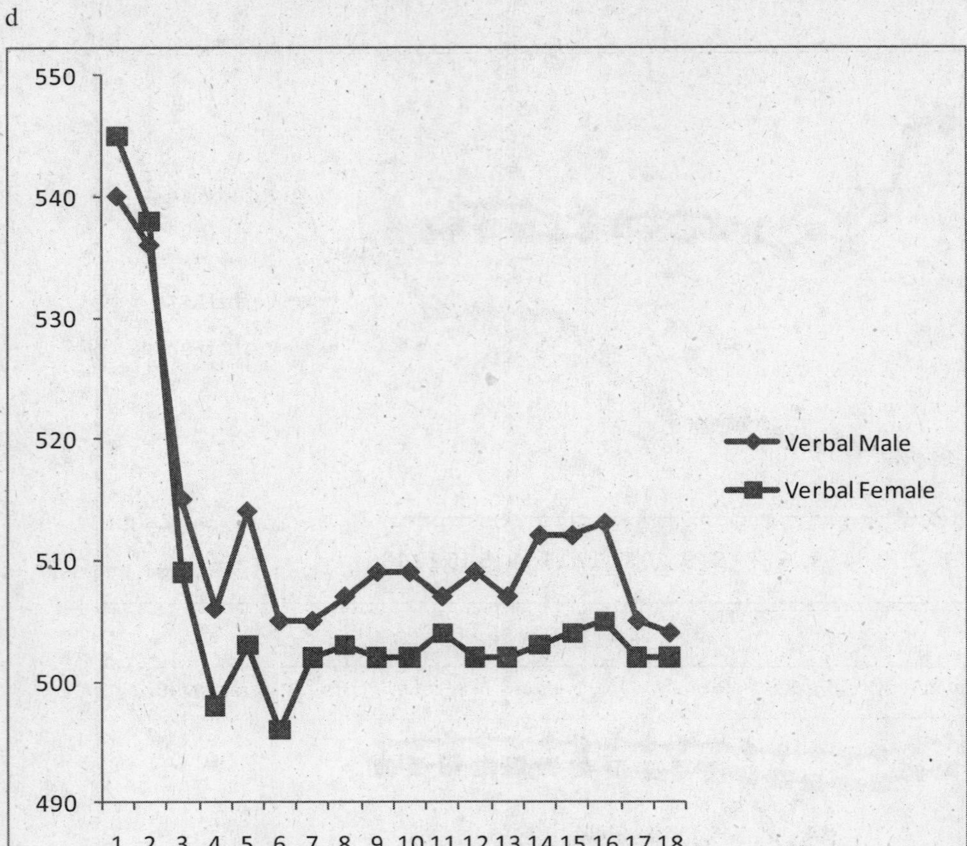

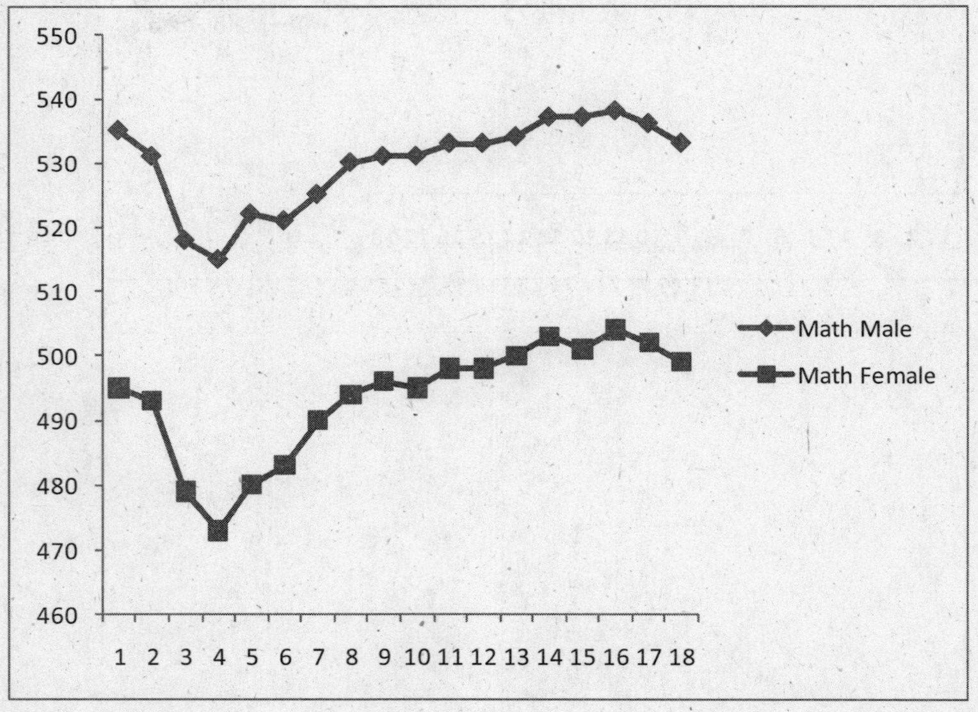

© 2012 Cengage Learning. All Rights Reserved. May not be scanned, copied or duplicated, or posted to a publicly accessible website, in whole or in part.

3.80 a

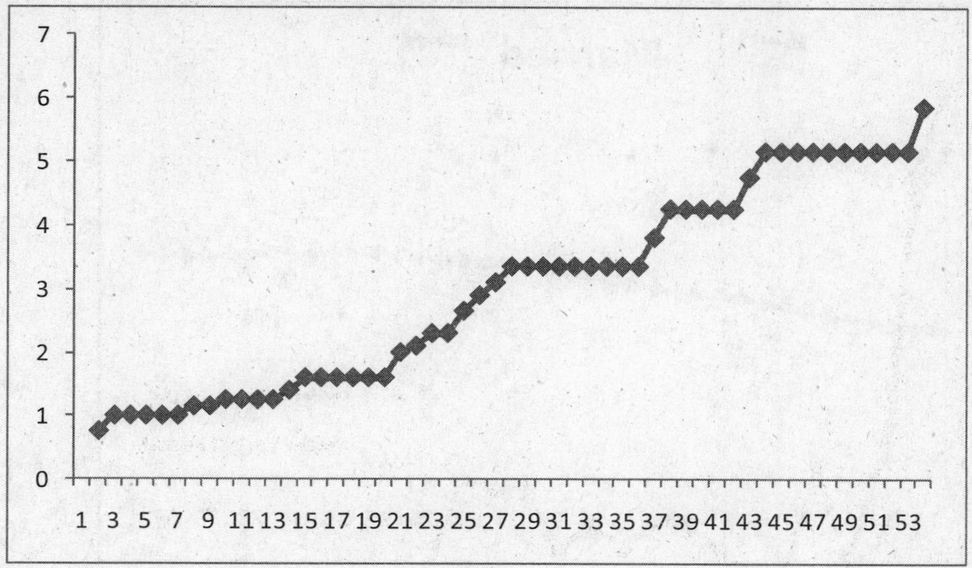

b To show actual changes it is probably best to show constant dollars on a graph with a 0.

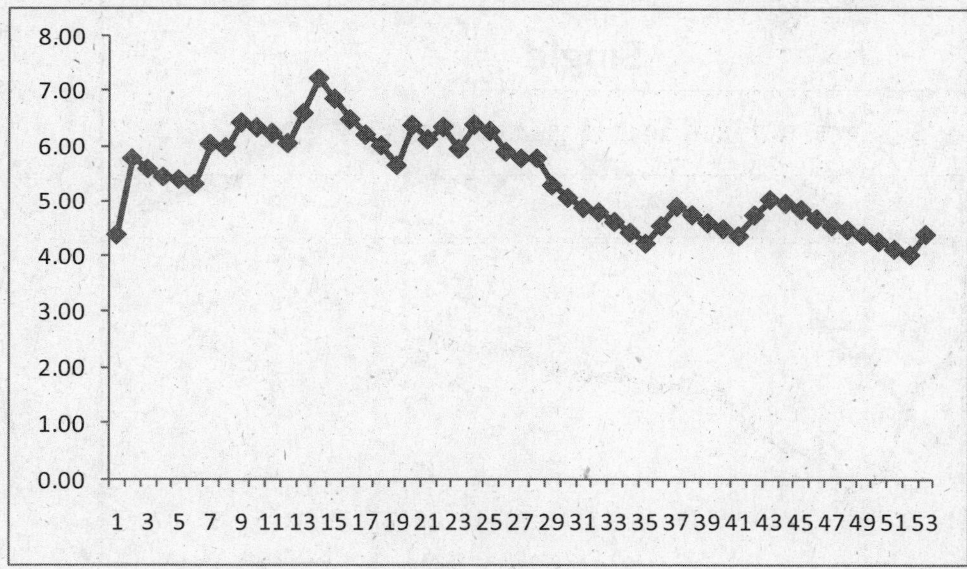

© 2012 Cengage Learning. All Rights Reserved. May not be scanned, copied or duplicated, or posted to a publicly accessible website, in whole or in part.

3.82 a

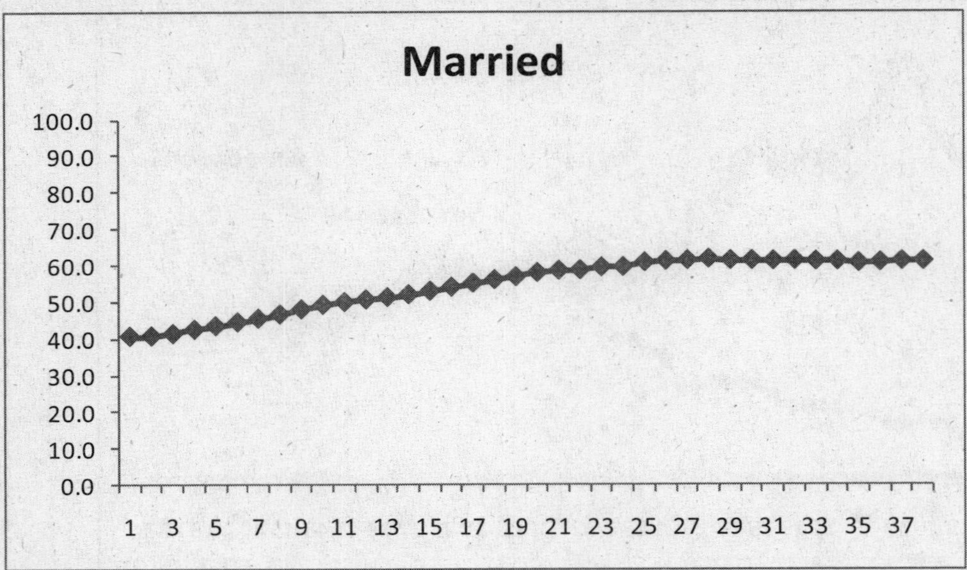

b

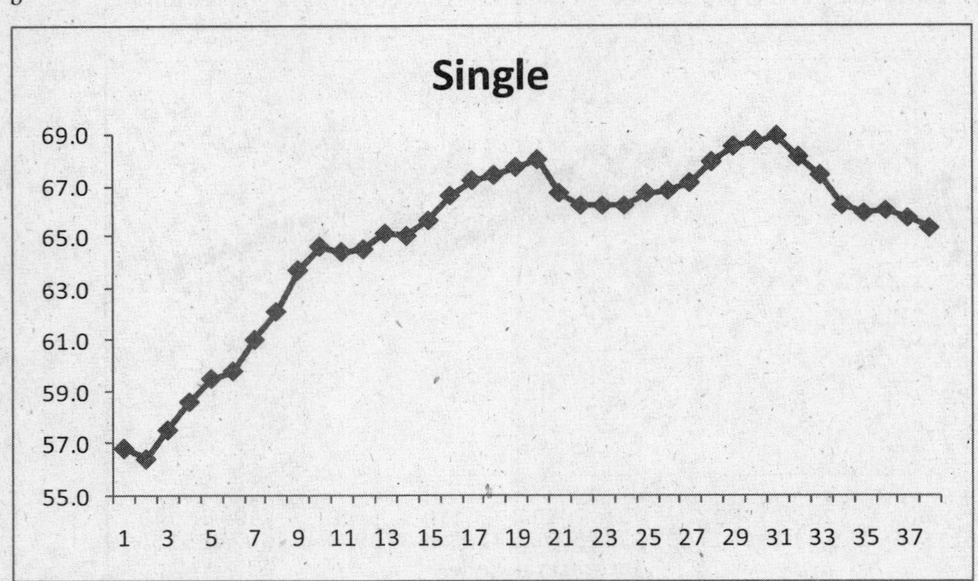

© 2012 Cengage Learning. All Rights Reserved. May not be scanned, copied or duplicated, or posted to a publicly accessible website, in whole or in part.

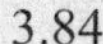

3.84

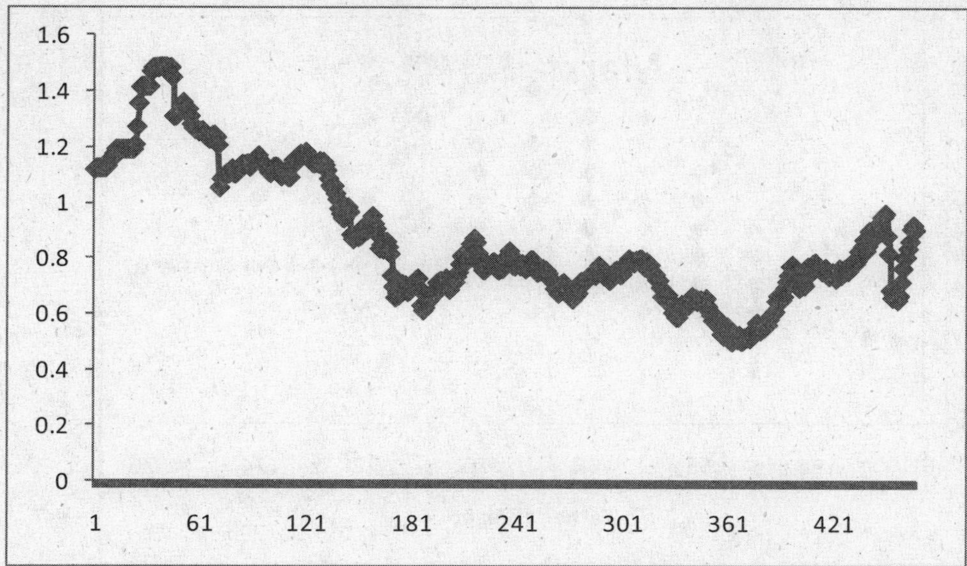

There has been a long-term decline in the value of the Australian dollar.

3.86

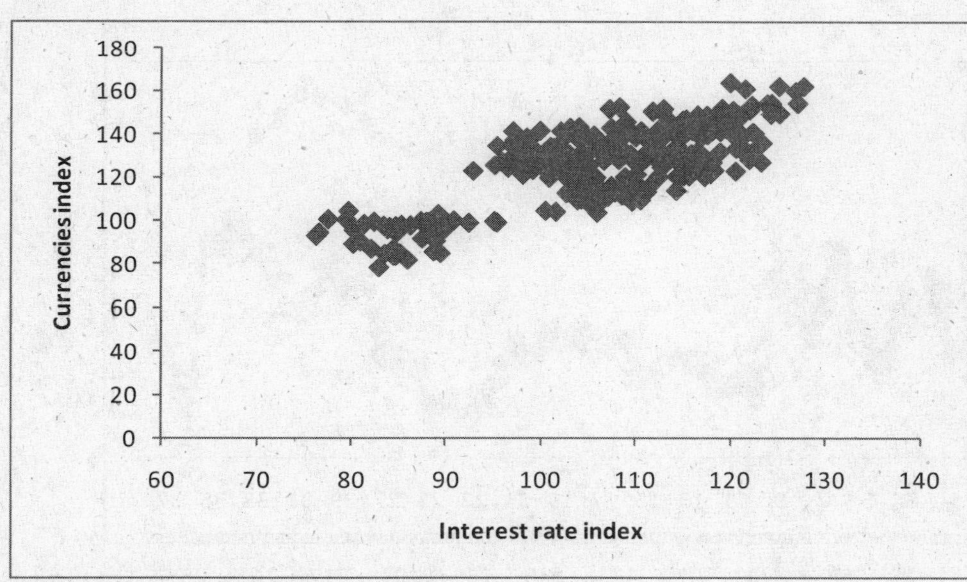

There is a very strong positive linear relationship.

© 2012 Cengage Learning. All Rights Reserved. May not be scanned, copied or duplicated, or posted to a publicly accessible website, in whole or in part.

3.88a

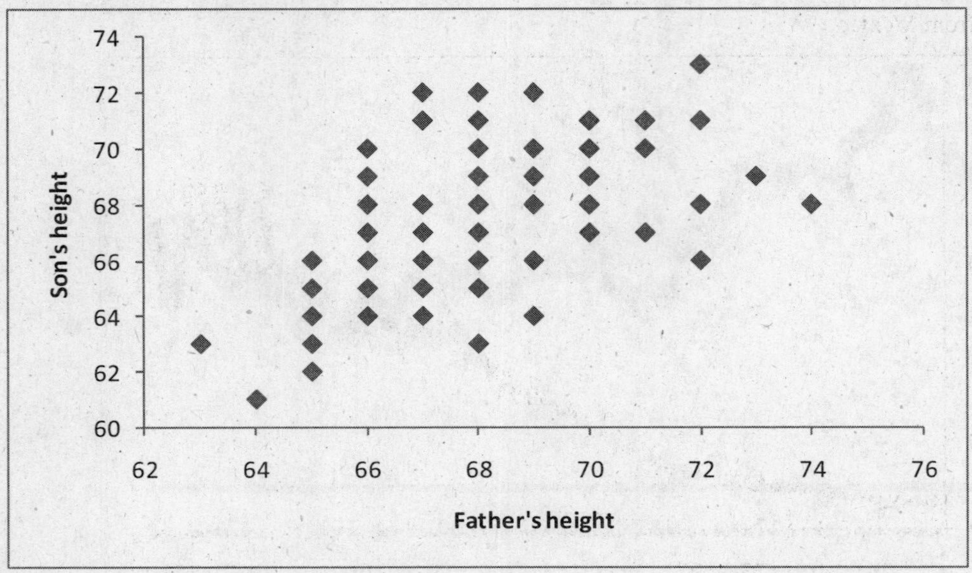

b. The slope is positive

c. There is a moderately strong linear relationship.

3.90

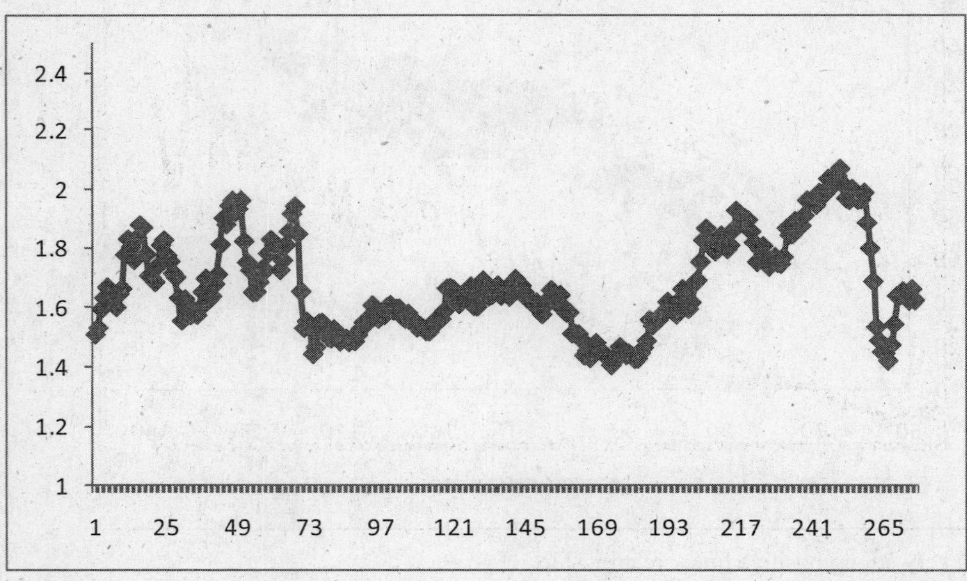

The value of the British pound has fluctuated quite a bit but the current exchange rate is close to the value in 1987.

© 2012 Cengage Learning. All Rights Reserved. May not be scanned, copied or duplicated, or posted to a publicly accessible website, in whole or in part.

3.92a

Imports from Mexico

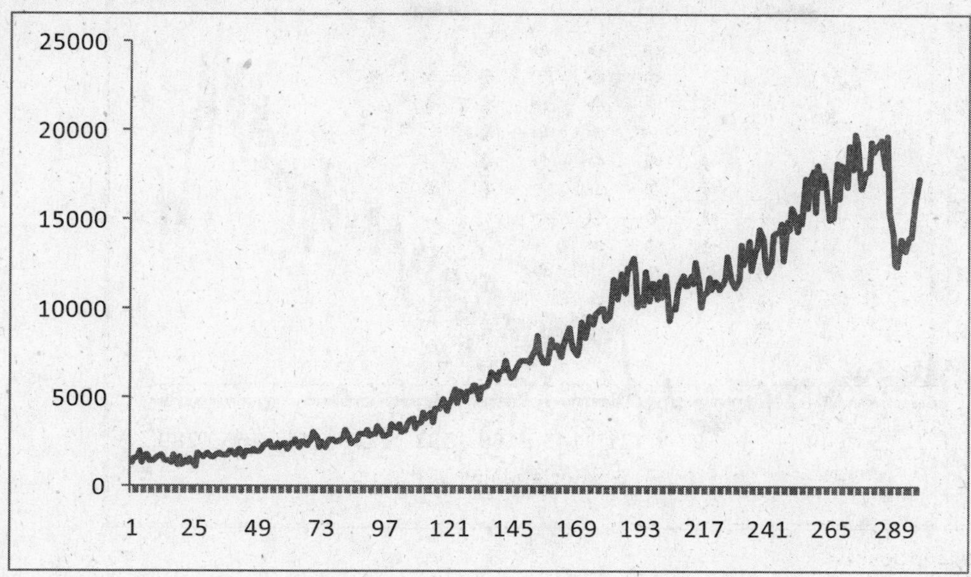

b. Exports to Mexico

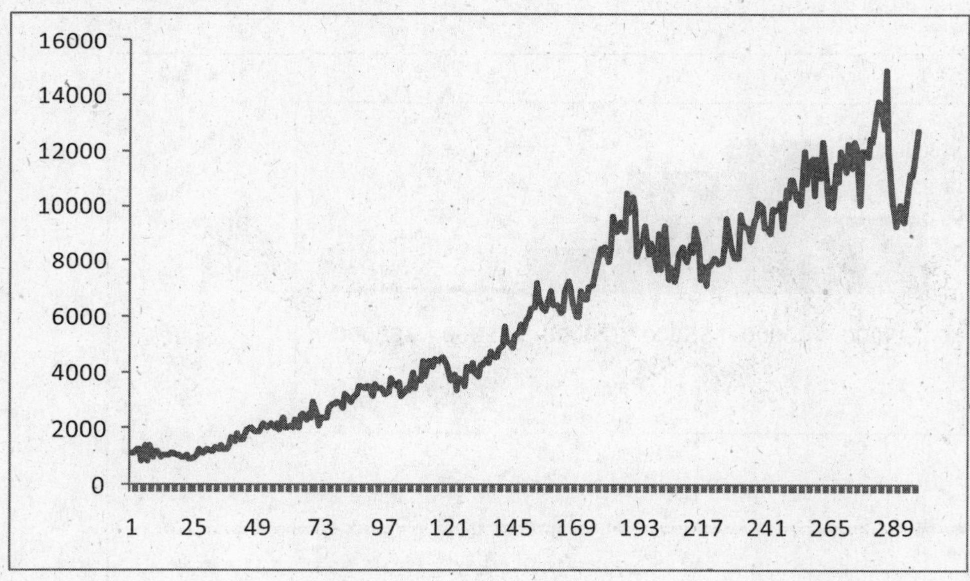

© 2012 Cengage Learning. All Rights Reserved. May not be scanned, copied or duplicated, or posted to a publicly accessible website, in whole or in part.

c. Balance of Trade (Imports from Mexico – exports to Mexico)

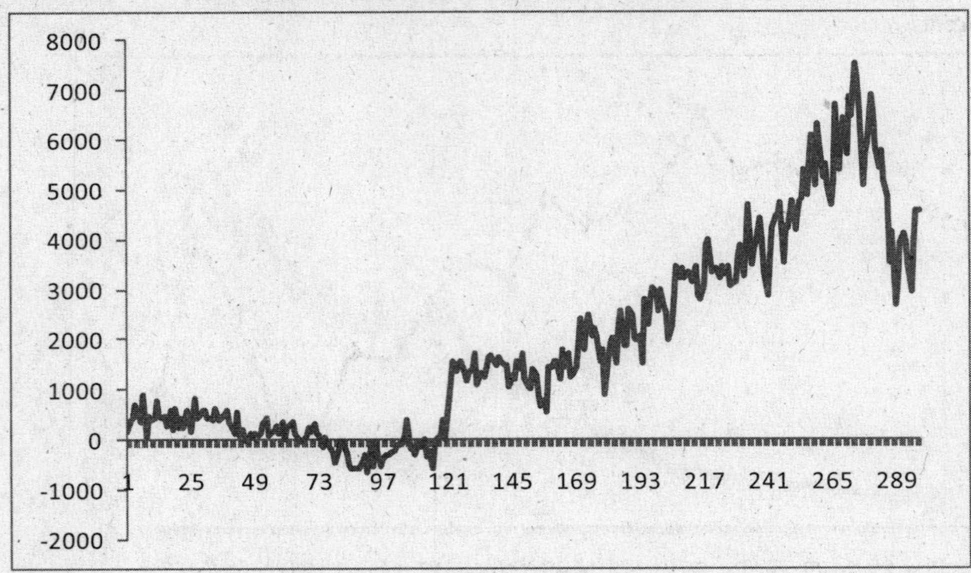

d. The United States imports more products from Mexico than it exports to Mexico. Moreover, the trade imbalance is worsening (only interrupted by the recession in 2008-2009).

3.94

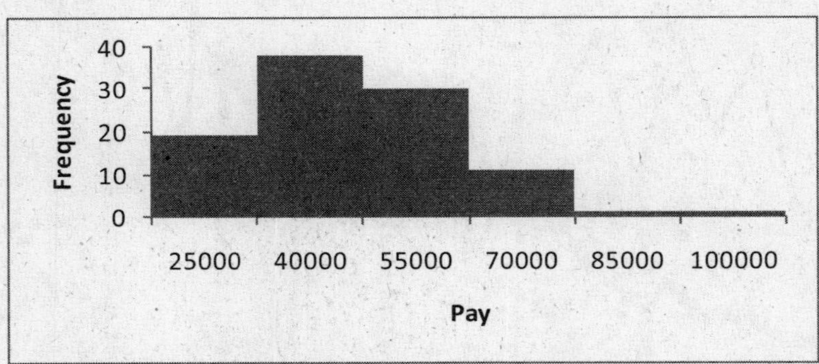

© 2012 Cengage Learning. All Rights Reserved. May not be scanned, copied or duplicated, or posted to a publicly accessible website, in whole or in part.

3.96

Fatal accidents

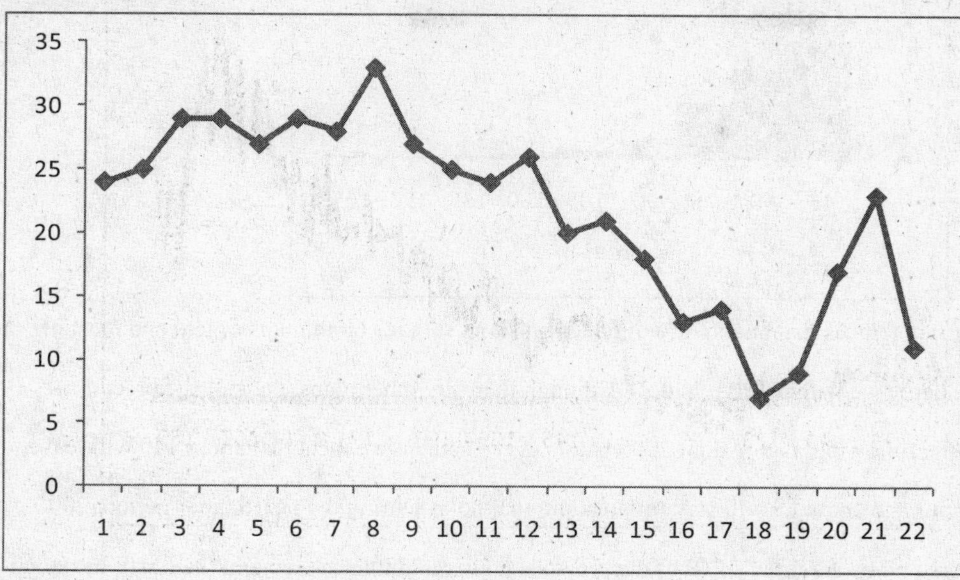

Passenger deaths

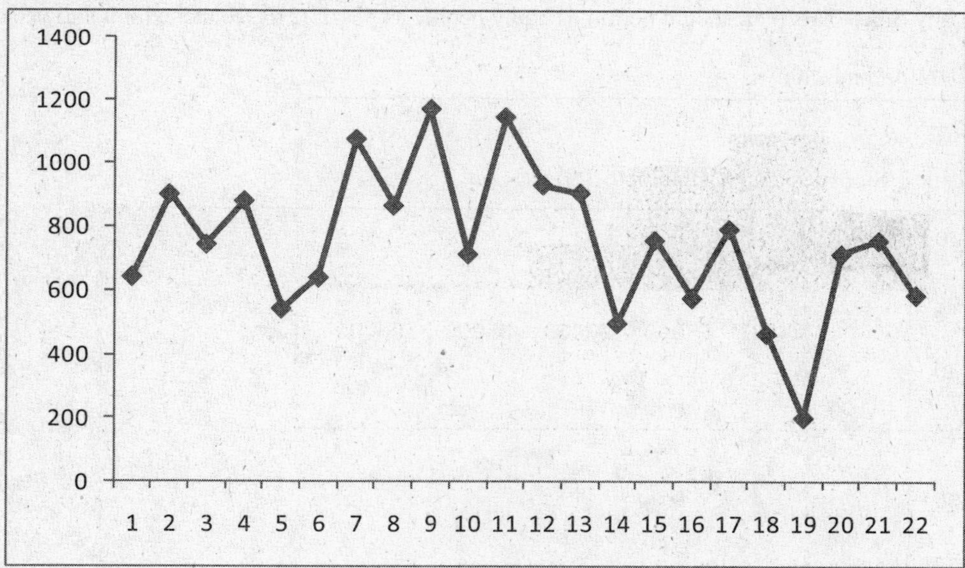

The number of fatal accidents and the number of deaths have been decreasing.

© 2012 Cengage Learning. All Rights Reserved. May not be scanned, copied or duplicated, or posted to a publicly accessible website, in whole or in part.

3.98

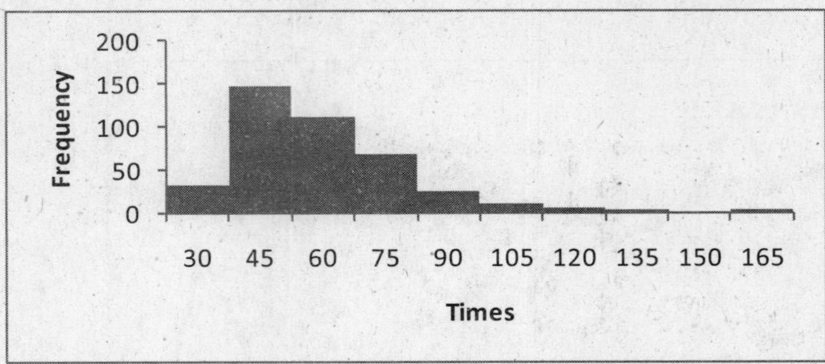

The histogram tells us that about 70% of gallery visitors stay for 60 minutes or less and most of the remainder leave within 120 minutes. Although there are other plans, the gallery director proposed the following plan. Admit 200 visitors every hour. We expect that about 140 will leave within 1 hour and about 60 will stay for an additional hour. During the next 1-hour period, 200 new visitors will be admitted. If 60 of the previous hour's admittances remain, there will be a total of 260 people in the gallery. If this pattern persists during the day, there will be a maximum of 260 visitors at any time. This plan should permit as many people as possible to see the exhibit and yet maintain comfort and safety.

3.100 Business Statistics course (Example 3.3)

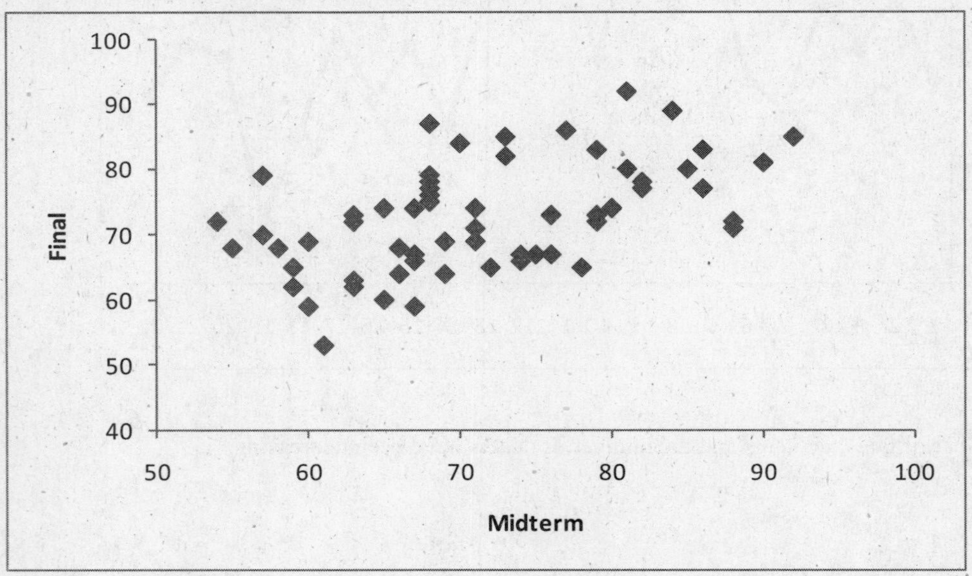

© 2012 Cengage Learning. All Rights Reserved. May not be scanned, copied or duplicated, or posted to a publicly accessible website, in whole or in part.

Mathematical Statistics course (Example 3.4)

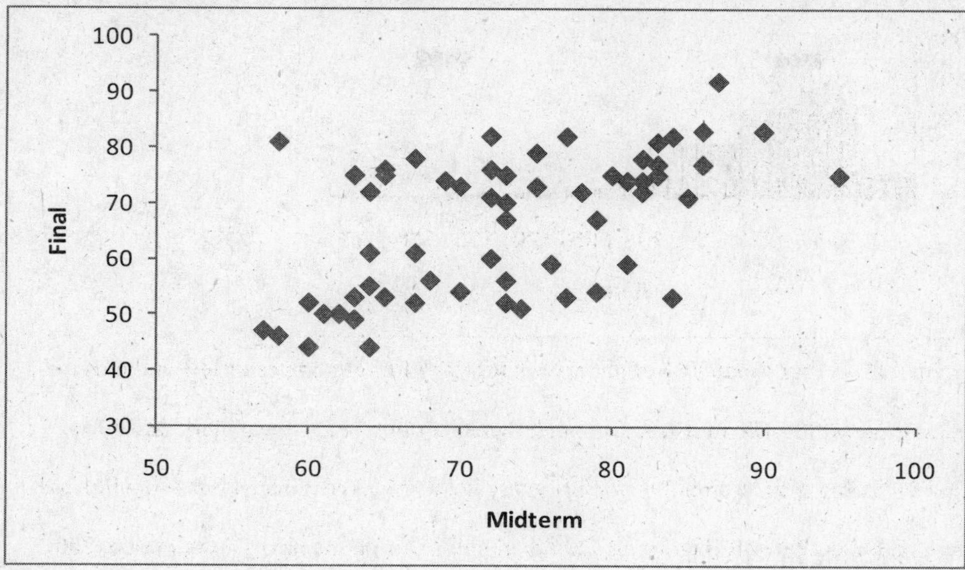

The relationship between midterm marks and final marks appear to be similar for both statistics courses. That is, there is weak positive linear relationship.

© 2012 Cengage Learning. All Rights Reserved. May not be scanned, copied or duplicated, or posted to a publicly accessible website, in whole or in part.

Chapter 4

4.2 $\bar{x} = \frac{\sum x_i}{n} = \frac{5+7+0+3+15+6+5+9+3+8+10+5+2+0+12}{15} = \frac{90}{15} = 6.0$

Ordered data: 0, 0, 2, 3, 3, 5, 5, 5, 6, 7, 8, 9, 10, 12, 15; Median = 5

Mode = 5

4.4a $\bar{x} = \frac{\sum x_i}{n} = \frac{33+29+45+60+42+19+52+38+36}{9} = \frac{354}{9} = 39.3$

Ordered data: 19, 29, 33, 36, 38, 42, 45, 52, 60; Median = 38

Mode: all

b The mean amount of time is 39.3 minutes. Half the group took less than 38 minutes.

4.6 $R_g = \sqrt[3]{(1+R_1)(1+R_2)(1+R_3)} - 1 = \sqrt[3]{(1+.25)(1-.10)(1+.50)} - 1 = .19$

4.8 a $\bar{x} = \frac{\sum x_i}{n} = \frac{.10+.22+.06-.05+.20}{5} = \frac{.53}{5} = .106$

Ordered data: –.05, .06, .10, .20, .22; Median = .10

b $R_g = \sqrt[5]{(1+R_1)(1+R_2)(1+R_3)(1+R_4)(1+R_5)} - 1 =$

$\sqrt[5]{(1+.10)(1+.22)(1+.06)(1-.05)(1+.20)} - 1 = .102$

c The geometric mean is best.

4.10a Year 1 rate of return = $\frac{1200-1000}{1000} = .20$

Year 2 rate of return = $\frac{1200-1200}{1200} = 0$

Year 3 rate of return = $\frac{1500-1200}{1200} = .25$

Year 4 rate of return = $\frac{2000-1500}{1500} = .33$

b $\bar{x} = \frac{\sum x_i}{n} = \frac{.20+0+.25+.33}{4} = \frac{.78}{4} = .195$

Ordered data: 0, .20, .25, .33; Median = .225

c $R_g = \sqrt[4]{(1+R_1)(1+R_2)(1+R_3)(1+R_4)} - 1 = \sqrt[4]{(1+.20)(1+0)(1+.25)(1+.33)} - 1 = .188$

© 2012 Cengage Learning. All Rights Reserved. May not be scanned, copied or duplicated, or posted to a publicly accessible website, in whole or in part.

d The geometric mean is best because $1000(1.188)^4 = 2000$.

4.12a $\bar{x} = 75{,}750$; median = 76,410

b The mean starting salary is \$75,750. Half the sample earned less than \$76,410.

4.14a $\bar{x} = 117.08$; median = 124.00

b The mean expenditure is \$117.08 and half the sample spent less than \$1246.00.

4.16a $\bar{x} = .81$; median = .83

b The mean percentage is .81. Half the sample paid less than .83.

4.18a $\bar{x} = 592.04$; median = 591.00

b The mean expenditure is \$592.04. Half the sample spent less than \$591.00

$$4.20\ \bar{x} = \frac{\sum x_i}{n} = \frac{4+5+3+6+5+6+5+6}{8} = \frac{40}{8} = 5$$

$$s^2 = \frac{\sum (x_i - \bar{x})^2}{n-1} = \frac{[(4-5)^2 + (5-5)^2 + ... + (6-5)^2}{8-1} = \frac{8}{7} = 1.14$$

$$4.22\ \bar{x} = \frac{\sum x_i}{n} = \frac{0+(-5)+(-3)+6+4+(-4)+1+(-5)+0+3}{10} = \frac{-3}{10} = -.30$$

$$s^2 = \frac{\sum (x_i - \bar{x})^2}{n-1} = \frac{[(0-(-.3))^2 + ((-5)-(-.3))^2 + ... + (3-(-.3))^2}{10-1} = \frac{136.1}{9} = 15.12$$

$$s = \sqrt{s^2} = \sqrt{15.12} = 3.89$$

4.24 a: $s^2 = 51.5$

b: $s^2 = 6.5$

c: $s^2 = 174.5$

4.26 6, 6, 6, 6, 6

4.28 a From the empirical rule we know that approximately 68% of the observations fall between 46 and 54. Thus 16% are less than 46 (the other 16% are above 54).

© 2012 Cengage Learning. All Rights Reserved. May not be scanned, copied or duplicated, or posted to a publicly accessible website, in whole or in part.

b Approximately 95% of the observations are between 42 and 58. Thus, only 2.5% are above 58 and all the rest, 97.5% are below 58.

c See (a) above; 16% are above 54.

4.30 a Nothing

b At least 75% lie between 60 and 180.

c At least 88.9% lie between 30 and 210.

4.32 $s^2 = 40.73 \text{ mph}^2$ and s = 6.38 mph; at least 75% of the speeds lie within 12.76 mph of the mean;

at least 88.9% of the speeds lie within 19.14 mph of the mean

4.34 $s^2 = .0858 \text{ cm}^2$, and s = .2929 cm; at least 75% of the lengths lie within .5858 of the mean; at least 88.9% of the rods will lie within .8787 cm of the mean.

4.36a s = 15.01

b In approximately 68% of the days the number of arrivals falls within 15.01 of the mean; in approximately 95% of the hours the number of arrivals falls within 30.02 of the mean; in approximately 99.7% of the hours the number of arrivals falls within 45.03 of the mean

4.38a $\bar{x} = 77.86$ and s = 85.35

b.

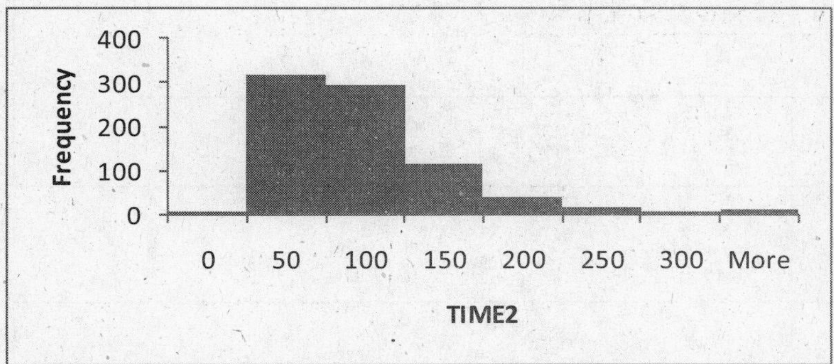

c. The histogram is positively skewed; we must use Chebysheff's Theorem. At least 75% of American adults watch between 0 and 249 minutes of television news.

4.40 First quartile: $L_{25} = (15+1)\frac{25}{100} = (16)(.25) = 4$; the fourth number is 3.

© 2012 Cengage Learning. All Rights Reserved. May not be scanned, copied or duplicated, or posted to a publicly accessible website, in whole or in part.

Second quartile: $L_{50} = (15+1)\frac{50}{100}$ = (16)(.5) = 8; the eighth number is 5.

Third quartile: $L_{75} = (15+1)\frac{75}{100}$ = (16)(.75) = 12; the twelfth number is 7.

4.42 20th percentile: $L_{20} = (10+1)\frac{20}{100}$ = (11)(.20) = 2.2; the 20th percentile is 43 + .2(51–43) = 44.6.

40th percentile: $L_{40} = (10+1)\frac{40}{100}$ = (11)(.40) = 4.4; the 40th percentile is 52 +.4(60–52) = 55.2.

4.44 Third decile: $L_{30} = (15+1)\frac{30}{100}$ = (16)(.30) = 4.8; the third decile is 5 + .8(7 – 5) = 6.6.

Sixth decile: $L_{60} = (15+1)\frac{60}{100}$ = (16)(.60) = 9.6; the sixth decile is 17 + .6(18 – 17) = 17.6.

4.46 Interquartile range = 7 – 3 = 4

4.48

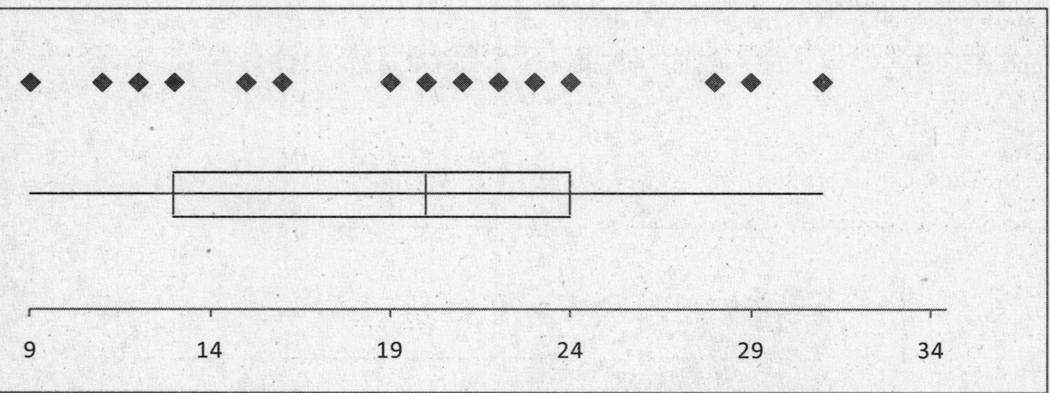

4.50

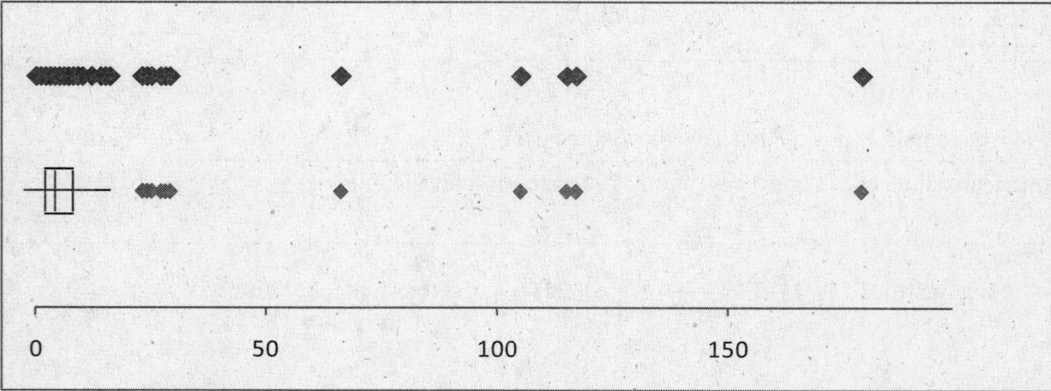

© 2012 Cengage Learning. All Rights Reserved. May not be scanned, copied or duplicated, or posted to a publicly accessible website, in whole or in part.

a First quartile = 2, second quartile = 4, and third quartile = 8.

b Most executives spend little time reading resumes. Keep it short.

4.52 First quartile = 50, second quartile = 125, and third quartile = 260. The amounts are positively skewed.

4.54a

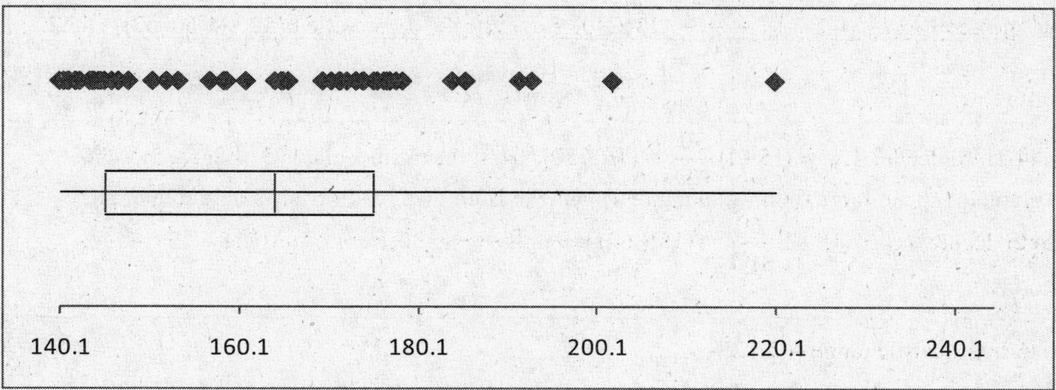

b The quartiles are 145.11, 164.17, and 175.18

c There are no outliers.

d The data are positively skewed. One-quarter of the times are below 145.11 and one-quarter are above 175.18.

4.56a The quartiles are 26, 28.5, and 32

b the times are positively skewed.

4.58 TIME1

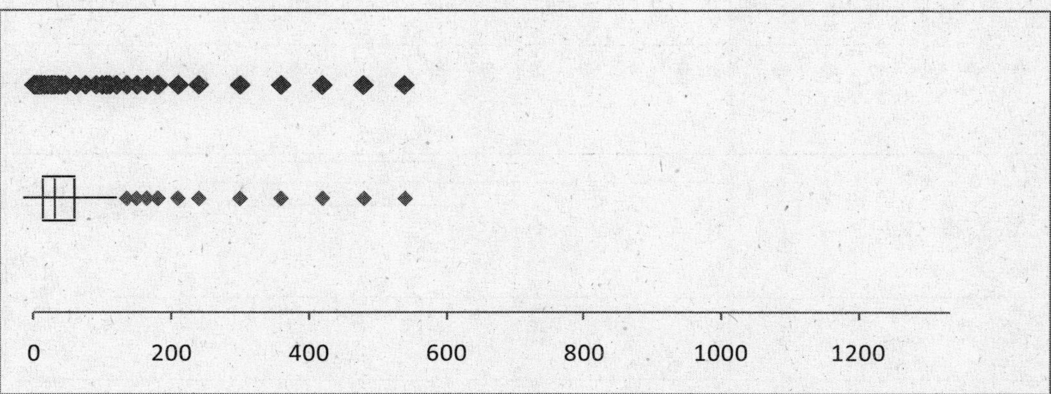

© 2012 Cengage Learning. All Rights Reserved. May not be scanned, copied or duplicated, or posted to a publicly accessible website, in whole or in part.

TIME2

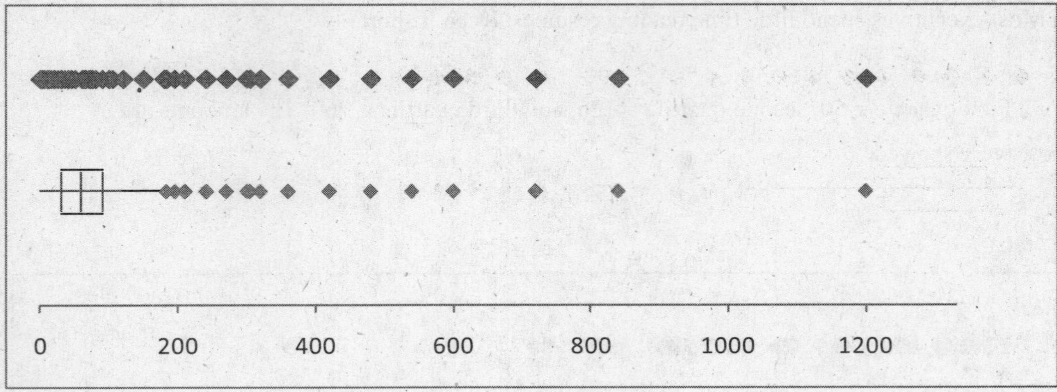

Americans spend more time watching news on television than reading news on the Internet.

4.60 EDUC

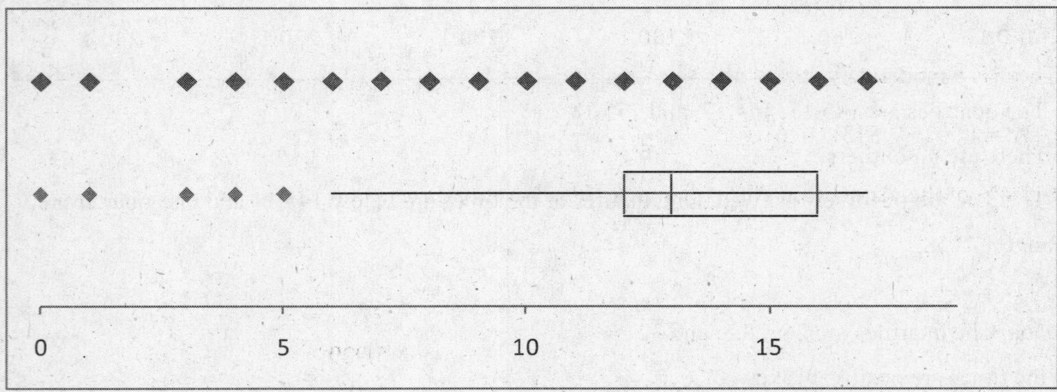

SPEDUC

The two sets of numbers are quite similar.

© 2012 Cengage Learning. All Rights Reserved. May not be scanned, copied or duplicated, or posted to a publicly accessible website, in whole or in part.

4.62 The quartiles are 1, 2, 4

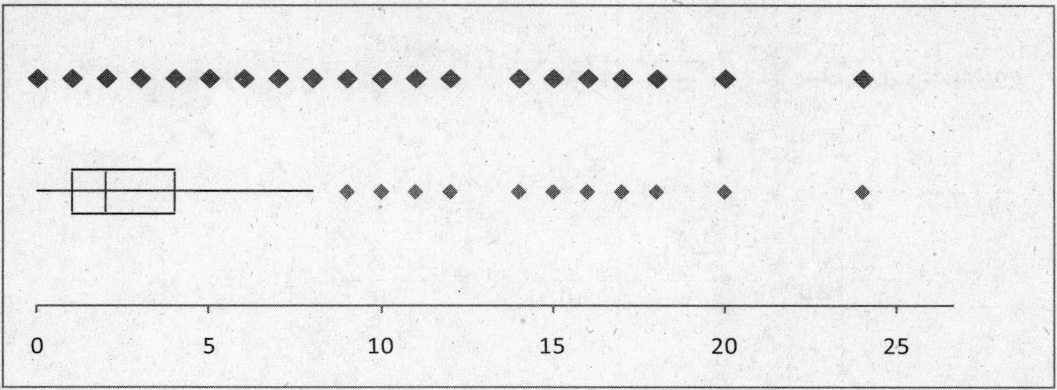

The number of hours of television watching is highly positively skewed.

4.64a $r = \frac{s_{xy}}{s_x s_y} = \frac{-150}{(16)(12)} = -.7813$

There is a moderately strong negative linear relationship.

b. $R^2 = r^2 = (-.7813)^2 = .6104$

61.04% of the variation in y is explained by the variation in x.

4.66	x_i	y_i	x_i^2	y_i^2	$x_i y_i$
	40	77	1,600	5,929	3,080
	42	63	1,764	3,969	2,646
	37	79	1,369	6,241	2,923
	47	86	2,209	7,396	4,041
	25	51	625	2,601	1,276
	44	78	1,936	6,084	3,432
	41	83	1,681	6,889	3,403
	48	90	2,304	8,100	4,320
	35	65	1,225	4,225	2,275
	28	47	784	2,209	1,316
Total	387	719	15,497	53,643	28,712

$\sum_{i=1}^{n} x_i = 387$ $\sum_{i=1}^{n} y_i = 719$ $\sum_{i=1}^{n} x_i^2 = 15{,}497$ $\sum_{i=1}^{n} y_i^2 = 53{,}643$ $\sum_{i=1}^{n} x_i y_i = 28{,}712$

a $$s_{xy} = \frac{1}{n-1}\left[\sum_{i=1}^{n} x_i y_i - \frac{\sum_{i=1}^{n} x_i \sum_{i=1}^{n} y_i}{n}\right] = \frac{1}{10-1}\left[28{,}712 - \frac{(387)(719)}{10}\right] = 98.52$$

© 2012 Cengage Learning. All Rights Reserved. May not be scanned, copied or duplicated, or posted to a publicly accessible website, in whole or in part.

$$s_x^2 = \frac{1}{n-1}\left[\sum_{i=1}^{n} x_i^2 - \frac{\left(\sum_{i=1}^{n} x_i\right)^2}{n}\right] = \frac{1}{10-1}\left[15{,}497 - \frac{(387)^2}{10}\right] = 57.79$$

$$s_y^2 = \frac{1}{n-1}\left[\sum_{i=1}^{n} y_i^2 - \frac{\left(\sum_{i=1}^{n} y_i\right)^2}{n}\right] = \frac{1}{10-1}\left[53{,}643 - \frac{(719)^2}{10}\right] = 216.32$$

b $$r = \frac{s_{xy}}{s_x s_y} = \frac{98.52}{\sqrt{(57.79)(216.32)}} = .8811$$

c $$R^2 = r^2 = .8811^2 = .7763$$

d $$b_1 = \frac{s_{xy}}{s_x^2} = \frac{98.52}{57.79} = 1.705$$

$$\bar{x} = \frac{\sum x_i}{n} = \frac{387}{10} = 38.7$$

$$\bar{y} = \frac{\sum y_i}{n} = \frac{719}{10} = 71.9$$

$$b_0 = \bar{y} - b_1\bar{x} = 71.9 - (1.705)(38.7) = 5.917$$

The least squares line is

$$\hat{y} = 5.917 + 1.705x$$

e There is a strong positive linear relationship between marks and study time. For each additional hour of study time marks increased on average by 1.705.

4.68

	A	B	C
1		*Unemployment Rate*	*Employment Rate*
2	Unemployment Rate	1	
3	Employment Rate	-0.6332	1

$R^2 = r^2 = (-.6332)^2 = .4009$; 40.09% of the variation in the employment rate is explained by the variation in the unemployment rate.

© 2012 Cengage Learning. All Rights Reserved. May not be scanned, copied or duplicated, or posted to a publicly accessible website, in whole or in part.

4.70

	A	B	C
1		*Rate*	*Houses*
2	Rate	1	
3	Houses	-0.2435	1

$R^2 = (-.2435)^2 = .0593$

Only 5.93% of the variation in the number of houses sold is explained by the variation in interest rates.

4.72

	A	B	C
1		*Unemployment rate*	*Help wanted index*
2	Unemployment rate	1	
3	Help wanted index	0.0830	1

$R^2 = (.0830)^2 = .0069.$

There is a very weak positive relationship between the two variables.

4.74

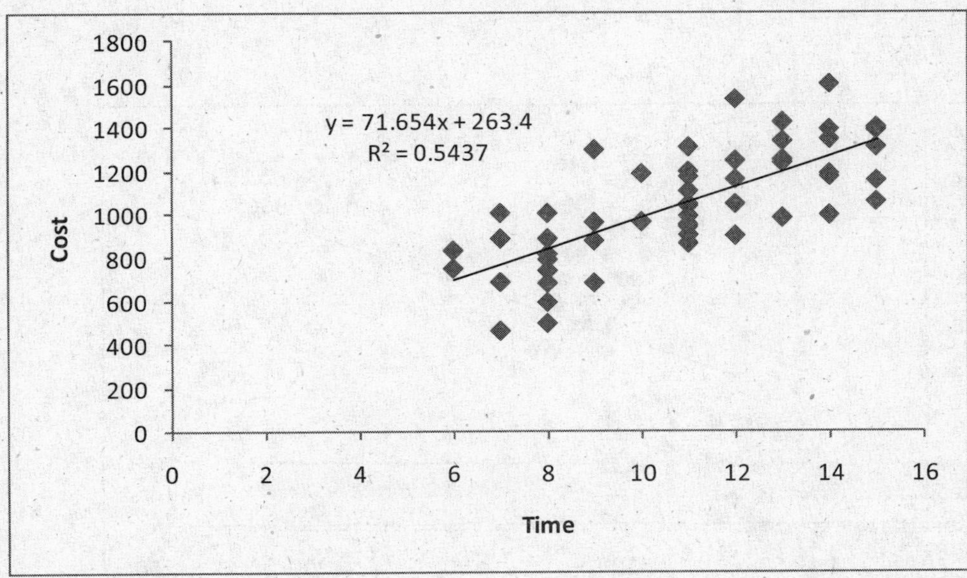

$\hat{y} = 263.4 + 71.65x$; Estimated fixed costs = \$263.40, estimated variable costs = \$71.65

© 2012 Cengage Learning. All Rights Reserved. May not be scanned, copied or duplicated, or posted to a publicly accessible website, in whole or in part.

4.76a

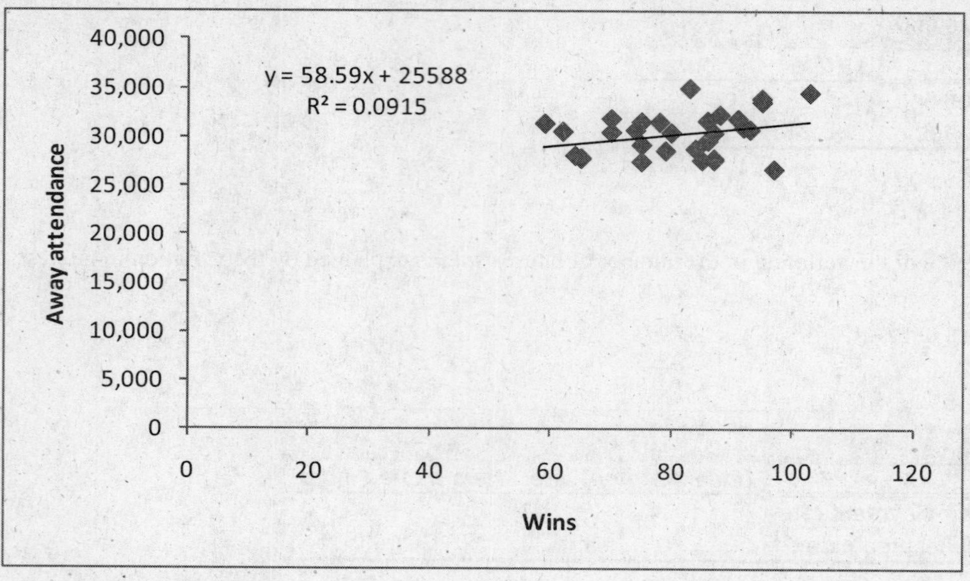

$R^2 = .0915$; there is a very weak relationship between the two variables.

b The slope coefficient is 58.59; away attendance increases on average by 58.59 for each win. However, the relationship is very weak.

4.78

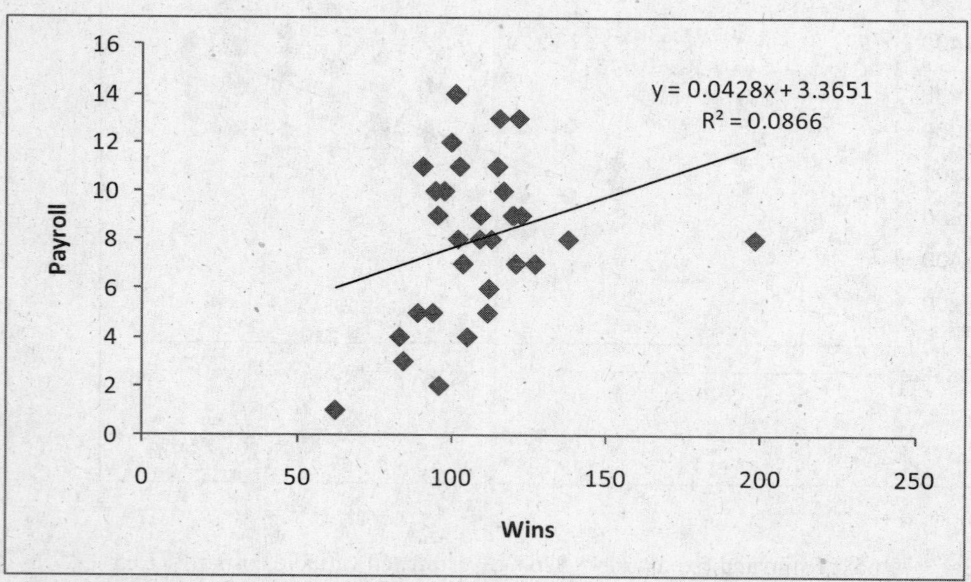

a. The slope coefficient is .0428; for each million dollars in payroll the number of wins increases on average by .0428. Thus, to cost of winning one addition game is 1/.0428 million = $23.364 million.

b. The coefficient of determination = .0866, which reveals that the linear relationship is very weak.

© 2012 Cengage Learning. All Rights Reserved. May not be scanned, copied or duplicated, or posted to a publicly accessible website, in whole or in part.

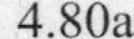

4.80a

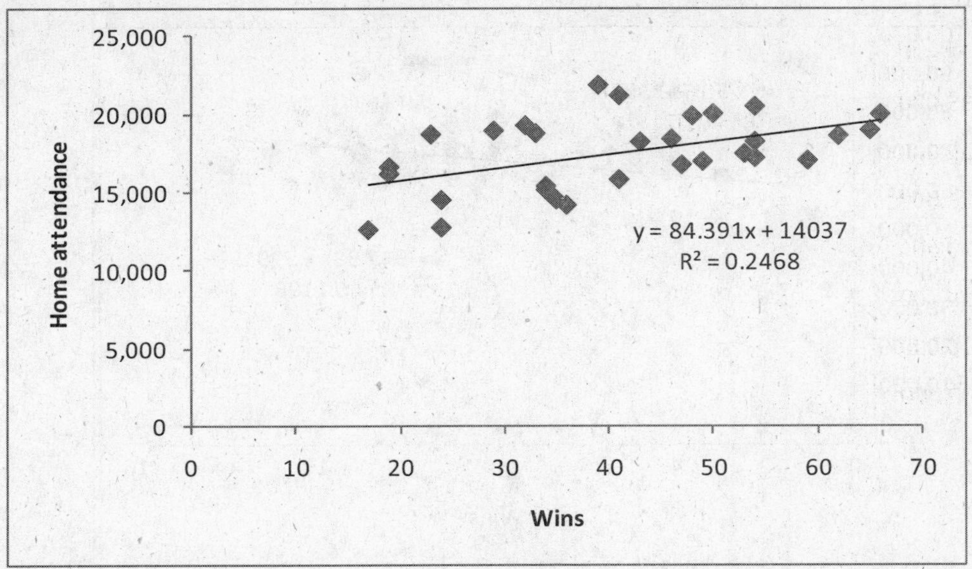

For each additional win home attendance increases on average by 84.391. The coefficient of determination is .2468; there is a weak relationship between the number of wins and home attendance.

b

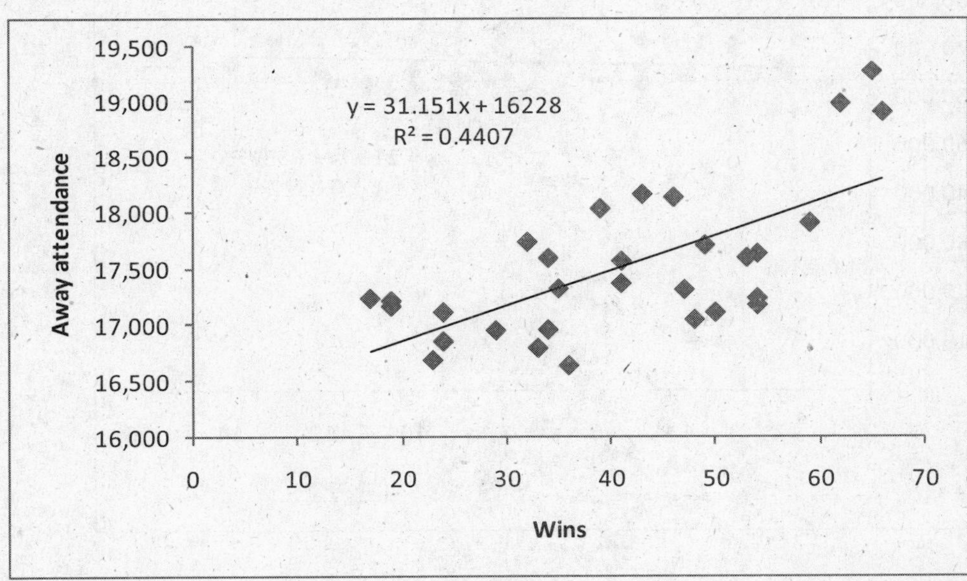

For each additional win away attendance increases on average by 31.151. The coefficient of determination is .4407; there is a moderately strong relationship between the number of wins and away attendance.

© 2012 Cengage Learning. All Rights Reserved. May not be scanned, copied or duplicated, or posted to a publicly accessible website, in whole or in part.

4.82

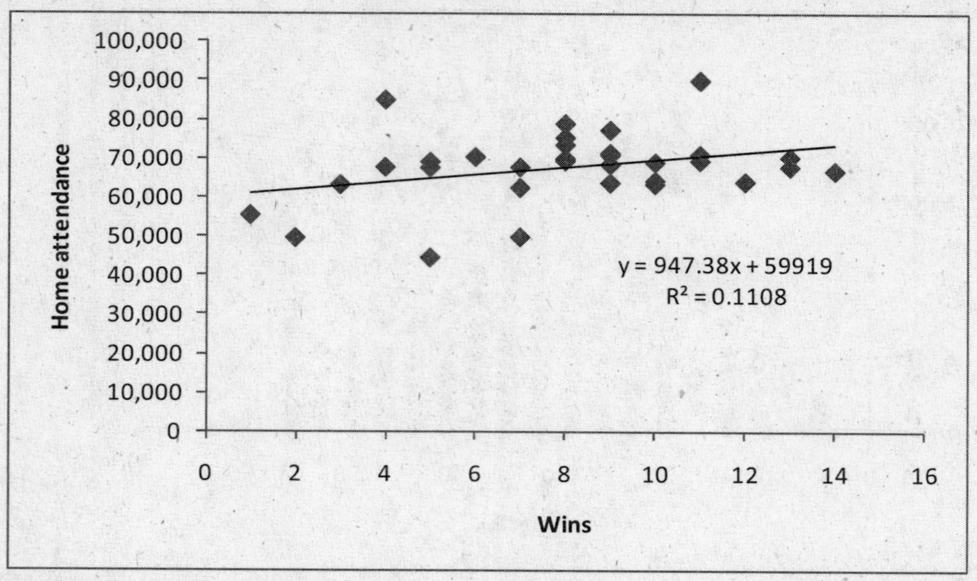

For each additional win home attendance increases on average by 947.38. The coefficient of determination is .1108; there is a very weak linear relationship between the number of wins and home attendance.

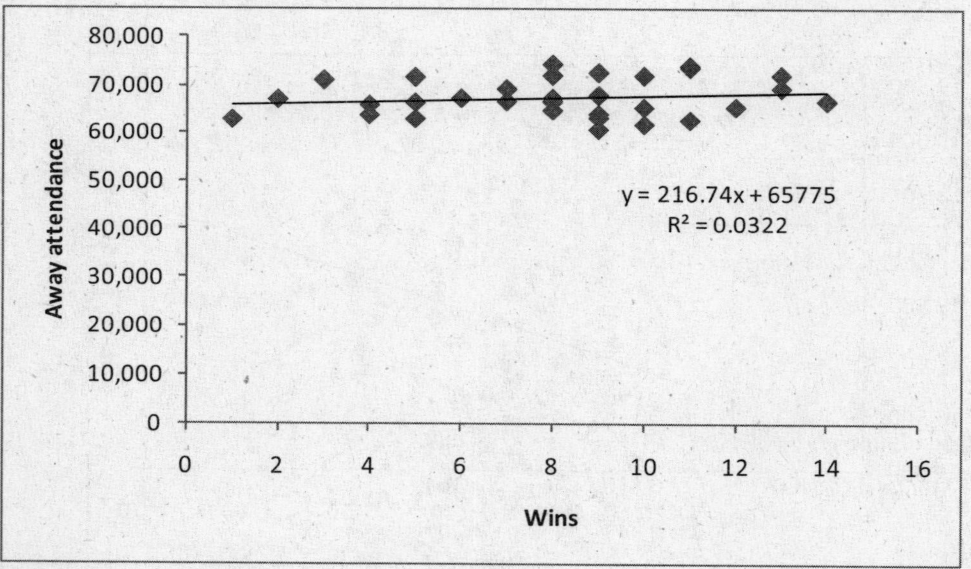

For each additional win away attendance increases on average by 216.74. The coefficient of determination is .0322; there is a very weak linear relationship between the number of wins and away attendance.

© 2012 Cengage Learning. All Rights Reserved. May not be scanned, copied or duplicated, or posted to a publicly accessible website, in whole or in part.

4.84a

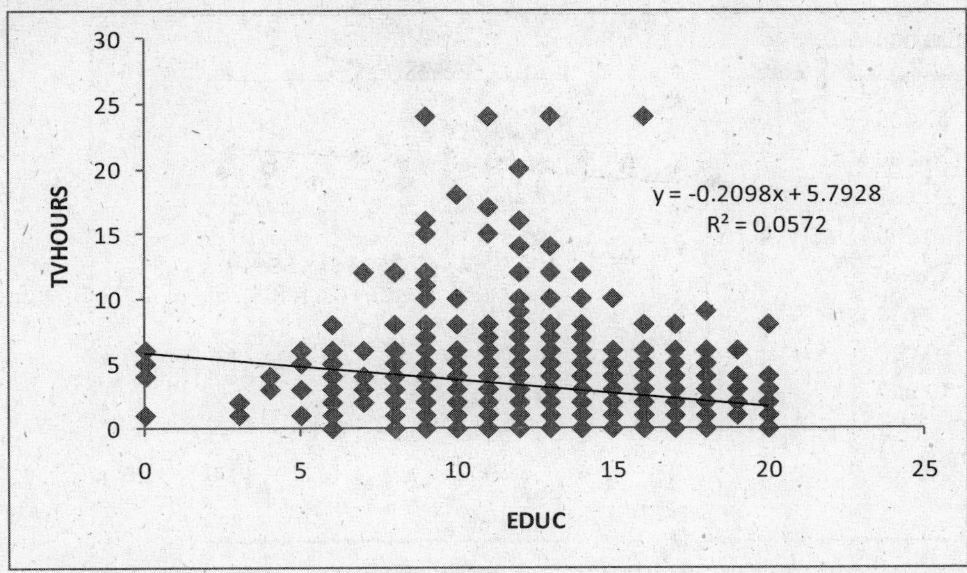

There is a weak negative linear relationship between education and television watching.

b R^2 = .0572; 5.72% of the variation in the amount of television is explained by the variation in education.

4.86 Correlation matrix

	A	B	C
1		*AGE*	*TIME2*
2	AGE	1	
3	TIME2	0.2107	1

There is a weak positive linear relationship between the two variables.

4.88	b_1	R^2
Barrick Gold	0.594	.071
Bell Canada Enterprises (BCE)	0.399	.089
Bank of Montreal (BMO)	0.610	.164
Enbridge	0.314	.109
Fortis	0.211	.032
Methanex	1.301	.270
Research in Motion (RIM)	1.465	.201
Telus	0.446	.097
Trans Canada Pipeline	0.393	.197

© 2012 Cengage Learning. All Rights Reserved. May not be scanned, copied or duplicated, or posted to a publicly accessible website, in whole or in part.

4.90a

D	E	F	G	H
Repaid			Defaulted	
Mean	755.21		Mean	626.30
Standard Error	4.62		Standard Error	7.23
Median	761		Median	633
Mode	767		Mode	693
Standard Deviation	68.59		Standard Deviation	64.67
Sample Variance	4705.23		Sample Variance	4181.76
Kurtosis	0.3177		Kurtosis	0.5666
Skewness	-0.3131		Skewness	-0.4416
Range	392		Range	354
Minimum	546		Minimum	436
Maximum	938		Maximum	790
Sum	166146		Sum	50104
Count	220		Count	80

b We can see that among those who repaid the mean score is larger than that of those who did not and the standard deviation is smaller. This information is similar but more precise than that obtained in Exercise 3.23.

4.92

	A	B	C
1		Calculus	Statistics
2	Calculus	1	
3	Statistics	0.6784	1

$R^2 = .6784^2 = .4603$; 46.03% of the variation in statistics marks is explained by the variation in calculus marks. The coefficient of determination provides a more precise indication of the strength of the linear relationship.

© 2012 Cengage Learning. All Rights Reserved. May not be scanned, copied or duplicated, or posted to a publicly accessible website, in whole or in part.

4.94

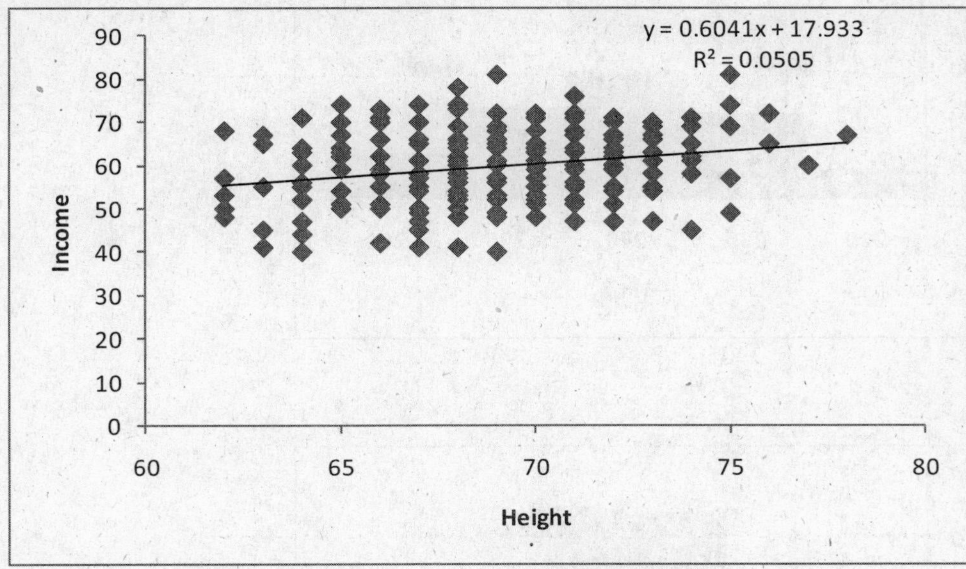

a $\hat{y}$ = 17.933 + .6041x

b The coefficient of determination is .0505, which indicates that only 5.05% of the variation in incomes is explained by the variation in heights.

4.96a

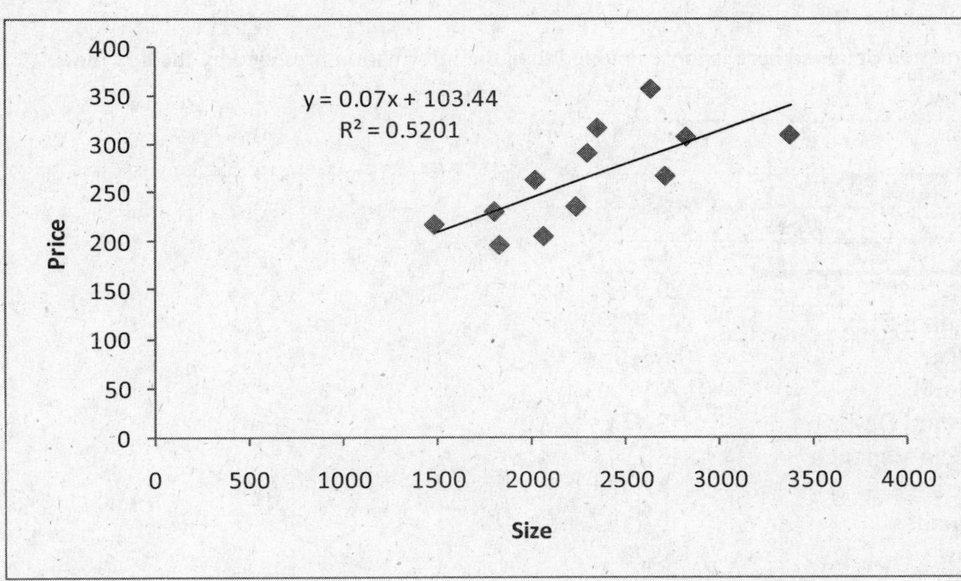

b. The slope coefficient is .07; For each additional square foot the price increases on average by $.07 thousand. More simply for each additional square foot the price increases on average by$70.

c. From the least squares line we can more precisely measure the relationship between the two variables.

© 2012 Cengage Learning. All Rights Reserved. May not be scanned, copied or duplicated, or posted to a publicly accessible website, in whole or in part.

4.98 Private course

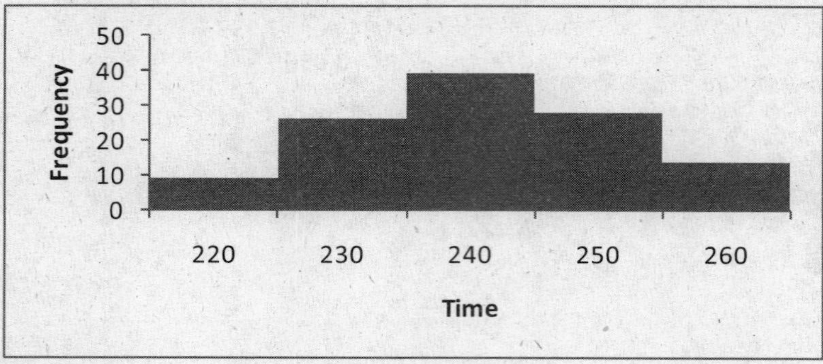

Public course

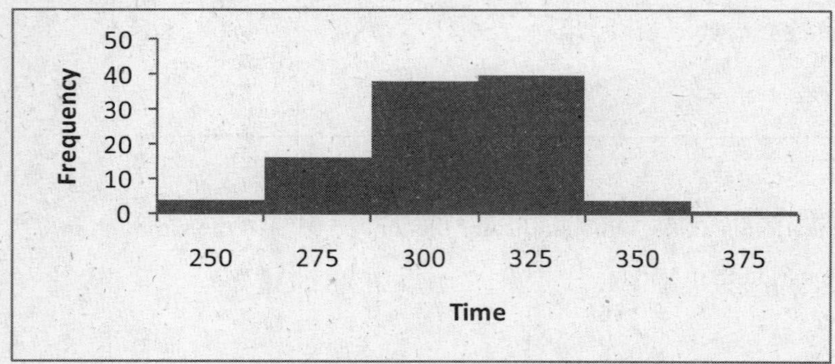

The information obtained here is more detailed than the information provided by the box plots.

4.100

	A	B
1	*Coffees*	
2		
3	Mean	29,913
4	Standard Error	1,722
5	Median	30,660
6	Mode	#N/A
7	Standard Deviation	12,174
8	Sample Variance	148,213,791
9	Kurtosis	0.117
10	Skewness	0.215
11	Range	59082
12	Minimum	3647
13	Maximum	62729
14	Sum	1,495,639
15	Count	50

a $\bar{x}$ = 29,913, median = 30,660

b s^2 = 148,213,791; s = 12,174

© 2012 Cengage Learning. All Rights Reserved. May not be scanned, copied or duplicated, or posted to a publicly accessible website, in whole or in part.

c

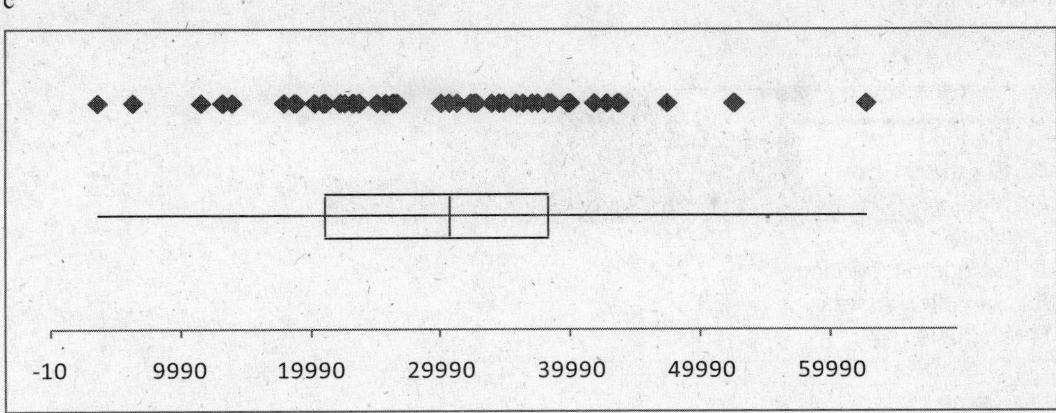

d The number of coffees sold varies considerably.

4.102 a & b

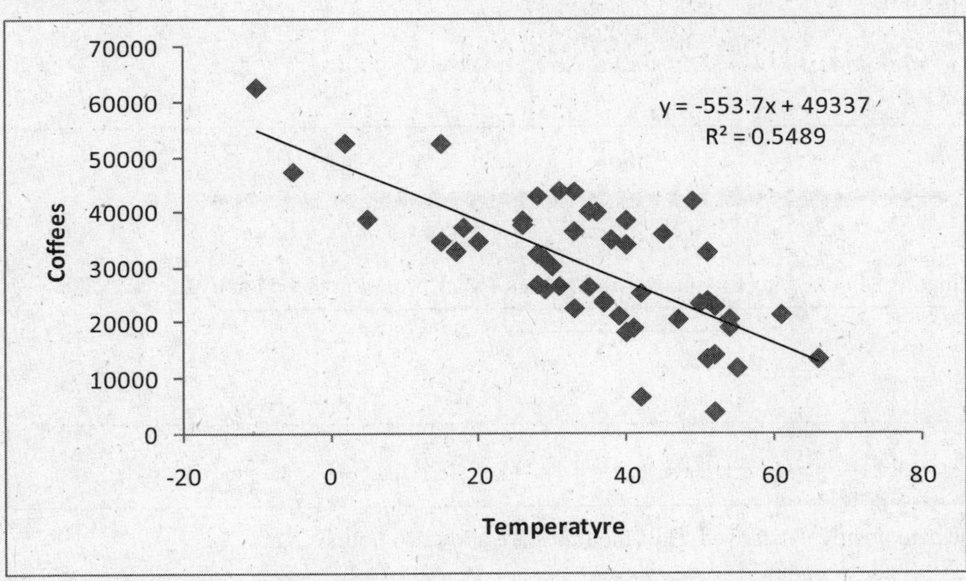

R^2 = .5489 and the least squares line is $\hat{y}$ = 49,337 – 553.7x

c 54.8% of the variation in the number of coffees sold is explained by the variation in temperature. For each additional degree of temperature the number of coffees sold decreases on average by 554 cups. Alternatively for each 1-degree drop in temperature the number of coffees increases on average, by 553.7 cups.

d We can measure the strength of the linear relationship accurately and the slope coefficient gives information about how temperature and the number of coffees sold are related.

© 2012 Cengage Learning. All Rights Reserved. May not be scanned, copied or duplicated, or posted to a publicly accessible website, in whole or in part.

4.104

	A	B
1	*Internet*	
2		
3	Mean	26.32
4	Standard Error	0.595
5	Median	26
6	Mode	21
7	Standard Deviation	9.41
8	Sample Variance	88.57
9	Kurtosis	-0.071
10	Skewness	0.154
11	Range	52
12	Minimum	2
13	Maximum	54
14	Sum	6579
15	Count	250

a $\bar{x} = 26.32$ and median = 26

b $s^2 = 88.57$, $s = 9.41$

c

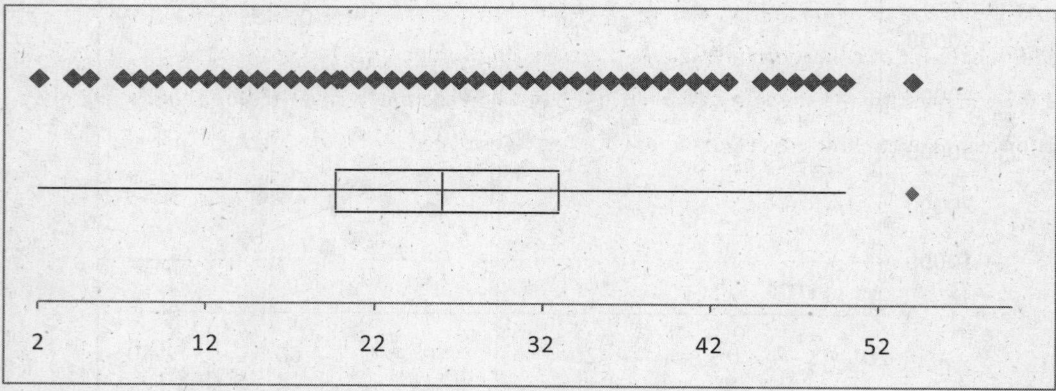

d The times are positively skewed. Half the times are above 26 hours.

© 2012 Cengage Learning. All Rights Reserved. May not be scanned, copied or duplicated, or posted to a publicly accessible website, in whole or in part.

4.106 a & b

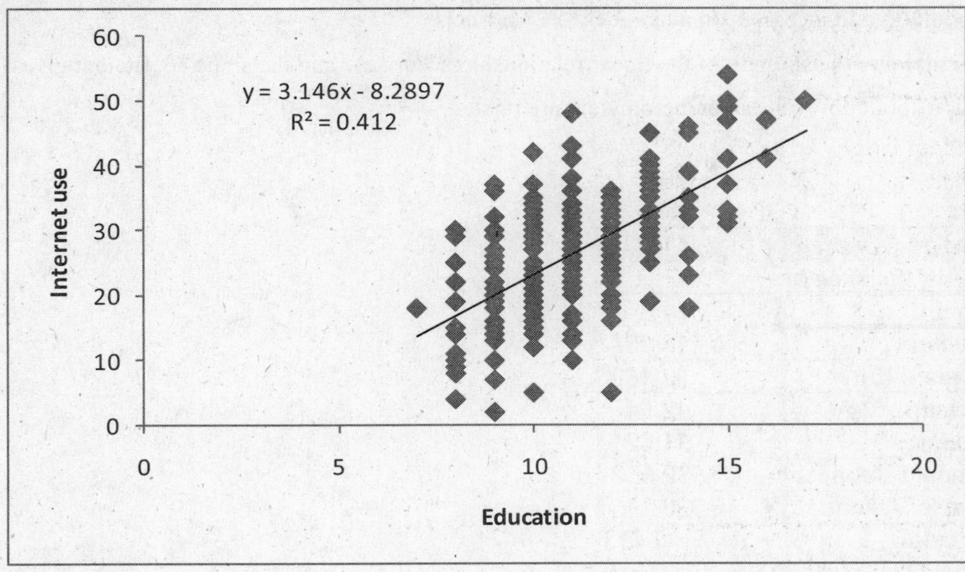

$R^2 = .412$ and the least squares line is $\hat{y} = -8.2897 + 3.146x$

c 41.2% of the variation in Internet use is explained by the variation in education. For each additional year of education Internet use increases on average by 3.146 hours.

d We can measure the strength of the linear relationship accurately and the slope coefficient gives information about how education and Internet use are related.

4.108a & b

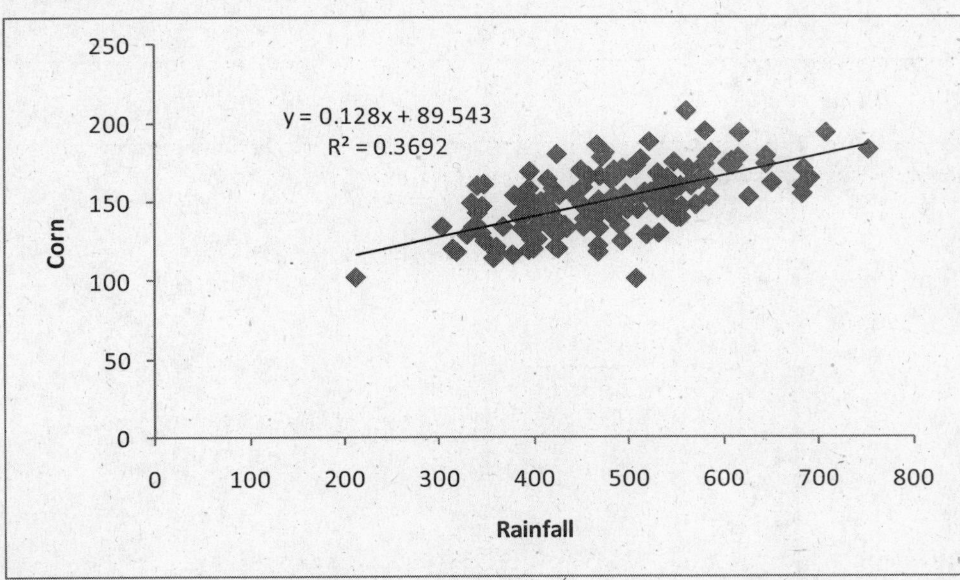

$R^2 = .369$ and the least squares line is $\hat{y} = 89.543 + .128$ Rainfall

© 2012 Cengage Learning. All Rights Reserved. May not be scanned, copied or duplicated, or posted to a publicly accessible website, in whole or in part.

c 36.92% of the variation in yield is explained by the variation in rainfall. For each additional inch of rainfall yield increases on average by .128 bushels.

d We can measure the strength of the linear relationship accurately and the slope coefficient gives information about how rainfall and crop yield are related.

4.110a

	A	B
1	*Debts*	
2		
3	Mean	12,067
4	Standard Error	180
5	Median	12,047
6	Mode	11,621
7	Standard Deviation	2,632
8	Sample Variance	6,929,745
9	Kurtosis	-0.413
10	Skewness	-0.210
11	Range	12,499
12	Minimum	4,626
13	Maximum	17,125
14	Sum	2,582,254
15	Count	214

b The mean debt is $12,067. Half the sample incurred debts below $12,047 and half incurred debts above. The mode is $11,621.

© 2012 Cengage Learning. All Rights Reserved. May not be scanned, copied or duplicated, or posted to a publicly accessible website, in whole or in part.

Chapter 5

5.2a The study is observational. The statistics practitioner did not randomly assign stores to buy Cans or bottles.

b Randomly assign some stores to receive only cans and others to receive only bottles.

5.4a A survey can be conducted by means of a personal interview, a telephone interview, or a self-administered questionnaire.

b A personal interview has a high response rate relative to other survey methods, but is expensive because of the need to hire well-trained interviewers and possibly pay travel-related costs if the survey is conducted over a large geographical area. A personal interview also will likely result in fewer incorrect responses that arise when respondents misunderstand some questions. A telephone interview is less expensive, but will likely result in a lower response rate. A self-administered questionnaire is least expensive, but suffers from lower response rates and accuracy than interviews.

5.6a The sampled population will exclude those who avoid large department stores in favor or smaller shops, as well as those who consider their time too valuable to spend participating in a survey. The sampled population will therefore differ from the target population of all customers who regularly shop at the mall.

b The sampled population will contain a disproportionate number of thick books, because of the manner in which the sample is selected.

c The sampled population consists of those eligible voters who are at home in the afternoon, thereby excluding most of those with full-time jobs (or at school).

5.8a A self-selected sample is a sample formed primarily on the basis of voluntary inclusion, with little control by the designer of the survey.

b Choose any recent radio or television poll based on responses of listeners who phone in on a volunteer basis.

c Self-selected samples are usually biased, because those who participate are more interested in the issue than those who don't, and therefore probably have a different opinion.

5.10 No, because the sampled population consists of the responses about the professor's course. We cannot make draw inferences about all courses.

© 2012 Cengage Learning. All Rights Reserved. May not be scanned, copied or duplicated, or posted to a publicly accessible website, in whole or in part.

5.12 We used Excel to generate 30 six-digit random numbers. Because we will ignore any duplicate numbers generated, we generated 30 six-digit random numbers and will use the first 20 unique random numbers to select our sample. The 30 numbers generated are shown below.

169,470	744,530	22,554	918,730	320,262	503,129
318,858	698,203	822,383	938,262	800,806	56,643
836,116	123,936	80,539	154,211	391,278	940,154
110,630	856,380	222,145	692,313	949,828	561,511
909,269	811,274	288,553	749,627	858,944	39,308

5.14 A stratified random sampling plan accomplishes the president's goals. The strata are the four areas enabling the statistics practitioner to learn about the entire population but also compare the four areas.

5.16 Use cluster sampling, letting each city block represent a cluster.

5.18 Three types of nonsampling errors:
(1) Error due to incorrect responses
(2) Nonresponse error, which refers to error introduced when responses are not obtained from some members of the sample. This may result in the sample being unrepresentative of the target population.
(3) Error due to selection bias, which arises when the sampling plan is such that some members of the target population cannot possibly be selected for inclusion in the sample.

© 2012 Cengage Learning. All Rights Reserved. May not be scanned, copied or duplicated, or posted to a publicly accessible website, in whole or in part.

Chapter 6

6.2 a Subjective approach

b If all the teams in major league baseball have exactly the same players the New York Yankees will win 25% of all World Series.

6.4 a Subjective approach

b The Dow Jones Industrial Index will increase on 60% of the days if economic conditions remain unchanged.

6.6 {Adams wins. Brown wins, Collins wins, Dalton wins}

6.8 a {0, 1, 2, 3, 4, 5}

b {4, 5}

c P(5) = .10

d P(2, 3, or 4) = P(2) + P(3) + P(4) = .26 + .21 + .18 = .65

e P(6) = 0

6.10 P(Contractor 1 wins) = 2/6, P(Contractor 2 wins) = 3/6, P(Contractor 3 wins) = 1/6

6.12 a P(shopper does not use credit card) = P(shopper pays cash) + P(shopper pays by debit card) = .30 + .10 = .40

b P(shopper pays cash or uses a credit card) = P(shopper pays cash) + P(shopper pays by credit card) = .30 + .60 = .90

6.14 a P(single) = .15, P(married) = .50, P(divorced) = .25, P(widowed) = .10

b Relative frequency approach

6.16 $P(A_1) = .1 + .2 = .3$, $P(A_2) = .3 + .1 = .4$, $P(A_3) = .2 + .1 = .3$.

$P(B_1) = .1 + .3 + .2 = .6$, $P(B_2) = .2 + .1 + .1 = .4$.

6.17 $P(A_1) = .4 + .2 = .6$, $P(A_2) = .3 + .1 = .4$. $P(B_1) = .4 + .3 = .7$, $P(B_2) = .2 + .1 = .3$.

6.18 a $P(A_1 \mid B_1) = \frac{P(A_1 \text{ and } B_1)}{P(B_1)} = \frac{.4}{.7} = .57$

© 2012 Cengage Learning. All Rights Reserved. May not be scanned, copied or duplicated, or posted to a publicly accessible website, in whole or in part.

b $P(A_2 \mid B_1) = \dfrac{P(A_2 \text{ and } B_1)}{P(B_1)} = \dfrac{.3}{.7} = .43$

c Yes. It is not a coincidence. Given B_1 the events A_1 and A_2 constitute the entire sample space.

6.20 The events are not independent because $P(A_1 \mid B_2) \neq P(A_1)$.

6.22 $P(A_1 \mid B_1) = \dfrac{P(A_1 \text{ and } B_1)}{P(B_1)} = \dfrac{.20}{.20+.60} = .25$; $P(A_1) = .20 + .05 = .25$; the events are independent.

6.24 $P(A_1) = .15 + .25 = .40$, $P(A_2) = .20 + .25 = .45$, $P(A_3) = .10 + .05 = .15$.

$P(B_1) = .15 + 20 + .10 = .45$, $P(B_2) = .25 + .25 + .05 = .55$.

6.26 a $P(A_1 \text{ or } A_2) = P(A_1) + P(A_2) = .40 + .45 = .85$

b $P(A_2 \text{ or } B_2) = P(A_2) + P(B_2) - P(A_2 \text{ and } B_2) = .45 + .55 - .25 = .75$

c $P(A_3 \text{ or } B_1) = P(A_3) + P(B_1) - P(A_3 \text{ and } B_1) = .15 + .45 - .10 = .50$

6.28 a P(debit card) = .04 + .18 + .14 = .36

b P(over \$100 | credit card) = $\dfrac{\text{P(credit card and over \$100}}{\text{P(credit card)}} = \dfrac{.23}{.03+.21+.23} = .49$

c P(credit card or debit card) = P(credit card) + P(debit card) = .47 + .36 = .83

6.30 a P(He is a smoker) = .12 + .19 = .31

b P(He does not have lung disease) = .19 + .66 = .85

c P(He has lung disease | he is a smoker) =

$\dfrac{\text{P(he has lung disease and he is a smo ker)}}{\text{P(he is a smo ker)}} = \dfrac{.12}{.31} = .387$

d P(He has lung disease | he does not smoke) =

$\dfrac{\text{P(he has lung disease and he does not smoke)}}{\text{P(he does not smoke)}} = \dfrac{.03}{.69} = .043$

6.32 a P(manual | math-stats) = $\dfrac{\text{P(manual and math} - \text{stats)}}{\text{P(math} - \text{stats)}} = \dfrac{.23}{.23+.36} = .390$

b P(computer) = .36 + .30 = .66

c No, because P(manual) = .23 + .11 = .34, which is not equal to P(manual | math-stats).

© 2012 Cengage Learning. All Rights Reserved. May not be scanned, copied or duplicated, or posted to a publicly accessible website, in whole or in part.

6.34 a P(ulcer) = .01 + .03 + .03 + .04 = .11

b $\text{P(ulcer | none)} = \dfrac{\text{P(ulcer and none)}}{\text{P(none)}} = \dfrac{.01}{.01+.22} = \dfrac{.01}{.23} = .043$

c $\text{P(none | ulcer)} = \dfrac{\text{P(ulcer and none)}}{\text{P(ulcer)}} = \dfrac{.01}{.01+.03+.03+.04} = \dfrac{.01}{.11} = .091$

d $\text{P(One, two, or more than two | no ulcer)} = 1 - \dfrac{\text{P(ulcer and none)}}{\text{P(ulcer)}} = 1 - .091 = .909$

6.36 a P(remember) = .15 + .18 = .33

b $\text{P(remember | violent)} = \dfrac{\text{P(remember and violent)}}{\text{P(violent)}} = \dfrac{.15}{.15+.35} = \dfrac{.15}{.50} = .30$

c Yes, the events are dependent.

6.38a P(Health insurance) = .167+.209+.225+.177 = .778

b. P(Person 55-64 | No health insurance)

$= \dfrac{\text{P(Person 55}-\text{64 and No health insurance)}}{\text{P(Person 55}-\text{64)}} = \dfrac{.026}{.177+.026} = \dfrac{.026}{.203} = .128$

c. P(Person 25-34|No health insurance) =

$\dfrac{\text{P(Person 25}-\text{34 and No health insurance)}}{\text{P(No health insurance)}} = \dfrac{.085}{.085+.061+.049+.026} = \dfrac{.085}{.221} = .385$

6.40a $\dfrac{\text{P(Violent crime and enrollment less than 300)}}{\text{P(Enrollment less than 300)}} = \dfrac{.159}{.159+.091} = \dfrac{.159}{.250} = .636$

b. $\dfrac{\text{P(Violent crime and enrollment less than 300)}}{\text{P(Violent crime)}} = \dfrac{.159}{.159+.221+.289+.108} = \dfrac{.159}{.777} = .205$

6.42 a P(under 20) = .464 + .147 + .237 = .848

b P(retail) = .237 + .035 + .005 = .277

c $\text{P(20 to 99 | construction)} = \dfrac{\text{P(20 to 99 and construction)}}{\text{P(construction)}} = \dfrac{.039}{.464+.039+.005} = \dfrac{.039}{.508} = .077$

6.44 $\text{P(purchase | see ad)} = \dfrac{\text{P(purchase and see ad)}}{\text{P(see ad)}} = \dfrac{.18}{.18+.42} = \dfrac{.18}{.60} = .30;$

P(purchase) = .18 + .12 = .30. The events are independent and thus, the ads are not effective.

© 2012 Cengage Learning. All Rights Reserved. May not be scanned, copied or duplicated, or posted to a publicly accessible website, in whole or in part.

6.46 a P(bachelor's degree | west)

$$= \frac{\text{P(bachelor's degree and west)}}{\text{P(west)}} = \frac{.046}{.036+.059+.045+.020+.046+.023} = \frac{.046}{.229} = .201$$

b P(northeast | high school graduate)

$$= \frac{\text{P(northeast and high school graduate)}}{\text{P(high school graduate)}} = \frac{.063}{.063+.078+.117+.059} = \frac{.063}{.317} = .199$$

c P(south) = .059 + .117 + .061 + .030 + .065 + .032 = .364

d P(not south) = 1 –P(south) = 1−.364 = .636

6.48

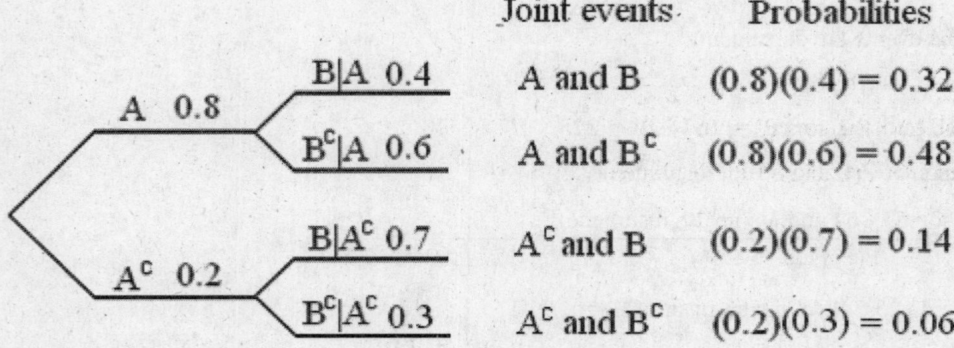

6.50

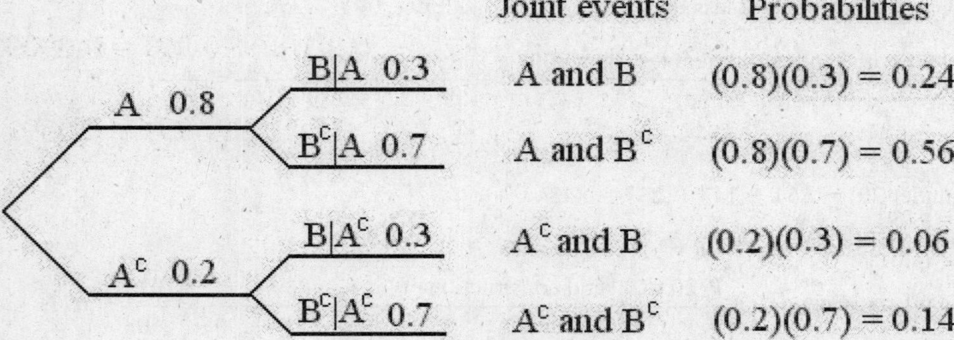

© 2012 Cengage Learning. All Rights Reserved. May not be scanned, copied or duplicated, or posted to a publicly accessible website, in whole or in part.

6.52

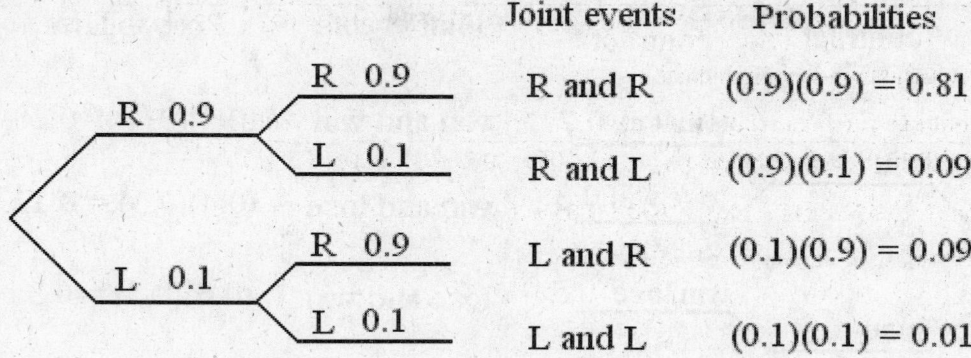

a P(R and R) = .81

b P(L and L) = .01

c P(R and L) + P(L and R) = .09 + .09 = .18

d P(Rand L) + P(L and R) + P(R and R) = .09 + .09 + .81 = .99

6.54a

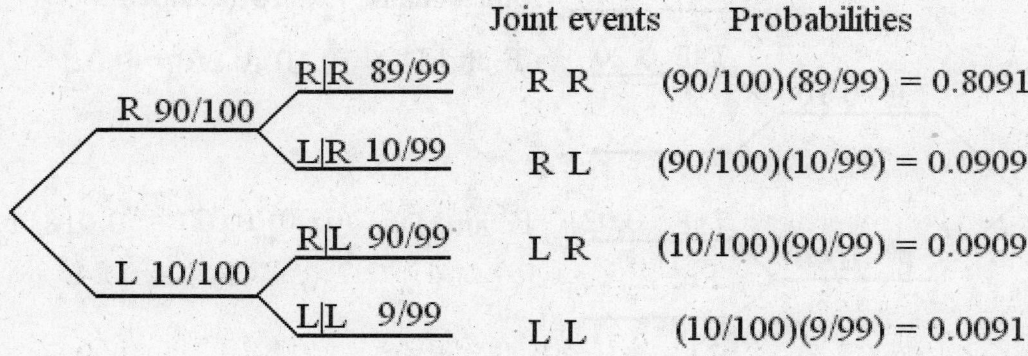

b P(RR) = .8091

c P(LL) = .0091

d P(RL) + P(LR) = .0909 + .0909 = .1818

e P(RL) + P(LR) + P(RR) = .0909 + .0909 + .8091 = .9909

© 2012 Cengage Learning. All Rights Reserved. May not be scanned, copied or duplicated, or posted to a publicly accessible website, in whole or in part.

6.56

First contract	Second contract	Joint events	Probabilities
win 0.4	win|win 0.7	win and win	(0.4)(0.7) = 0.28
	lose|win 0.3	win and lose	(0.4)(0.3) = 0.12
lose 0.6	win|lose 0.5	lose and win	(0.6)(0.5) = 0.3
	lose|lose 0.5	lose and lose	(0.6)(0.5) = 0.3

a P(win both) = .28

b P(lose both) = .30

c P(win only one) = .12 + .30 = .42

6.58

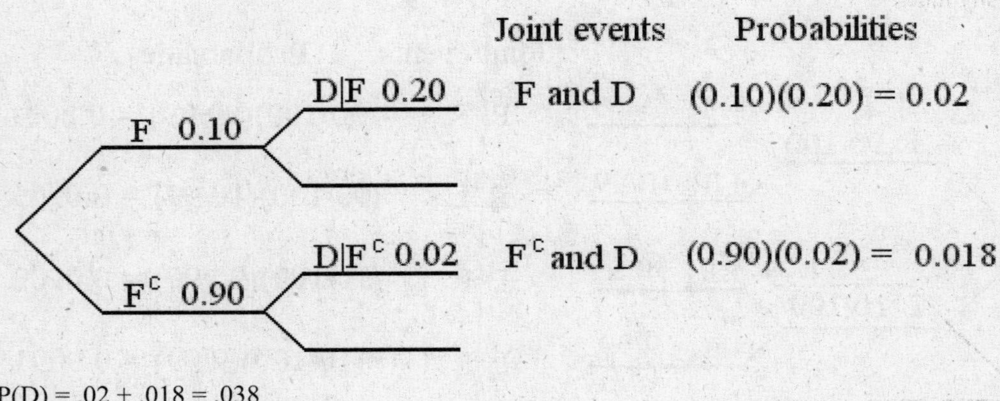

P(D) = .02 + .018 = .038

© 2012 Cengage Learning. All Rights Reserved. May not be scanned, copied or duplicated, or posted to a publicly accessible website, in whole or in part.

6.60

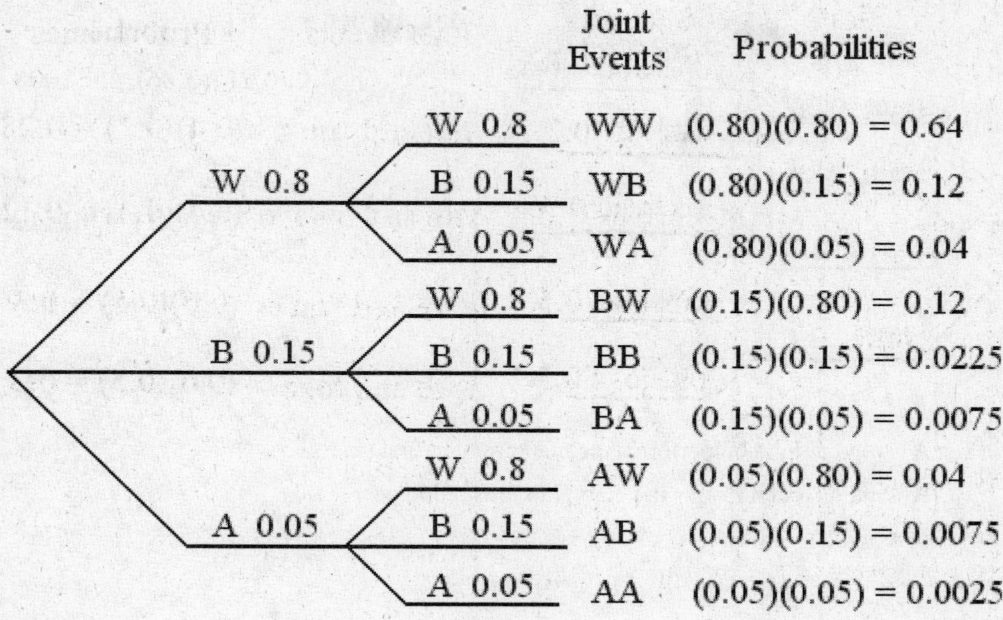

Diversity index = .12 + .04 + .12 + .0075 + .04 + .0075 = .335

6.62

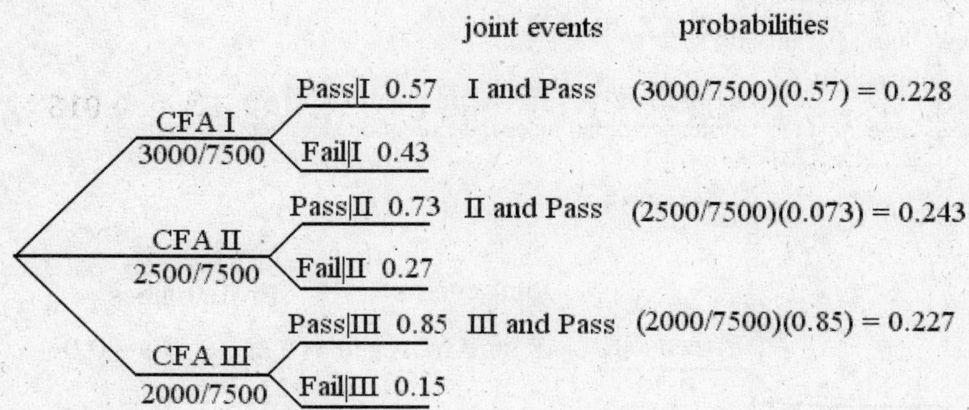

P(pass) = .228 + .243 + .227 = .698

© 2012 Cengage Learning. All Rights Reserved. May not be scanned, copied or duplicated, or posted to a publicly accessible website, in whole or in part.

6.64

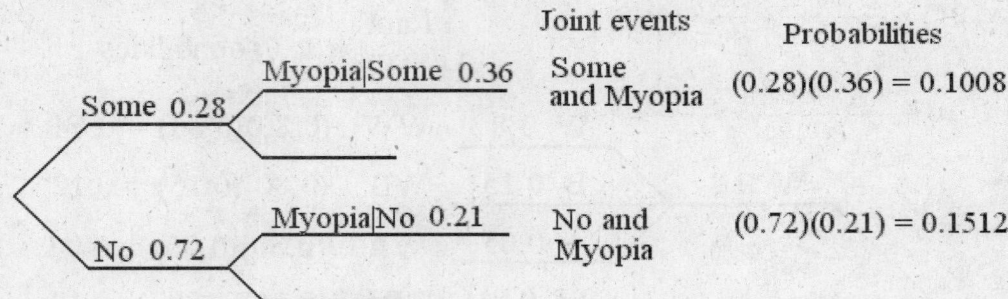

P(myopic) = .1008 + .1512 = .2520

6.66 Let A = mutual fund outperforms the market in the first year

B = mutual outperforms the market in the second year

P(A and B) = P(A)P(B | A) = (.15)(.22) = .033

6.68 Define the events:

M: The main control will fail.

B_1: The first backup will fail.

B_2: The second backup will fail

The probability that the plane will crash is

P(M and B_1 and B_2) = [P(M)][P(B_1)][P(B_2)]

= (.0001) (.01) (.01)

= .00000001

We have assumed that the 3 systems will fail independently of one another.

6.70

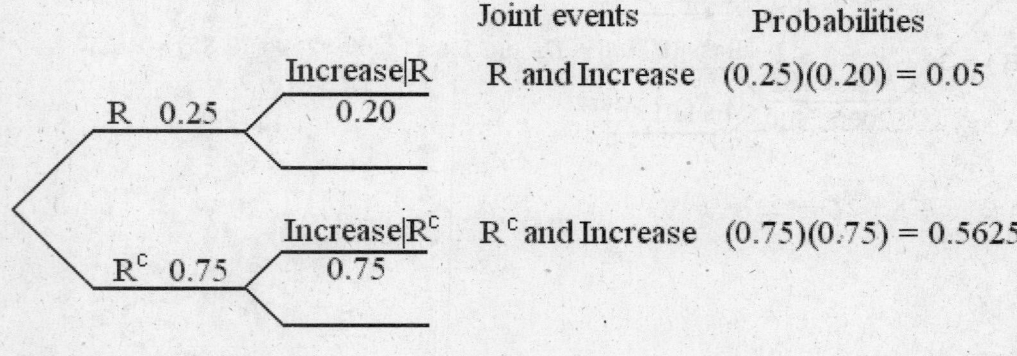

P(Increase) = .05 + .5625 = .6125

© 2012 Cengage Learning. All Rights Reserved. May not be scanned, copied or duplicated, or posted to a publicly accessible website, in whole or in part.

6.72 $P(A \text{ and } B) = .32$, $P(A^C \text{ and } B) = .14$, $P(B) = .46$, $P(B^C) = .54$

a $P(A \mid B) = \dfrac{P(A \text{ and } B)}{P(B)} = \dfrac{.32}{.46} = .696$

b $P(A^C \mid B) = \dfrac{P(A^C \text{ and } B)}{P(B)} = \dfrac{.14}{.46} = .304$

c $P(A \text{ and } B^C) = .48$; $P(A \mid B^C) = \dfrac{P(A \text{ and } B^C)}{P(B^C)} = \dfrac{.48}{.54} = .889$

d $P(A^C \text{ and } B^C) = .06$; $P(A^C \mid B^C) = \dfrac{P(A^C \text{ and } B^C)}{P(B^C)} = \dfrac{.06}{.54} = .111$

6.74 $P(F \mid D) = \dfrac{P(F \text{ and } D)}{P(D)} = \dfrac{.020}{.038} = .526$

6.76 $P(\text{CFA I} \mid \text{passed}) = \dfrac{P(\text{CFA I and passed})}{P(\text{passed})} = \dfrac{.228}{.698} = .327$

6.78 $P(A) = .40$, $P(B \mid A) = .85$, $P(B \mid A^C) = .29$

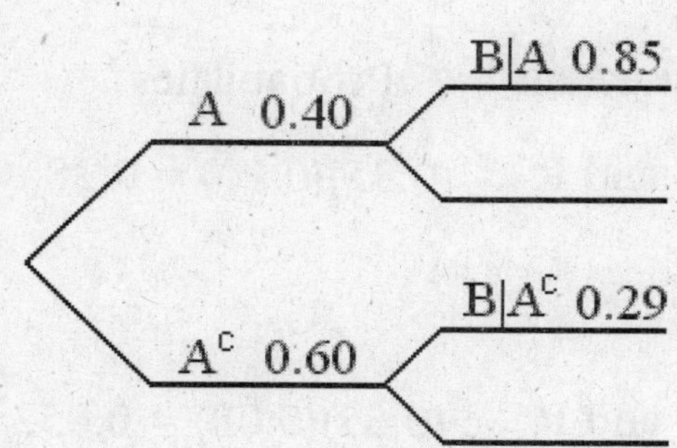

Joint events	Probabilities
A and B	$(0.40)(0.85) = 0.34$
A^C and B	$(0.60)(0.29) = 0.174$

$P(B) = .34 + .174 = .514$

$P(A \mid B) = \dfrac{P(A \text{ and } B)}{P(B)} = \dfrac{.34}{.514} = .661$

© 2012 Cengage Learning. All Rights Reserved. May not be scanned, copied or duplicated, or posted to a publicly accessible website, in whole or in part.

6.80 Define events: A, B, C = airlines A, B, and C, D = on time

P(A) = .50, P(B) = .30, P(C) = .20, P(D | A) = .80, P(D | B) = .65, P(D | C) = .40

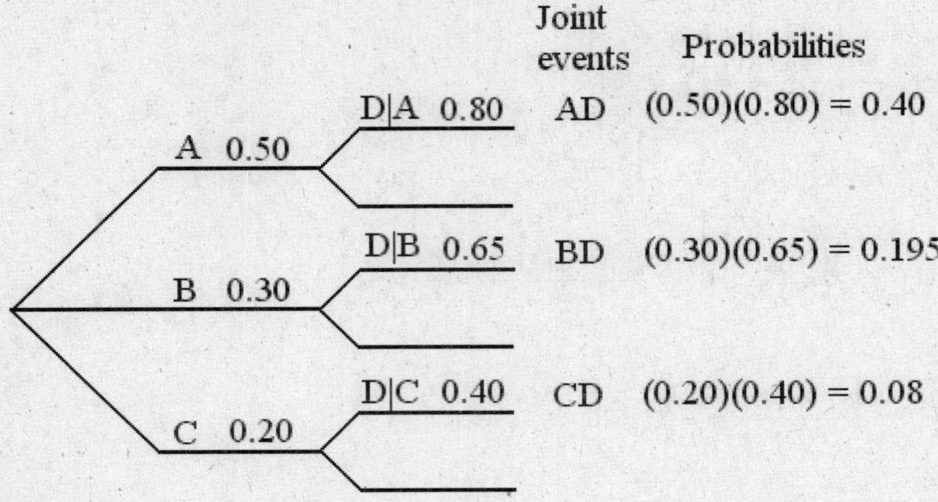

P(D) = .40 + .195 + .08 = .675

$$P(A \mid D) = \frac{P(A \text{ and } D)}{P(D)} = \frac{.40}{.675} = .593$$

6.82

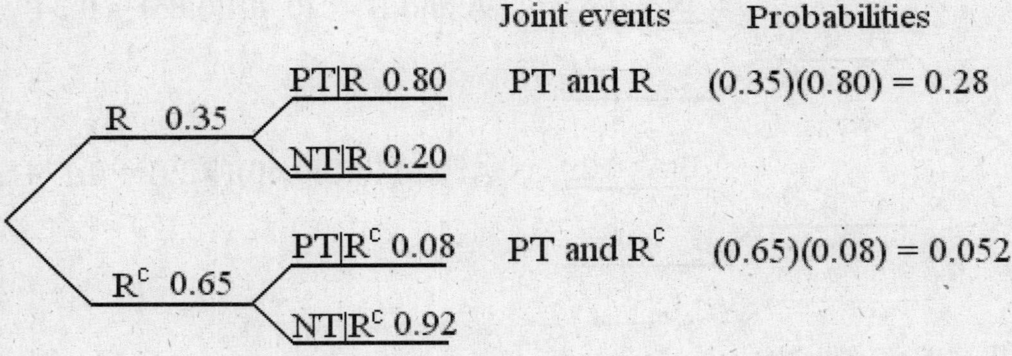

P(PT) = .28 + .052 = .332

$$P(R \mid PT) = \frac{P(R \text{ and } PT)}{P(PT)} = \frac{.28}{.332} = .843$$

© 2012 Cengage Learning. All Rights Reserved. May not be scanned, copied or duplicated, or posted to a publicly accessible website, in whole or in part.

6.84 Sensitivity = P(PT | H) = .920

Specificity = $P(NT \mid H^C) = .973$

Positive predictive value = P(H | PT) = .1460

Negative predictive value = $P H^C \mid NT) = \frac{P(H^C \text{ and } NT)}{P(NT)} = \frac{.9681}{.0004 + .9681} = \frac{.9681}{.9685} = .9996$

6.86 a P(Marketing A) = .053 + .237 = .290

b P(Marketing A | Statistics not A) =

$$\frac{P(\text{Marketing A and Statistics not A})}{P(\text{Statistics not A})} = \frac{.23}{.237 + .580} = \frac{.237}{.817} = .290$$

c Yes, the probabilities in Parts a and b are the same.

6.88 a P(second) = .05 + .14 = .19

b $P(\text{successful} \mid -8 \text{ or less}) = \frac{P(\text{successful and } -8 \text{ or less})}{P(-8 \text{ or less})} = \frac{.15}{.15 + .14} = \frac{.15}{.29} = .517$

c No, because P(successful) = .66 + .15 = .81, which is not equal to P(successful | –8 or less) .

6.90 $P(A^C \mid B) = \frac{P(A^C \text{ and } B)}{P(B)} = \frac{.221}{.749} = .295$

6.92

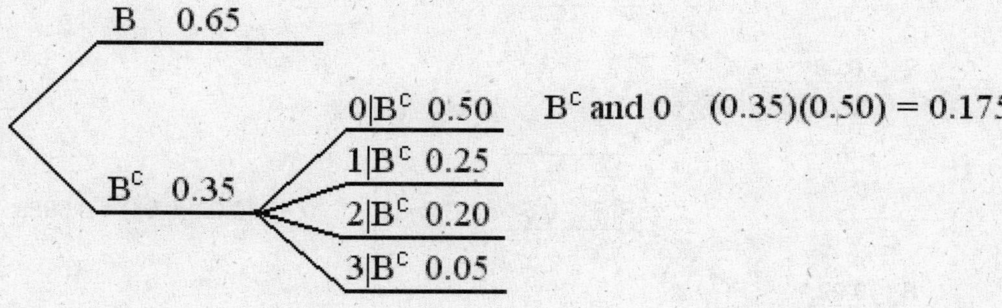

P(no sale) = .65 + .175 = .825

© 2012 Cengage Learning. All Rights Reserved. May not be scanned, copied or duplicated, or posted to a publicly accessible website, in whole or in part.

6.94 Define events: R = reoffend, D = detained

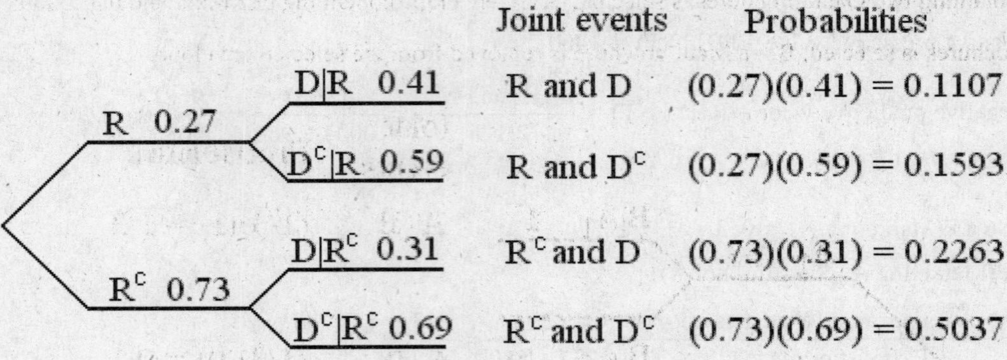

a $P(D) = P(R \text{ and } D) + P(R^C \text{ and } D) = .1107 + .2263 = .3370$

$$P(R|\,D) = \frac{P(R \text{ and } D)}{P(D)} = \frac{.1107}{.3370} = .3285$$

b $P(D^C) = P(R \text{ and } D^C) + P(R^C \text{ and } D^C) = .1593 + .5037 = .6630$

$$P(R|\,D^C) = \frac{P(R \text{ and } D^C)}{P(D^C)} = \frac{.1593}{.6630} = .2403$$

6.96

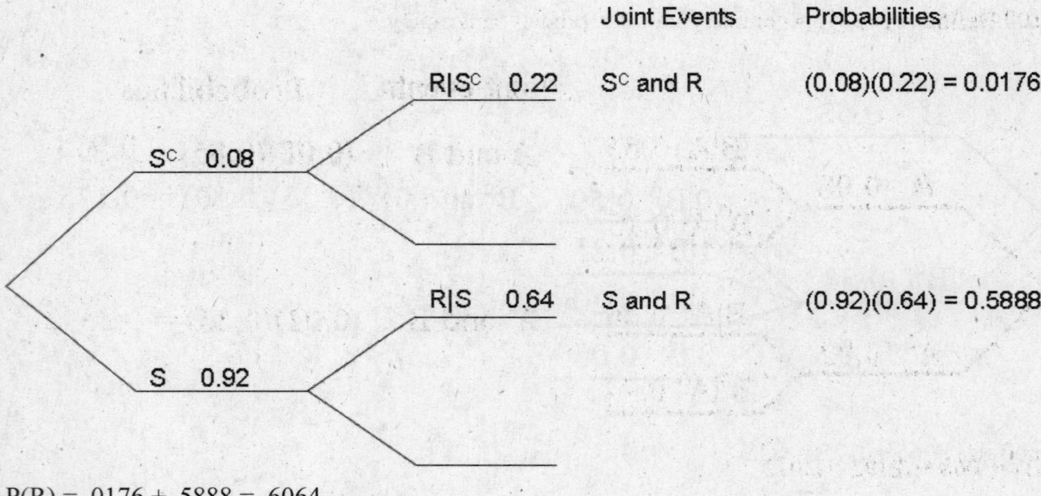

$P(R) = .0176 + .5888 = .6064$

$$P(S \mid R) = \frac{P(S \text{ and } R)}{P(R)} = \frac{.5888}{.6064} = .9710$$

© 2012 Cengage Learning. All Rights Reserved. May not be scanned, copied or duplicated, or posted to a publicly accessible website, in whole or in part.

6.98 Define the events: A_1 = envelope containing two Maui brochures is selected, A_2 = envelope containing two Oahu brochures is selected, A_3 = envelope containing one Maui and one Oahu brochures is selected. B = a Maui brochure is removed from the selected envelope.

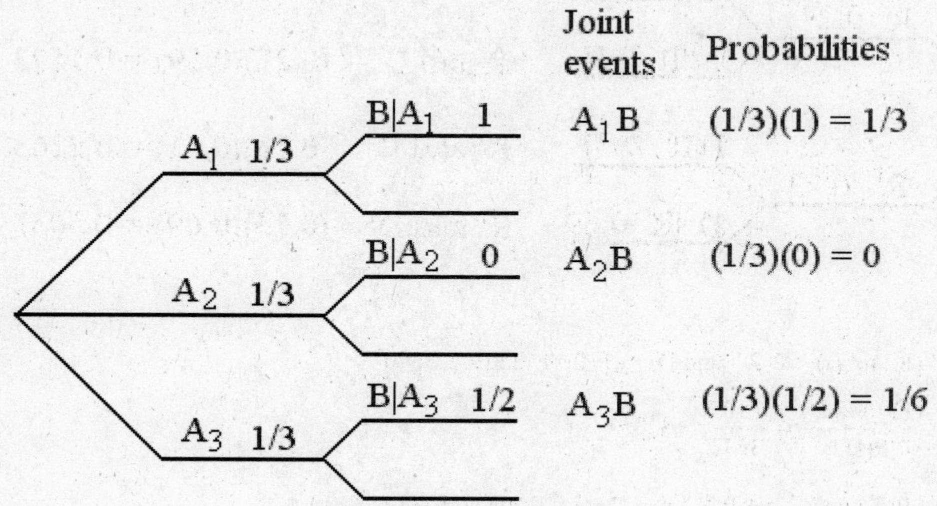

P(B) = 1/3 + 0 + 1/6 = 1/2

$$P(A_1 \mid B) = \frac{P(A_1 \text{ and } B)}{P(B)} = \frac{1/3}{1/2} = 2/3$$

6.100 Define events: A = company fail, B = predict bankruptcy

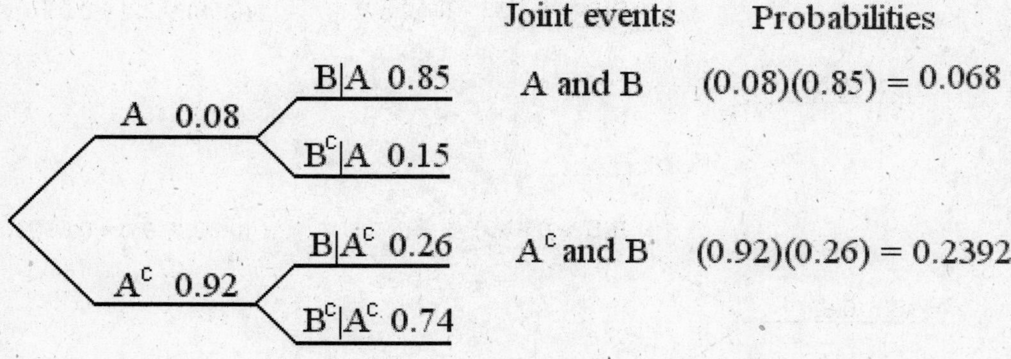

P(B) = .068 + .2392 = .3072

$$P(A \mid B) = \frac{P(A \text{ and } B)}{P(B)} = \frac{.068}{.3072} = .2214$$

6.102 Probabilities of outcomes: P(HH) = .25, P(HT) = .25, P(TH) = .25, P(TT) = .25

P(TT | HH is not possible) = .25/(.25 + .25 + .25) = .333

© 2012 Cengage Learning. All Rights Reserved. May not be scanned, copied or duplicated, or posted to a publicly accessible website, in whole or in part.

Chapter 7

7.2 a any value between 0 and several hundred miles

b No, because we cannot identify the second value or any other value larger than 0.

c No, uncountable means infinite.

d The variable is continuous.

7.4 a 0, 1, 2, …, 100

b Yes.

c Yes, there are 101 values.

d The variable is discrete because it is countable.

7.6 P(x) = 1/6 for x = 1, 2, 3, 4, 5, and 6

7.8 a $P(2 \le X \le 5) = P(2) + P(3) + P(4) + P(5) = .310 + .340 + .220 + .080 = .950$

$P(X > 5) = P(6) + P(7) = .019 + .001 = .020$

$P(X < 4) = P(0) + P(1) + P(2) + P(3) = .005 + .025 + .310 + .340 = .680$

b $E(X) = \sum xP(x) = 0(.005) + 1(.025) + 2(.310) + 4(.340) + 5(.080) + 6(.019) + 7(.001)$

$= 3.066$

c $\sigma^2 = V(X) = \sum (x-\mu)^2 P(x) = (0–3.066)^2(.005) + (1–3.066)^2(.025) + (2–3.066)^2(.310)$

$+ (3–3.066)^2(.340) + (4–3.066)^2(.220) + (5–3.066)^2(.080) + (6–3.066)^2(.019)$

$+ (7–3.066)^2(.001) = 1.178$

$\sigma = \sqrt{\sigma^2} = \sqrt{1.178} = 1.085$

7.10 a $P(X > 0) = P(2) + P(6) + P(8) = .3 + .4 + .1 = .8$

b $P(X \ge 1) = P(2) + P(6) + P(8) = .3 + .4 + .1 = .8$

c $P(X \ge 2) = P(2) + P(6) + P(8) = .3 + .4 + .1 = .8$

d $P(2 \le X \le 5) = P(2) = .3$

7.12 P(Losing 6 in a row) = $.5^6 = .0156$

© 2012 Cengage Learning. All Rights Reserved. May not be scanned, copied or duplicated, or posted to a publicly accessible website, in whole or in part.

7.14

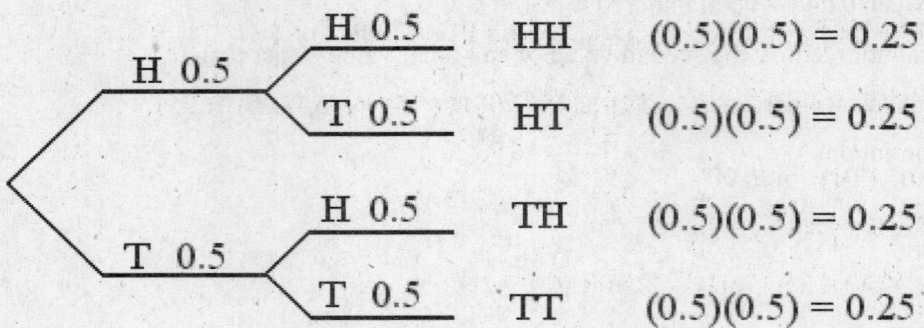

a P(HH) = .25

b P(HT) = .25

c P(TH) = .25

d P(TT) = .25

7.16

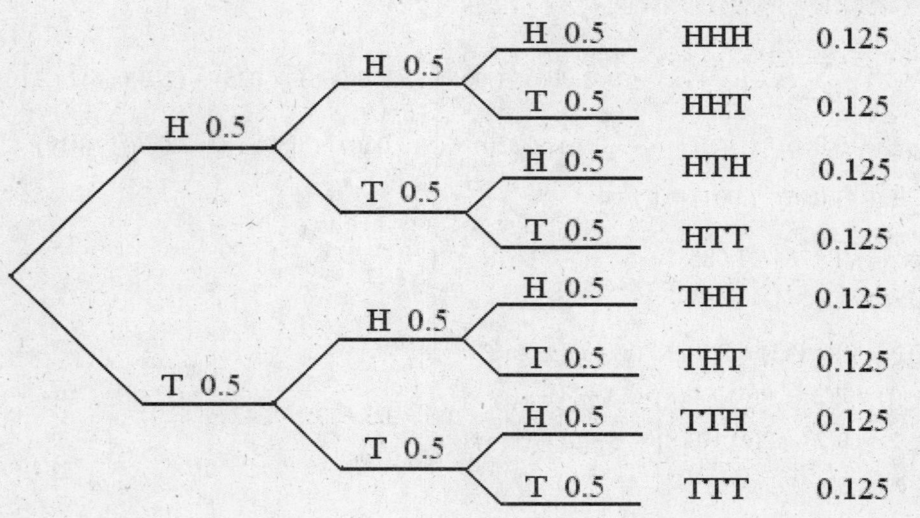

7.18a $\mu = E(X) = \sum xP(x) = -2(.59) + 5(.15) + 7(.25) + 8(.01) = 1.40$

$\sigma^2 = V(X) = \sum (x-\mu)^2 P(x) = (-2-1.4)^2(.59) + (5-1.4)^2(.15) + (7-1.4)^2(.25) + (8-1.4)^2(.01)$

$= 17.04$

© 2012 Cengage Learning. All Rights Reserved. May not be scanned, copied or duplicated, or posted to a publicly accessible website, in whole or in part.

b

x	−2	5	7	8
y	−10	25	35	40
P(y)	.59	.15	.25	.01

c $E(Y) = \sum yP(y) = -10(.59) + 25(.15) + 35(.25) + 40(.01) = 7.00$

$V(Y) = \sum (y-\mu)^2 P(y) = (-10-7.00)^2(.59) + (25-7.00)^2(.15) + (35-7.00)^2(.25)$

$+ (40-7.00)^2(.01) = 426.00$

d $E(Y) = E(5X) = 5E(X) = 5(1.4) = 7.00$

$V(Y) = V(5X) = 5^2 V(X) = 25(17.04) = 426.00.$

7.20a $P(X \geq 2) = P(2) + P(3) = .4 + .2 = .6$

b. $\mu = E(X) = \sum xP(x) = 0(.1) + 1(.3) + 2(.4) + 3(.2) = 1.7$

$\sigma^2 = V(X) = \sum (x-\mu)^2 P(x) = (0-1.7)^2(.1) + (1-1.7)^2(.3) + (2-1.7)^2(.4) + (3-1.7)^2(.2) = .81$

7.22 a $P(X > 4) = P(5) + P(6) + P(7) = .20 + .10 + .10 = .40$

b $P(X \geq 2) = 1 - P(X \leq 1) = 1 - P(1) = 1 - .05 = .95$

7.24 $Y = .25X$; $E(Y) = .25E(X) = .25(4.1) = 1.025$

$V(Y) = V(.25X) = (.25)^2(2.69) = .168$

7.26 a $P(4) = .06$

b $P(8) = 0$

c $P(0) = .35$

d $P(X \geq 1) = 1 - P(0) = 1 - .35 = .65$

7.28 a $P(X = 3) = P(3) = .21$

b $P(X \geq 5) = P(5) + P(6) + P(7) + P(8) = .12 + .08 + .06 + .05 = .31$

c $P(5 \leq X \leq 7) = P(5) + P(6) + P(7) = .12 + .08 + .06 = .26$

7.30 $\mu = E(X) = \sum xP(x) = 0(.04) + 1(.19) + 2(.22) + 3(.28) + 4(.12) + 5(.09) + 6(.06) = 2.76$

$\sigma^2 = V(X) = \sum (x-\mu)^2 P(x) = (1-2.76)^2(.04) + (2-2.76)^2(.19) + (3-2.76)^2(.28)$

$+ (4-2.76)^2(.12) + (5-2.76)^2(.09) + (6-2.76)^2(.06) = 2.302$

$\sigma = \sqrt{\sigma^2} = \sqrt{2.302} = 1.517$

© 2012 Cengage Learning. All Rights Reserved. May not be scanned, copied or duplicated, or posted to a publicly accessible website, in whole or in part.

7.32 $\mu = E(X) = \sum xP(x) = 1(.24) + 2(.18) + 3(.13) + 4(.10) + 5(.07) + 6(.04) + 7(.04) + 8(.20)$

$= 3.86$

$\sigma^2 = V(X) = \sum (x-\mu)^2 P(x) = (1-3.86)^2(.24) + (2-3.86)^2(.18) + (3-3.86)^2(.13) +$

$(4-3.86)^2(.10) + (5-3.86)^2(.07) + (6-3.86)^2(.04) + (7-3.86)^2(.04) + (8-3.86)^2(.20) = 6.78$

$\sigma = \sqrt{\sigma^2} = \sqrt{6.78} = 2.60$

7.34 E(Value of coin) = 400(.40) + 900(.30) + 100(.30) = 460. Take the $500.

7.36 E(damage costs) = .01(400) + .02(200) + .10(100) + .87(0) = 18. The owner should pay up to $18 for the device.

7.38 $\mu = E(X) = \sum xP(x) = 1(.05) + 2(.12) + 3(.20) + 4(.30) + 5(.15) + 6(.10) + 7(.08) = 4.00$

$\sigma^2 = V(X) = \sum (x-\mu)^2 P(x) = (1-4.0)^2(.05) + (2-4.0)^2(.12) + (3-4.0)^2(.20) + (4-4.0)^2(.30)$

$+ (5-4.0)^2(.15) + (6-4.0)^2(.10) + (7-4.0)^2(.08) = 2.40$

7.40 $\mu = E(X) = \sum xP(x) = 0(.10) + 1(.25) + 2(.40) + 3(.20) + 4(.05) = 1.85$

7.42 Breakeven point = 15,000/(7.40 – 3.00) = 3,409

7.44 a $\sum_{\text{all x}} \sum_{\text{all y}} xyP(x, y) = (1)(1)(.5) + (1)(2)(.1) + (2)(1)(.1) + (2)(2)(.3) = 2.1$

$COV(X, Y) = \sum_{\text{all x}} \sum_{\text{all y}} xyP(x, y) - \mu_x\mu_y = 2.1 - (1.4)(1.4) = .14$

$\sigma_x = \sqrt{\sigma_x^2} = \sqrt{.24} = .49, \ \sigma_y = \sqrt{\sigma_y^2} = \sqrt{.24} = .49$

$\rho = \frac{COV(X,Y)}{\sigma_x\sigma_y} = \frac{.14}{(.49)(.49)} = .58$

7.46 a

x + y	P(x + y)
2	.5
3	.2
4	.3

© 2012 Cengage Learning. All Rights Reserved. May not be scanned, copied or duplicated, or posted to a publicly accessible website, in whole or in part.

b $\mu_{x+y} = E(X+Y) = \sum (x+y)P(x+y) = 2(.5) + 3(.2) + 4(.3) = 2.8$

$\sigma^2_{x+y} = V(X+Y) = \sum [(x+y) - \mu_{x+y}]^2 P(x+y) = (2–2.8)^2 (.5) + (3–2.8)^2 (.2) + (4–2.8)^2 (.3) =$

.76

c Yes

7.48 a $\sum_{\text{all x}} \sum_{\text{all y}} xyP(x, y) = (1)(1)(.28) + (1)(2)(.12) + (2)(1)(.42) + (2)(2)(.18) = 2.08$

$COV(X, Y) = \sum_{\text{all x}} \sum_{\text{all y}} xyP(x, y) - \mu_x \mu_y = 2.08 - (1.6)(1.3) = 0$

$\sigma_x = \sqrt{\sigma_x^2} = \sqrt{.24} = .49,\ \sigma_y = \sqrt{\sigma_y^2} = \sqrt{.21} = .46$

$$\rho = \frac{COV(X, Y)}{\sigma_x \sigma_y} = \frac{0}{(.49)(.46)} = 0$$

7.50 a

x + y	P(x + y)
2	.28
3	.54
4	.18

b $\mu_{x+y} = E(X+Y) = \sum (x+y)P(x+y) = 2(.28) + 3(.54) + 4(.18) = 2.9$

$\sigma^2_{x+y} = V(X+Y) = \sum [(x+y) - \mu_{x+y}]^2 P(x+y) = (2–2.9)^2 (.28) + (3–2.9)^2 (.54) + (4–2.9)^2 (.18)$

$= .45$

c Yes

7.52

	x		
y	0	1	2
1	.42	.21	.07
2	.18	.09	.03

7.54 a

Refrigerators, x	P(x)
0	.22
1	.49
2	.29

b

Stoves, y	P(y)
0	.34
1	.39
2	.27

© 2012 Cengage Learning. All Rights Reserved. May not be scanned, copied or duplicated, or posted to a publicly accessible website, in whole or in part.

c $\mu_x = E(X) = \sum xP(x) = 0(.22) + 1(.49) + 2(.29) = 1.07$

$\sigma^2 = V(X) = \sum (x-\mu)^2 P(x) = (0-1.07)^2(.22) + (1-1.07)^2(.49) + (2-1.07)^2(.29) = .505$

d $\mu_y = E(Y) = \sum yP(y) = 0(.34) + 1(.39) + 2(.27) = .93$

$\sigma^2 = V(Y) = \sum (y-\mu)^2 P(y) = (0-.93)^2(.34) + (1-.93)^2(.39) + (2-.93)^2(.27) = .605$

e $\sum_{\text{all x}} \sum_{\text{all y}} xyP(x,y) = (0)(0)(.08) + (0)(1)(.09) + (0)(2)(.05) + (1)(0)(.14) + (1)(1)(.17)$

$+ (1)(2)(.18) + (2)(0)(.12) + (2)(1)(.13) + (2)(2)(.04) = .95$

$COV(X, Y) = \sum_{\text{all x}} \sum_{\text{all y}} xyP(x,y) - \mu_x\mu_y = .95 - (1.07)(.93) = -.045$

$\sigma_x = \sqrt{\sigma_x^2} = \sqrt{.505} = .711, \ \sigma_y = \sqrt{\sigma_y^2} = \sqrt{.605} = .778$

$\rho = \frac{COV(X,Y)}{\sigma_x \sigma_y} = \frac{-.045}{(.711)(.778)} = -.081$

7.56 a $P(X = 1 \mid Y = 0) = P(X = 1 \text{ and } Y = 0)/P(Y = 0) = .14/.34 = .412$

b $P(Y = 0 \mid X = 1) = P(X = 1 \text{ and } Y = 0)/P(X = 1) = .14/.49 = .286$

c $P(X = 2 \mid Y = 2) = P(X = 2 \text{ and } Y = 2)/P(Y = 2) = .04/.27 = .148$

7.58 $E\left(\sum X_i\right) = \sum E(X_i) = 35 + 20 + 20 + 50 + 20 = 145$

$V\left(\sum X_i\right) = \sum V(X_i) = 8 + 5 + 4 + 12 + 2 = 31$

7.60 $E\left(\sum X_i\right) = \sum E(X_i) = 10 + 3 + 30 + 5 + 100 + 20 = 168$

$V\left(\sum X_i\right) = \sum V(X_i) = 9 + 0 + 100 + 1 + 400 + 64 = 574$

7.62 $E(R_p) = w_1E(R_1) + w_2E(R_2) = (.30)(.12) + (.70)(.25) = .2110$

a $V(R_p) = w_1^2\sigma_1^2 + w_2^2\sigma_2^2 + 2w_1w_2\rho\sigma_1\sigma_2$

$= (.30)^2(.02)^2 + (.70)^2(.15^2) + 2(.30)(.70)(.5)(.02)(.15) = .0117$

$\sigma_{R_p} = \sqrt{.0117} = .1081$

b $V(R_p) = w_1^2\sigma_1^2 + w_2^2\sigma_2^2 + 2w_1w_2\rho\sigma_1\sigma_2$

$= (.30)^2(.02)^2 + (.70)^2(.15^2) + 2(.30)(.70)(.2)(.02)(.15) = .0113$

$\sigma_{R_p} = \sqrt{.0113} = .1064$

© 2012 Cengage Learning. All Rights Reserved. May not be scanned, copied or duplicated, or posted to a publicly accessible website, in whole or in part.

c $V(R_p) = w_1^2\ \sigma_1^2 + w_2^2\ \sigma_2^2 + 2\, w_1\, w_2\, \rho\, \sigma_1\, \sigma_2$

$$= (.30)^2(.02)^2 + (.70)^2(.15^2) + 2(.30)(.70)(0)(.02)(.15) = .0111$$

$\sigma_{R_p} = \sqrt{.0111} = .1052$

7.64 $E(R_p) = w_1E(R_1) + w_2E(R_2) = (.60)(.09) + (.40)(.13) = .1060$

$V(R_p) = w_1^2\ \sigma_1^2 + w_2^2\ \sigma_2^2 + 2\, w_1\, w_2\, \rho\, \sigma_1\, \sigma_2$

$$= (.60)^2(.15)^2 + (.40)^2(.21^2) + 2(.60)(.40)(.4)(.15)(.21) = .0212$$

$\sigma_{R_p} = \sqrt{.0212} = .1456$

The statistics used in Exercises 7.66 to 7.78 were computed by Excel. The variances were taken from the variance-covariance matrix. As a result they are the population parameters. To convert to statistics multiply the variance of the portfolio returns by n/(n–1).

7.66 a

Stock	Mean	Variance
AT&T	.00717	.00318
Aetna	.00627	.01147
Cigna	.01327	.01550
Coca-Cola	.00881	.00239
Disney	.00562	.00442
Ford	.01555	.05104
McDonald's	.01478	.00277

b

	AT&T	Aetna	Cigna	Coca Cola	Disney	Ford	McDonalds
AT&T	0.00318						
Aetna	0.00111	0.01147					
Cigna	0.00162	0.01071	0.01550				
Coca Cola	0.00105	0.00154	0.00173	0.00239			
Disney	0.00120	0.00308	0.00389	0.00144	0.00442		
Ford	0.00332	0.00168	0.00982	0.00284	0.00741	0.05104	
McDonalds	0.00103	0.00196	0.00183	0.00148	0.00148	0.00157	0.00277

7.68 The stocks with the smallest variances are Coca-Cola (.00239) and McDonalds (.00277).

© 2012 Cengage Learning. All Rights Reserved. May not be scanned, copied or duplicated, or posted to a publicly accessible website, in whole or in part.

Portfolio of 2 Stocks			
		Coca Cola	*McDonalds*
Variance-Covariance Matrix	Coca Cola	0.00235	
	McDonalds	0.00145	0.00273
Expected Returns		0.00881	0.01478
Weights		0.5000	0.5000
Portfolio Return			
Expected Value	**0.01180**		
Variance	**0.00200**		
Standard Deviation	**0.04469**		

The expected value is .01180 and the standard deviation is .04469.

7.70

Portfolio of 3 Stocks				
		AT&T	*Coca Cola*	*Disney*
Variance-Covariance Matrix	AT&T	0.00313		
	Coca Cola	0.00103	0.00235	
	Disney	0.00118	0.00141	0.00434
Expected Returns		0.00717	0.00881	0.00562
Weights		0.33333	0.33333	0.33333
Portfolio Return				
Expected Value	**0.00720**			
Variance	**0.00190**			
Standard Deviation	**0.04355**			

The expected value is .00720 and the standard deviation is .04355.

© 2012 Cengage Learning. All Rights Reserved. May not be scanned, copied or duplicated, or posted to a publicly accessible website, in whole or in part.

7.72

Portfolio of 4 Stocks					
		AT&T	*Cigna*	*Disney*	*Ford*
Variance-Covariance Matrix	AT&T	0.003130			
	Cigna	0.001594	0.015245		
	Disney	0.001178	0.003829	0.004342	
	Ford	0.003267	0.009658	0.007288	0.050194
Expected Returns		0.00717	0.01327	0.00562	0.01555
Weights		0.30000	0.10000	0.40000	0.20000
Portfolio Return					
Expected Value	**0.00884**				
Variance	**0.00577**				
Standard Deviation	**0.07593**				

The expected value is .00884 and the standard deviation is .07593.

7.74 The stocks with the largest means are Fortis (.01254) and Research in Motion (.02536).

Portfolio of 2 Stocks			
		Fortis	**RIM**
Variance-Covariance Matrix	**Fortis**	0.00322	
	RIM	0.00003	0.02509
Expected Returns		0.01254	0.02536
Weights		0.50000	0.50000
Portfolio Return			
Expected Value	**0.01895**		
Variance	**0.00709**		
Standard Deviation	**0.08421**		

The expected value is .01895 and the standard deviation is .08421.

7.76 The two-stock portfolio with the largest expected value is composed of Fortis and Research in Motion , the two stocks with the highest means. Its expected value is .01895 and its standard deviation is .08421. The two-stock portfolio with the smallest variance is composed of Enbridge and Trans Canada Pipelines, the two stocks with the smallest variances. The expect value is .00969 and the standard deviation is .04103.

© 2012 Cengage Learning. All Rights Reserved. May not be scanned, copied or duplicated, or posted to a publicly accessible website, in whole or in part.

7.78

Portfolio of 4 Stocks					
		Barrick	BCE	Telus	TRP
Variance-Covariance Matrix	Barrick	0.01174			
	BCE	-0.00257	0.00421		
	Telus	-0.00085	0.00178	0.00480	
	TRP	0.00069	0.00091	0.00069	0.00184
Expected Returns		0.01253	0.00590	0.00436	0.00741
Weights		0.50000	0.25000	0.15000	0.10000
Portfolio Return					
Expected Value	0.00913				
Variance	0.00282				
Standard Deviation	0.05313				

The expected value is .00913 and the standard deviation is .05313.

7.80 a

Stock	Mean	Variance
Amazon	.02834	.02055
Amgen	.00150	.00788
Apple	.03927	.01442
Cisco Systems	.00664	.00628
Google	.02497	.01109
Intel	.00288	.00651
Microsoft	.00618	.00538
Oracle	.01203	.00446
Research in Motion	.02953	.02990

b Stocks, Amazon, Apple, Google, and Research in Motion have the largest means.

c Stocks Cisco, Intel, Microsoft, and Oracle have the smallest variances.

7.84 $P(X = x) = \frac{n!}{x!(n-x)!} p^x (1-p)^{n-x}$

a $P(X = 3) = \frac{10!}{3!(10-3)!} (.3)^3 (1-.3)^{10-3} = .2668$

b $P(X = 5) = \frac{10!}{5!(10-5)!} (.3)^5 (1-.3)^{10-5} = .1029$

c $P(X = 8) = \frac{10!}{8!(10-8)!} (.3)^8 (1-.3)^{10-8} = .0014$

© 2012 Cengage Learning. All Rights Reserved. May not be scanned, copied or duplicated, or posted to a publicly accessible website, in whole or in part.

7.86 a .26683

b .10292

c .00145

7.88 a $P(X = 2) = P(X \le 2) - P(X \le 1) = .9011 - .6554 = .2457$

b $P(X = 3) = P(X \le 3) - P(X \le 2) = .9830 - .9011 = .0819$

c $P(X = 5) = P(X \le 5) - P(X \le 4) = .9999 - 9984 = .0015$

7.90 a $P(X = 18) = P(X \le 18) - P(X \le 17) = .6593 - .4882 = .1711$

b $P(X = 15) = P(X \le 15) - P(X \le 14) = .1894 - .0978 = .0916$

c $P(X \le 20) = .9095$

d $P(X \ge 16) = 1 - P(X \le 15) = 1 - .1894 = .8106$

7.92 Binomial distribution with p = .25

a $P(X = 1) = \frac{4!}{1!(4-1)!}(.25)^1(1-.25)^{4-1} = .4219$

b Table 1 with n = 8: $p(2) = P(X \le 2) - P(X \le 1) = .6785 - .3671 = .3114$

c Excel: p(3) = .25810

7.94 Table 1 with n = 25 and p = .90

a $P(X = 20) = P(X \le 20) - P(X \le 19) = .0980 - .0334 = .0646$

b $P(X \ge 20) = 1 - P(X \le 19) = 1 - .0334 = .9666$

c $P(X \le 24) = .9282$

d $E(X) = np = 25(.90) = 22.5$

7.96 $P(X = 0) = \frac{4!}{0 1!(4-0)!}(.7)^0(1-.7)^{4-0} = .0081$

7.98 $P(X = 0) = \frac{25!}{0!(25-0)!}(.08)^0(1-.08)^{25-0} = .1244$

7.100 $P(X = 20) = \frac{20!}{20!(20-20)!}(.75)^{20}(1-.75)^{20-20} = .00317$

© 2012 Cengage Learning. All Rights Reserved. May not be scanned, copied or duplicated, or posted to a publicly accessible website, in whole or in part.

7.102 a $P(X = 2) = \frac{5!}{2!(5-2)!}(.45)^2(1-.45)^{5-2} = .3369$

b Excel with n = 25 and p = .45: $P(X \geq 10) = 1 - P(X \leq 9) = 1 - .24237 = .75763$

7.104 a $P(X = 2) = \frac{5!}{2!(5-2)!}(.52)^2(1-.52)^{5-2} = .2990$

b Excel with n = 25 and p = .52: $P(X \geq 10) = 1 - P(X \leq 9) = 1 - .08033 = .91967$

7.106 a Excel with n = 100 and p = .52: $P(X \geq 50) = 1 - P(X \leq 49) = 1 - .30815 = .69185$

b Excel with n = 100 and p = .36: $P(X \leq 30) = .12519$

c Excel with n = 100 and p = .06: $P(X \leq 5) = .44069$

7.108a. Excel with n = 10 and p = .23: $P(X \geq 5) = 1 - P(X \leq 4) = 1 - .94308 = .05692$

b. Excel with n = 25 and p = .23: $P(X \leq 5) = .47015$

7.110 a $P(X = 0) = \frac{e^{-\mu}\mu^x}{x!} = \frac{e^{-2}2^0}{0!} = .1353$

b $P(X = 3) = \frac{e^{-\mu}\mu^x}{x!} = \frac{e^{-2}2^3}{3!} = .1804$

c $P(X = 5) = \frac{e^{-\mu}\mu^x}{x!} = \frac{e^{-2}2^5}{5!} = .0361$

7.112 a Table 2 with $\mu = 3.5$: $P(X = 0) = P(X \leq 0) = .0302$

b Table 2 with $\mu = 3.5$: $P(X \geq 5) = 1 - P(X \leq 4) = 1 - .7254 = .2746$

c Table 2 with $\mu = 3.5/7$: $P(X = 1) = P(X \leq 1) - P(X \leq 0) = .9098 - .6065 = .3033$

7.114 a $P(X = 0 \text{ with } \mu = 2) = \frac{e^{-\mu}\mu^x}{x!} = \frac{e^{-2}(2)^0}{0!} = .1353$

b $P(X = 10 \text{ with } \mu = 14) = \frac{e^{-\mu}\mu^x}{x!} = \frac{e^{-14}(14)^{10}}{10!} = .0663$

7.116 a Excel with $\mu = 30$: $P(X \geq 35) = 1 - P(X \leq 34) = 1 - .79731 = .20269$

b Excel with $\mu = 15$:$P(X \leq 12 = .26761$

© 2012 Cengage Learning. All Rights Reserved. May not be scanned, copied or duplicated, or posted to a publicly accessible website, in whole or in part.

7.118 P(X = 0 with μ = 80/200) = $\frac{e^{-\mu}\mu^{x}}{x!} = \frac{e^{-.4}(.4)^{0}}{0!}$ =.6703

7.120 a Table 2 with μ = 1.5: P(X $\geq$ 2) = 1 – P(X $\leq$ 1) = 1 – .5578 = .4422

b Table 2 μ = 6: P(X < 4) = P(X $\leq$ 3) = .1512

7.122 a P(X = 0 with μ = 1.5) = $\frac{e^{-\mu}\mu^{x}}{x!} = \frac{e^{-1.5}(1.5)^{0}}{0!}$ = .2231

b Table 2 with μ = 4.5: P(X $\leq$ 5) = .7029

c Table 2 with μ = 3.0: P(X $\geq$ 3) = 1 – P(X $\leq$ 2 = 1 – .4232 = .5768

7.124 a E(X) = np = 40(.02) = .8

b P(X = 0) = $\frac{40!}{0!(40-0)!}(.02)^{0}(1-.02)^{40-0}$ = .4457

7.126 a P(X = 10 with μ = 8) = $\frac{e^{-\mu}\mu^{x}}{x!} = \frac{e^{-8}(8)^{10}}{10!}$ = .0993

b Table 2 with μ = 8: P(X > 5) = P(X $\geq$ 6) = 1 – P(X $\leq$ 5) = 1 – .1912 = .8088

c Table 2 with μ = 8: P(X < 12) = P(X $\leq$ 11) = .8881

7.128 Table 1 with n = 10 and p = .3: P(X > 5) = P(X $\geq$ 6) = 1 – P(X $\leq$ 5) = 1 – .9527 = .0473

7.130 Table 1 with n = 10 and p = .20: P(X $\geq$ 6) = 1 – P(X $\leq$ 5) = 1 – .9936 = .0064

7.132 a Excel with n = 80 and p = .70: P(X > 65) = P(X $\geq$ 66) = 1 – P(X $\leq$ 65) = 1 – .99207 = .00793

b E(X) = np = 80(.70) = 56

c $\sigma = \sqrt{np(1-p)} = \sqrt{80(.70)(1-.70)}$ = 4.10

7.134 Table 1 with n = 25 and p = .40:

a P(X = 10) = P(X $\leq$10) – P(X $\leq$ 9) = .5858 – .4246 = .1612

b P(X < 5) = P(X $\leq$ 4) = .0095

c P(X > 15) = P(X $\geq$ 16) = 1 – P(X $\leq$ 15) = 1 – .9868 = .0132

© 2012 Cengage Learning. All Rights Reserved. May not be scanned, copied or duplicated, or posted to a publicly accessible website, in whole or in part.

7.136 a $\mu = E(X) = \sum xP(x) = 0(.36) + 1(.22) + 2(.20) + 3(.09) + 4(.08) + 5(.05) = 1.46$

$\sigma^2 = V(X) = \sum (x-\mu)^2 P(x) = (0-1.46)^2(.36) + (1-1.46)^2(.22) + (2-1.46)^2(.20)$

$+ (3-1.46)^2(.09) + (4-1.46)^2(.08) + (5-1.46)^2(.05) = 2.23$

$\sigma = \sqrt{\sigma^2} = \sqrt{2.23} = 1.49$

b $\mu = E(X) = \sum xP(x) = 0(.15) + 1(.18) + 2(.23) + 3(.26) + 4(.10) + 5(.08) = 2.22$

$\sigma^2 = V(X) = \sum (x-\mu)^2 P(x) = (0-2.22)^2(.15) + (1-2.22)^2(.18) + (2-2.22)^2(.23)$

$+ (3-2.22)^2(.26) + (4-2.22)^2(.10) + (5-2.22)^2(.08) = 2.11$

$\sigma = \sqrt{\sigma^2} = \sqrt{2.11} = 1.45$

7.138 p = .08755 because $P(X \geq 1) = 1 - P(X = 0$ with n = 10 and p = .08755) = 1 – .40 = .60

7.140 Binomial with n = 5 and p = .01. (using Excel)

x	p(x)
0	.95099
1	.04803
2	.00097
3	.00001
4	0
5	0

© 2012 Cengage Learning. All Rights Reserved. May not be scanned, copied or duplicated, or posted to a publicly accessible website, in whole or in part.

Chapter 8

8.2a. $P(X > 45) \approx \frac{(60-45)\times 3}{50\times 15} + \frac{(75-60)\times 3}{50\times 15} = .1200$

b. $P(10 < X < 40) \approx \frac{(15-10)\times 16}{50\times 15} + \frac{(30-15)\times 8}{50\times 15} + \frac{(40-30)\times 8}{50\times 15} = .4800$

c. $P(X < 25) \approx \frac{(-30-[-45])\times 5}{50\times 15} + \frac{(-15-[-30])\times 5}{50\times 15} + \frac{(0-[-15])\times 2}{50\times 15} + \frac{(15-0)\times 16}{50\times 15} + \frac{(25-15)\times 8}{50\times 15}$

$= .6667$

d. $P(35 < X < 65) \approx \frac{(45-35)\times 8}{50\times 15} + \frac{(60-45)\times 3}{50\times 15} + \frac{(65-60)\times 3}{50\times 15} = .1867$

8.4a.

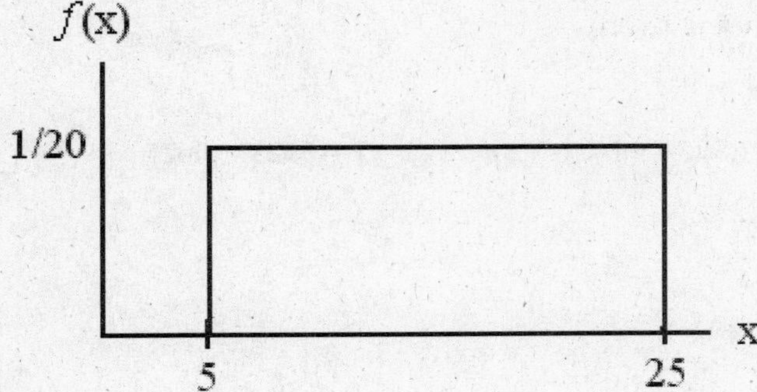

b. $P(X > 25) = 0$

c. $P(10 < X < 15) = (15-10)\frac{1}{20} = .25$

d. $P(5.0 < X < 5.1) = (5.1-5)\frac{1}{20} = .005$

8.6 $f(x) = \frac{1}{(60-30)} = \frac{1}{30} \quad 30 < x < 60$

a. $P(X > 55) = (60-55)\frac{1}{30} = .1667$

b. $P(30 < X < 40) = (40-30)\frac{1}{30} = .3333$

c. $P(X = 37.23) = 0$

8.8 $.10\times(60-30) = 3$; The top decile = 60–3 = 57 minutes

© 2012 Cengage Learning. All Rights Reserved. May not be scanned, copied or duplicated, or posted to a publicly accessible website, in whole or in part.

8.10 .20(175–110) = 13. Bottom 20% lie below (110 + 13) = 123

For Exercises 8.12 and 8.14 we calculate probabilities by determining the area in a triangle. That is,

Area in a triangle = (.5)(height)(base)

8.12a

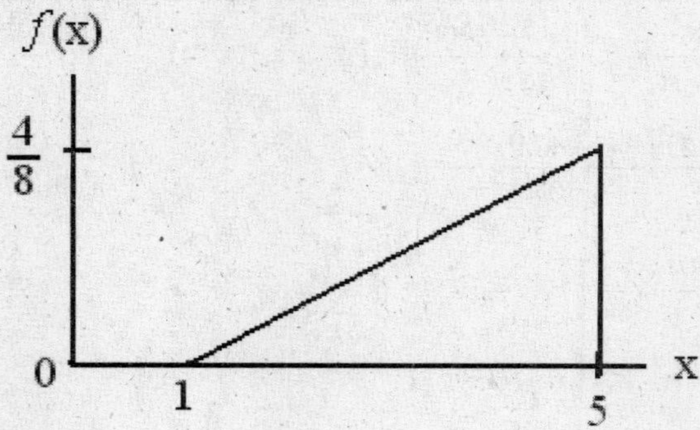

b. P(2 < X < 4) = P(X < 4) – P(X < 2) = (.5)(3/8)(4–1) – (.5)(1/8)(2–1) = .5625 – .0625 = .5

c. P(X < 3) = (.5)(2/8)(3–1) = .25

8.14a. f(x) = .10 – .005x $0 \leq x \leq 20$

b. P(X > 10) = (.5)(.05)(20–10) = .25

c. P(6 < X < 12) = P(X > 6) – PX > 12) = (.5)(.07)(20–6) – (.5)(.04)(20–12) = .49 – .16 = .33

8.16 P(Z < 1.51) = .9345

8.18 P(Z < −1.59) = .0559

8.20 P(Z < − 2.30) = .0107

8.22 P(Z > −1.44) = 1 – P(Z < −1.44) = 1 − .0749 = .9251

8.24 P(Z > 1.67) = 1 – P(Z < 1.67) = 1 – .9525 = .0475

8.26 P(1.14 < Z < 2.43) = P(Z < 2.43) – P(Z < 1.14) = .9925 – .8729 = .1196

8.28 P(Z > 3.09) = 1 – P(Z < 3.09) = 1 – .9990 = .0010

© 2012 Cengage Learning. All Rights Reserved. May not be scanned, copied or duplicated, or posted to a publicly accessible website, in whole or in part.

8.30 $P(Z > 4.0) = 0$

8.32 $P(Z < z_{.045}) = 1 - .045 = .9550$; $z_{.045} = 1.70$

8.34 $P(X > 145) = P\left(\frac{X-\mu}{\sigma} > \frac{145-100}{20}\right) = P(Z > 2.25) = 1 - P(Z < 2.25) = 1 - .9878 = .0122$

8.36 $P(800 < X < 1100) = P\left(\frac{800-1,000}{250} < \frac{X-\mu}{\sigma} < \frac{1,100-1,000}{250}\right) = P(-.8 < Z < .4)$

$= P(Z < .4) - P(Z < -.8) = .6554 - .2119 = .4435$

8.38 a $P(5 < X < 10) = P\left(\frac{5-6.3}{2.2} < \frac{X-\mu}{\sigma} < \frac{10-6.3}{2.2}\right) = P(-.59 < Z > 1.68)$

$= P(Z < 1.68) - P(Z < -.59) = .9535 - .2776 = .6759$

b $P(X > 7) = P\left(\frac{X-\mu}{\sigma} > \frac{7-6.3}{2.2}\right) = P(Z > .32) = 1 - P(Z < .32) = 1 - .6255 = .3745$

c $P(X < 4) = P\left(\frac{X-\mu}{\sigma} < \frac{4-6.3}{2.2}\right) = P(Z < -1.05) = .1469$

8.40 $P(X > 5,000) = P\left(\frac{X-\mu}{\sigma} > \frac{5,000-5,100}{200}\right) = P(Z > -.5) = 1 - P(Z < -.5) = 1 - .3085 = .6915$

8.42 a $P(X > 12,000) = P\left(\frac{X-\mu}{\sigma} > \frac{12,000-10,000}{2,400}\right) = P(Z > .83) = 1 - P(Z < .83) = 1 - .7967$

$= .2033$

b $P(X < 9,000) = P\left(\frac{X-\mu}{\sigma} < \frac{9,000-10,000}{2,400}\right) = P(Z < -.42) = .3372$

8.44 a $P(X > 70) = P\left(\frac{X-\mu}{\sigma} > \frac{70-65}{4}\right) = P(Z > 1.25) = 1 - P(Z < 1.25) = 1 - .8944 = .1056$

b $P(X < 60) = P\left(\frac{X-\mu}{\sigma} < \frac{60-65}{4}\right) = P(Z < -1.25) = .1056$

c $P(55 < X < 70) = P\left(\frac{55-65}{4} < \frac{X-\mu}{\sigma} < \frac{70-65}{4}\right) = P(-2.50 < Z < 1.25)$

$= P(Z < 1.25) - P(Z < -2.50) = .8944 - .0062 = .8882$

© 2012 Cengage Learning. All Rights Reserved. May not be scanned, copied or duplicated, or posted to a publicly accessible website, in whole or in part.

8.46 Top 5%: $P(Z < z_{.05}) = 1 - .05 = .9500$; $z_{.05} = 1.645$; $z_{.05} = \frac{x-\mu}{\sigma}$; $1.645 = \frac{x-32}{1.5}$;

x = 34.4675

Bottom 5%: $P(Z < -z_{.05}) = .0500$; $-z_{.05} = -1.645$; $-z_{.05} = \frac{x-\mu}{\sigma}$; $-1.645 = \frac{x-32}{1.5}$;

x = 29.5325

8.48 $P(X > 8) = P\left(\frac{X-\mu}{\sigma} > \frac{8-7.2}{.667}\right) = P(Z > 1.20) = 1 - P(Z < 1.20) = 1 - .8849 = .1151$

8.50 a $P(X > 10) = P\left(\frac{X-\mu}{\sigma} > \frac{10-7.5}{2.1}\right) = P\,Z > 1.19) = 1 - P(Z < 1.19) = 1 - .8830 = .1170$

b $P(7 < X < 9) = P\left(\frac{7-7.5}{2.1} < \frac{X-\mu}{\sigma} < \frac{9-7.5}{2.1}\right) = P(-.24 < Z < .71)$

$= P(Z < .71) - P(0 < Z < -.24) = .7611 - .4052 = .3559$

c $P(X < 3) = P\left(\frac{X-\mu}{\sigma} < \frac{3-7.5}{2.1}\right) = P\,Z < -2.14) = .0162$

d $P(Z < -z_{.05}) = .0500$; $-z_{.05} = -1.645$; $-z_{.05} = \frac{x-\mu}{\sigma}$; $-1.645 = \frac{x-7.5}{2.1}$; x = 4.05 hours

8.52 $P(Z < -z_{.01}) = .0100$; $-z_{.05} = -2.33$; $-z_{.01} = \frac{x-\mu}{\sigma}$; $-2.33 = \frac{x-11{,}500}{800}$; x = 9,636

8.54 a $P(X > 30) = P\left(\frac{X-\mu}{\sigma} > \frac{30-27}{7}\right) = P(Z > .43) = 1 - P(Z < .43) = 1 - .6664 = .3336$

b $P(X > 40) = P\left(\frac{X-\mu}{\sigma} > \frac{40-27}{7}\right) = P(Z > 1.86) = 1 - P(Z < 1.86) = 1 - .9686 = .0314$

c $P(X < 15) = P\left(\frac{X-\mu}{\sigma} < \frac{15-27}{7}\right) = P(Z < -1.71) = .0436$

d $P(Z < z_{.20}) = 1 - .20 = .8000$; $z_{.20} = .84$; $z_{.20} = \frac{x-\mu}{\sigma}$; $.84 = \frac{x-27}{7}$; x = 32.88

8.56 a $P(X < 10) = P\left(\frac{X-\mu}{\sigma} < \frac{10-16.40}{2.75}\right) = P(Z < -2.33) = .0099$

b $P(Z < -z_{.10}) = .1000$; $-z_{.10} = -1.28$; $-z_{.10} = \frac{x-\mu}{\sigma}$; $-1.28 = \frac{x-16.40}{2.75}$; x = 12.88

© 2012 Cengage Learning. All Rights Reserved. May not be scanned, copied or duplicated, or posted to a publicly accessible website, in whole or in part.

8.58 $P(Z < z_{.02}) = 1 - .02 = .9800;\ z_{.02} = 2.05;\ z_{.02} = \frac{x-\mu}{\sigma};\ 2.05 = \frac{x-100}{16};\ x = 132.80$

(rounded to 133)

8.60 $P(X < 45{,}000) = P\left(\frac{X-\mu}{\sigma} < \frac{45{,}000-41{,}825}{13{,}444}\right) = P(Z < .24) = .5948$

8.62 $P(x > 150{,}000) = P\left(\frac{X-\mu}{\sigma} < \frac{150{,}000-99{,}700}{30{,}000}\right) = P(Z > 1.68) = 1 - P(Z < 1.68) = 1 - .9535$

$= .0465$

8.64 $P(Z < z_{.20}) = 1 - .20 = .8000;\ z_{.20} = .84;\ z_{.20} = \frac{x-\mu}{\sigma};\ .84 = \frac{x-150}{25};\ x = 171$

8.66 $P(Z < z_{.40}) = 1 - .40 = .6000;\ z_{.40} = .25;\ z_{.40} = \frac{x-\mu}{\sigma};\ .25 = \frac{x-850}{90};\ .x = 872.5$

(rounded to 873)

8.68 $P(X < 150) = P\left(\frac{X-\mu}{\sigma} < \frac{150-145}{5.57}\right) = P(Z < .90) = .8159$

8.70 a. $P(X < 0) = P\left(\frac{X-\mu}{\sigma} < \frac{0-10.60}{14.56}\right) = P(Z < -.73) = .2327$

b. $P(X > 20) = P\left(\frac{X-\mu}{\sigma} > \frac{20-10.60}{14.56}\right) = P(Z > .65) = 1 - P(Z < .65) = 1 - .7422 = .2578$

© 2012 Cengage Learning. All Rights Reserved. May not be scanned, copied or duplicated, or posted to a publicly accessible website, in whole or in part.

8.72

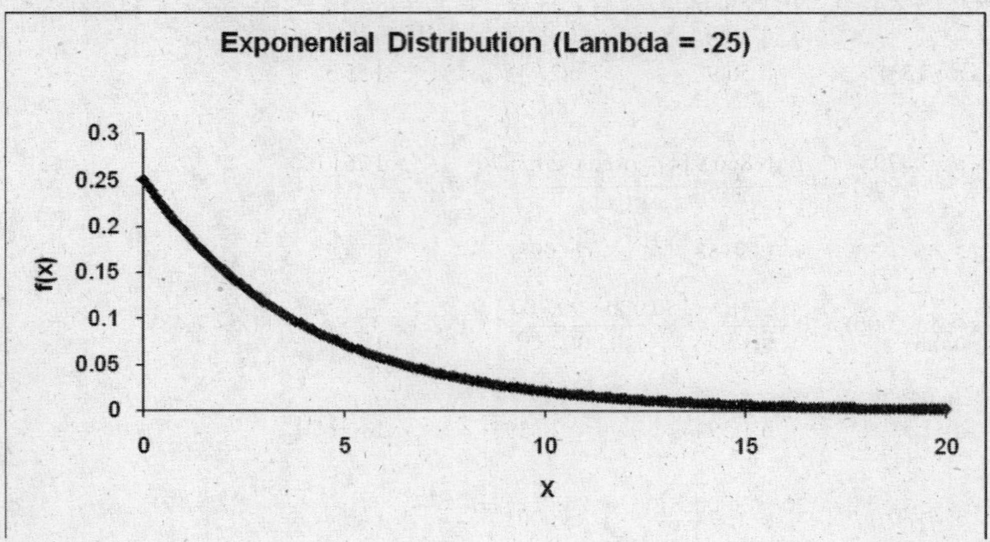

8.74 a $P(X > 2) = e^{-.3(2)} = e^{-.6} = .5488$

b $P(X < 4) = 1 - e^{-.3(4)} = 1 - e^{-1.2} = 1 - .3012 = .6988$

c $P(1 < X < 2) = e^{-.3(1)} - e^{-.3(2)} = e^{-.3} - e^{-.6} = .7408 - .5488 = .1920$

d $P(X = 3) = 0$

8.76 $\mu = 1/\lambda = 25$ hours; $\lambda = .04$ breakdowns/hour

$P(X > 50) = e^{-.04(50)} = e^{-2} = .1353$

8.78 $\mu = 1/\lambda = 5$ minutes; $\lambda = .2$ customer/minute

$P(X < 10) = 1 - e^{-.2(10)} = 1 - e^{-2} = 1 - .1353 = .8647$

8.80 $\mu = 1/\lambda = 7.5$ minutes; $\lambda = .133$ service/minute

$P(X < 5) = 1 - e^{-.133(5)} = 1 - e^{-.665} = 1 - .5143 = .4857$

8.82 $\mu = 1/\lambda = 6$ minutes; $\lambda = .167$ customers/minute

$P(X > 10) = e^{-.167(10)} = e^{-1.67} = .1889$

8.84 a 2.750 b 1.282 c 2.132 d 2.528

8.86 a 1.6556 b 2.6810 c 1.9600 d 1.6602

© 2012 Cengage Learning. All Rights Reserved. May not be scanned, copied or duplicated, or posted to a publicly accessible website, in whole or in part.

8.88	a .1744	b .0231	c .0251	d .0267
8.90	a 17.3	b 50.9	c 2.71	d 53.5
8.92	a 33.5705	b 866.911	c 24.3976	d 261.058
8.94	a .4881	b .9158	c .9988	d .9077
8.96	a 2.84	b 1.93	c 3.60	d 3.37
8.98	a 1.5204	b 1.5943	c 2.8397	d 1.1670
8.100	a .1050	b .1576	c .0001	d .0044

© 2012 Cengage Learning. All Rights Reserved. May not be scanned, copied or duplicated, or posted to a publicly accessible website, in whole or in part.

Chapter 9

9.2 a $P(\overline{X}=1) = P(1,1) = 1/36$

b $P(\overline{X}=6) = P(6,6) = 1/36$

9.4 The variance of $\overline{X}$ is smaller than the variance of X.

9.6 No, because the sample mean is approximately normally distributed.

9.8 a $P(\overline{X}>1050) = P\left(\frac{\overline{X}-\mu}{\sigma/\sqrt{n}} > \frac{1050-1000}{200/\sqrt{25}}\right) = P(Z>1.25) = 1-P(Z<1.25) = 1-.8944$

$= .1056$

b $P(\overline{X}<960) = P\left(\frac{\overline{X}-\mu}{\sigma/\sqrt{n}} < \frac{960-1000}{200/\sqrt{25}}\right) = P(Z<-1.00) = .1587$

c $P(\overline{X}>1100) = P\left(\frac{\overline{X}-\mu}{\sigma/\sqrt{n}} > \frac{1100-1000}{200/\sqrt{25}}\right) = P(Z>2.50) = 1-P(Z<2.50) = 1-.9938 = .0062$

9.10 a $P(49<\overline{X}<52) = P\left(\frac{49-50}{5/\sqrt{4}} < \frac{\overline{X}-\mu}{\sigma/\sqrt{n}} < \frac{52-50}{5/\sqrt{4}}\right) = P(-.40<Z<.80)$

$= P(Z<.80) - P(Z<-.40) = .7881 - .3446 = .4435$

b $P(49<\overline{X}<52) = P\left(\frac{49-50}{5/\sqrt{16}} < \frac{\overline{X}-\mu}{\sigma/\sqrt{n}} < \frac{52-50}{5/\sqrt{16}}\right) = P(-.80<Z<1.60)$

$= P(Z<1.60) - P(Z<-.80) = .9452 - .2119 = .7333$

c $P(49<\overline{X}<52) = P\left(\frac{49-50}{5/\sqrt{25}} < \frac{\overline{X}-\mu}{\sigma/\sqrt{n}} < \frac{52-50}{5/\sqrt{25}}\right) = P(-1.00<Z<2.00)$

$= P(Z<2.00) - P(Z<-1.00) = .9772 - .1587 = .8185$

9.12 a $P(49<\overline{X}<52) = P\left(\frac{49-50}{20/\sqrt{4}} < \frac{\overline{X}-\mu}{\sigma/\sqrt{n}} < \frac{52-50}{20/\sqrt{4}}\right) = P(-.10<Z<.20)$

$= P(Z<.20) - P(Z<-.10) = .5793 - .4602 = .1191$

b $P(49<\overline{X}<52) = P\left(\frac{49-50}{20/\sqrt{16}} < \frac{\overline{X}-\mu}{\sigma/\sqrt{n}} < \frac{52-50}{20/\sqrt{16}}\right) = P(-.20<Z<.40)$

$= P(Z<.40) - P(Z<-.20) = .6554 - .4207 = .2347$

© 2012 Cengage Learning. All Rights Reserved. May not be scanned, copied or duplicated, or posted to a publicly accessible website, in whole or in part.

c $P(49 < \overline{X} < 52) = P\left(\frac{49-50}{20/\sqrt{25}} < \frac{\overline{X}-\mu}{\sigma/\sqrt{n}} < \frac{52-50}{20/\sqrt{25}}\right) = P(-.25 < Z < .50)$

$= P(Z < .50) - P(Z < -.25) = .6915 - .4013 = .2902$

9.14 a $\sigma_{\bar{x}} = \frac{\sigma}{\sqrt{n}}\sqrt{\frac{N-n}{N-1}} = \frac{500}{\sqrt{1,000}}\sqrt{\frac{10,000-1,000}{10,000-1}} = 15.00$

b $\sigma_{\bar{x}} = \frac{\sigma}{\sqrt{n}}\sqrt{\frac{N-n}{N-1}} = \frac{500}{\sqrt{500}}\sqrt{\frac{10,000-500}{10,000-1}} = 21.80$

c $\sigma_{\bar{x}} = \frac{\sigma}{\sqrt{n}}\sqrt{\frac{N-n}{N-1}} = \frac{500}{\sqrt{100}}\sqrt{\frac{10,000-100}{10,000-1}} = 49.75$

9.16 We can answer part (c) and possibly part (b) depending on how nonnormal the population is.

9.18 a $P(X > 60) = P\left(\frac{X-\mu}{\sigma} > \frac{60-52}{6}\right) = P(Z > 1.33) = 1 - P(Z < 1.33) = 1 - .9082 = .0918$

b $P(\overline{X} > 60) = P\left(\frac{\overline{X}-\mu}{\sigma/\sqrt{n}} > \frac{60-52}{6/\sqrt{3}}\right) = P(Z > 2.31) = 1 - P(Z < 2.31) = 1 - .9896 = .0104$

c $[P(X > 60)]^3 = [.0918]^3 = .00077$

9.20 a $P(X < 75) = P\left(\frac{X-\mu}{\sigma} < \frac{75-78}{6}\right) = P(Z < -.50) = .3085$

b $P(\overline{X} < 75) = P\left(\frac{\overline{X}-\mu}{\sigma/\sqrt{n}} < \frac{75-78}{6/\sqrt{50}}\right) = P(Z < -3.54) = 1 - P(Z < 3.54) = 1 - 1 = 0$

9.22 a $P(\overline{X} < 5.97) = P\left(\frac{\overline{X}-\mu}{\sigma/\sqrt{n}} < \frac{5.97-6.05}{.18/\sqrt{36}}\right) = P(Z < -2.67) = .0038$

b It appears to be false.

9.24 The professor needs to know the mean and standard deviation of the population of the weights of elevator users and that the distribution is not extremely nonnormal.

9.26 $P(\text{Total time} > 300) = P(\overline{X} > 300/60) = P(\overline{X} > 5) = P\left(\frac{\overline{X}-\mu}{\sigma/\sqrt{n}} > \frac{5-4.8}{1.3/\sqrt{60}}\right) = P(Z > 1.19)$

$= 1 - P(Z < 1.19) = 1 - .8830 = .1170$

© 2012 Cengage Learning. All Rights Reserved. May not be scanned, copied or duplicated, or posted to a publicly accessible website, in whole or in part.

9.28 $P(\text{Total number of cups} > 240) = P(\overline{X} > 240/125) = P(\overline{X} > 1.92) = P\left(\frac{\overline{X}-\mu}{\sigma/\sqrt{n}} > \frac{1.92-2.0}{.6/\sqrt{125}}\right)$

$= P(Z > -1.49) = 1 - P(Z < -1.49) = 1 - .0681 = .9319$

9.30a $P(\hat{P} > .60) = P\left(\frac{\hat{P}-p}{\sqrt{p(1-p)/n}} > \frac{.60-.5}{\sqrt{(.5)(1-.5)/300}}\right) = P(Z > 3.46) = 0$

b. $P(\hat{P} > .60) = P\left(\frac{\hat{P}-p}{\sqrt{p(1-p)/n}} > \frac{.60-.55}{\sqrt{(.55)(1-.55)/300}}\right) = P(Z > 1.74) = 1 - P(Z < 1.74)$

$= 1 - .9591 = .0409$

c. $P(\hat{P} > .60) = P\left(\frac{\hat{P}-p}{\sqrt{p(1-p)/n}} > \frac{.60-.6}{\sqrt{(.6)(1-.6)/300}}\right) = P(Z > 0) = 1 - P(Z < 0) = 1 - .5 = .5$

9.32 $P(\hat{P} < .75) = P\left(\frac{\hat{P}-p}{\sqrt{p(1-p)/n}} > \frac{.75-.80}{\sqrt{(.80)(1-.80)/100}}\right) = P(Z < -1.25) = .1056$

9.34 $P(\hat{P} < .49) = P\left(\frac{\hat{P}-p}{\sqrt{p(1-p)/n}} < \frac{.49-.55}{\sqrt{(.55)(1-.55)/500}}\right) = P(Z < -2.70) = .0035$

9.36 a $P(\hat{P} < .50) = P\left(\frac{\hat{P}-p}{\sqrt{p(1-p)/n}} < \frac{.50-.53}{\sqrt{(.53)(1-.53)/400}}\right) = P(Z < -1.20) = .1151$; the claim may be true

b $P(\hat{P} < .50) = P\left(\frac{\hat{P}-p}{\sqrt{p(1-p)/n}} < \frac{.50-.53}{\sqrt{(.53)(1-.53)/1,000}}\right) = P(Z < -1.90) = .0287$; the claim appears to be false

9.38 $P(\hat{P} > .05) = P\left(\frac{\hat{P}-p}{\sqrt{p(1-p)/n}} > \frac{.05-.03}{\sqrt{(.03)(1-.03)/400}}\right) = P(Z > 2.34) = 1 - P(Z < 2.34)$

$= 1 - .9904 = .0096$; the commercial appears to be dishonest

9.40 a $P(\hat{P} < .45) = P\left(\frac{\hat{P}-p}{\sqrt{p(1-p)/n}} < \frac{.45-.50}{\sqrt{(.50)(1-.50)/600}}\right) = P(Z < -2.45) = .0071$

b The claim appears to be false.

© 2012 Cengage Learning. All Rights Reserved. May not be scanned, copied or duplicated, or posted to a publicly accessible website, in whole or in part.

9.42 $P(\hat{P} < .70) = P\left(\frac{\hat{P}-p}{\sqrt{p(1-p)/n}} < \frac{.70-.75}{\sqrt{(.75)(1-.75)/460}}\right) = P(Z < -2.48) = .0066$

9.44 The claim appears to be false.

9.46 $P(\overline{X}_1 - \overline{X}_2 > 25) = P\left(\frac{(\overline{X}_1 - \overline{X}_2) - (\mu_1 - \mu_2)}{\sqrt{\frac{\sigma_1^2}{n_1} + \frac{\sigma_2^2}{n_2}}} > \frac{25-(280-270)}{\sqrt{\frac{25^2}{50} + \frac{30^2}{50}}}\right) = P(Z > 2.72)$

$= 1 - P(Z < 2.72) = 1 - .9967 = .0033$

9.48 $P(\overline{X}_1 - \overline{X}_2 > 0) = P\left(\frac{(\overline{X}_1 - \overline{X}_2) - (\mu_1 - \mu_2)}{\sqrt{\frac{\sigma_1^2}{n_1} + \frac{\sigma_2^2}{n_2}}} > \frac{0-(40-38)}{\sqrt{\frac{6^2}{25} + \frac{8^2}{25}}}\right) = P(Z > -1.00) = 1 - P(Z < -1.00)$

$= 1 - .1587 = .8413$

9.50 $P(\overline{X}_1 - \overline{X}_2 > 0) = P\left(\frac{(\overline{X}_1 - \overline{X}_2) - (\mu_1 - \mu_2)}{\sqrt{\frac{\sigma_1^2}{n_1} + \frac{\sigma_2^2}{n_2}}} > \frac{0-(140-138)}{\sqrt{\frac{6^2}{25} + \frac{8^2}{25}}}\right) = P(Z > -1.00)$

$= 1 - P(Z < -1.00) = 1 - .1587 = .8413$

9.52 $P(\overline{X}_1 - \overline{X}_2 > 0) = P\left(\frac{(\overline{X}_1 - \overline{X}_2) - (\mu_1 - \mu_2)}{\sqrt{\frac{\sigma_1^2}{n_1} + \frac{\sigma_2^2}{n_2}}} > \frac{0-(73-77)}{\sqrt{\frac{12^2}{4} + \frac{10^2}{4}}}\right) = P(Z > .51) = 1 - P(Z < .51)$

$= 1 - .6950 = .3050$

9.54 $P(\overline{X}_1 - \overline{X}_2 < 0) = P\left(\frac{(\overline{X}_1 - \overline{X}_2) - (\mu_1 - \mu_2)}{\sqrt{\frac{\sigma_1^2}{n_1} + \frac{\sigma_2^2}{n_2}}} < \frac{0-(10-15)}{\sqrt{\frac{3^2}{25} + \frac{3^2}{25}}}\right) = P(Z < 5.89) = 1$

© 2012 Cengage Learning. All Rights Reserved. May not be scanned, copied or duplicated, or posted to a publicly accessible website, in whole or in part.

Chapter 10

10.2 An unbiased estimator of a parameter is an estimator whose expected value equals the parameter.

10.4

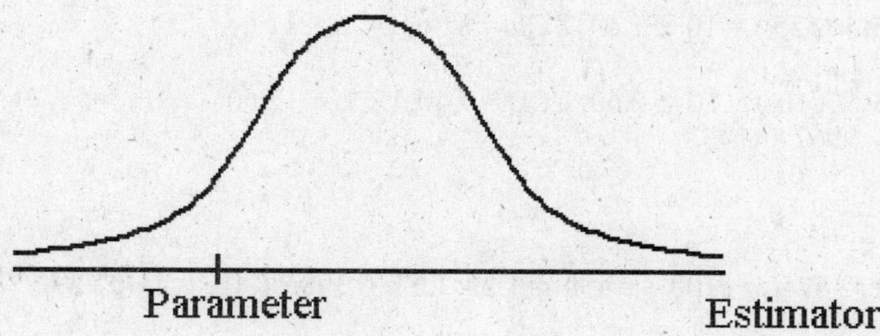

10.6

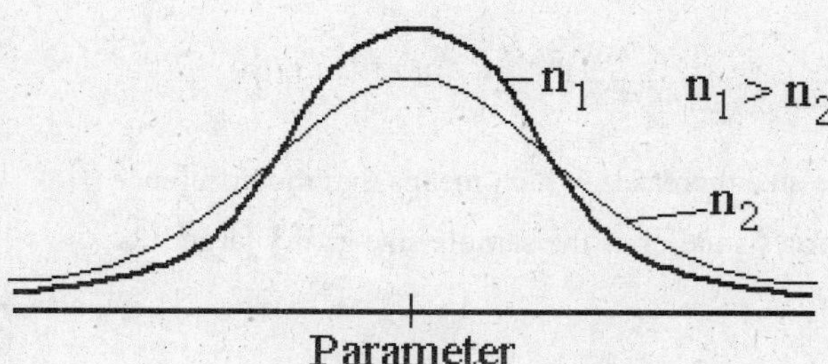

10.8

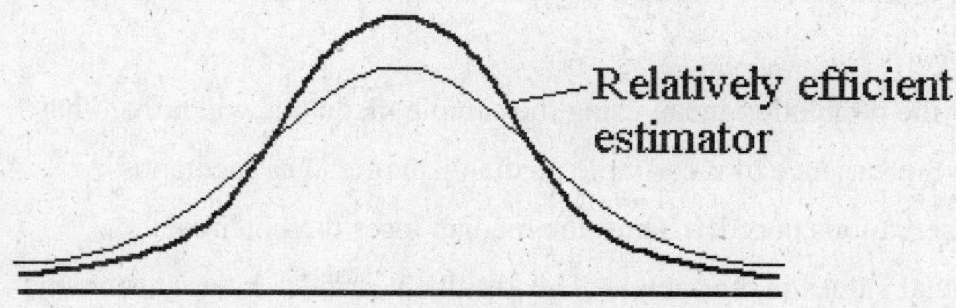

10.10a. $\bar{x} \pm z_{\alpha/2}\sigma/\sqrt{n} = 200 \pm 1.96(50/\sqrt{25}) = 200 \pm 19.60$; LCL = 180.40, UCL = 219.60

b. $\bar{x} \pm z_{\alpha/2}\sigma/\sqrt{n} = 200 \pm 1.96(25/\sqrt{25}) = 200 \pm 9.80$; LCL = 190.20, UCL = 209.80

c. $\bar{x} \pm z_{\alpha/2}\sigma/\sqrt{n} = 200 \pm 1.96(10/\sqrt{25}) = 200 \pm 3.92$; LCL = 196.08, UCL = 203.92

d. The interval narrows.

© 2012 Cengage Learning. All Rights Reserved. May not be scanned, copied or duplicated, or posted to a publicly accessible website, in whole or in part.

10.12a. $\bar{x} \pm z_{\alpha/2}\sigma/\sqrt{n} = 500 \pm 2.33(12/\sqrt{50}) = 500 \pm 3.95$; LCL = 496.05, UCL = 503.95

b. $\bar{x} \pm z_{\alpha/2}\sigma/\sqrt{n} = 500 \pm 1.96(12/\sqrt{50}) = 500 \pm 3.33$; LCL = 496.67, UCL = 503.33

c. $\bar{x} \pm z_{\alpha/2}\sigma/\sqrt{n} = 500 \pm 1.645(12/\sqrt{50}) = 500 \pm 2.79$; LCL = 497.21, UCL = 502.79

d. The interval narrows.

10.14a. $\bar{x} \pm z_{\alpha/2}\sigma/\sqrt{n} = 10 \pm 1.645(5/\sqrt{100}) = 10 \pm .82$; LCL = 9.18, UCL = 10.82

b. $\bar{x} \pm z_{\alpha/2}\sigma/\sqrt{n} = 10 \pm 1.645(5/\sqrt{25}) = 10 \pm 1.64$; LCL = 8.36, UCL = 11.64

c. $\bar{x} \pm z_{\alpha/2}\sigma/\sqrt{n} = 10 \pm 1.645(5/\sqrt{10}) = 10 \pm 2.60$; LCL = 7.40, UCL = 12.60

d. The interval widens.

10.16a. $\bar{x} \pm z_{\alpha/2}\sigma/\sqrt{n} = 400 \pm 2.575(5/\sqrt{100}) = 400 \pm 1.29$; LCL = 398.71, UCL = 401.29

b. $\bar{x} \pm z_{\alpha/2}\sigma/\sqrt{n} = 200 \pm 2.575(5/\sqrt{100}) = 200 \pm 1.29$; LCL = 198.71, UCL = 201.29

c. $\bar{x} \pm z_{\alpha/2}\sigma/\sqrt{n} = 100 \pm 2.575(5/\sqrt{100}) = 100 \pm 1.29$; LCL = 98.71, UCL = 101.29

d. The width of the interval is unchanged.

10.18 The variance decreases as the sample size increases, which means that the difference between the estimator and the parameter grows smaller as the sample size grows larger.

10.20a. sample median $\pm z_{\alpha/2} \frac{1.2533\,\sigma}{\sqrt{n}} = 500 \pm 1.645 \frac{1.2533(12)}{\sqrt{50}} = 500 \pm 3.50$

b. The 90% confidence interval estimate of the population mean using the sample mean is 500 $\pm$ 2.79.

The 90% confidence interval of the population mean using the sample median is wider than that using the sample mean because the variance of the sample median is larger. The median is calculated by placing all the observations in order. Thus, the median loses the potential information contained in the actual values in the sample. This results in a wider interval estimate.

10.22 $\bar{x} \pm z_{\alpha/2}\sigma/\sqrt{n} = 43.75 \pm 1.96(10/\sqrt{8}) = 43.75 \pm 6.93$; LCL = 36.82, UCL = 50.68

We estimate that the mean age of men who frequent bars lies between 36.82 and 50.68. This type of estimate is correct 95% of the time.

10.24 $\bar{x} \pm z_{\alpha/2}\sigma/\sqrt{n} = 9.85 \pm 1.645(8/\sqrt{20}) = 9.85 \pm 2.94$; LCL = 6.91, UCL = 12.79

© 2012 Cengage Learning. All Rights Reserved. May not be scanned, copied or duplicated, or posted to a publicly accessible website, in whole or in part.

10.26 $\bar{x} \pm z_{\alpha/2}\sigma/\sqrt{n}$ = 16.9 ± 2.575(5/$\sqrt{10}$) = 16.9 ± 4.07; LCL = 12.83, UCL = 20.97

10.28 $\bar{x} \pm z_{\alpha/2}\sigma/\sqrt{n}$ = 13.15 ± 1.645(6/$\sqrt{13}$) = 13.15 ± 2.74; LCL = 10.41, UCL = 15.89

10.30 $\bar{x} \pm z_{\alpha/2}\sigma/\sqrt{n}$ = 252.38 ± 1.96(30/$\sqrt{400}$) = 252.38 ± 2.94; LCL = 249.44, UCL = 255.32

10.32 $\bar{x} \pm z_{\alpha/2}\sigma/\sqrt{n}$ = 12.10 ± 1.645(2.1/$\sqrt{200}$) = 12.10 ± .24; LCL = 11.86, UCL = 12.34. We estimate that the mean rate of return on all real estate investments lies between 11.86% and 12.34%. This type of estimate is correct 90% of the time.

10.34 $\bar{x} \pm z_{\alpha/2}\sigma/\sqrt{n}$ = .510 ± 2.575(.1/$\sqrt{250}$) = .510 ± .016; LCL = .494, UCL = .526. We estimate that the mean growth rate of this type of grass lies between .494 and .526 inch . This type of estimate is correct 99% of the time.

10.36 $\bar{x} \pm z_{\alpha/2}\sigma/\sqrt{n}$ = 19.28 ± 1.645(6/$\sqrt{250}$) = 19.28 ± .62; LCL = 18.66, UCL = 19.90. We estimate that the mean leisure time per week of Japanese middle managers lies between 18.66 and 19.90 hours. This type of estimate is correct 90% of the time.

10.38 $\bar{x} \pm z_{\alpha/2}\sigma/\sqrt{n}$ = 585,063 ± 1.645(30,000/$\sqrt{80}$) = 585,063 ± 5,518; LCL = 579,545, UCL = 590,581. We estimate that the mean annual income of all company presidents lies between $579,545 and $590,581. This type of estimate is correct 90% of the time.

10.40 $\bar{x} \pm z_{\alpha/2}\sigma/\sqrt{n}$ = 27.19 ± 1.96(8/$\sqrt{100}$) = 27.19 ± 1.57; LCL = 25.62, UCL = 28.76

10.42a The sample size increases.
b The sample size increases.
c The sample size decreases.

10.44a The sample size decreases.
b The sample size decreases.
c The sample size increases.

© 2012 Cengage Learning. All Rights Reserved. May not be scanned, copied or duplicated, or posted to a publicly accessible website, in whole or in part.

10.46 a. $\bar{x} \pm z_{\alpha/2}\frac{\sigma}{\sqrt{n}} = 150 \pm 1.645\frac{5}{\sqrt{271}} = 150 \pm .5$

b. $\bar{x} \pm z_{\alpha/2}\frac{\sigma}{\sqrt{n}} = 150 \pm 1.645\frac{20}{\sqrt{271}} = 150 \pm 2$

10.48a. $n = \left(\frac{z_{\alpha/2}\sigma}{W}\right)^2 = \left(\frac{1.96 \times 200}{10}\right)^2 = 1{,}537$

b. 500 ± 10

10.50a The width of the confidence interval estimate is equal to what was specified.

b The width of the confidence interval estimate is smaller than what was specified.

c The width of the confidence interval estimate is larger than what was specified.

10.52 $n = \left(\frac{z_{\alpha/2}\sigma}{B}\right)^2 = \left(\frac{2.575 \times 360}{20}\right)^2 = 2{,}149$

10.54 $n = \left(\frac{z_{\alpha/2}\sigma}{B}\right)^2 = \left(\frac{1.645 \times 20}{1}\right)^2 = 1{,}083$

10.56 $n = \left(\frac{z_{\alpha/2}\sigma}{B}\right)^2 = \left(\frac{1.96 \times 15}{2}\right)^2 = 217$

© 2012 Cengage Learning. All Rights Reserved. May not be scanned, copied or duplicated, or posted to a publicly accessible website, in whole or in part.

Chapter 11

11.2 H_0: I will complete the Ph.D.

H_1: I will not be able to complete the Ph.D.

11.4 H_0: Risky investment is more successful

H_1: Risky investment is not more successful

11.6 The defendant in both cases was O. J. Simpson. The verdicts were logical because in the criminal trial the amount of evidence to convict is greater than the amount of evidence required in a civil trial. The two juries concluded that there was enough (preponderance of) evidence in the civil trial, but not enough evidence (beyond a reasonable doubt) in the criminal trial.

All p-values and probabilities of Type II errors were calculated manually using Table 3 in Appendix B.

11.8 Rejection region: $z > z_{.03} = 1.88$

$$z = \frac{\bar{x} - \mu}{\sigma / \sqrt{n}} = \frac{51 - 50}{5 / \sqrt{9}} = .60$$

p-value = P(Z > .60) = 1 – .7257 = .2743

There is not enough evidence to infer that $\mu > 50$.

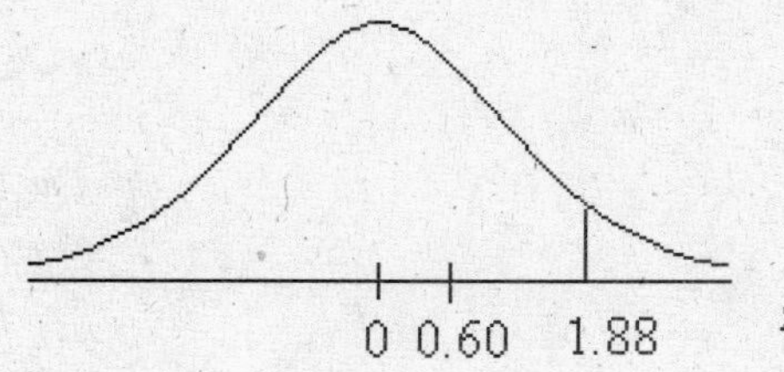

11.10 Rejection region: $z < -z_{.025} = -1.96$ or $z > z_{.025} = 1.96$

$$z = \frac{\bar{x} - \mu}{\sigma / \sqrt{n}} = \frac{100 - 100}{10 / \sqrt{100}} = 0$$

p-value = 2P(Z > 0) = 2(.5) = 1.00

There is not enough evidence to infer that $\mu \neq 100$.

© 2012 Cengage Learning. All Rights Reserved. May not be scanned, copied or duplicated, or posted to a publicly accessible website, in whole or in part.

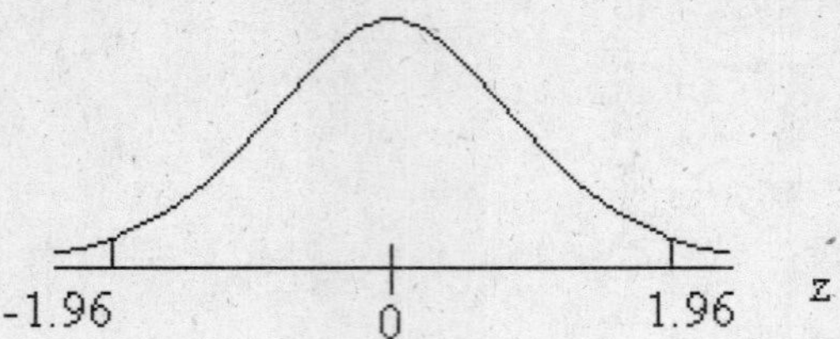

11.12 Rejection region: $z < -z_{.05} = -1.645$

$$z = \frac{\bar{x}-\mu}{\sigma/\sqrt{n}} = \frac{48-50}{15/\sqrt{100}} = -1.33$$

p-value = P(Z < −1.33) = .0918

There is not enough evidence to infer that $\mu < 50$.

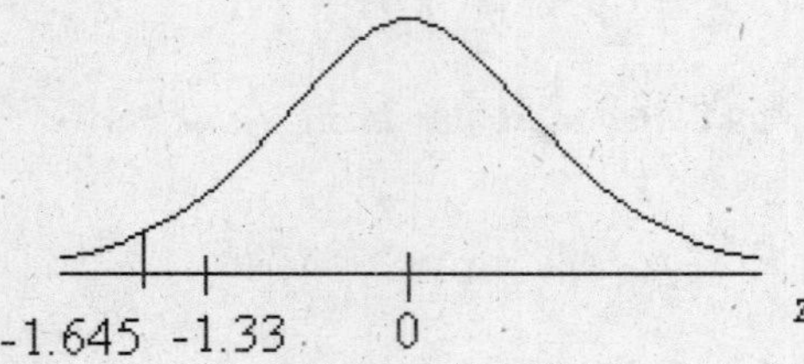

11.14 a. $z = \frac{\bar{x}-\mu}{\sigma/\sqrt{n}} = \frac{190-200}{50/\sqrt{9}} = -.60$

p-value = P(Z < −.60) = .5 − .2257 = .2743

b. $z = \frac{\bar{x}-\mu}{\sigma/\sqrt{n}} = \frac{190-200}{30/\sqrt{9}} = -1.00$

p-value = P(Z < −1.00) = .1587

c $z = \frac{\bar{x}-\mu}{\sigma/\sqrt{n}} = \frac{190-200}{10/\sqrt{9}} = -3.00$

p-value = P(Z < −3.00) = .0013

d. The value of the test statistic decreases and the p-value decreases.

11.16 a. $z = \frac{\bar{x}-\mu}{\sigma/\sqrt{n}} = \frac{99-100}{8/\sqrt{100}} = -1.25$

p-value = 2P(Z < −1.25) = 2(.1056) = .2112

b. $z = \frac{\bar{x}-\mu}{\sigma/\sqrt{n}} = \frac{99-100}{8/\sqrt{50}} = -.88$

p-value = 2P(Z < −.88) = 2(.1894) = .3788

© 2012 Cengage Learning. All Rights Reserved. May not be scanned, copied or duplicated, or posted to a publicly accessible website, in whole or in part.

c. $z = \frac{\bar{x} - \mu}{\sigma / \sqrt{n}} = \frac{99 - 100}{8 / \sqrt{20}} = -.56$

p-value = 2P(Z < –.56) = 2(.2877) = .5754

d. The value of the test statistic increases and the p-value increases.

11.18 a. $z = \frac{\bar{x} - \mu}{\sigma / \sqrt{n}} = \frac{72 - 60}{20 / \sqrt{25}} = 3.00$

p-value = P(Z > 3.00) = 1 – .9987 = .0013

b. $z = \frac{\bar{x} - \mu}{\sigma / \sqrt{n}} = \frac{68 - 60}{20 / \sqrt{25}} = 2.00$

p-value = P(Z > 2.00) = 1 – .9772 = .0228

c. $z = \frac{\bar{x} - \mu}{\sigma / \sqrt{n}} = \frac{64 - 60}{20 / \sqrt{25}} = 1.00$

p-value = P(Z > 1.00) = 1 – .8413 = .1587

d. The value of the test statistic decreases and the p-value increases.

11.20 a $z = \frac{\bar{x} - \mu}{\sigma / \sqrt{n}} = \frac{178 - 170}{35 / \sqrt{400}} = 4.57$

p-value = P(Z > 4.57) = 0.

b $z = \frac{\bar{x} - \mu}{\sigma / \sqrt{n}} = \frac{178 - 170}{100 / \sqrt{400}} = 1.60$

p-value = P(Z > 1.60) = 1 – .9452 = .0548

The value of the test statistic decreases and the p-value increases.

11.22 a $z = \frac{\bar{x} - \mu}{\sigma / \sqrt{n}} = \frac{21.63 - 22}{6 / \sqrt{100}} = -.62$

p-value = P(Z < –.62) = .2676

b $z = \frac{\bar{x} - \mu}{\sigma / \sqrt{n}} = \frac{21.63 - 22}{6 / \sqrt{500}} = -1.38$

p-value = P(Z < –1.38) = .0838

The value of the test statistic decreases and the p-value decreases.

© 2012 Cengage Learning. All Rights Reserved. May not be scanned, copied or duplicated, or posted to a publicly accessible website, in whole or in part.

11.24

$\bar{x}$	$z = \dfrac{\bar{x} - 22}{6 / \sqrt{220}}$	p-value
22.0	0	.5
21.8	–.49	.3121
21.6	–.99	.1611
21.4	–1.48	.0694
21.2	–1.98	.0239
21.0	–2.47	.0068
20.8	–2.97	.0015
20.6	–3.46	0
20.4	–3.96	0

11.26 a $z = \dfrac{\bar{x} - \mu}{\sigma / \sqrt{n}} = \dfrac{17.55 - 17.09}{2 / \sqrt{100}} = 2.30$

p-value = 2P(Z > 2.30) = 2(1 – .9893) = 2(.0107) = .0214

b $z = \dfrac{\bar{x} - \mu}{\sigma / \sqrt{n}} = \dfrac{17.55 - 17.09}{10 / \sqrt{100}} = .46$

p-value = 2P(Z > .46) = 2(1 – .6772) = 2(.3228) = .6456

The value of the test statistic decreases and the p-value increases.

11.28 $H_0 : \mu = 5$

$H_1 : \mu > 5$

$z = \dfrac{\bar{x} - \mu}{\sigma / \sqrt{n}} = \dfrac{6 - 5}{1.5 / \sqrt{10}} = 2.11$

p-value = P(Z > 2.11) = 1 – .9826 = .0174

There is enough evidence to infer that the mean is greater than 5 cases.

11.30 $H_0 : \mu = 12$

$H_1 : \mu < 12$

$z = \dfrac{\bar{x} - \mu}{\sigma / \sqrt{n}} = \dfrac{11.00 - 12}{3 / \sqrt{15}} = -1.29$

p-value = P(Z < –1.29) = .0985

There is enough evidence to infer that the average number of golf balls lost is less than 12.

11.32 $H_0 : \mu = 6$

$H_1 : \mu > 6$

$z = \dfrac{\bar{x} - \mu}{\sigma / \sqrt{n}} = \dfrac{6.60 - 6}{2 / \sqrt{10}} = .95$

p-value = P(Z > .95) = 1 – .8289 = .1711

© 2012 Cengage Learning. All Rights Reserved. May not be scanned, copied or duplicated, or posted to a publicly accessible website, in whole or in part.

There is not enough evidence to infer that the mean time spent putting on the 18th green is greater than 6 minutes.

11.34 $H_0 : \mu = 25$

$H_1 : \mu > 25$

$$z = \frac{\bar{x} - \mu}{\sigma / \sqrt{n}} = \frac{30.22 - 25}{12 / \sqrt{18}} = 1.85$$

p-value = P(Z > 1.85) = 1 – .9678 =.0322

There is not enough evidence to conclude that the manager is correct.

11.36 $H_0 : \mu = 30{,}000$

$H_1 : \mu < 30{,}000$

$$z = \frac{\bar{x} - \mu}{\sigma / \sqrt{n}} = \frac{29{,}120 - 30{,}000}{8{,}000 / \sqrt{350}} = -2.06$$

p-value = (P(Z < –2.06) = .0197

There is enough evidence to infer that the president is correct

11.38a $H_0 : \mu = 17.85$

$H_1 : \mu > 17.85$

$$z = \frac{\bar{x} - \mu}{\sigma / \sqrt{n}} = \frac{19.13 - 17.85}{3.87 / \sqrt{25}} = 1.65$$

p-value = P(Z > 1.65) = 1 – .9505 = .0495

There is enough evidence to infer that the campaign was successful.

b We must assume that the population standard deviation is unchanged.

11.40 $H_0 : \mu = 55$

$H_1 : \mu > 55$

$$z = \frac{\bar{x} - \mu}{\sigma / \sqrt{n}} = \frac{55.80 - 55}{5 / \sqrt{200}} = 2.26$$

p-value = P(Z > 2.26) = 1 – .9881 = .0119

There is not enough evidence to support the officer's belief.

11.42 $H_0 : \mu = 20$

$H_1 : \mu < 20$

© 2012 Cengage Learning. All Rights Reserved. May not be scanned, copied or duplicated, or posted to a publicly accessible website, in whole or in part.

$$z = \frac{\bar{x} - \mu}{\sigma / \sqrt{n}} = \frac{19.39 - 20}{3 / \sqrt{36}} = -1.22$$

p-value = P(Z < –1.22) = .1112

There is not enough evidence to infer that the manager is correct.

11.44 $H_0: \mu = 4$

$H_1: \mu \neq 4$

$$z = \frac{\bar{x} - \mu}{\sigma / \sqrt{n}} = \frac{4.84 - 4}{2 / \sqrt{63}} = 3.33$$

p-value = 2P(Z > 3.33) = 0

There is enough evidence to infer that the average Alpine skier does not ski 4 times per year.

11.46 $H_0: \mu = 32$

$H_1: \mu < 32$

$$z = \frac{\bar{x} - \mu}{\sigma / \sqrt{n}} = \frac{29.92 - 32}{8 / \sqrt{110}} = -2.73$$

p-value = P(Z < –2.73) = 1– .9968 = .0032

There is enough evidence to infer that there has been a decrease in the mean time away from desks. A type I error occurs when we conclude that the plan decreases the mean time away from desks when it actually does not. This error is quite expensive. Consequently we demand a low p-value. The p-value is small enough to infer that there has been a decrease.

11.48 Rejection region: $\frac{\bar{x} - \mu}{\sigma / \sqrt{n}} > z_{\alpha/2}$ or $\frac{\bar{x} - \mu}{\sigma / \sqrt{n}} < -z_{\alpha/2}$

$$\frac{\bar{x} - 200}{10 / \sqrt{100}} > z_{.025} = 1.96 \text{ or } \frac{\bar{x} - 200}{10 / \sqrt{100}} < -1.96$$

$\bar{x} > 201.96$ or $\bar{x} < 198.04$

$\beta = P(198.04 < \bar{x} < 201.96 \text{ given } \mu = 203)$

$$= P\left(\frac{198.04 - 203}{10 / \sqrt{100}} < \frac{\bar{x} - \mu}{\sigma / \sqrt{n}} < \frac{201.96 - 203}{10 / \sqrt{100}}\right) = P(-4.96 < z < -1.04) = .1492 - 0 = .1492$$

11.50 Rejection region: $\frac{\bar{x} - \mu}{\sigma / \sqrt{n}} < -z_{\alpha}$

$$\frac{\bar{x} - 50}{10 / \sqrt{40}} < -z_{.05} = -1.645$$

$\bar{x} < 47.40$

© 2012 Cengage Learning. All Rights Reserved. May not be scanned, copied or duplicated, or posted to a publicly accessible website, in whole or in part.

$\beta = P(\bar{x} > 47.40 \text{ given } \mu = 48) = P\left(\frac{\bar{x}-\mu}{\sigma/\sqrt{n}} > \frac{47.40-48}{10/\sqrt{40}}\right) = P(z > -.38) = 1 - .3520 = .6480$

11.52 a. Rejection region: $\frac{\bar{x}-\mu}{\sigma/\sqrt{n}} > z_{\alpha}$

$\frac{\bar{x}-100}{20/\sqrt{100}} > z_{.10} = 1.28$

$\bar{x} > 102.56$

$\beta = P(\bar{x} < 102.56 \text{ given } \mu = 102) = P\left(\frac{\bar{x}-\mu}{\sigma/\sqrt{n}} < \frac{102.56-102}{20/\sqrt{100}}\right) = P(z < .28) = .6103$

b. Rejection region: $\frac{\bar{x}-\mu}{\sigma/\sqrt{n}} > z_{\alpha}$

$\frac{\bar{x}-100}{20/\sqrt{100}} > z_{.02} = 2.55$

$\bar{x} > 104.11$

$\beta = P(\bar{x} < 104.11 \text{ given } \mu = 102) = P\left(\frac{\bar{x}-\mu}{\sigma/\sqrt{n}} < \frac{104.11-102}{20/\sqrt{100}}\right) = P(z < 1.06) = .8554$

c. β increases.

11.54

Exercise 11.52 a

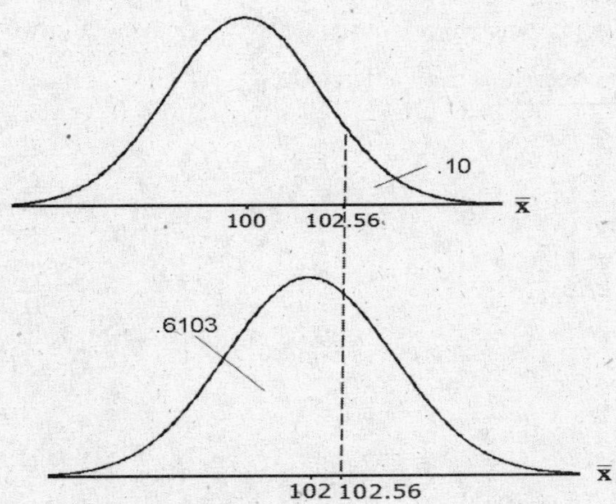

© 2012 Cengage Learning. All Rights Reserved. May not be scanned, copied or duplicated, or posted to a publicly accessible website, in whole or in part.

Exercise 11.52 b

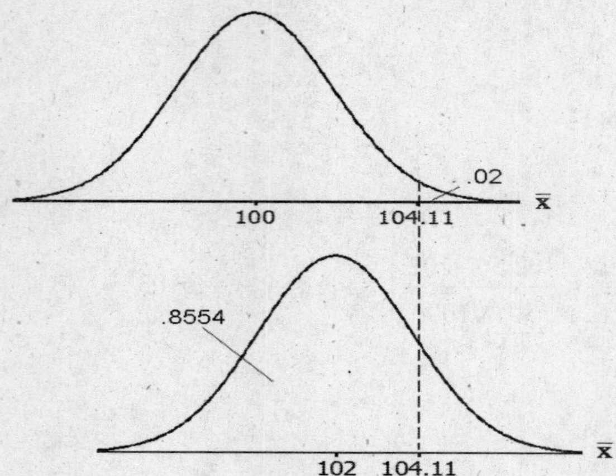

Exercise 11.53 a

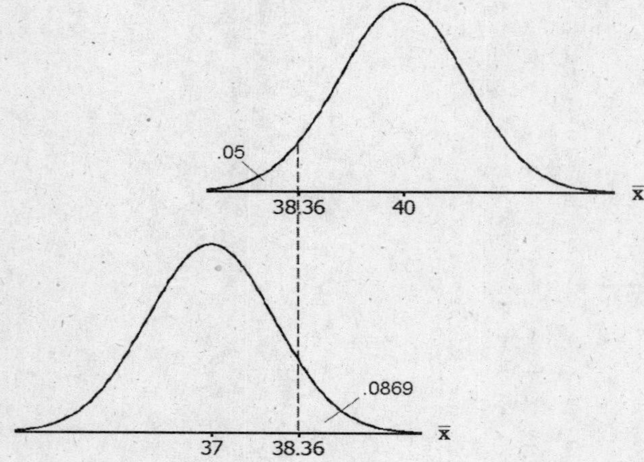

© 2012 Cengage Learning. All Rights Reserved. May not be scanned, copied or duplicated, or posted to a publicly accessible website, in whole or in part.

Exercise 11.53 b

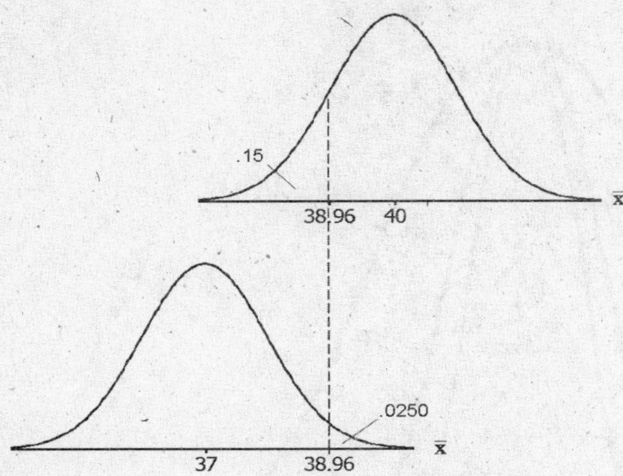

11.56 a. Rejection region: $\frac{\bar{x}-\mu}{\sigma/\sqrt{n}} > z_{\alpha}$

$\frac{\bar{x}-300}{50/\sqrt{81}} > z_{.05} = 1.645$

$\bar{x} > 309.14$

$\beta = P(\bar{x} < 309.14 \text{ given } \mu = 310) = P\left(\frac{\bar{x}-\mu}{\sigma/\sqrt{n}} < \frac{309.14-310}{50/\sqrt{81}}\right) = P(z < -.15) = .4404$

b. Rejection region: $\frac{\bar{x}-\mu}{\sigma/\sqrt{n}} > z_{\alpha}$

$\frac{\bar{x}-300}{50/\sqrt{36}} > z_{.05} = 1.645$

$\bar{x} > 313.71$

$\beta = P(\bar{x} < 313.71 \text{ given } \mu = 310) = P\left(\frac{\bar{x}-\mu}{\sigma/\sqrt{n}} < \frac{313.71-310}{50/\sqrt{36}}\right) = P(z < .45) = .6736$

c. β increases.

© 2012 Cengage Learning. All Rights Reserved. May not be scanned, copied or duplicated, or posted to a publicly accessible website, in whole or in part.

11.58

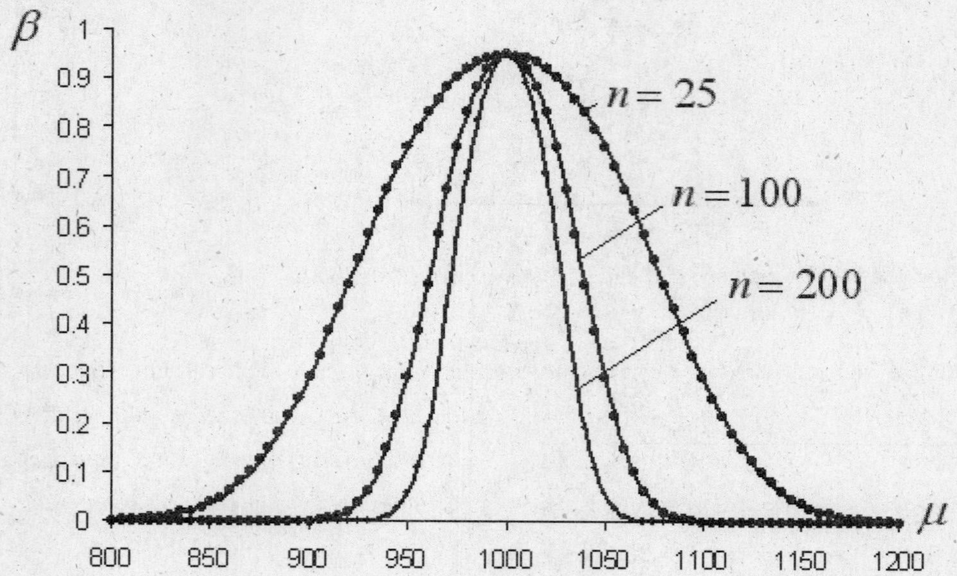

11.60 $H_0: \mu = 170$

$H_1: \mu < 170$

A Type I error occurs when we conclude that the new system is not cost effective when it actually is. A Type II error occurs when we conclude that the new system is cost effective when it actually is not.

The test statistic is the same. However, the p-value equals 1 minus the p-value calculated Example 11.1. That is,

p-value = 1 – .0069 = .9931

We conclude that there is no evidence to infer that the mean is less than 170. That is, there is no evidence to infer that the new system will not be cost effective.

11.62 Rejection region: $\frac{\bar{x}-\mu}{\sigma/\sqrt{n}} < -z_\alpha$

$$\frac{\bar{x}-22}{6/\sqrt{220}} < -z_{.10} = -1.28$$

$\bar{x} < 21.48$

$$\beta = P(\bar{x} > 21.48 \text{ given } \mu = 21) = P\left(\frac{\bar{x}-\mu}{\sigma/\sqrt{n}} > \frac{21.48-21}{6/\sqrt{220}}\right) = P(z > 1.19) = 1 - .8830 = .1170$$

The company can decide whether the sample size and significance level are appropriate.

© 2012 Cengage Learning. All Rights Reserved. May not be scanned, copied or duplicated, or posted to a publicly accessible website, in whole or in part.

11.64 Rejection region: $\frac{\bar{x}-\mu}{\sigma/\sqrt{n}} < -z_\alpha$

$$\frac{\bar{x}-32}{8/\sqrt{110}} < -z_{.05} = -1.645$$

$\bar{x} < 30.75$

$$\beta = P(\bar{x} > 30.75 \text{ given } \mu = 30) = P\left(\frac{\bar{x}-\mu}{\sigma/\sqrt{n}} > \frac{30.75-30)}{8/\sqrt{110}}\right) = P(z > .98) = 1 - .8365 = .1635$$

β can be decreased by increasing α and/or increasing the sample size.

11.66 A Type I error occurs when we conclude that the site is feasible when it is not. The consequence of this decision is to conduct further testing. A Type II error occurs when we do not conclude that a site is feasible when it actually is. We will do no further testing on this site, and as a result we will not build on a good site. If there are few other possible sits, this could be an expensive mistake.

© 2012 Cengage Learning. All Rights Reserved. May not be scanned, copied or duplicated, or posted to a publicly accessible website, in whole or in part.

Chapter 12

12.4 a $\bar{x} \pm t_{\alpha/2} s/\sqrt{n}$ = 1,500 ± 1.984(300/$\sqrt{100}$) = 1,500 ± 59.52; LCL = 1,440.48, UCL = 1,559.52

b $\bar{x} \pm t_{\alpha/2} s/\sqrt{n}$ = 1,500 ± 1.984(200/$\sqrt{100}$) = 1,500 ± 39.68; LCL = 1,460.32, UCL = 1,539.68

c $\bar{x} \pm t_{\alpha/2} s/\sqrt{n}$ = 1,500 ± 1.984(100/$\sqrt{100}$) = 1,500 ± 19.84; LCL = 1,480.16, UCL = 1,519.84

d The interval narrows.

12.6 a $\bar{x} \pm t_{\alpha/2} s/\sqrt{n}$ = 10 ± 1.984(1/$\sqrt{100}$) = 10 ± .20; LCL = 9.80, UCL = 10.20

b $\bar{x} \pm t_{\alpha/2} s/\sqrt{n}$ = 10 ± 1.984(4/$\sqrt{100}$) = 10 ± .79; LCL = 9.21, UCL = 10.79

c $\bar{x} \pm t_{\alpha/2} s/\sqrt{n}$ = 10 ± 1.984(10/$\sqrt{100}$) = 10 ± 1.98; LCL = 8.02, UCL = 11.98

d The interval widens.

12.8 a $\bar{x} \pm t_{\alpha/2} s/\sqrt{n}$ = 63 ± 1.990(8/$\sqrt{81}$) = 63 ± 1.77; LCL = 61.23, UCL = 64.77

b $\bar{x} \pm t_{\alpha/2} s/\sqrt{n}$ = 63 ± 2.000(8/$\sqrt{64}$) = 63 ± 2.00; LCL = 61.00, UCL = 65.00

c $\bar{x} \pm t_{\alpha/2} s/\sqrt{n}$ = 63 ± 2.030(8/$\sqrt{36}$) = 63 ± 2.71; LCL = 60.29, UCL = 65.71

d The interval widens.

12.10 $H_0: \mu = 180$

$H_1: \mu \neq 180$

Rejection region: $t < -t_{\alpha/2,n-1} = -t_{.025,199} \approx -1.972$ or $t > t_{\alpha/2,n-1} = t_{.025,199} = 1.972$

a $t = \dfrac{\bar{x}-\mu}{s/\sqrt{n}} = \dfrac{175-180}{22/\sqrt{200}} = -3.21$, p-value = .0015. There is enough evidence to infer that the population mean is not equal to 180.

b $t = \dfrac{\bar{x}-\mu}{s/\sqrt{n}} = \dfrac{175-180}{45/\sqrt{200}} = -1.57$, p-value = .1177. There is not enough evidence to infer that the population mean is not equal to 180.

c $t = \dfrac{\bar{x}-\mu}{s/\sqrt{n}} = \dfrac{175-180}{60/\sqrt{200}} = -1.18$, p-value = .2400. There is not enough evidence to infer that the population mean is not equal to 180.

d. As the s increases, the test statistic increases and the p-value increases.

© 2012 Cengage Learning. All Rights Reserved. May not be scanned, copied or duplicated, or posted to a publicly accessible website, in whole or in part.

12.12 $H_0: \mu = 50$

$H_0: \mu \neq 50$

a Rejection region: $t < -t_{\alpha/2,n-1} = -t_{.05,24} = -1.711$ or $t > t_{\alpha/2,n-1} = t_{.05,24} = 1.711$

$t = \frac{\bar{x}-\mu}{s/\sqrt{n}} = \frac{52-50}{15/\sqrt{25}} = .67$, p-value = .5113. There is not enough evidence to infer that the population mean is not equal to 50.

b Rejection region: $t < -t_{\alpha/2,n-1} = -t_{.05,14} = -1.761$ or $t > t_{\alpha/2,n-1} = t_{.05,14} = 1.761$

$t = \frac{\bar{x}-\mu}{s/\sqrt{n}} = \frac{52-50}{15/\sqrt{15}} = .52$, p-value = .6136. There is not enough evidence to infer that the population mean is not equal to 50.

c Rejection region: $t < -t_{\alpha/2,n-1} = -t_{.05,4} = -2.132$ or $t > t_{\alpha/2,n-1} = t_{.05,4} = -2.132$

$t = \frac{\bar{x}-\mu}{s/\sqrt{n}} = \frac{52-50}{15/\sqrt{5}} = .30$, p-value = .7804. There is not enough evidence to infer that the population mean is not equal to 50.

d The test statistic decreases and the p-value increases.

12.14 Rejection region: $t > t_{\alpha,n-1} = t_{.01,99} \approx 2.364$

a $t = \frac{\bar{x}-\mu}{s/\sqrt{n}} = \frac{106-100}{35/\sqrt{100}} = 1.71$, p-value = .0448. There is not enough evidence to infer that the population mean is greater than 100.

b $t = \frac{\bar{x}-\mu}{s/\sqrt{n}} = \frac{106-100}{25/\sqrt{100}} = 2.40$, p-value = .0091. There is enough evidence to infer that the population mean is greater than 100.

c $t = \frac{\bar{x}-\mu}{s/\sqrt{n}} = \frac{106-100}{15/\sqrt{100}} = 4.00$, p-value = .0001. There is enough evidence to infer that the population mean is greater than 100

d The test statistic increases and the p-value decreases.

12.16 a $\bar{x} \pm t_{\alpha/2} s/\sqrt{n}$ = 175 ± 2.132(30/$\sqrt{5}$) = 175 ± 28.60; LCL = 146.40, UCL = 203.60

b $\bar{x} \pm z_{\alpha/2} \sigma/\sqrt{n}$ = 175 ± 1.645(30/$\sqrt{5}$) = 175 ± 22.07; LCL = 152.93, UCL = 197.07

c The student t distribution is more widely dispersed than the standard normal; thus, $z_{\alpha/2}$ is smaller than $t_{\alpha/2}$.

© 2012 Cengage Learning. All Rights Reserved. May not be scanned, copied or duplicated, or posted to a publicly accessible website, in whole or in part.

12.18 a $\bar{x} \pm t_{\alpha/2} s/\sqrt{n}$ = 350 ± 2.576(100/$\sqrt{500}$) = 350 ± 11.52; LCL = 338.48, UCL = 361.52

b $\bar{x} \pm z_{\alpha/2} \sigma/\sqrt{n}$ = 350 ± 2.575(100/$\sqrt{500}$) = 350 ± 11.52; LCL = 338.48, UCL = 361.52

c With n = 500 the student t distribution with 999 degrees of freedom is almost identical to the standard normal distribution.

12.20 $H_0: \mu = 110$

$H_0: \mu < 110$

a Rejection region: $t < -t_{\alpha,n-1} = -t_{.10,9} = -1.383$

$t = \frac{\bar{x}-\mu}{s/\sqrt{n}} = \frac{103-110}{17/\sqrt{10}} = -1.30$, p-value = .1126. There is not enough evidence to infer that the population mean is less than 110.

b Rejection region: $z < -z_{\alpha} = z_{.10} = -1.28$

$z = \frac{\bar{x}-\mu}{\sigma/\sqrt{n}} = \frac{103-110}{17/\sqrt{10}} = -1.30$, p-value = P(Z < –1.30) = .0968. There is enough evidence to infer that the population mean is less than 110.

c The Student t distribution is more dispersed than the standard normal.

12.22 a Rejection region: $t > t_{\alpha,n-1} = t_{.05,999} = 1.645$

$t = \frac{\bar{x}-\mu}{s/\sqrt{n}} = \frac{405-400}{100/\sqrt{1,000}} = 1.58$, p-value = .0569. There is not enough evidence to infer that the population mean is less than 15.

b Rejection region: $z > z_{\alpha} = z_{.05} = 1.645$

$t = \frac{\bar{x}-\mu}{s/\sqrt{n}} = \frac{405-400}{100/\sqrt{1,000}} = 1.58$, p-value = P(Z > 1.58) = 1 – .9429 = .0571. There is not enough evidence to infer that the population mean is less than 15.

c With n = 1,000 the student t distribution with 999 degrees of freedom is almost identical to the standard normal distribution.

12.24 $\bar{x} \pm t_{\alpha/2} s/\sqrt{n}$ = 24,051 ± 2.145(17,386/$\sqrt{15}$) = 24,051 ± 9,628; LCL = 14,422, UCL = 33,680

12.26 $H_0: \mu = 8$

$H_0: \mu < 8$

Rejection region: $t < -t_{\alpha,n-1} = -t_{.01,17} = -2.567$

© 2012 Cengage Learning. All Rights Reserved. May not be scanned, copied or duplicated, or posted to a publicly accessible website, in whole or in part.

$t = \frac{\bar{x}-\mu}{s/\sqrt{n}} = \frac{7.91-8}{.085/\sqrt{18}}$ = –4.49, p-value = .0002. There is enough evidence to conclude that the average container is mislabeled.

12.28 $\bar{x} \pm t_{\alpha/2} s/\sqrt{n}$ = 26.67 ± 1.796(16.52/ $\sqrt{12}$) = 26.67 ± 8.56; LCL = 18.11, UCL = 35.23

12.30 $H_0: \mu = 10$

$H_0: \mu < 10$

Rejection region: $t < -t_{\alpha,n-1} = -t_{.10,9} = -1.383$

$t = \frac{\bar{x}-\mu}{s/\sqrt{n}} = \frac{7.10-10}{3.75/\sqrt{10}}$ = –2.45, p-value = .0185. There is enough evidence to infer that the mean proportion of returns is less than 10%.

12.32 $\bar{x} \pm t_{\alpha/2} s/\sqrt{n}$ = 4.66 ± 2.576(2.37/ $\sqrt{240}$) = 4.66 ± .39; LCL = 4.27, UCL = 5.05

Total number: LCL = 100 million (4.27) = 427 million, UCL = 100 million (5.05) = 505 million

12.34 $\bar{x} \pm t_{\alpha/2} s/\sqrt{n}$ = 15,137 ± 1.96(5,263/ $\sqrt{306}$ = 15,137 ± 590; LCL = 14,547, UCL = 15,727

Total credit card debt: LCL = 50 million (14,547) = $727,350 million, UCL = 50 million (15,727) = $786,350 million

12.36 $\bar{x} \pm t_{\alpha/2} s/\sqrt{n}$ = 2.67 ± 1.973(2.50/ $\sqrt{188}$) = 2.67 ± .36; LCL = 2.31, UCL = 3.03

12.38 $\bar{x} \pm t_{\alpha/2} s/\sqrt{n}$ = 422.36 ± 1.973(122.77/ $\sqrt{176}$) = 422.36 ± 18.26; LCL = 404.10, UCL = 440.62

Total cost of congestion: LCL = 128 million (404.10) = $51,725 million, UCL = 128 million (440.62) = $56,399 million

12.40 $H_0: \mu = 15$

$H_0: \mu > 15$

Rejection region: $t > t_{\alpha,n-1} = t_{.05,115} \approx 1.658$

$t = \frac{\bar{x}-\mu}{s/\sqrt{n}} = \frac{15.27-15}{5.72/\sqrt{116}}$ = .51, p-value = .3061. There is not enough evidence to infer that the mean number of commercials is greater than 15.

© 2012 Cengage Learning. All Rights Reserved. May not be scanned, copied or duplicated, or posted to a publicly accessible website, in whole or in part.

12.42 $H_0: \mu = 85$

$H_0: \mu > 85$

Rejection region: $t > t_{\alpha,n-1} = t_{.05,84} \approx 1.663$

$t = \frac{\bar{x} - \mu}{s/\sqrt{n}} = \frac{89.27 - 85}{17.30/\sqrt{85}} = 2.28$, p-value = .0127. There is enough evidence to infer that an e-grocery will be successful.

12.44 $\bar{x} \pm t_{\alpha/2} s/\sqrt{n} = 96{,}100 \pm 1.960(34{,}468/\sqrt{473}) = 96{,}100 \pm 3106$; LCL = 92,994, UCL = 99,206

Total amount of debt: LCL = 7 million(92,994) = 650,958 million UCL = 7 million(99,206) = 694,442 million

12.46 $H_0: \mu = 12$

$H_0: \mu > 12$

	A	B
1	**t-Test: Mean**	
2		
3		*EDUC*
4	Mean	13.43
5	Standard Deviation	3.08
6	Hypothesized Mean	12
7	df	2017
8	t Stat	20.89
9	P(T<=t) one-tail	0
10	t Critical one-tail	1.6456
11	P(T<=t) two-tail	0
12	t Critical two-tail	1.9611

t = 20.89, p-value = 0; there is enough evidence to conclude that the average American adult completed more than 12 years of education.

12.48 $H_0: \mu = 40$

$H_0: \mu > 40$

© 2012 Cengage Learning. All Rights Reserved. May not be scanned, copied or duplicated, or posted to a publicly accessible website, in whole or in part.

	A	B
1	**t-Test: Mean**	
2		
3		*HRS*
4	Mean	42.00
5	Standard Deviation	14.48
6	Hypothesized Mean	40
7	df	1202
8	t Stat	4.80
9	P(T<=t) one-tail	0
10	t Critical one-tail	1.6461
11	P(T<=t) two-tail	0
12	t Critical two-tail	1.9619

t = 4.80, p-value = 0; there is enough evidence to conclude that the mean number of hours worked is greater than 40.

12.50

	A	B
1	**t-Estimate: Mean**	
2		
3		*TVHOURS*
4	Mean	2.94
5	Standard Deviation	2.29
6	LCL	2.85
7	UCL	3.02

LCL = 2.85, UCL = 3.02

12.52

	A	B
1	**t-Estimate: Mean**	
2		
3		*DAYS8*
4	Mean	4.96
5	Standard Deviation	2.48
6	LCL	4.80
7	UCL	5.12

LCL = 4.80, UCL = 5.12

12.56 $H_0: \sigma^2 = 300$

$H_1: \sigma^2 \neq 300$

a Rejection region: $\chi^2 < \chi^2_{1-\alpha/2,n-1} = \chi^2_{.975,99} \approx 74.2$ or $\chi^2 > \chi^2_{\alpha/2,n-1} = \chi^2_{.025,99} \approx 130$

© 2012 Cengage Learning. All Rights Reserved. May not be scanned, copied or duplicated, or posted to a publicly accessible website, in whole or in part.

$\chi^2 = \frac{(n-1)s^2}{\sigma^2} = \frac{(100-1)(220)}{300} = 72.60$, p-value = .0427. There is enough evidence to infer that the population variance differs from 300.

b Rejection region: $\chi^2 < \chi^2_{1-\alpha/2,n-1} = \chi^2_{.975,49} \approx 32.4$ or $\chi^2 > \chi^2_{\alpha/2,n-1} = \chi^2_{.025,49} \approx 71.4$

$\chi^2 = \frac{(n-1)s^2}{\sigma^2} = \frac{(50-1)(220)}{300} = 35.93$, p-value = .1643. There is not enough evidence to infer that the population variance differs from 300.

c Decreasing the sample size decreases the test statistic and increases the p-value of the test.

12.58 a LCL = $\frac{(n-1)s^2}{\chi^2_{\alpha/2,n-1}} = \frac{(n-1)s^2}{\chi^2_{.05,14}} = \frac{(15-1)(12)}{23.7} = 7.09$

UCL = $\frac{(n-1)s^2}{\chi^2_{1-\alpha/2,n-1}} = \frac{(n-1)s^2}{\chi^2_{.95,14}}\ \frac{(15-1)(12)}{6.57} = 25.57$

b LCL = $\frac{(n-1)s^2}{\chi^2_{\alpha/2,n-1}} = \frac{(n-1)s^2}{\chi^2_{.05,29}} = \frac{(30-1)(12)}{42.6} = 8.17$

UCL = $\frac{(n-1)s^2}{\chi^2_{1-\alpha/2,n-1}} = \frac{(n-1)s^2}{\chi^2_{.95,29}} = \frac{(30-1)(12)}{17.7} = 19.66$

c Increasing the sample size narrows the interval.

12.60 $H_0: \sigma^2 = 250$

$H_1: \sigma^2 < 250$

Rejection region: $\chi^2 < \chi^2_{1-\alpha,n-1} = \chi^2_{.90,9} = 4.17$

$\chi^2 = \frac{(n-1)s^2}{\sigma^2} = \frac{(10-1)(210.22)}{250} = 7.57$, p-value = .4218. There is not enough evidence to infer that the population variance has decreased.

12.62 LCL = $\frac{(n-1)s^2}{\chi^2_{\alpha/2,n-1}} = \frac{(n-1)s^2}{\chi^2_{.025,9}} = \frac{(10-1)(15.43)}{19.0} = 7.31$

UCL = $\frac{(n-1)s^2}{\chi^2_{1-\alpha/2,n-1}} = \frac{(n-1)s^2}{\chi^2_{.975,9}} = \frac{(10-1)(15.43)}{2.70} = 51.43$

© 2012 Cengage Learning. All Rights Reserved. May not be scanned, copied or duplicated, or posted to a publicly accessible website, in whole or in part.

12.64 $H_0 : \sigma^2 = 18$

$H_1 : \sigma^2 > 18$

Rejection region: $\chi^2 > \chi^2_{\alpha,n-1} = \chi^2_{.10,244} = 272.704$ (from Excel)

$\chi^2 = \frac{(n-1)s^2}{\sigma^2} = \frac{(245-1)(22.56)}{18} = 305.81$; p-value = .0044. There is enough evidence to infer that the population variance is greater than 18.

12.66 $H_0 : \sigma^2 = 200$

$H_1 : \sigma^2 < 200$

Rejection region: $\chi^2 < \chi^2_{1-\alpha,n-1} = \chi^2_{.95,99} \approx 77.9$

$\chi^2 = \frac{(n-1)s^2}{\sigma^2} = \frac{(100-1)(174.47)}{200} = 86.36$; p-value = .1863. There is not enough evidence to infer that the population variance is less than 200. Replace the bulbs as they burn out.

12.70 a $\hat{p} \pm z_{\alpha/2}\sqrt{\hat{p}(1-\hat{p})/n} = .48 \pm 1.96\sqrt{.48(1-.48)/500} = .48 \pm .0438$

b $\hat{p} \pm z_{\alpha/2}\sqrt{\hat{p}(1-\hat{p})/n} = .48 \pm 1.96\sqrt{.48(1-.48)/200} = .48 \pm .0692$

c $\hat{p} \pm z_{\alpha/2}\sqrt{\hat{p}(1-\hat{p})/n} = .48 \pm 1.96\sqrt{.48(1-.48)/1000} = .48 \pm .0310$

d The interval narrows.

12.72 $H_0 : p = .60$

$H_1 : p > .60$

a $z = \frac{\hat{p}-p}{\sqrt{p(1-p)/n}} = \frac{.63-.60}{\sqrt{.60(1-.60)/100}} = .61$, p-value = P(Z > .61) = 1 – .7291 =.2709

b $z = \frac{\hat{p}-p}{\sqrt{p(1-p)/n}} = \frac{.63-.60}{\sqrt{.60(1-.60)/200}} = .87$, p-value = P(Z > .87) = 1 – .8078 = .1922

c $z = \frac{\hat{p}-p}{\sqrt{p(1-p)/n}} = \frac{.63-.60}{\sqrt{.60(1-.60)/400}} = 1.22$, p-value = P(Z > 1.22) = 1 – .8888 = .1112

d The p-value decreases.

12.74 $n = \left(\frac{z_{\alpha/2}\sqrt{\hat{p}(1-\hat{p})}}{B}\right)^2 = \left(\frac{1.645\sqrt{.5(1-.5)}}{.03}\right)^2 = 752$

© 2012 Cengage Learning. All Rights Reserved. May not be scanned, copied or duplicated, or posted to a publicly accessible website, in whole or in part.

12.76 a $\hat{p} \pm z_{\alpha/2}\sqrt{\hat{p}(1-\hat{p})/n} = .75 \pm 1.645\sqrt{.75(1-.75)/752} = .75 \pm .0260$

b The interval is narrower.

c Yes, because the interval estimate is better than specified.

12.78a .75 ± .03

b Yes, because the sample size was chosen to produce this interval.

12.80a $\hat{p} \pm z_{\alpha/2}\sqrt{\hat{p}(1-\hat{p})/n} = .5 \pm 1.645\sqrt{.5(1-.5)/564} = .5 \pm .0346$

b The interval is wider.

c No because the interval estimate is wider (worse) than specified.

12.82 $H_0: p = .25$

$H_1: p < .25$

$\hat{p} = 41/200 = .205$

$z = \frac{\hat{p}-p}{\sqrt{p(1-p)/n}} = \frac{.205-.25}{\sqrt{.25(1-.25)/200}} = -1.47$, p-value = $P(Z < -1.47) = .0708$. There is enough evidence to support the officer's belief.

12.84 $H_0: p = .92$

$H_1: p > .92$

$\hat{p} = 153/165 = .927$

$z = \frac{\hat{p}-p}{\sqrt{p(1-p)/n}} = \frac{.927-.92}{\sqrt{.92(1-.92)/165}} = .33$, p-value = $P(Z > .33) = 1 - .6293 = .3707$. There is not enough evidence to conclude that the airline's on-time performance has improved.

12.86 $\hat{p} = 68/400 = .17$

$\hat{p} \pm z_{\alpha/2}\sqrt{\hat{p}(1-\hat{p})/n} = .17 \pm 1.96\sqrt{.17(1-.17)/400} = .17 \pm .0368$; LCL = .1332, UCL = .2068

12.88 $\tilde{p} = \frac{x+2}{n+4} = \frac{1+2}{200+4} = .0147$

$\tilde{p} \pm z_{\alpha/2}\sqrt{\frac{\tilde{p}(1-\tilde{p})}{n+4}} = .0147 \pm 1.96\sqrt{\frac{.0147(1-.0147)}{200+4}} = .0147 \pm .0165$; LCL = 0 (increased from –.0018), UCL = .0312

© 2012 Cengage Learning. All Rights Reserved. May not be scanned, copied or duplicated, or posted to a publicly accessible website, in whole or in part.

12.90 $\tilde{p} = \frac{x+2}{n+4} = \frac{1+2}{385+4} = .0077$

$\tilde{p} \pm z_{\alpha/2}\sqrt{\frac{\tilde{p}(1-\tilde{p})}{n+4}} = .0077 \pm 2.575\sqrt{\frac{.0077(1-.0077)}{385+4}} = .0077 \pm .0114$; LCL = 0 (increased from –.0037), UCL = .0191

12.92 LCL = 75,000(.0792) = 5,940, UCL = 75,000(.1320) = 9,900

12.94 $H_0: p = .90$

$H_1: p < .90$

$z = \frac{\hat{p}-p}{\sqrt{p(1-p)/n}} = \frac{.8644-.90}{\sqrt{.90(1-.90)/177}} = -1.58$, p-value = P(Z < –1.58) = .0571. There is not enough evidence to infer that the satisfaction rate is less than 90%.

12.96 $\hat{p} \pm z_{\alpha/2}\sqrt{\hat{p}(1-\hat{p})/n} = .600 \pm 1.96\sqrt{.600(1-.600)/1508} = .600 \pm .025$; LCL = .575, UCL = .625

Total number of Canadians who prefer artificial Christmas trees: LCL = 6 million(.575) = 3.45 million, UCL = 6 million (.625) = 3.75 million

12.98 $H_0: p = .50$

$H_1: p > .50$

$z = \frac{\hat{p}-p}{\sqrt{p(1-p)/n}} = \frac{.57-.50}{\sqrt{.50(1-.50)/100}} = 1.40$, p-value = P(Z > 1.40) = 1 – .9192 =.0808. There is enough evidence to conclude that more than 50% of all business students would rate the book as excellent.

12.100 $\hat{p} \pm z_{\alpha/2}\sqrt{\hat{p}(1-\hat{p})/n} = .0490 \pm 1.96\sqrt{.0490(1-.0490)/5000} = .0490 \pm .0060$; LCL = .0430, UCL = .0550

Total number of television households: LCL = 115 million(.0430) = 4.945 million, UCL = 115 million(.0550) = 6.325 million

12.102a. $\hat{p} \pm z_{\alpha/2}\sqrt{\hat{p}(1-\hat{p})/n} = .2031 \pm 1.96\sqrt{.2031(1-.2031)/650} = .2031 \pm .0309$; LCL = .1722, UCL = .2340

Number: LCL = 5 million (.1722) = .861 million, UCL = 5 million (.2340) = 1.17 million

© 2012 Cengage Learning. All Rights Reserved. May not be scanned, copied or duplicated, or posted to a publicly accessible website, in whole or in part.

12.104a

	A	B
1	**z-Estimate: Proportion**	
2		*WRKSTAT*
3	Sample Proportion	0.4963
4	Observations	2021
5	LCL	0.4780
6	UCL	0.5146

LCL = .4780, UCL = .5146

b

	A	B
1	**z-Estimate: Proportion**	
2		*WRKSTAT*
3	Sample Proportion	0.0366
4	Observations	2021
5	LCL	0.0284
6	UCL	0.0448

LCL = .0284, UCL = .0448

12.106

	A	B
1	**z-Estimate: Proportion**	
2		*WRKGOVT*
3	Sample Proportion	0.1791
4	Observations	1915
5	LCL	0.1647
6	UCL	0.1935

LCL = .1647, UCL = .1935

12.108 $H_0: p = .50$

$H_1: p > .50$

© 2012 Cengage Learning. All Rights Reserved. May not be scanned, copied or duplicated, or posted to a publicly accessible website, in whole or in part.

	A	B
1	**z-Test: Proportion**	
2		
3		*PARTYID*
4	Sample Proportion	0.5592
5	Observations	2568
6	Hypothesized Proportion	0.5
7	z Stat	6.00
8	P(Z<=z) one-tail	0
9	z Critical one-tail	1.6449
10	P(Z<=z) two-tail	0
11	z Critical two-tail	1.96

$z = 6.00$, p-value = 0. There is enough evidence to infer that in 2006 more Americans saw themselves as Democrats than Republicans.

12.110 $H_0: p = .50$

$H_1: p > .50$

	A	B
1	**z-Test: Proportion**	
2		
3		*PARTYID*
4	Sample Proportion	0.5471
5	Observations	1687
6	Hypothesized Proportion	0.5
7	z Stat	3.87
8	P(Z<=z) one-tail	0.0001
9	z Critical one-tail	1.6449
10	P(Z<=z) two-tail	0.0002
11	z Critical two-tail	1.96

$z = 3.87$, p-value = .0001. There is enough evidence to infer that in 2002 more Americans saw themselves as Democrats than Republicans.

12.112 $H_0: p = .50$

$H_1: p > .50$

© 2012 Cengage Learning. All Rights Reserved. May not be scanned, copied or duplicated, or posted to a publicly accessible website, in whole or in part.

	A	B
1	**z-Test: Proportion**	
2		
3		*POLVIEW*
4	Sample Proportion	0.5547
5	Observations	2650
6	Hypothesized Proportion	0.5
7	z Stat	5.63
8	P(Z<=z) one-tail	0
9	z Critical one-tail	1.6449
10	P(Z<=z) two-tail	0
11	z Critical two-tail	1.96

z = 5.63, p-value = 0. There is enough evidence to infer that in 2006 more Americans saw themselves as conservatives than liberals.

12.114 $H_0: p = .50$

$H_1: p > .50$

	A	B
1	**z-Test: Proportion**	
2		
3		*POLVIEW*
4	Sample Proportion	0.7651
5	Observations	809
6	Hypothesized Proportion	0.5
7	z Stat	15.08
8	P(Z<=z) one-tail	0
9	z Critical one-tail	1.6449
10	P(Z<=z) two-tail	0
11	z Critical two-tail	1.96

z = 15.08, p-value = 0. There is enough evidence to infer that in 2002 more Americans saw themselves as conservatives than liberals.

12.116 $H_0: p = .50$

$H_1: p > .50$

© 2012 Cengage Learning. All Rights Reserved. May not be scanned, copied or duplicated, or posted to a publicly accessible website, in whole or in part.

	A	B
1	**z-Test: Proportion**	
2		
3		*PARTY*
4	Sample Proportion	0.6115
5	Observations	1058
6	Hypothesized Proportion	0.5
7	z Stat	7.26
8	P(Z<=z) one-tail	0
9	z Critical one-tail	1.6449
10	P(Z<=z) two-tail	0
11	z Critical two-tail	1.96

z = 7.26, p-value = 0. There is enough evidence to infer that in 2008 more Americans saw themselves as Democrats than Republicans.

12.118 $H_0: p = .50$

$H_1: p > .50$

	A	B
1	**z-Test: Proportion**	
2		
3		*LIBCON*
4	Sample Proportion	0.5834
5	Observations	917
6	Hypothesized Proportion	0.5
7	z Stat	5.05
8	P(Z<=z) one-tail	0
9	z Critical one-tail	1.6449
10	P(Z<=z) two-tail	0
11	z Critical two-tail	1.96

z = 5.05, p-value = 0. There is enough evidence to infer that in 2008 more Americans saw themselves as conservatives than liberals.

12.120

	A	B
1	**z-Estimate: Proportion**	
2		*HEALTH*
3	Sample Proportion	0.1700
4	Observations	1794
5	LCL	0.1526
6	UCL	0.1874

LCL = .1526, UCL = .1874

Total number: LCL = 230,151,000(.1526) = 35,121,043, UCL = 230,151,000(.1874) = 43,130,297

© 2012 Cengage Learning. All Rights Reserved. May not be scanned, copied or duplicated, or posted to a publicly accessible website, in whole or in part.

12.122 $H_0 : p = .51$

$H_1 : p \neq .51$

	A	B
1	**z-Test: Proportion**	
2		
3		*WHOVOTED*
4	Sample Proportion	0.5006
5	Observations	823
6	Hypothesized Proportion	0.51
7	z Stat	-0.539
8	P(Z<=z) one-tail	0.2949
9	z Critical one-tail	1.6449
10	P(Z<=z) two-tail	0.5898
11	z Critical two-tail	1.96

z =-.539, p-value = .5898. There is not enough evidence to infer that the survey results differ from the actual results.

12.124 Codes 3 and 4 were changed to 5

$\hat{p} \pm z_{\alpha/2}\sqrt{\hat{p}(1-\hat{p})/n} = .7305 \pm 1.96\sqrt{.7305(1-.7305)/475} = .7305 \pm .0399$; LCL = .6906, UCL = .7704; Market segment size: LCL = 19,108,000 (.6906) = 13,195,985, UCL = 19,108,000 (.7704) = 14,720,803

12.126a. $\hat{p} \pm z_{\alpha/2}\sqrt{\hat{p}(1-\hat{p})/n} = .2919 \pm 1.96\sqrt{.2919(1-.2919)/1836} = .2919 \pm .0208$; LCL = .2711, UCL = .3127

b LCL = 107,194,000 (.2711) = 29,060,293, UCL = 107,194,000 (.3127) = 33,519,564

12.128 $\hat{p} \pm z_{\alpha/2}\sqrt{\hat{p}(1-\hat{p})/n} = .1748 \pm 1.645\sqrt{.1748(1-.1748)/412} = .1748 \pm .0308$; LCL = .1440, UCL = .2056; Number: LCL = 187 million(.1440) = 26.928 million, UCL = 187 million(.2056) = 38.447 million

12.130 a $H_0 : \mu = 30$

$H_1 : \mu > 30$

© 2012 Cengage Learning. All Rights Reserved. May not be scanned, copied or duplicated, or posted to a publicly accessible website, in whole or in part.

	A	B	C	D
1	**t-Test: Mean**			
2				
3				*Costs*
4	Mean			31.95
5	Standard Deviation			7.19
6	Hypothesized Mean			30
7	df			124
8	t Stat			3.04
9	P(T<=t) one-tail			0.0015
10	t Critical one-tail			1.6572
11	P(T<=t) two-tail			0.0030
12	t Critical two-tail			1.9793

t = 3.04, p-value = .0015; there is enough evidence to infer that the candidate is correct.

	A	B	C	D
1	**t-Estimate: Mean**			
2				
3				*Costs*
4	Mean			31.95
5	Standard Deviation			7.19
6	LCL			30.68
7	UCL			33.23

b LCL = 30.68, UCL = 33.23

c The costs are required to be normally distributed.

12.132 $H_0: \sigma^2 = 17$

$H_1: \sigma^2 > 17$

	A	B	C	D
1	**Chi Squared Test: Variance**			
2				
3				*Times*
4	Sample Variance			27.47
5	Hypothesized Variance			17
6	df			19
7	chi-squared Stat			30.71
8	P (CHI<=chi) one-tail			0.0435
9	chi-squared Critical one tail	Left-tail		10.1170
10		Right-tail		30.1435
11	P (CHI<=chi) two-tail			0.0869
12	chi-squared Critical two tail	Left-tail		8.9065
13		Right-tail		32.8523

$\chi^2 = 30.71$, p-value = .0435. There is enough evidence to infer that problems are likely.

© 2012 Cengage Learning. All Rights Reserved. May not be scanned, copied or duplicated, or posted to a publicly accessible website, in whole or in part.

12.134 a

	A	B	C	D
1	**t-Estimate: Mean**			
2				
3				*Marks*
4	Mean			71.88
5	Standard Deviation			10.03
6	LCL			69.03
7	UCL			74.73

LCL = 69.03, UCL = 74.73

b $H_0: \mu = 68$

$H_1: \mu > 68$

	A	B	C	D
1	**t-Test: Mean**			
2				
3				*Marks*
4	Mean			71.88
5	Standard Deviation			10.03
6	Hypothesized Mean			68
7	df			49
8	t Stat			2.74
9	P(T<=t) one-tail			0.0043
10	t Critical one-tail			1.6766
11	P(T<=t) two-tail			0.0086
12	t Critical two-tail			2.0096

t = 2.74, p-value = .0043; there is enough evidence to infer that students with a calculus background would perform better in statistics than students with no calculus.

12.136

	A	B
1	**z-Estimate: Proportion**	
2		*Insurance*
3	Sample Proportion	0.632
4	Observations	250
5	LCL	0.582
6	UCL	0.682

LCL = .582, UCL = .682

© 2012 Cengage Learning. All Rights Reserved. May not be scanned, copied or duplicated, or posted to a publicly accessible website, in whole or in part.

12.138

	A	B	C	D
1	**t-Estimate: Mean**			
2				
3				*Time*
4	Mean			6.35
5	Standard Deviation			2.16
6	LCL			6.05
7	UCL			6.65

LCL = 6.05, UCL = 6.65

12.140

	A	B
1	**z-Estimate: Proportion**	
2		*Tourist*
3	Sample Proportion	0.667
4	Observations	72
5	LCL	0.558
6	UCL	0.776

LCL = .558, UCL = .776

12.142 $H_0: p = .90$

$H_1: p < .90$

	A	B	C	D
1	**z-Test: Proportion**			
2				
3				*Springs*
4	Sample Proportion			0.86
5	Observations			100
6	Hypothesized Proportion			0.9
7	z Stat			-1.33
8	P(Z<=z) one-tail			0.0912
9	z Critical one-tail			1.2816
10	P(Z<=z) two-tail			0.1824
11	z Critical two-tail			1.6449

z = –1.33, p-value = .0912; there is enough evidence to infer that less than 90% of the springs are the correct length.

12.144 a $H_0: \mu = 9.8$

$H_1: \mu < 9.8$

© 2012 Cengage Learning. All Rights Reserved. May not be scanned, copied or duplicated, or posted to a publicly accessible website, in whole or in part.

	A	B	C	D
1	**t-Test: Mean**			
2				
3				*Time*
4	Mean			9.16
5	Standard Deviation			2.64
6	Hypothesized Mean			9.8
7	df			149
8	t Stat			-2.97
9	P(T<=t) one-tail			0.0018
10	t Critical one-tail			1.2873
11	P(T<=t) two-tail			0.0036
12	t Critical two-tail			1.6551

t = –2.97, p-value = .0018; there is enough evidence to infer that enclosure of preaddressed envelopes improves the average speed of payments.

b $H_0: \sigma^2 = (3.2^2) = 10.24$

$H_1: \sigma^2 < 10.24$

	A	B	C	D
1	**Chi Squared Test: Variance**			
2				
3				*Time*
4	Sample Variance			6.98
5	Hypothesized Variance			10.24
6	df			149
7	chi-squared Stat			101.58
8	P (CHI<=chi) one-tail			0.0011
9	chi-squared Critical one tail	Left-tail		127.3493
10		Right-tail		171.5069
11	P (CHI<=chi) two-tail			0.0021
12	chi-squared Critical two tail	Left-tail		121.7870
13		Right-tail		178.4854

$\chi^2 = 101.58$, p-value = .0011; there is enough evidence to infer that the variability in payment speeds decreases when a preaddressed envelope is sent.

12.146

	A	B
1	**z-Estimate: Proportion**	
2		*Concert*
3	Sample Proportion	0.1533
4	Observations	600
5	LCL	0.1245
6	UCL	0.1822

Proportion: LCL = .1245, UCL = .1822

Total: LCL = 400,000(.1245) = 49,800 UCL = 400,000(.1822) = 72,880

© 2012 Cengage Learning. All Rights Reserved. May not be scanned, copied or duplicated, or posted to a publicly accessible website, in whole or in part.

12.148 a

	A	B	C	D
1	**t-Estimate: Mean**			
2				
3				*Percent Gain/Loss*
4	Mean			12.03
5	Standard Deviation			37.55
6	LCL			-5.54
7	UCL			29.61

LCL = -5.54%, UCL = 29.61%

b. $H_0 : \mu = 16$

$H_1 : \mu < 16$

	A	B	C	D
1	**t-Test: Mean**			
2				
3				*Percent Gain/Loss*
4	Mean			12.03
5	Standard Deviation			37.55
6	Hypothesized Mean			16
7	df			19
8	t Stat			-0.47
9	P(T<=t) one-tail			0.3210
10	t Critical one-tail			1.7291
11	P(T<=t) two-tail			0.6420
12	t Critical two-tail			2.0930

t = -.47, p-value = .3210; there is not enough evidence to infer that Mr. Cramer does less well than the S&P 500 index.

12.150 $H_0 : \mu = 14.35$

$H_1 : \mu > 14.35$

	A	B
1	**t-Test: Mean**	
2		
3		*Debt ratio*
4	Mean	14.6144
5	Standard Deviation	4.4716
6	Hypothesized Mean	14.35
7	df	235
8	t Stat	0.908
9	P(T<=t) one-tail	0.1823
10	t Critical one-tail	1.6514
11	P(T<=t) two-tail	0.3646
12	t Critical two-tail	1.9701

© 2012 Cengage Learning. All Rights Reserved. May not be scanned, copied or duplicated, or posted to a publicly accessible website, in whole or in part.

t = .908, p-value = .1823. There is not enough evidence to conclude that the debt service ratio has increased since 2006.

12.152 $H_0: \mu = 25.97$

$H_1: \mu > 25.97$

	A	B
1	**t-Test: Mean**	
2		
3		*Obligations*
4	Mean	26.55
5	Standard Deviation	8.10
6	Hypothesized Mean	25.97
7	df	177
8	t Stat	0.959
9	P(T<=t) one-tail	0.1693
10	t Critical one-tail	1.6535
11	P(T<=t) two-tail	0.3386
12	t Critical two-tail	1.9735

t = .959, p-value = .1693. There is not enough evidence to conclude that the financial obligations ratio for renters has increased since 2005.

12.154 $H_0: \mu = 65.8$

$H_1: \mu > 65.8$

	A	B
1	**t-Test: Mean**	
2		
3		*Percentage*
4	Mean	66.30
5	Standard Deviation	2.10
6	Hypothesized Mean	65.8
7	df	103
8	t Stat	2.44
9	P(T<=t) one-tail	0.0083
10	t Critical one-tail	1.6598
11	P(T<=t) two-tail	0.0166
12	t Critical two-tail	1.9833

t = 2.44, p-value = .0083. There is enough evidence to conclude that the percentage of total compensation for wages and salaries increased between 2007 and 2008.

© 2012 Cengage Learning. All Rights Reserved. May not be scanned, copied or duplicated, or posted to a publicly accessible website, in whole or in part.

Chapter 13

13.6 $H_0: (\mu_1 - \mu_2) = 0$

$H_1: (\mu_1 - \mu_2) \neq 0$

a Equal-variances test statistic

Rejection region: $t < -t_{\alpha/2,\nu} = -t_{.025,22} = -2.074$ or $t > t_{\alpha/2,\nu} = t_{.025,22} = 2.074$

$$t = \frac{(\bar{x}_1 - \bar{x}_2) - (\mu_1 - \mu_2)}{\sqrt{s_p^2\left(\frac{1}{n_1} + \frac{1}{n_2}\right)}} = \frac{(74 - 71) - 0}{\sqrt{\left(\frac{(12-1)18^2 + (12-1)16^2}{12+12-2}\right)\left(\frac{1}{12} + \frac{1}{12}\right)}} = .43, \text{ p-value} = .6703.$$ There

is not enough evidence to infer that the population means differ.

b Equal-variances test statistic

Rejection region: $t < -t_{\alpha/2,\nu} = -t_{.025,22} = -2.074$ or $t > t_{\alpha/2,\nu} = t_{.025,22} = 2.074$

$$t = \frac{(\bar{x}_1 - \bar{x}_2) - (\mu_1 - \mu_2)}{\sqrt{s_p^2\left(\frac{1}{n_1} + \frac{1}{n_2}\right)}} = \frac{(74 - 71) - 0}{\sqrt{\left(\frac{(12-1)210^2 + (12-1)198^2}{12+12-2}\right)\left(\frac{1}{12} + \frac{1}{12}\right)}} = .04, \text{ p-value} = .9716.$$

There is not enough evidence to infer that the population means differ.

c The value of the test statistic decreases and the p-value increases.

d Equal-variances test statistic

Rejection region: $t < -t_{\alpha/2,\nu} = -t_{.025,298} = -1.960$ or $t > t_{\alpha/2,\nu} = t_{.025,298} = 1.960$

$$t = \frac{(\bar{x}_1 - \bar{x}_2) - (\mu_1 - \mu_2)}{\sqrt{s_p^2\left(\frac{1}{n_1} + \frac{1}{n_2}\right)}} = \frac{(74 - 71) - 0}{\sqrt{\left(\frac{(150-1)18^2 + (150-1)16^2}{150+150-2}\right)\left(\frac{1}{150} + \frac{1}{150}\right)}} = 1.53, \text{ p-value} = .1282.$$

There is not enough evidence to infer that the population means differ.

e The value of the test statistic increases and the p-value decreases.

f Rejection region: $t < -t_{\alpha/2,\nu} = -t_{.025,22} = -2.074$ or $t > t_{\alpha/2,\nu} = t_{.025,22} = 2.074$

$$t = \frac{(\bar{x}_1 - \bar{x}_2) - (\mu_1 - \mu_2)}{\sqrt{s_p^2\left(\frac{1}{n_1} + \frac{1}{n_2}\right)}} = \frac{(76 - 71) - 0}{\sqrt{\left(\frac{(12-1)18^2 + (12-1)16^2}{12+12-2}\right)\left(\frac{1}{12} + \frac{1}{12}\right)}} = .72, \text{ p-value} = .4796.$$ There

is not enough evidence to infer that the population means differ.

g The value of the test statistic increases and the p-value decreases.

13.8 $H_0: (\mu_1 - \mu_2) = 0$

$H_1: (\mu_1 - \mu_2) > 0$

a Unequal-variances test statistic

© 2012 Cengage Learning. All Rights Reserved. May not be scanned, copied or duplicated, or posted to a publicly accessible website, in whole or in part.

$$\nu = \frac{(s_1^2/n_1 + s_2^2/n_2)^2}{\frac{(s_1^2/n_1)^2}{n_1 - 1} + \frac{(s_2^2/n_2)^2}{n_2 - 1}} = 200.4 \text{ (rounded to 200)}$$

Rejection region: $t > t_{\alpha,\nu} = t_{.05,200} = 1.653$

$$t = \frac{(\bar{x}_1 - \bar{x}_2) - (\mu_1 - \mu_2)}{\sqrt{\left(\frac{s_1^2}{n_1} + \frac{s_2^2}{n_2}\right)}} = \frac{(412 - 405) - 0}{\sqrt{\left(\frac{128^2}{150} + \frac{54^2}{150}\right)}} = .62$$, p-value = .2689. There is not enough evidence to infer that μ_1 is greater than μ_2.

b Unequal-variances test statistic

$$\nu = \frac{(s_1^2/n_1 + s_2^2/n_2)^2}{\frac{(s_1^2/n_1)^2}{n_1 - 1} + \frac{(s_2^2/n_2)^2}{n_2 - 1}} = 223.1 \text{ (rounded to 223)}$$

Rejection region: $t > t_{\alpha,\nu} = t_{.05,223} \approx 1.645$

$$t = \frac{(\bar{x}_1 - \bar{x}_2) - (\mu_1 - \mu_2)}{\sqrt{\left(\frac{s_1^2}{n_1} + \frac{s_2^2}{n_2}\right)}} = \frac{(412 - 405) - 0}{\sqrt{\left(\frac{31^2}{150} + \frac{16^2}{150}\right)}} = 2.46$$, p-value = .0074. There is enough evidence to infer that μ_1 is greater than μ_2.

c The value of the test statistic increases and the p-value decreases.

d Unequal-variances test statistic

$$\nu = \frac{(s_1^2/n_1 + s_2^2/n_2)^2}{\frac{(s_1^2/n_1)^2}{n_1 - 1} + \frac{(s_2^2/n_2)^2}{n_2 - 1}} = 25.6 \text{ (rounded to 26)}$$

Rejection region: $t > t_{\alpha,\nu} = t_{.05,26} = 1.706$

$$t = \frac{(\bar{x}_1 - \bar{x}_2) - (\mu_1 - \mu_2)}{\sqrt{\left(\frac{s_1^2}{n_1} + \frac{s_2^2}{n_2}\right)}} = \frac{(412 - 405) - 0}{\sqrt{\left(\frac{128^2}{20} + \frac{54^2}{20}\right)}} = .23$$, p-value = .4118. There is not enough evidence to infer that μ_1 is greater than μ_2.

e The value of the test statistic decreases and the p-value increases.

f Unequal-variances test statistic

Rejection region: $t > t_{\alpha,\nu} = t_{.05,200} = 1.653$

$$t = \frac{(\bar{x}_1 - \bar{x}_2) - (\mu_1 - \mu_2)}{\sqrt{\left(\frac{s_1^2}{n_1} + \frac{s_2^2}{n_2}\right)}} = \frac{(409 - 405) - 0}{\sqrt{\left(\frac{128^2}{150} + \frac{54^2}{150}\right)}} = .35$$, p-value = .3624. There is not enough evidence to infer that μ_1 is greater than μ_2.

© 2012 Cengage Learning. All Rights Reserved. May not be scanned, copied or duplicated, or posted to a publicly accessible website, in whole or in part.

g The value of the test statistic decreases and the p-value increases.

13.10 a In all cases the equal-variances t-test degrees of freedom is greater than the unequal-variances t-test degrees of freedom.

13.12 $H_0: (\mu_1 - \mu_2) = 0$

$H_1: (\mu_1 - \mu_2) < 0$

Two-tail F test: F = 1.02, p-value = .9823; use equal-variances test statistic

Rejection region: $t < -t_{\alpha,\nu} = -t_{.10,18} = -1.330$

$$t = \frac{(\bar{x}_1 - \bar{x}_2) - (\mu_1 - \mu_2)}{\sqrt{s_p^2\left(\frac{1}{n_1} + \frac{1}{n_2}\right)}} = \frac{(5.10 - 7.30) - 0}{\sqrt{\left(\frac{(10-1)5.88 + (10-1)5.79}{10+10-2}\right)\left(\frac{1}{10} + \frac{1}{10}\right)}} = -2.04, \text{ p-value} = .0283.$$

There is enough evidence to infer that there are fewer errors when the yellow ball is used.

13.14 $H_0: (\mu_1 - \mu_2) = 0$

$H_1: (\mu_1 - \mu_2) \neq 0$

Two-tail F test: F = 1.04, p-value = .9873; use equal-variances test statistic

Rejection region: $t < -t_{\alpha/2,\nu} = -t_{.05,13} = -1.771$ or $t > t_{\alpha/2,\nu} = t_{.05,13} = 1.771$

$$t = \frac{(\bar{x}_1 - \bar{x}_2) - (\mu_1 - \mu_2)}{\sqrt{s_p^2\left(\frac{1}{n_1} + \frac{1}{n_2}\right)}} = \frac{(3{,}372 - 4{,}093) - 0}{\sqrt{\left(\frac{(9-1)755{,}196 + (6-1)725{,}778}{9+6-2}\right)\left(\frac{1}{9} + \frac{1}{6}\right)}} = -1.59, \text{ p-value} = .1368.$$

There is not enough evidence to infer a difference between the two types of vacation expenses.

13.16 $H_0: (\mu_1 - \mu_2) = 0$

$H_1: (\mu_1 - \mu_2) \neq 0$

Two-tail F test: F = 1.67, p-value = .4060; use equal-variances test statistic

Rejection region: $t < -t_{\alpha/2,\nu} = -t_{.025,22} = -2.074$ or $t > t_{\alpha/2,\nu} = t_{.025,22} = 2.074$

$$t = \frac{(\bar{x}_1 - \bar{x}_2) - (\mu_1 - \mu_2)}{\sqrt{s_p^2\left(\frac{1}{n_1} + \frac{1}{n_2}\right)}} = \frac{(33.33 - 31.50) - 0}{\sqrt{16.1667\left(\frac{1}{12} + \frac{1}{12}\right)}} = 1.12, \text{ p-value} = .2761.$$ There is not enough evidence to infer that the speeds differ.

13.18 $H_0: (\mu_1 - \mu_2) = 0$

$H_1: (\mu_1 - \mu_2) \neq 0$

© 2012 Cengage Learning. All Rights Reserved. May not be scanned, copied or duplicated, or posted to a publicly accessible website, in whole or in part.

Two-tail F test: F = .99, p-value = .9571; use equal-variances test statistic

Rejection region: $t < -t_{\alpha/2,\nu} = -t_{.025,238} = -1.960$ or $t > t_{\alpha/2,\nu} = t_{.025,238} = 1.960$

$$t = \frac{(\bar{x}_1 - \bar{x}_2) - (\mu_1 - \mu_2)}{\sqrt{s_p^2\left(\frac{1}{n_1} + \frac{1}{n_2}\right)}} = \frac{(10.01 - 9.12) - 0}{\sqrt{\left(\frac{(120-1)4.43^2 + (120-1)4.45^2}{120+120-2}\right)\left(\frac{1}{120} + \frac{1}{120}\right)}} = 1.55, \text{ p-value}$$

= .1204. There is not enough evidence to infer that oat bran is different from other cereals in terms of cholesterol reduction?

13.20 a $H_0: (\mu_1 - \mu_2) = 0$

$H_1: (\mu_1 - \mu_2) > 0$

Two-tail F test: F = 1.01, p-value = .9619; use equal-variances test statistic

Rejection region: $t > t_{\alpha,\nu} = t_{.05,282} \approx 1.645$

$$t = \frac{(\bar{x}_1 - \bar{x}_2) - (\mu_1 - \mu_2)}{\sqrt{s_p^2\left(\frac{1}{n_1} + \frac{1}{n_2}\right)}} = \frac{(59.81 - 57.40) - 0}{\sqrt{\left(\frac{(125-1)7.02^2 + (159-1)6.99^2}{125+159-2}\right)\left(\frac{1}{125} + \frac{1}{159}\right)}} = 2.88, \text{ p-value}$$

= .0021. There is enough evidence to infer that the cruise ships are attracting younger customers.

b $(\bar{x}_1 - \bar{x}_2) \pm t_{\alpha/2}\sqrt{s_p^2\left(\frac{1}{n_1} + \frac{1}{n_2}\right)} = (59.81 - 57.40)$

$$\pm 2.576\sqrt{\left(\frac{(125-1)7.02^2 + (159-1)6.99^2}{125+159-2}\right)\left(\frac{1}{125} + \frac{1}{159}\right)} = 2.41 \pm 2.16;$$

LCL = .25, UCL = 4.57

13.22 $H_0: (\mu_1 - \mu_2) = 0$

$H_1: (\mu_1 - \mu_2) > 0$

Two-tail F test: F = .98, p-value = .9520; use equal-variances test statistic

Rejection region: $t > t_{\alpha,\nu} = t_{.05,58} \approx 1.671$

$$t = \frac{(\bar{x}_1 - \bar{x}_2) - (\mu_1 - \mu_2)}{\sqrt{s_p^2\left(\frac{1}{n_1} + \frac{1}{n_2}\right)}} = \frac{(115.50 - 110.20) - 0}{\sqrt{\left(\frac{(30-1)21.69^2 + (30-1)21.93^2}{30+30-2}\right)\left(\frac{1}{30} + \frac{1}{30}\right)}} = .94, \text{ p-value} = .1753.$$

There is not enough evidence to retain supplier A - switch to supplier B.

13.24 a $H_0: (\mu_1 - \mu_2) = 0$

$H_1: (\mu_1 - \mu_2) \neq 0$

© 2012 Cengage Learning. All Rights Reserved. May not be scanned, copied or duplicated, or posted to a publicly accessible website, in whole or in part.

Two-tail F test: F = 5.18, p-value = .0019; use unequal-variances test statistic

$$\nu = \frac{(s_1^2/n_1 + s_2^2/n_2)^2}{\frac{(s_1^2/n_1)^2}{n_1 - 1} + \frac{(s_2^2/n_2)^2}{n_2 - 1}} = 33.9 \text{ (rounded to 34)}$$

Rejection region: $t < -t_{\alpha/2,\nu} = -t_{.005,34} \approx -2.724$ or $t > t_{\alpha/2,\nu} = t_{.005,34} \approx 2.724$

$$t = \frac{(\bar{x}_1 - \bar{x}_2) - (\mu_1 - \mu_2)}{\sqrt{\left(\frac{s_1^2}{n_1} + \frac{s_2^2}{n_2}\right)}} = \frac{(70.42 - 56.44) - 0}{\sqrt{\left(\frac{20.54^2}{24} + \frac{9.03^2}{16}\right)}} = 2.94, \text{ p-value} = .0060.$$

There is enough evidence to conclude that the two packages differ in the amount of time needed to learn how to use them.

b $(\bar{x}_1 - \bar{x}_2) \pm t_{\alpha/2}\sqrt{\left(\frac{s_1^2}{n_1} + \frac{s_2^2}{n_2}\right)} = (70.42 - 56.44) \pm 2.030\sqrt{\left(\frac{20.54^2}{24} + \frac{9.03^2}{16}\right)} = 13.98 \pm 9.67;$

LCL = 4.31, UCL = 23.65

c The amount of time is required to be normally distributed.

d The histograms are somewhat bell shaped.

13.26 $H_0: (\mu_1 - \mu_2) = 0$

$H_1: (\mu_1 - \mu_2) > 0$

Two-tail F test: F = .73, p-value = .0699; use equal-variances test statistic

Rejection region: $t > t_{\alpha,\nu} = t_{.05,268} \approx 1.645$

$$t = \frac{(\bar{x}_1 - \bar{x}_2) - (\mu_1 - \mu_2)}{\sqrt{s_p^2\left(\frac{1}{n_1} + \frac{1}{n_2}\right)}} = \frac{(.646 - .601) - 0}{\sqrt{\left(\frac{(125-1).045^2 + (145-1).053^2}{125 + 145 - 2}\right)\left(\frac{1}{125} + \frac{1}{145}\right)}} = 7.54, \text{ p-value} = 0.$$

There is enough evidence to conclude that the reaction time of drivers using cell phones is slower that for non-cell phone users.

13.28 $H_0: (\mu_1 - \mu_2) = 0$

$H_1: (\mu_1 - \mu_2) > 0$

Two-tail F test: F = .97, p-value = .9054; use equal-variances test statistic

Rejection region: $t > t_{\alpha,\nu} = t_{.05,143} \approx 1.656$

© 2012 Cengage Learning. All Rights Reserved. May not be scanned, copied or duplicated, or posted to a publicly accessible website, in whole or in part.

$$t = \frac{(\bar{x}_1 - \bar{x}_2) - (\mu_1 - \mu_2)}{\sqrt{s_p^2\left(\frac{1}{n_1} + \frac{1}{n_2}\right)}} = \frac{(6.18 - 5.94) - 0}{\sqrt{\left(\frac{(64-1)1.59^2 + (81-1)1.61^2}{64+81-2}\right)\left(\frac{1}{64} + \frac{1}{81}\right)}} = .90, \text{ p-value} = .1858.$$

There is not enough evidence to infer that people spend more time researching for a financial planner than they do for a stock broker.

13.30 $H_0: (\mu_1 - \mu_2) = 0$

$H_1: (\mu_1 - \mu_2) \neq 0$

Two-tail F test: F = .85, p-value = .2494; use equal-variances test statistic

Rejection region: $t < -t_{\alpha/2,\nu} = -t_{.025,413} \approx -1.960$ or $t > t_{\alpha/2,\nu} = t_{.025,413} \approx 1.960$

$$t = \frac{(\bar{x}_1 - \bar{x}_2) - (\mu_1 - \mu_2)}{\sqrt{s_p^2\left(\frac{1}{n_1} + \frac{1}{n_2}\right)}} = \frac{(149.85 - 154.43) - 0}{\sqrt{\left(\frac{(213-1)21.82^2 + (202-1)23.64^2}{213+202-2}\right)\left(\frac{1}{213} + \frac{1}{202}\right)}} = -2.05,$$

p-value = .0412. There is enough evidence to conclude that there are differences in service times between the two chains.

13.32 a $H_0: (\mu_1 - \mu_2) = 0$

$H_1: (\mu_1 - \mu_2) \neq 0$

Two-tail F test: F = 1.51, p-value = .0402; use unequal-variances test statistic

$$\nu = \frac{(s_1^2/n_1 + s_2^2/n_2)^2}{\frac{(s_1^2/n_1)^2}{n_1 - 1} + \frac{(s_2^2/n_2)^2}{n_2 - 1}} = 190$$

Rejection region: $t < -t_{\alpha/2,\nu} = -t_{.025,190} \approx -1.973$ or $t > t_{\alpha/2,\nu} = t_{.025,190} \approx 1.973$

$$t = \frac{(\bar{x}_1 - \bar{x}_2) - (\mu_1 - \mu_2)}{\sqrt{\left(\frac{s_1^2}{n_1} + \frac{s_2^2}{n_2}\right)}} = \frac{(130.93 - 126.14) - 0}{\sqrt{\left(\frac{31.99^2}{100} + \frac{26.00^2}{100}\right)}} = 1.16, \text{ p-value} = .2467.$$ There is not enough evidence to infer that differences exist between the two types of customers.

13.34 $H_0: (\mu_1 - \mu_2) = 0$

$H_1: (\mu_1 - \mu_2) < 0$

Two-tail F test: F = .95, p-value = .8252; use equal-variances test statistic

Rejection region: $t > t_{\alpha,\nu} = t_{.05,178} \approx 1.653$

© 2012 Cengage Learning. All Rights Reserved. May not be scanned, copied or duplicated, or posted to a publicly accessible website, in whole or in part.

$$t = \frac{(\bar{x}_1 - \bar{x}_2) - (\mu_1 - \mu_2)}{\sqrt{s_p^2\left(\frac{1}{n_1} + \frac{1}{n_2}\right)}} = \frac{60{,}245 - 63{,}563) - 0}{\sqrt{\left(\frac{(90-1)10{,}506^2 + (90-1)10{,}755^2}{90+90-2}\right)\left(\frac{1}{90} + \frac{1}{90}\right)}} = -2.09$$

$t = -2.09$, p-value = .0189. There is enough evidence to conclude that commission salespeople outperform fixed-salary salespersons

13.36 $H_0: (\mu_1 - \mu_2) = 0$

$H_1: (\mu_1 - \mu_2) > 0$

Two-tail F test: F = .41, p-value = 0; use unequal-variances test statistic

$$\nu = \frac{(s_1^2/n_1 + s_2^2/n_2)^2}{\frac{(s_1^2/n_1)^2}{n_1 - 1} + \frac{(s_2^2/n_2)^2}{n_2 - 1}} = 222$$

Rejection region: $t > t_{\alpha,\nu} = t_{.05,222} \approx 1.645$

$$t = \frac{(\bar{x}_1 - \bar{x}_2) - (\mu_1 - \mu_2)}{\sqrt{\left(\frac{s_1^2}{n_1} + \frac{s_2^2}{n_2}\right)}} = \frac{(14.20 - 11.27) - 0}{\sqrt{\left(\frac{2.84^2}{130} + \frac{4.42^2}{130}\right)}} = 6.28$$, p-value = 0. There is enough evidence to conclude that bottles of wine with metal caps are perceived to be cheaper.

13.38 Two-tail F test: F = 2.13, p-value = 0; use unequal-variances test statistic.

	A	B	C	D
1	**t-Estimate: Two Means**	**(Unequal Variances)**		
2				
3		*Men*	*Women*	
4	Mean	50,294	32,741	
5	Variance	1,934,263,981	906,683,965	
6	Observations	610	579	
7				
8	Degrees of Freedom	1081.2		
9	Confidence Level	0.95		
10	Confidence Interval Estimate	17552	±	4271
11	LCL	13282		
12	UCL	21823		

LCL = 13,281.97, UCL = 21,823.01.

13.40 Using the CPI annual data, 2008 dollars are adjusted to the 2006 base year. The nominal differential in salaries is summarized below. Without adjusting for inflation, the mean salary differential between men and women grew by 21.5% in 2008 compared to the mean salary differentials in 2006. However, after adjusting for inflation, this differential is reduced to 13.8%.

© 2012 Cengage Learning. All Rights Reserved. May not be scanned, copied or duplicated, or posted to a publicly accessible website, in whole or in part.

The data show that men earn significantly higher nominal and real incomes than women, and this differential has grown larger over the years between 2006 and 2008.

	Nominal Values (Unadjusted)					Real Values (CPI Adjusted)		
Year	Mean Salary Difference			CPI Index	CPI Ratio	Mean Salary Difference		
2006	$14,446.68	±	$2,410.51	201.6	1	$14,446.68	±	$2,410.51
2008	$17,552.49	±	$4,270.52	215.2	1.0677	$16,439.96	±	$3,999.84
Differential	*21.50%*			*6.77%*		*13.80%*		

13.42 $H_0: (\mu_1 - \mu_2) = 0$

$H_1: (\mu_1 - \mu_2) < 0$

Two-tail F test: F = .765, p-value = .00321; use unequal-variances test statistic

	A	B	C
1	t-Test: Two-Sample Assuming Unequal Variances		
2			
3		*Democrat*	*Republican*
4	Mean	13.09	13.84
5	Variance	7.75	5.93
6	Observations	643	409
7	Hypothesized Mean Difference	0.00	
8	df	951.00	
9	t Stat	-4.65	
10	P(T<=t) one-tail	1.88E-06	
11	t Critical one-tail	1.6465	
12	P(T<=t) two-tail	3.77E-06	
13	t Critical two-tail	1.9625	

t = -4.65, p-value = 1.88E-06 ≈ 0. There is enough evidence to conclude that Republicans have more years of education than do Democrats.

13.44 $H_0: (\mu_1 - \mu_2) = 0$

$H_1: (\mu_1 - \mu_2) > 0$

Two-tail F test: F = 1.917, p-value = 0; use unequal-variances test statistic

© 2012 Cengage Learning. All Rights Reserved. May not be scanned, copied or duplicated, or posted to a publicly accessible website, in whole or in part.

	A	B	C
1	t-Test: Two-Sample Assuming Unequal Variances		
2			
3		Men	Women
4	Mean	44,542	27,128
5	Variance	1,264,085,479	659,397,880
6	Observations	514	588
7	Hypothesized Mean Difference	0	
8	df	920	
9	t Stat	9.20	
10	P(T<=t) one-tail	1.15E-19	
11	t Critical one-tail	1.6465	
12	P(T<=t) two-tail	2.30E-19	
13	t Critical two-tail	1.9625	

t = 9.20, p-value = 1.15E-19 ≈ 0. There is enough evidence to conclude that men draw higher incomes than women in 2004 (ANES).

13.46 Assuming that the volunteers were randomly assigned to eat either oat bran or another grain cereal the data are experimental.

13.48 a Let students select the section they wish to attend and compare test results.

b Randomly assign students to either section and compare test results.

13.50 a Randomly select finance and marketing MBA graduates and determine their starting salaries.

b Randomly assign some MBA students to major in finance and others to major in marketing. Compare starting salaries after they graduate.

c Better students may be attracted to finance and better students draw higher starting salaries.

13.52 $H_0: \mu_D = 0$

$H_1: \mu_D < 0$

Rejection region: $t < -t_{\alpha,\nu} = -t_{.05,7} = -1.895$

$t = \frac{\bar{x}_D - \mu_D}{s_D / \sqrt{n_D}} = \frac{-4.75 - 0}{4.17/\sqrt{8}} = -3.22$, p-value = .0073. There is enough evidence to infer that the Brand A is better than Brand B.

13.54 $H_0: \mu_D = 0$

$H_1: \mu_D > 0$

© 2012 Cengage Learning. All Rights Reserved. May not be scanned, copied or duplicated, or posted to a publicly accessible website, in whole or in part.

Rejection region: $t > t_{\alpha,\nu} = t_{.05,6} = 1.943$

$t = \frac{\bar{x}_D - \mu_D}{s_D / \sqrt{n_D}} = \frac{1.86 - 0}{2.48 / \sqrt{7}} = 1.98$, p-value = .0473. There is enough evidence to infer that the camera reduces the number of red-light runners.

13.56 a $H_0 : \mu_D = 0$

$H_1 : \mu_D > 0$

Rejection region: $t > t_{\alpha,\nu} = t_{.05,11} = 1.796$

$t = \frac{\bar{x}_D - \mu_D}{s_D / \sqrt{n_D}} = \frac{3.08 - 0}{5.88 / \sqrt{12}} = 1.82$, p-value = .0484. There is enough evidence to infer that companies with exercise programs have lower medical expenses.

b $\bar{x}_D \pm t_{\alpha/2} \frac{s_D}{\sqrt{n_D}} = 3.08 \pm 2.201 \frac{5.88}{\sqrt{12}} = 3.08 \pm 3.74$; LCL = –.66, UCL = 6.82

c Yes because medical expenses will vary by the month of the year.

13.58 $H_0 : \mu_D = 0$

$H_1 : \mu_D \neq 0$

Rejection region: $t < -t_{\alpha/2,\nu} = -t_{.025,49} \approx -2.009$ or $t > t_{\alpha/2,\nu} = t_{.025,49} \approx 2.009$

$t = \frac{\bar{x}_D - \mu_D}{s_D / \sqrt{n_D}} = \frac{-1.16 - 0}{2.22 / \sqrt{50}} = -3.70$, p-value = .0006. There is enough evidence to infer that waiters and waitresses earn different amounts in tips.

13.60 a $H_0 : \mu_D = 0$

$H_1 : \mu_D > 0$

Rejection region: $t > t_{\alpha,\nu} = t_{.10,14} = 1.345$

$t = \frac{\bar{x}_D - \mu_D}{s_D / \sqrt{n_D}} = \frac{57.40 - 0}{13.14 / \sqrt{15}} = 16.92$, p-value = 0. There is enough evidence to conclude that heating costs for insulated homes is less than that for uninsulated homes.

b $\bar{x}_D \pm t_{\alpha/2} \frac{s_D}{\sqrt{n_D}} = 57.40 \pm 2.145 \frac{13.14}{\sqrt{15}} = 57.40 \pm 7.28$; LCL = 50.12, UCL = 64.68

c Differences are required to be normally distributed.

© 2012 Cengage Learning. All Rights Reserved. May not be scanned, copied or duplicated, or posted to a publicly accessible website, in whole or in part.

13.62 $H_0: \mu_D = 0$

$H_1: \mu_D < 0$

Rejection region: $t < -t_{\alpha,\nu} = -t_{.05,169} \approx -1.654$

$t = \dfrac{\bar{x}_D - \mu_D}{s_D / \sqrt{n_D}} = \dfrac{-183.35 - 0}{1568.94 / \sqrt{170}} = -1.52$, p-value = .0647. There is not enough to infer stock holdings have decreased.

13.64 $H_0: \mu_D = 0$

$H_1: \mu_D > 0$

Rejection region: $t > t_{\alpha,\nu} = t_{.05,54} \approx 1.676$

$t = \dfrac{\bar{x}_D - \mu_D}{s_D / \sqrt{n_D}} = \dfrac{520.85 - 0}{1854.92 / \sqrt{55}} = 2.08$, p-value = .0210. There is enough evidence to infer that company 1's calculated tax payable is higher than company 2's.

13.66 The matched pairs experiment reduced the variation caused by different drivers.

13.68 Salary offers and undergraduate GPA are not as strongly linked as are salary offers and MBA GPA.

13.70 $H_0: \mu_D = 0$

$H_1: \mu_D > 0$

	A	B	C
1	t-Test: Paired Two Sample for Means		
2			
3		*EDUC*	*PAEDUC*
4	Mean	13.80	11.49
5	Variance	9.21	17.64
6	Observations	1485	1485
7	Pearson Correlation	0.4814	
8	Hypothesized Mean Difference	0	
9	df	1484	
10	t Stat	23.35	
11	P(T<=t) one-tail	2.99E-103	
12	t Critical one-tail	1.6459	
13	P(T<=t) two-tail	5.98E-103	
14	t Critical two-tail	1.9616	

t = 23.35, p-value = 2.99E-103 ≈ 0. There is enough evidence to infer that this generation is more educated than their fathers.

© 2012 Cengage Learning. All Rights Reserved. May not be scanned, copied or duplicated, or posted to a publicly accessible website, in whole or in part.

13.72 $H_0: \mu_D = 0$

$H_1: \mu_D > 0$

	A	B	C
1	t-Test: Paired Two Sample for Means		
2			
3		*PRESTG80*	*PAPRES80*
4	Mean	44.33	43.38
5	Variance	193.75	160.22
6	Observations	1527	1527
7	Pearson Correlation	0.2077	
8	Hypothesized Mean Difference	0	
9	df	1526	
10	t Stat	2.22	
11	P(T<=t) one-tail	0.0132	
12	t Critical one-tail	1.6459	
13	P(T<=t) two-tail	0.0264	
14	t Critical two-tail	1.9615	

t = 2.22, p-value = .0132. There is enough evidence to infer that this generation has more prestigious occupations than their fathers.

13.76 a $H_0: \sigma_1^2 / \sigma_2^2 = 1$

$H_1: \sigma_1^2 / \sigma_2^2 \neq 1$

Rejection region: $F > F_{\alpha/2,\nu_1,\nu_2} = F_{.05,29,29} \approx 1.88$ or

$F < F_{1-\alpha/2,\nu_1,\nu_2} = 1/F_{\alpha/2,\nu_2,\nu_1} = 1/F_{.05,29,29} \approx 1/1.88 = .53$

$F = s_1^2 / s_2^2 = 350/700 = .50$, p-value = .0669. There is enough evidence to conclude that the population variances differ.

b Rejection region: $F > F_{\alpha/2,\nu_1,\nu_2} = F_{.025,14,14} = 2.98$ or

$F < F_{1-\alpha/2,\nu_1,\nu_2} = 1/F_{\alpha/2,\nu_2,\nu_1} = 1/F_{.025,14,14} = 1/2.98 = .34$

$F = s_1^2 / s_2^2 = 350/700 = .50$, p-value = .2071. There is not enough evidence to conclude that the population variances differ.

c The value of the test statistic is unchanged and in this exercise the conclusion changed as well.

13.78 $H_0: \sigma_1^2 / \sigma_2^2 = 1$

$H_1: \sigma_1^2 / \sigma_2^2 \neq 1$

Rejection region: $F > F_{\alpha/2,\nu_1,\nu_2} = F_{.025,9,10} = 3.78$ or

$F < F_{1-\alpha/2,\nu_1,\nu_2} = 1/F_{\alpha/2,\nu_2,\nu_1} = 1/F_{.025,10,9} = 1/3.96 = .25$

© 2012 Cengage Learning. All Rights Reserved. May not be scanned, copied or duplicated, or posted to a publicly accessible website, in whole or in part.

$F = s_1^2 / s_2^2$ = .0000057/.0000114 =.50, p-value = .3179. There is not enough evidence to conclude that the two machines differ in their consistency of fills.

13.80 $H_0: \sigma_1^2 / \sigma_2^2 = 1$

$H_1: \sigma_1^2 / \sigma_2^2 \neq 1$

Rejection region: $F > F_{\alpha/2, \nu_1, \nu_2} = F_{.025,10,10} = 3.72$ or

$F < F_{1-\alpha/2, \nu_1, \nu_2} = 1/F_{\alpha/2, \nu_2, \nu_1} = 1/F_{.025,10,10} = 1/3.72 = .269$

$F = s_1^2 / s_2^2$ = 193.67/60.00 = 3.23, p-value = .0784. There is not enough evidence to infer that the variances of the marks differ between the two sections.

13.82 $H_0: \sigma_1^2 / \sigma_2^2 = 1$

$H_1: \sigma_1^2 / \sigma_2^2 \neq 1$

Rejection region: $F > F_{\alpha/2, \nu_1, \nu_2} = F_{.025,99,99} \approx 1.48$ or

$F < F_{1-\alpha/2, \nu_1, \nu_2} = 1/F_{\alpha/2, \nu_2, \nu_1} = 1/F_{.025,99,99} \approx 1/1.48 = .68$

$F = s_1^2 / s_2^2$ = 41,309/19,850 = 2.08, p-value = .0003. There is enough evidence to conclude that the variances differ.

13.84 $H_0: \sigma_1^2 / \sigma_2^2 = 1$

$H_1: \sigma_1^2 / \sigma_2^2 \neq 1$

Rejection region: $F > F_{\alpha/2, \nu_1, \nu_2} = F_{.05,99,99} \approx 1.39$ or

$F < F_{1-\alpha, \nu_1, \nu_2} = 1/F_{\alpha, \nu_2, \nu_1} = 1/F_{.05,99,99} \approx 1/1.39 = .72$

$F = s_1^2 / s_2^2$ = 3.35/10.95 = .31, p-value = 0. There is enough evidence to conclude that the variance in service times differ.

13.88 $H_0: (p_1 - p_2) = 0$

$H_1: (p_1 - p_2) \neq 0$

a $z = \frac{(\hat{p}_1 - \hat{p}_2)}{\sqrt{\hat{p}(1-\hat{p})\left(\frac{1}{n_1} + \frac{1}{n_2}\right)}} = \frac{(.60 - .55)}{\sqrt{.575(1-.575)\left(\frac{1}{225} + \frac{1}{225}\right)}} = 1.07,$

p-value = 2P(Z > 1.07) = 2(1 – .8577) = .2846

© 2012 Cengage Learning. All Rights Reserved. May not be scanned, copied or duplicated, or posted to a publicly accessible website, in whole or in part.

b $z=\frac{(\hat{p}_1-\hat{p}_2)}{\sqrt{\hat{p}(1-\hat{p})\left(\frac{1}{n_1}+\frac{1}{n_2}\right)}}=\frac{(.95-.90)}{\sqrt{.925(1-.925)\left(\frac{1}{225}+\frac{1}{225}\right)}}=2.01,$

p-value = 2P(Z > 2.01) = 2(1 – .9778) = .0444.

c The p-value decreases.

d $z=\frac{(\hat{p}_1-\hat{p}_2)}{\sqrt{\hat{p}(1-\hat{p})\left(\frac{1}{n_1}+\frac{1}{n_2}\right)}}=\frac{(.10-.05)}{\sqrt{.075(1-.075)\left(\frac{1}{225}+\frac{1}{225}\right)}}=2.01,$

p-value = 2P(Z > 2.01) = 2(1 – .94778) = .0444.

e The p-value decreases.

13.90 $H_0:(p_1-p_2)=0$

$H_1:(p_1-p_2)>0$

$$z=\frac{(\hat{p}_1-\hat{p}_2)}{\sqrt{\hat{p}(1-\hat{p})\left(\frac{1}{n_1}+\frac{1}{n_2}\right)}}=\frac{(.205-.140)}{\sqrt{.177(1-.177)\left(\frac{1}{229}+\frac{1}{178}\right)}}=1.70,$$

p-value = P(Z > 1.70) = 1 – .9554 = .0446.

There is enough evidence to conclude that those who paid the regular price are more likely to buy an extended warranty.

13.92 $H_0:(p_1-p_2)=0$

$H_1:(p_1-p_2)>0$

$$z=\frac{(\hat{p}_1-\hat{p}_2)}{\sqrt{\hat{p}(1-\hat{p})\left(\frac{1}{n_1}+\frac{1}{n_2}\right)}}=\frac{(.0196-.0087)}{\sqrt{.0132(1-.0132)\left(\frac{1}{562}+\frac{1}{804}\right)}}=1.74,$$

p-value = P(Z > 1.74) = 1 – .9591 = .0409.

There is enough evidence to conclude that those who score under 600 are more likely to default than those who score 60 or more.

13.94 $H_0:(p_1-p_2)=-.08$

$H_1:(p_1-p_2)<-.08$

Rejection region: $z<-z_{\alpha}=-z_{.01}=-2.33$

$$z=\frac{(\hat{p}_1-\hat{p}_2)-(p_1-p_2)}{\sqrt{\frac{\hat{p}_1(1-\hat{p}_1)}{n_1}+\frac{\hat{p}_2(1-\hat{p}_2)}{n_2}}}=\frac{(.11-.28)-(-.08)}{\sqrt{\frac{.11(1-.11)}{300}+\frac{.28(1-.28)}{300}}}=-2.85,$$

© 2012 Cengage Learning. All Rights Reserved. May not be scanned, copied or duplicated, or posted to a publicly accessible website, in whole or in part.

p-value =P(Z < –2.85) = 1 – .9978 = .0022.

There is enough evidence to conclude that management should adopt process 1.

13.96 a $H_0: (p_1 - p_2) = 0$

$H_1: (p_1 - p_2) < 0$

Rejection region: $z < -z_\alpha = -z_{.05} = -1.645$

$$z = \frac{(\hat{p}_1 - \hat{p}_2)}{\sqrt{\hat{p}(1-\hat{p})\left(\frac{1}{n_1} + \frac{1}{n_2}\right)}} = \frac{(.093 - .115)}{\sqrt{.104(1-.104)\left(\frac{1}{6281} + \frac{1}{6281}\right)}} = -4.04$$, p-value = 0. There is enough

evidence to infer that Plavix is effective.

13.98 $H_0: (p_1 - p_2) = 0$

$H_1: (p_1 - p_2) > 0$

Rejection region: $z > z_\alpha = z_{.05} = 1.645$

$$\hat{p}_1 = \frac{1{,}084}{11{,}000} = .0985 \quad \hat{p}_2 = \frac{997}{11{,}000} = .0906 \quad \hat{p} = \frac{1{,}084 + 997}{22{,}000} = .0946$$

$$z = \frac{(\hat{p}_1 - \hat{p}_2)}{\sqrt{\hat{p}(1-\hat{p})\left(\frac{1}{n_1} + \frac{1}{n_2}\right)}} = \frac{(.0985 - .0906)}{\sqrt{.0946(1-.0946)\left(\frac{1}{11{,}000} + \frac{1}{11{,}000}\right)}} = 2.00,$$

p-value = P(Z > 2.00) = 1 – .9772 = .0228.

There is enough evidence to infer that aspirin leads to more cataracts.

13.100 $H_0: (p_1 - p_2) = 0$

$H_1: (p_1 - p_2) < 0$

Rejection region: $z < -z_\alpha = -z_{.05} = -1.645$

$$\hat{p}_1 = \frac{88}{395} = .2228 \quad \hat{p}_2 = \frac{105}{406} = .2586 \quad \hat{p} = \frac{88 + 105}{395 + 406} = .2409$$

$$z = \frac{(\hat{p}_1 - \hat{p}_2)}{\sqrt{\hat{p}(1-\hat{p})\left(\frac{1}{n_1} + \frac{1}{n_2}\right)}} = \frac{(.2228 - .2586)}{\sqrt{.2409(1-.2409)\left(\frac{1}{395} + \frac{1}{406}\right)}} = -1.19$$, p-value = P(Z < –1.19)

= .1170. There is not enough evidence to infer that exercise training reduces mortality.

13.102 a $H_0: (p_1 - p_2) = 0$

$H_1: (p_1 - p_2) > 0$

© 2012 Cengage Learning. All Rights Reserved. May not be scanned, copied or duplicated, or posted to a publicly accessible website, in whole or in part.

Rejection region: $z > z_\alpha = z_{.10} = 1.28$

$$z = \frac{(\hat{p}_1 - \hat{p}_2)}{\sqrt{\hat{p}(1-\hat{p})\left(\frac{1}{n_1}+\frac{1}{n_2}\right)}} = \frac{(.2632 - .0741)}{\sqrt{.11(1-.11)\left(\frac{1}{38}+\frac{1}{162}\right)}} = 3.35$$, p-value = 0. There is enough

evidence to conclude that smokers have a higher incidence of heart diseases than nonsmokers.

b $(\hat{p}_1 - \hat{p}_2) \pm z_{\alpha/2}\sqrt{\frac{\hat{p}_1(1-\hat{p}_1)}{n_1}+\frac{\hat{p}_2(1-\hat{p}_2)}{n_2}}$

$= (.2632–0741) \pm 1.645\sqrt{\frac{.2632(1-.2632)}{38}+\frac{.0741(1-.0741)}{162}} = .1891 \pm .1223$; LCL = .0668,

UCL = .3114

13.104 $H_0: (p_1 - p_2) = 0$

$H_1: (p_1 - p_2) \neq 0$

Rejection region: $z < -z_{\alpha/2}, z > z_{\alpha/2}, z_{.025} = 1.96$

1 = Success

$$z = \frac{(\hat{p}_1 - \hat{p}_2)}{\sqrt{\hat{p}(1-\hat{p})\left(\frac{1}{n_1}+\frac{1}{n_2}\right)}} = \frac{(.5169 - .375)}{\sqrt{.4463(1-.4463)\left(\frac{1}{445}+\frac{1}{440}\right)}} = 4.24$$, p-value = $P(Z > 4.24) = 0$

There is enough evidence to infer that Canadians and Americans differ in their responses to the survey question.

13.106 $H_0: (p_1 - p_2) = 0$

$H_1: (p_1 - p_2) > 0$

Rejection region: $z > z_\alpha = z_{.05} = 1.645$

2 = Success

$$z = \frac{(\hat{p}_1 - \hat{p}_2)}{\sqrt{\hat{p}(1-\hat{p})\left(\frac{1}{n_1}+\frac{1}{n_2}\right)}} = \frac{(.8608 - .7875)}{\sqrt{.8394(1-.8394)\left(\frac{1}{194}+\frac{1}{80}\right)}} = 1.50$$, p-value = 0.0664

There is not enough evidence to infer that those with more education are less likely to work 11 hours or more per day.

13.108 1 = Success

<u>Canada</u> $H_0: (p_1 - p_2) = 0$

$H_1: (p_1 - p_2) > 0$

© 2012 Cengage Learning. All Rights Reserved. May not be scanned, copied or duplicated, or posted to a publicly accessible website, in whole or in part.

Rejection region: $z > z_\alpha = z_{.05} = 1.645$

$$z = \frac{(\hat{p}_1 - \hat{p}_2)}{\sqrt{\hat{p}(1-\hat{p})\left(\frac{1}{n_1}+\frac{1}{n_2}\right)}} = \frac{(.6305 - .5243)}{\sqrt{.5834(1-.5834)\left(\frac{1}{387}+\frac{1}{309}\right)}} = 2.82, \text{ p-value} = .0024$$

There is enough evidence to infer that the proportion of Canadians who believe that global warming is a fact, has fallen in the period between November 2009 and December 2009.

<u>USA</u> $H_0: (p_1 - p_2) = 0$

$H_1: (p_1 - p_2) > 0$

Rejection region: $z > z_\alpha = z_{.05} = 1.645$

$$z = \frac{(\hat{p}_1 - \hat{p}_2)}{\sqrt{\hat{p}(1-\hat{p})\left(\frac{1}{n_1}+\frac{1}{n_2}\right)}} = \frac{(.4947 - .4613)}{\sqrt{.4793(1-.4793)\left(\frac{1}{469}+\frac{1}{401}\right)}} = 0.981, \text{ p-value} = .1634$$

There is not enough evidence to infer that the proportion of Americans who believe that global warming is a fact, has fallen in the period between November 2009 and December 2009.

<u>Britain</u> $H_0: (p_1 - p_2) = 0$

$H_1: (p_1 - p_2) > 0$

Rejection region: $z > z_\alpha = z_{.05} = 1.645$

$$z = \frac{(\hat{p}_1 - \hat{p}_2)}{\sqrt{\hat{p}(1-\hat{p})\left(\frac{1}{n_1}+\frac{1}{n_2}\right)}} = \frac{(.4692 - .4300)}{\sqrt{.4509(1-.4509)\left(\frac{1}{341}+\frac{1}{300}\right)}} = 1.00, \text{ p-value} = .1587$$

There is not enough evidence to infer that the proportion of British who believe that global warming is a fact, has fallen in the period between November 2009 and December 2009.

13.110 $H_0: (p_1 - p_2) = 0$

$H_1: (p_1 - p_2) > 0$

Rejection region: $z > z_\alpha = z_{.05} = 1.645$

$$z = \frac{(\hat{p}_1 - \hat{p}_2)}{\sqrt{\hat{p}(1-\hat{p})\left(\frac{1}{n_1}+\frac{1}{n_2}\right)}} = \frac{(.1385 - .0905)}{\sqrt{.1035(1-.1035)\left(\frac{1}{231}+\frac{1}{619}\right)}} \quad z = 2.04,$$

p-value = $P(Z > 2.04) = 1 - .9793 = .0207$. There is enough evidence to conclude that health conscious adults are more likely to buy Special X.

© 2012 Cengage Learning. All Rights Reserved. May not be scanned, copied or duplicated, or posted to a publicly accessible website, in whole or in part.

13.112 $H_0: (p_1 - p_2) = 0$

$H_1: (p_1 - p_2) \neq 0$

Rejection region: $z < -z_{\alpha/2} = -z_{.025} = -1.96$ or $z > z_{\alpha/2} = z_{.025} = 1.96$

$$z = \frac{(\hat{p}_1 - \hat{p}_2)}{\sqrt{\hat{p}(1-\hat{p})\left(\frac{1}{n_1} + \frac{1}{n_2}\right)}} = \frac{(.0995 - .1297)}{\sqrt{.1132(1-.1132)\left(\frac{1}{382} + \frac{1}{316}\right)}} = -1.25,$$

p-value = 2P(Z < –1.25) = 2(.1056) = .2112.

There is not enough evidence to infer differences between the two sources.

13.114 $H_0: (p_1 - p_2) = 0$

$H_1: (p_1 - p_2) \neq 0$

	A	B	C
1	**z-Test: Two Proportions**		
2			
3		*Men*	*Women*
4	Sample Proportions	0.1510	0.0843
5	Observations	914	1044
6	Hypothesized Difference	0	
7	z Stat	4.61	
8	P(Z<=z) one tail	0	
9	z Critical one-tail	1.6449	
10	P(Z<=z) two-tail	0	
11	z Critical two-tail	1.96	

z = 4.61, p-value = 0. There is enough evidence to infer a difference in the proportion of men and women who decide to work for themselves.

13.116 $H_0: (p_1 - p_2) = 0$

$H_1: (p_1 - p_2) \neq 0$

	A	B	C
1	**z-Test: Two Proportions**		
2			
3		*Men*	*Women*
4	Sample Proportions	0.7931	0.7607
5	Observations	667	723
6	Hypothesized Difference	0	
7	z Stat	1.45	
8	P(Z<=z) one tail	0.0739	
9	z Critical one-tail	1.6449	
10	P(Z<=z) two-tail	0.1478	
11	z Critical two-tail	1.96	

© 2012 Cengage Learning. All Rights Reserved. May not be scanned, copied or duplicated, or posted to a publicly accessible website, in whole or in part.

z = 1.45, p-value = .1478. There is not enough evidence to infer a difference in the proportion of men and women who answer the question correctly.

13.118 $H_0: (p_1 - p_2) = 0$

$H_1: (p_1 - p_2) \neq 0$

	A	B	C
1	**z-Test: Two Proportions**		
2			
3		*Men*	*Women*
4	Sample Proportions	0.8346	0.7195
5	Observations	671	713
6	Hypothesized Difference	0	
7	z Stat	5.13	
8	P(Z<=z) one tail	0	
9	z Critical one-tail	1.6449	
10	P(Z<=z) two-tail	0	
11	z Critical two-tail	1.96	

z = 5.13, p-value = 0. There is enough evidence to infer a difference in the proportion of men and women who answer the question correctly.

13.120 $H_0: (p_1 - p_2) = 0$

$H_1: (p_1 - p_2) \neq 0$

	A	B	C
1	**z-Test: Two Proportions**		
2			
3		*Year 2006*	*Year 2008*
4	Sample Proportions	0.6696	0.664
5	Observations	2815	1902
6	Hypothesized Difference	0	
7	z Stat	0.400	
8	P(Z<=z) one tail	0.3447	
9	z Critical one-tail	1.6449	
10	P(Z<=z) two-tail	0.6894	
11	z Critical two-tail	1.96	

z = .40, p-value = .6894. There is not enough evidence to infer a difference in the proportion of those favoring capital punishment between 2006 and 2008.

13.122

<u>GSS2002</u> $H_0: (p_1 - p_2) = 0$

$H_1: (p_1 - p_2) \neq 0$

© 2012 Cengage Learning. All Rights Reserved. May not be scanned, copied or duplicated, or posted to a publicly accessible website, in whole or in part.

	A	B	C
1	**z-Test: Two Proportions**		
2			
3		*Democrat*	*Republican*
4	Sample Proportions	0.1041	0.0707
5	Observations	922	764
6	Hypothesized Difference	0	
7	z Stat	2.40	
8	P(Z<=z) one tail	0.0082	
9	z Critical one-tail	1.6449	
10	P(Z<=z) two-tail	0.0164	
11	z Critical two-tail	1.96	

z = 2.40, p-value = .0164. There is enough evidence to infer a difference in the proportion of those completing a graduate degree between Democrats and Republicans in 2002.

GSS2004 $H_0: (p_1 - p_2) = 0$

$H_1: (p_1 - p_2) \neq 0$

	A	B	C
1	**z-Test: Two Proportions**		
2			
3		*Democrat*	*Republican*
4	Sample Proportions	0.1127	0.1084
5	Observations	958	821
6	Hypothesized Difference	0	
7	z Stat	0.290	
8	P(Z<=z) one tail	0.3858	
9	z Critical one-tail	1.6449	
10	P(Z<=z) two-tail	0.7716	
11	z Critical two-tail	1.96	

z = 0.29, p-value = .7716. In 2004, there is not enough evidence to infer a difference in the proportion of Democrats versus Republicans who have completed a graduate degree.

GSS2006 $H_0: (p_1 - p_2) = 0$

$H_1: (p_1 - p_2) \neq 0$

© 2012 Cengage Learning. All Rights Reserved. May not be scanned, copied or duplicated, or posted to a publicly accessible website, in whole or in part.

	A	B	C
1	**z-Test: Two Proportions**		
2			
3		*Democrat*	*Republican*
4	Sample Proportions	0.1115	0.0848
5	Observations	1435	1132
6	Hypothesized Difference	0	
7	z Stat	2.24	
8	P(Z<=z) one tail	0.0125	
9	z Critical one-tail	1.6449	
10	P(Z<=z) two-tail	0.0250	
11	z Critical two-tail	1.96	

z = 2.24, p-value = .0250. In 2006, there is enough evidence to infer a difference in the proportion of Democrats versus Republicans who have completed a graduate degree, with Democrats corresponding to the larger proportion.

GSS2008 $H_0: (p_1 - p_2) = 0$

$H_1: (p_1 - p_2) \neq 0$

	A	B	C
1	**z-Test: Two Proportions**		
2			
3		*Democrat*	*Republican*
4	Sample Proportions	0.1151	0.0972
5	Observations	721	504
6	Hypothesized Difference	0	
7	z Stat	0.994	
8	P(Z<=z) one tail	0.1601	
9	z Critical one-tail	1.6449	
10	P(Z<=z) two-tail	0.3202	
11	z Critical two-tail	1.96	

z = .99, p-value = .3202. In 2008, there is not enough evidence to infer a difference in the proportion of Democrats versus Republicans who have completed a graduate degree.

13.124 $H_0: (p_1 - p_2) = 0$

$H_1: (p_1 - p_2) \neq 0$

© 2012 Cengage Learning. All Rights Reserved. May not be scanned, copied or duplicated, or posted to a publicly accessible website, in whole or in part.

	A	B	C
1	**z-Test: Two Proportions**		
2			
3		*Democrat*	*Republican*
4	Sample Proportions	0.8326	0.9124
5	Observations	645	411
6	Hypothesized Difference	0	
7	z Stat	-3.69	
8	P(Z<=z) one tail	0.0001	
9	z Critical one-tail	1.6449	
10	P(Z<=z) two-tail	0.0002	
11	z Critical two-tail	1.96	

z = -3.69, p-value = 0. In 2008, there is enough evidence to infer a difference in the proportion of Democrats versus Republicans who have health insurance.

13.126 a $H_0 : (p_1 - p_2) = 0$

$H_1 : (p_1 - p_2) > 0$

	A	B	C
1	**z-Test: Two Proportions**		
2			
3		*Year 2001 Boys*	*Year 2011 Boys*
4	Sample Proportions	0.6568	0.5559
5	Observations	271	313
6	Hypothesized Difference	0	
7	z Stat	2.49	
8	P(Z<=z) one tail	0.0065	
9	z Critical one-tail	1.6449	
10	P(Z<=z) two-tail	0.0130	
11	z Critical two-tail	1.96	

z = 2.49, p-value = .0065. There is enough evidence to conclude that there has been a decrease in participation among boys over the past 10 years.

b $H_0 : (p_1 - p_2) = 0$

$H_1 : (p_1 - p_2) > 0$

© 2012 Cengage Learning. All Rights Reserved. May not be scanned, copied or duplicated, or posted to a publicly accessible website, in whole or in part.

	A	B	C
1	z-Test: Two Proportions		
2			
3		Year 2001 Girls	Year 2011 Girls
4	Sample Proportions	0.4875	0.4507
5	Observations	281	304
6	Hypothesized Difference	0	
7	z Stat	0.893	
8	P(Z<=z) one tail	0.1859	
9	z Critical one-tail	1.6449	
10	P(Z<=z) two-tail	0.3718	
11	z Critical two-tail	1.96	

z = .893, p-value = .1859. There is not enough evidence to conclude that there has been a decrease in participation among girls over the past 10 years.

c $H_0: (p_1 - p_2) = 0$

$H_1: (p_1 - p_2) > 0$

	A	B	C
1	z-Test: Two Proportions		
2			
3		Year 2011 Boys	Year 2011 Girls
4	Sample Proportions	0.5559	0.4507
5	Observations	313	304
6	Hyothesized Difference	0	
7	z Statistic	2.61	
8	P(Z<=z) One-Tail	0.0045	
9	z Critical One-Tail	1.6449	
10	P(Z<=z) Two-Tail	0.0089	
11	z Critical Two-Tail	1.96	

z = 2.61, p-value = .0045. There is enough evidence to infer girls are less likely to participate in sports than boys in 2011.

13.128 Gross sales must increase by 50/.20 = $250 to pay for ads.

$H_0: (\mu_1 - \mu_2) = 250$

$H_1: (\mu_1 - \mu_2) > 250$

© 2012 Cengage Learning. All Rights Reserved. May not be scanned, copied or duplicated, or posted to a publicly accessible website, in whole or in part.

	A	B	C
1	t-Test: Two-Sample Assuming Equal Variances		
2			
3		*During*	*Before*
4	Mean	5746.07	5372.13
5	Variance	167289	194772
6	Observations	15	24
7	Pooled Variance	184373	
8	Hypothesized Mean Difference	250	
9	df	37	
10	t Stat	0.88	
11	P(T<=t) one-tail	0.1931	
12	t Critical one-tail	1.6871	
13	P(T<=t) two-tail	0.3862	
14	t Critical two-tail	2.0262	

t = .88, p-value = .1931. There is not enough evidence to conclude that the ads are profitable.

13.130 $H_0: \mu_D = 0$

$H_1: \mu_D < 0$

	A	B	C
1	t-Test: Paired Two Sample for Means		
2			
3		*Drug*	*Placebo*
4	Mean	18.43	22.03
5	Variance	30.39	66.37
6	Observations	100	100
7	Pearson Correlation	0.69	
8	Hypothesized Mean Difference	0	
9	df	99	
10	t Stat	-6.09	
11	P(T<=t) one-tail	0.0000	
12	t Critical one-tail	1.6604	
13	P(T<=t) two-tail	0.0000	
14	t Critical two-tail	1.9842	

t = –6.09, p-value = 0. There is enough evidence to infer that the new drug is effective.

13.132 $H_0: (p_1 - p_2) = 0$

$H_1: (p_1 - p_2) < 0$

© 2012 Cengage Learning. All Rights Reserved. May not be scanned, copied or duplicated, or posted to a publicly accessible website, in whole or in part.

	A	B	C	D
1	**z-Test: Two Proportions**			
2				
3			*Last Year*	*This Year*
4	Sample Proportions		0.6758	0.7539
5	Observations		327	382
6	Hypothesized Difference		0	
7	z Stat		-2.30	
8	P(Z<=z) one tail		0.0106	
9	z Critical one-tail		1.6449	
10	P(Z<=z) two-tail		0.0212	
11	z Critical two-tail		1.96	

z = –2.30, p-value = .0106. There is enough evidence to infer an increase in seatbelt use.

13.134 a $H_0: (\mu_1 - \mu_2) = 0$

$H_1: (\mu_1 - \mu_2) \neq 0$

Two-tail F test: F = 1.10, p-value = .8430; use equal-variances t-test

	A	B	C
1	t-Test: Two-Sample Assuming Equal Variances		
2			
3		*Male*	*Female*
4	Mean	39.75	49.00
5	Variance	803.88	733.16
6	Observations	20	20
7	Pooled Variance	768.52	
8	Hypothesized Mean Difference	0	
9	df	38	
10	t Stat	-1.06	
11	P(T<=t) one-tail	0.1490	
12	t Critical one-tail	1.3042	
13	P(T<=t) two-tail	0.2980	
14	t Critical two-tail	1.6860	

t = –1.06, p-value = .2980. There is not enough evidence to conclude that men and women differ in the amount of time spent reading magazines.

b $H_0: (\mu_1 - \mu_2) = 0$

$H_1: (\mu_1 - \mu_2) < 0$

Two-tail F test: F = .266, p-value = .0053; use unequal-variances t-test

© 2012 Cengage Learning. All Rights Reserved. May not be scanned, copied or duplicated, or posted to a publicly accessible website, in whole or in part.

	A	B	C
1	t-Test: Two-Sample Assuming Unequal Variances		
2			
3		*Low*	*High*
4	Mean	33.10	56.84
5	Variance	278.69	1047.81
6	Observations	21.00	19
7	Hypothesized Mean Difference	0.00	
8	df	26.00	
9	t Stat	-2.87	
10	P(T<=t) one-tail	0.0040	
11	t Critical one-tail	1.3150	
12	P(T<=t) two-tail	0.0080	
13	t Critical two-tail	1.7056	

t = –2.87, p-value = .0040. There is enough evidence to conclude that high-income individuals devote more time to reading magazines than do low-income individuals.

13.136 $H_0: (p_1 - p_2) = 0$

$H_1: (p_1 - p_2) > 0$

	A	B	C	D
1	**z-Test: Two Proportions**			
2				
3			*This Year*	*3 Years Ago*
4	Sample Proportions		0.4351	0.3558
5	Observations		393	385
6	Hypothesized Difference		0	
7	z Stat		2.26	
8	P(Z<=z) one tail		0.0119	
9	z Critical one-tail		1.2816	
10	P(Z<=z) two-tail		0.0238	
11	z Critical two-tail		1.6449	

z = 2.26, p-value = .0119. There is enough evidence to infer that Americans have become more distrustful of television and newspaper reporting this year than they were three years ago.

13.138 $H_0: (p_1 - p_2) = 0$

$H_1: (p_1 - p_2) \neq 0$

The totals in columns A through D are 5788, 265, 5154, and 332, respectively.

© 2012 Cengage Learning. All Rights Reserved. May not be scanned, copied or duplicated, or posted to a publicly accessible website, in whole or in part.

	A	B	C	D	E
1	**z-Test of the Difference Between Two Proportions (Case 1)**				
2					
3		**Sample 1**	**Sample 2**	**z Stat**	**-4.28**
4	**Sample proportion**	0.045800	0.064400	**P(Z<=z) one-tail**	**0.0000**
5	**Sample size**	5788	5154	**z Critical one-tail**	**1.6449**
6	**Alpha**	0.05		**P(Z<=z) two-tail**	**0.0000**
7				**z Critical two-tail**	**1.9600**

z = –4.28, p-value = 0. There is enough evidence to infer that the defective rate differs between the two machines.

13.140 $H_0: (\mu_1 - \mu_2) = 0$

$H_1: (\mu_1 - \mu_2) > 0$

Two-tail F test: F = 1.77, p-value = .0084; use unequal-variances test statistic

	A	B	C
1	t-Test: Two-Sample Assuming Unequal Variances		
2			
3		*Facebook*	*No Facebook*
4	Mean	3.24	3.48
5	Variance	0.199	0.113
6	Observations	148	71
7	Hypothesized Mean Difference	0	
8	df	178	
9	t Stat	-4.53	
10	P(T<=t) one-tail	5.43E-06	
11	t Critical one-tail	1.6535	
12	P(T<=t) two-tail	1.09E-05	
13	t Critical two-tail	1.9734	

z = -4.53, p-value = 5.43E-06 ≈ 0. There is enough evidence to conclude that Facebook users maintain lower GPA scores.

13.142 a $H_0: (\mu_1 - \mu_2) = 0$

$H_1: (\mu_1 - \mu_2) > 0$

Two-tail F test: F = .438, p-value = .0482; use unequal-variances t-test

© 2012 Cengage Learning. All Rights Reserved. May not be scanned, copied or duplicated, or posted to a publicly accessible website, in whole or in part.

	A	B	C
1	t-Test: Two-Sample Assuming Unequal Variances		
2			
3		*Exercise*	*Drug*
4	Mean	13.52	9.92
5	Variance	5.76	13.16
6	Observations	25	25
7	Hypothesized Mean Difference	0	
8	df	42	
9	t Stat	4.14	
10	P(T<=t) one-tail	0.0001	
11	t Critical one-tail	2.4185	
12	P(T<=t) two-tail	0.0002	
13	t Critical two-tail	2.6981	

t = 4.14, p-value = .0001. There is enough evidence that exercise is more effective than medication in reducing hypertension.

b

	A	B	C	D	E	F
1	**t-Estimate of the Difference Between Two Means (Unequal-Variances)**					
2						
3		**Sample 1**	**Sample 2**	**Confidence Interval Estimate**		
4	**Mean**	13.52	9.92	**3.60**	±	**1.76**
5	**Variance**	5.76	13.16	**Lower confidence limit**		**1.84**
6	**Sample size**	25	25	**Upper confidence limit**		**5.36**
7	**Degrees of freedom**	**41.63**				
8	**Confidence level**	0.95				

LCL = 1.84, UCL = 5.36

c The histograms are bell shaped.

13.144 $H_0: \mu_D = 0$

$H_1: \mu_D < 0$

	A	B	C
1	t-Test: Paired Two Sample for Means		
2			
3		*Group 1*	*Group 2*
4	Mean	7.53	8.57
5	Variance	29.77	43.37
6	Observations	50	50
7	Pearson Correlation	0.89	
8	Hypothesized Mean Difference	0	
9	df	49	
10	t Stat	-2.40	
11	P(T<=t) one-tail	0.0100	
12	t Critical one-tail	1.6766	
13	P(T<=t) two-tail	0.0201	
14	t Critical two-tail	2.0096	

© 2012 Cengage Learning. All Rights Reserved. May not be scanned, copied or duplicated, or posted to a publicly accessible website, in whole or in part.

t = –2.40, p-value = .0100. There is enough evidence to conclude that people who exercise moderately more frequently lose weight faster

13.146 $H_0: (p_1 - p_2) = 0$

$H_1: (p_1 - p_2) > 0$

	A	B	C	D
1	**z-Test: Two Proportions**			
2				
3			*Special K*	*Other*
4	Sample Proportions		0.575	0.515
5	Observations		200	200
6	Hypothesized Difference		0	
7	z Stat		1.20	
8	P(Z<=z) one tail		0.1141	
9	z Critical one-tail		1.6449	
10	P(Z<=z) two-tail		0.2282	
11	z Critical two-tail		1.9600	

z = 1.20, p-value = .1141. There is not enough evidence to conclude that Special K buyers are more likely to think the ad is effective.

13.148 $H_0: (\mu_1 - \mu_2) = 0$

$H_1: (\mu_1 - \mu_2) > 0$

Two-tail F test: F = .624, p-value = .0431; use unequal-variances t-test

	A	B	C
1	t-Test: Two-Sample Assuming Unequal Variances		
2			
3		*Computer*	*No Computer*
4	Mean	69,933	48,246
5	Variance	63,359,040	101,588,525
6	Observations	89	61
7	Hypothesized Mean Difference	0	
8	df	109	
9	t Stat	14.07	
10	P(T<=t) one-tail	0.0000	
11	t Critical one-tail	1.2894	
12	P(T<=t) two-tail	0.0000	
13	t Critical two-tail	1.6590	

t = 14.07, p-value = 0. There is enough evidence to conclude that single-person businesses that use a PC earn more.

13.150 $H_0: (\mu_1 - \mu_2) = 0$

$H_1: (\mu_1 - \mu_2) < 0$

© 2012 Cengage Learning. All Rights Reserved. May not be scanned, copied or duplicated, or posted to a publicly accessible website, in whole or in part.

Two-tail F test: F = 1.62, p-value = .1008; use equal-variances t-test

	A	B	C
1	t-Test: Two-Sample Assuming Equal Variances		
2			
3		*Supplement*	*Placebo*
4	Mean	19.02	21.85
5	Variance	41.34	25.49
6	Observations	48	48
7	Pooled Variance	33.41	
8	Hypothesized Mean Difference	0	
9	df	94	
10	t Stat	-2.40	
11	P(T<=t) one-tail	0.0092	
12	t Critical one-tail	1.6612	
13	P(T<=t) two-tail	0.0183	
14	t Critical two-tail	1.9855	

t = –2.40, p-value = .0092. There is enough evidence to infer that taking vitamin and mineral supplements daily increases the body's immune system?

13.152 $H_0: (\mu_1 - \mu_2) = 0$

$H_1: (\mu_1 - \mu_2) \neq 0$

Two-tail F test: F = 1.43, p-value = 0; use unequal-variances test statistic

	A	B	C
1	t-Test: Two-Sample Assuming Unequal Variances		
2			
3		*Men*	*Women*
4	Mean	99.93	99.58
5	Variance	139.0	97.45
6	Observations	963	1059
7	Hypothesized Mean Difference	0	
8	df	1883	
9	t Stat	0.71	
10	P(T<=t) one-tail	0.2382	
11	t Critical one-tail	1.6457	
12	P(T<=t) two-tail	0.4763	
13	t Critical two-tail	1.9612	

t = 0.71, p-value = .4763. There is not enough evidence to conclude that math test scores differ between males and females.

13.154 $H_0: (\mu_1 - \mu_2) = 0$

$H_1: (\mu_1 - \mu_2) > 0$

Two-tail F test: F = 1.41, p-value = .1433; use equal-variances t-test

© 2012 Cengage Learning. All Rights Reserved. May not be scanned, copied or duplicated, or posted to a publicly accessible website, in whole or in part.

	A	B	C
1	t-Test: Two-Sample Assuming Equal Variances		
2			
3		*City*	*Suburb*
4	Mean	2.42	1.97
5	Variance	1.08	0.77
6	Observations	70	78
7	Pooled Variance	0.92	
8	Hypothesized Mean Difference	0	
9	df	146	
10	t Stat	2.85	
11	P(T<=t) one-tail	0.0025	
12	t Critical one-tail	1.6554	
13	P(T<=t) two-tail	0.0050	
14	t Critical two-tail	1.9763	

t = 2.85, p-value = .0025. There is enough evidence to infer that city households discard more newspaper than do suburban households.

13.156 $H_0: (p_1 - p_2) = 0$

$H_1: (p_1 - p_2) < 0$

	A	B	C	D
1	**z-Test: Two Proportions**			
2				
3			*No HS*	*HS*
4	Sample Proportions		0.127	0.358
5	Observations		63	257
6	Hypothesized Difference		0	
7	z Stat		-3.54	
8	P(Z<=z) one tail		0.0002	
9	z Critical one-tail		1.6449	
10	P(Z<=z) two-tail		0.0004	
11	z Critical two-tail		1.96	

z = –3.54, p-value = .0002. There is enough evidence to conclude that Californians who did not complete high school are less likely to take a course in the university's evening program.

13.158 $H_0: (\mu_1 - \mu_2) = 0$

$H_1: (\mu_1 - \mu_2) < 0$

Two-tail F test: F = .501, p-value = 0; use unequal-variances t-test

© 2012 Cengage Learning. All Rights Reserved. May not be scanned, copied or duplicated, or posted to a publicly accessible website, in whole or in part.

	A	B	C
1	t-Test: Two-Sample Assuming Unequal Variances		
2			
3		*Sale-CDs*	*Sale-fax*
4	Mean	59.04	65.57
5	Variance	425.4	849.7
6	Observations	122	144
7	Hypothesized Mean Difference	0	
8	df	256	
9	t Stat	-2.13	
10	P(T<=t) one-tail	0.0171	
11	t Critical one-tail	1.6508	
12	P(T<=t) two-tail	0.0341	
13	t Critical two-tail	1.9693	

t = –2.13, p-value = .0171. There is enough evidence to conclude that those who buy the fax/copier outspend those who buy the package of CD-ROMS.

13.160 $H_0: (p_1 - p_2) = 0$

$H_1: (p_1 - p_2) \neq 0$

The data must first be unstacked. Success = 2

	A	B	C	D
1	**z-Test: Two Proportions**			
2				
3			*Female*	*Male*
4	Sample Proportions		0.5945	0.6059
5	Observations		762	746
6	Hypothesized Difference		0	
7	z Stat		-0.45	
8	P(Z<=z) one tail		0.3256	
9	z Critical one-tail		1.6449	
10	P(Z<=z) two-tail		0.6512	
11	z Critical two-tail		1.96	

z = –.45, p-value = .6512. There is not enough evidence to conclude that men and women differ in their choices of Christmas trees.

© 2012 Cengage Learning. All Rights Reserved. May not be scanned, copied or duplicated, or posted to a publicly accessible website, in whole or in part.

Appendix 13

A13.2 a z-test of $p_1 - p_2$ (case 1)

H_0: $(p_1 - p_2) = 0$

H_1: $(p_1 - p_2) > 0$

	A	B	C	D	E
1	**z-Test of the Difference Between Two Proportions (Case 1)**				
2					
3		**Sample 1**	**Sample 2**	**z Stat**	**2.83**
4	**Sample proportion**	0.4336	0.2414	**P(Z<=z) one-tail**	**0.0024**
5	**Sample size**	113	87	**z Critical one-tail**	**1.6449**
6	**Alpha**	0.05		**P(Z<=z) two-tail**	**0.0047**
7				**z Critical two-tail**	**1.9600**

z = 2.83, p-value = .0024. There is enough evidence to infer that customers who see the ad are more likely to make a purchase than those who do not see the ad.

b Equal-variances t-test of $\mu_1 - \mu_2$

$H_0: (\mu_1 - \mu_2) = 0$

$H_1: (\mu_1 - \mu_2) > 0$

Two-tail F test: F = 2.20, p-value = .0577; use equal-variances t-test

	A	B	C
1	t-Test: Two-Sample Assuming Equal Variances		
2			
3		*Ad*	*No Ad*
4	Mean	97.38	92.01
5	Variance	621.97	283.26
6	Observations	49	21
7	Pooled Variance	522.35	
8	Hypothesized Mean Difference	0	
9	df	68	
10	t Stat	0.90	
11	P(T<=t) one-tail	0.1853	
12	t Critical one-tail	1.6676	
13	P(T<=t) two-tail	0.3705	
14	t Critical two-tail	1.9955	

t = .90, p-value = .1853. There is not enough evidence to infer that customers who see the ad and make a purchase spend more than those who do not see the ad and make a purchase.

c z-estimator of p

© 2012 Cengage Learning. All Rights Reserved. May not be scanned, copied or duplicated, or posted to a publicly accessible website, in whole or in part.

	A	B	C	D	E
1	**z-Estimate of a Proportion**				
2					
3	**Sample proportion**	0.4336	**Confidence Interval Estimate**		
4	**Sample size**	113	**0.4336**	±	**0.0914**
5	**Confidence level**	0.95	**Lower confidence limit**		**0.3423**
6			**Upper confidence limit**		**0.5250**

We estimate that between 34.23% and 52.50% of all customers who see the ad will make a purchase.

d t-estimator of μ

	A	B	C	D
1	**t-Estimate: Mean**			
2				
3				*Ad*
4	Mean			97.38
5	Standard Deviation			24.94
6	LCL			90.22
7	UCL			104.55

We estimate that the mean amount spent by customers who see the ad and make a purchase lies between $90.22 and $104.55.

A13.4 Frequency of accidents: z -test of $p_1 - p_2$ (case 1)

$$H_0: (p_1 - p_2) = 0$$

$$H_1: (p_1 - p_2) > 0$$

	A	B	C	D	E
1	**z-Test of the Difference Between Two Proportions (Case 1)**				
2					
3		**Sample 1**	**Sample 2**	**z Stat**	**0.47**
4	**Sample proportion**	0.0840	0.0760	**P(Z<=z) one-tail**	**0.3205**
5	**Sample size**	500	500	**z Critical one-tail**	**1.6449**
6	**Alpha**	0.05		**P(Z<=z) two-tail**	**0.6410**
7				**z Critical two-tail**	**1.9600**

z = .47, p-value = .32053. There is not enough evidence to infer that ABS-equipped cars have fewer accidents than cars without ABS.

Severity of accidents Equal-variances t-test of $\mu_1 - \mu_2$

$$H_0: (\mu_1 - \mu_2) = 0$$

$$H_1: (\mu_1 - \mu_2) > 0$$

Two-tail F test: F = 1.15, p-value = .6626; use equal-variances t-test

© 2012 Cengage Learning. All Rights Reserved. May not be scanned, copied or duplicated, or posted to a publicly accessible website, in whole or in part.

	A	B	C
1	t-Test: Two-Sample Assuming Equal Variances		
2			
3		*No ABS*	*ABS*
4	Mean	2075	1714
5	Variance	450,343	390,409
6	Observations	42	38
7	Pooled Variance	421,913	
8	Hypothesized Mean Difference	0	
9	df	78	
10	t Stat	2	
11	P(T<=t) one-tail	0.0077	
12	t Critical one-tail	1.6646	
13	P(T<=t) two-tail	0.0153	
14	t Critical two-tail	1.9908	

Estimate of the difference between two means (equal-variances)

	A	B	C	D	E	F
1	**t-Estimate of the Difference Between Two Means (Equal-Variances)**					
2						
3		**Sample 1**	**Sample 2**	**Confidence Interval Estimate**		
4	**Mean**	2075	1714	**360.48**	±	**290**
5	**Variance**	450,343	390,409	**Lower confidence limit**		**71**
6	**Sample size**	42	38	**Upper confidence limit**		**650**
7	**Pooled Variance**	**421,913**				
8	**Confidence level**	0.95				

We estimate that the mean repair cost for non-ABS-equipped cars will be between $71 and $650 more than the mean repair cost for ABS-equipped cars.

A13.6 Speeds: Equal-variances t-test of $\mu_1 - \mu_2$

$$H_0: (\mu_1 - \mu_2) = 0$$

$$H_1: (\mu_1 - \mu_2) > 0$$

Two-tail F test: F = .993, p-value = .9738; use equal-variances t-test

© 2012 Cengage Learning. All Rights Reserved. May not be scanned, copied or duplicated, or posted to a publicly accessible website, in whole or in part.

	A	B	C
1	t-Test: Two-Sample Assuming Equal Variances		
2			
3		*Speeds Before*	*Speeds After*
4	Mean	31.74	31.42
5	Variance	4.50	4.41
6	Observations	100	100
7	Pooled Variance	4.45	
8	Hypothesized Mean Difference	0	
9	df	198	
10	t Stat	1.07	
11	P(T<=t) one-tail	0.1424	
12	t Critical one-tail	1.6526	
13	P(T<=t) two-tail	0.2849	
14	t Critical two-tail	1.9720	

t = 1.07, p-value = .1424. There is not enough evidence to infer that speed bumps reduce speeds.

Proper stops: Equal-variances t-test of $\mu_1 - \mu_2$

$$H_0 : (\mu_1 - \mu_2) = 0$$

$$H_1 : (\mu_1 - \mu_2) < 0$$

Two-tail F test: F =.99, p-value = .9784; use equal-variances t-test

	A	B	C
1	t-Test: Two-Sample Assuming Equal Variances		
2			
3		*Stops Before*	*Stops After*
4	Mean	7.82	7.98
5	Variance	1.83	1.84
6	Observations	100	100
7	Pooled Variance	1.83	
8	Hypothesized Mean Difference	0	
9	df	198	
10	t Stat	-0.84	
11	P(T<=t) one-tail	0.2021	
12	t Critical one-tail	1.6526	
13	P(T<=t) two-tail	0.4042	
14	t Critical two-tail	1.9720	

t = –.84, p-value = .2021. There is not enough evidence to infer that speed bumps increase the number of proper stops.

A13.8 t-test of μ_D

$$H_0 : \mu_D = 0$$

$$H_1 : \mu_D > 0$$

© 2012 Cengage Learning. All Rights Reserved. May not be scanned, copied or duplicated, or posted to a publicly accessible website, in whole or in part.

	A	B	C
1	t-Test: Paired Two Sample for Means		
2			
3		*Before*	*After*
4	Mean	28.94	26.22
5	Variance	61.45	104.30
6	Observations	50	50
7	Pearson Correlation	0.87	
8	Hypothesized Mean Difference	0	
9	df	49	
10	t Stat	3.73	
11	P(T<=t) one-tail	0.000	
12	t Critical one-tail	1.677	
13	P(T<=t) two-tail	0.000	
14	t Critical two-tail	2.010	

t = 3.73, p-value = .0002. There is enough evidence to infer that the law discourages bicycle use.

A13.10 t-test of μ

$H_0: \mu = 200$

$H_1: \mu > 200$

	A	B	C	D
1	**t-Test: Mean**			
2				
3				*Pedestrians*
4	Mean			209.13
5	Standard Deviation			60.01
6	Hypothesized Mean			200
7	df			39
8	t Stat			0.96
9	P(T<=t) one-tail			0.1711
10	t Critical one-tail			1.6849
11	P(T<=t) two-tail			0.3422
12	t Critical two-tail			2.0227

t = .96, p-value = .1711. There is not enough evidence to infer that the franchiser should build on this site.

A13.12 F-test of σ_1^2 / σ_2^2

$H_0: \sigma_1^2 / \sigma_2^2 = 1$

$H_1: \sigma_1^2 / \sigma_2^2 > 1$

© 2012 Cengage Learning. All Rights Reserved. May not be scanned, copied or duplicated, or posted to a publicly accessible website, in whole or in part.

	A	B	C
1	F-Test Two-Sample for Variances		
2			
3		*Brand A*	*Brand B*
4	Mean	145.95	144.78
5	Variance	16.45	4.25
6	Observations	100	100
7	df	99	99
8	F	3.87	
9	P(F<=f) one-tail	0.0000	
10	F Critical one-tail	1.3941	

F = 3.87, p-value = 0. There is overwhelming evidence to infer that Brand B is superior to Brand A.

A13.14 z-test of $p_1 - p_2$ (case 1)

H_0: $(p_1 - p_2) = 0$

H_1: $(p_1 - p_2) > 0$

	A	B	C	D
1	**z-Test: Two Proportions**			
2				
3			*Exercisers*	*Watchers*
4	Sample Proportions		0.4250	0.3675
5	Observations		400	400
6	Hypothesized Difference		0	
7	z Stat		1.66	
8	P(Z<=z) one tail		0.0482	
9	z Critical one-tail		1.6449	
10	P(Z<=z) two-tail		0.0964	
11	z Critical two-tail		1.9600	

z = 1.66, p-value = .0482. There is evidence to infer that exercisers are more likely to remember the sponsor's brand name than those who only watch.

A13.16 t-tests of μ_D

a $H_0: \mu_D = 40$

$H_1: \mu_D > 40$

© 2012 Cengage Learning. All Rights Reserved. May not be scanned, copied or duplicated, or posted to a publicly accessible website, in whole or in part.

	A	B	C
1	t-Test: Paired Two Sample for Means		
2			
3		*SAT after*	*SAT before*
4	Mean	1235	1162
5	Variance	37970	28844
6	Observations	40	40
7	Pearson Correlation	0.94	
8	Hypothesized Mean Difference	40	
9	df	39	
10	t Stat	2.98	
11	P(T<=t) one-tail	0.0024	
12	t Critical one-tail	1.6849	
13	P(T<=t) two-tail	0.0049	
14	t Critical two-tail	2.0227	

t = 2.98, p-value = .0024. There is enough evidence to conclude that the ETS claim is false.

b $H_0: \mu_D = 110$

$H_1: \mu_D < 110$

	A	B	C
1	t-Test: Paired Two Sample for Means		
2			
3		*SAT after*	*SAT before*
4	Mean	1235	1162
5	Variance	37970	28844
6	Observations	40	40
7	Pearson Correlation	0.94	
8	Hypothesized Mean Difference	110	
9	df	39	
10	t Stat	-3.39	
11	P(T<=t) one-tail	0.0008	
12	t Critical one-tail	1.6849	
13	P(T<=t) two-tail	0.0016	
14	t Critical two-tail	2.0227	

t = –3.39, p-value = .0008. There is enough evidence to conclude that the Kaplan claim is also false.

A13.18

Two-tail F test: F = 1.05, p-value = .6509; use equal-variances t-test

© 2012 Cengage Learning. All Rights Reserved. May not be scanned, copied or duplicated, or posted to a publicly accessible website, in whole or in part.

	A	B	C
1	t-Test: Two-Sample Assuming Equal Variances		
2			
3		*Government*	*Private*
4	Mean	41.92	42.09
5	Variance	213.72	203.73
6	Observations	189	985
7	Pooled Variance	205.33	
8	Hypothesized Mean Difference	0	
9	df	1172	
10	t Stat	-0.155	
11	P(T<=t) one-tail	0.4385	
12	t Critical one-tail	1.6462	
13	P(T<=t) two-tail	0.8771	
14	t Critical two-tail	1.9620	

t= -.155, p-value = .4385. There is not enough evidence …

A19.20 H_0: $(p_1 - p_2) = 0$

H_1: $(p_1 - p_2) \neq 0$

	A	B	C	D
1	**z-Test: Two Proportions**			
2				
3			*Democrats*	*Republicans*
4	Sample Proportions		0.7587	0.8058
5	Observations		489	345
6	Hypothesized Difference		0	
7	z Stat		-1.61	
8	P(Z<=z) one tail		0.0534	
9	z Critical one-tail		1.6449	
10	P(Z<=z) two-tail		0.1068	
11	z Critical two-tail		1.96	

z = -1.61, p-value = .0534. There is not enough evidence to conclude that Democrats and Republicans differ in their correct answer to this question.

A13.22 H_0: $(p_1 - p_2) = 0$

H_1: $(p_1 - p_2) \neq 0$

© 2012 Cengage Learning. All Rights Reserved. May not be scanned, copied or duplicated, or posted to a publicly accessible website, in whole or in part.

	A	B	C	D
1	z-Test: Two Proportions			
2				
3			*Democrats*	*Republicans*
4	Sample Proportions		0.738	0.8116
5	Observations		481	345
6	Hypothesized Difference		0	
7	z Stat		-2.47	
8	P(Z<=z) one tail		0.0067	
9	z Critical one-tail		1.6449	
10	P(Z<=z) two-tail		0.0134	
11	z Critical two-tail		1.96	

z = -2.41, p-value = .0067. There is enough evidence to conclude that Democrats and Republicans differ in their correct answer to this question.

A13.24

	A	B
1	t-Estimate: Mean	
2		
3		*CUREMPYR*
4	Mean	8.51
5	Standard Deviation	8.61
6	LCL	7.93
7	UCL	9.10

LCL = 7.93, UCL = 9.10

A13.26 H_0: $(p_1 - p_2) = 0$

H_1: $(p_1 - p_2) > 0$

	A	B	C
1	z-Test: Two Proportions		
2			
3		*Year 2008*	*Year 2006*
4	Sample Proportions	0.2807	0.2523
5	Observations	1774	3873
6	Hypothesized Difference	0	
7	z Stat	2.26	
8	P(Z<=z) one tail	0.0119	
9	z Critical one-tail	1.2816	
10	P(Z<=z) two-tail	0.0238	
11	z Critical two-tail	1.6449	

z = 2.26, p-value = .0119. There is sufficient evidence to infer that the proportion of Americans earning at least $75,000 is greater in 2008 than in 2006.

© 2012 Cengage Learning. All Rights Reserved. May not be scanned, copied or duplicated, or posted to a publicly accessible website, in whole or in part.

A13.28

	A	B
1	**t-Estimate: Mean**	
2		
3		*TIME2*
4	Mean	77.86
5	Standard Deviation	85.35
6	LCL	70.12
7	UCL	85.61

LCL = 70.12, UCL = 85.61

A13.30

	A	B
1	**z-Estimate: Proportion**	
2		*INC*
3	Sample Proportion	0.0582
4	Observations	1683
5	LCL	0.0470
6	UCL	0.0694

LCL = .0470, UCL = .0694

© 2012 Cengage Learning. All Rights Reserved. May not be scanned, copied or duplicated, or posted to a publicly accessible website, in whole or in part.

Chapter 14

14.2 a $\bar{\bar{x}} = \frac{4(20)+4(22)+4(25)}{4+4+4} = 22.33$

SST = $\sum n_j(\bar{x}_j - \bar{\bar{x}})^2 = 4(20 - 22.33)^2 + 4(22 - 22.33)^2 + 4(25 - 22.33)^2 = 50.67$

SSE = $\sum (n_j - 1)s_j^2 = (4-1)(10) + (4-1)(10) + (4-1)(10) = 90$

ANOVA Table

Source	Degrees of Freedom	Sum of Squares	Mean Squares	F
Treatments	$k-1=2$	SST = 50.67	MST = 25.33	F = 2.53
Error	$n-k=9$	SSE = 90	MSE = 10	

b SSE = $\sum (n_j - 1)s_j^2 = (4-1)(25) + (4-1)(25) + (4-1)(25) = 225$

ANOVA Table

Source	Degrees of Freedom	Sum of Squares	Mean Squares	F
Treatments	$k-1=2$	SST = 50.67	MST = 25.33	F = 1.01
Error	$n-k=9$	SSE = 225	MSE = 25.0	

c The F statistic decreases.

14.4 $H_0: \mu_1 = \mu_2 = \mu_3$

H_1: At least two means differ.

Rejection region: $F > F_{\alpha,k-1,n-k} = F_{.05,2,9} = 4.26$

	Finance	Marketing	Management
Mean	2.25	3.25	5.75
Variance	2.25	2.92	2.92

Grand mean = 3.75

SST = $\sum n_j(\bar{x}_j - \bar{\bar{x}})^2 = 4(2.25-3.75)^2 + 4(3.25 - 3.75)^2 + 4(5.75 - 3.75)^2 = 26.00$

SSE = $\sum (n_j - 1)s_j^2 = (4-1)(2.25) + (4-1)(2.92) + (4-1)(2.92) = 24.25$

ANOVA table

Source	Degrees of Freedom	Sum of Squares	Mean Squares	F
Treatments	$k-1=2$	SST = 26.00	MST = 13.00	F = 4.82
Error	$n-k=9$	SSE = 24.25	MSE = 2.69	

F = 4.82, p-value = .0377. There is enough evidence to conclude that there are differences in the number of job offers between the three MBA majors.

© 2012 Cengage Learning. All Rights Reserved. May not be scanned, copied or duplicated, or posted to a publicly accessible website, in whole or in part.

14.6 $H_0: \mu_1 = \mu_2 = \mu_3$

H_1 : At least two means differ.

Rejection region: $F > F_{\alpha,k-1,n-k} = F_{.05,2,12} = 3.89$

	BA	BSc	BBA
Mean	3.94	4.78	5.76
Variance	1.26	.92	1.00

Grand mean = 4.83

$SST = \sum n_j(\bar{x}_j - \bar{\bar{x}})^2 = 5(3.94 - 4.83)^2 + 5(4.78 - 4.83)^2 + 5(5.76 - 4.83)^2 = 8.30$

$SSE = \sum (n_j - 1)s_j^2 = (5 - 1)(1.26) + (5 - 1)(.92) + (5 - 1)(1.00) = 12.73$

ANOVA table

Source	Degrees of Freedom	Sum of Squares	Mean Squares	F
Treatments	$k - 1 = 2$	SST = 8.30	MST = 4.15	F = 3.91
Error	$n - k = 12$	SSE = 12.73	MSE = 1.06	

F = 3.91, p-value = .0493. There is enough evidence to conclude that students in different degree program differ in their summer earnings.

14.8 $H_0: \mu_1 = \mu_2 = \mu_3$

H_1 : At least two means differ.

Rejection region: $F > F_{\alpha,k-1,n-k} = F_{.05,3,8} = 4.07$

	IBM	Dell	HP	Other
Mean	13.33	11.00	9.67	17.00
Variance	12.33	79.00	22.33	39.00

Grand mean = 12.75

$SST = \sum n_j(\bar{x}_j - \bar{\bar{x}})^2 = 3(13.33 - 12.75)^2 + 3(11.00 - 12.75)^2 + 3(9.67 - 12.75)^2 + 3(17.00 - 12.75)^2 = 92.92$

$SSE = \sum (n_j - 1)s_j^2 = (3 - 1)(12.33) + (3 - 1)(79.00) + (3 - 1)(22.33) + (3 - 1)(39.00) = 305.33$

ANOVA table

Source	Degrees of Freedom	Sum of Squares	Mean Squares	F
Treatments	$k - 1 = 3$	SST = 92.92	MST = 30.97	F = .81
Error	$n - k = 8$	SSE = 305.33	MSE = 38.17	

F = .81, p-value = .5224. There is not enough evidence to conclude that there are differences in age between the computer brands.

© 2012 Cengage Learning. All Rights Reserved. May not be scanned, copied or duplicated, or posted to a publicly accessible website, in whole or in part.

14.10a $H_0: \mu_1 = \mu_2 = \mu_3 = \mu_4$

H_1: At least two means differ.

Rejection region: $F > F_{\alpha,k-1,n-k} = F_{.05,3,116} \approx 2.68$

Grand mean = 101.0

$SST = \sum n_j(\bar{x}_j - \bar{\bar{x}})^2$

$= 30(90.17 - 101.0)^2 + 30(95.77 - 101.0)^2 + 30(106.8 - 101.0)^2 + 30(111.17 - 101.0)^2 = 8{,}464$

$SSE = \sum (n_j - 1)s_j^2$

= (30 –1)(991.52) + (30 – 1)(900.87) + (30 – 1)(928.70) + (30 – 1)(1,023.04) = 111,480

ANOVA table

Source	Degrees of Freedom	Sum of Squares	Mean Squares	F
Treatments	$k - 1 = 3$	SST = 8,464	MST = 2821	F = 2.94
Error	$n - k = 116$	SSE = 111,480	MSE = 961	

F = 2.94, p-value = .0363. There is enough evidence to infer that there are differences between the completion times of the four income tax forms.

b The times for each form must be normally distributed with the same variance.

c The histograms are approximately bell-shaped and the sample variances are similar.

14.12 $H_0: \mu_1 = \mu_2 = \mu_3 = \mu_4 = \mu_5$

H_1: At least two means differ.

Rejection region: $F > F_{\alpha,k-1,n-k} = F_{.01,4,120} = 3.48$

Grand mean = 173.3

$SST = \sum n_j(\bar{x}_j - \bar{\bar{x}})^2 = 25(164.6 - 173.3)^2 + 25(185.6 - 173.3)^2 + 25(154.8 - 173.3)^2$

$+ 25(182.6 - 173.3)^2 + 25(178.9 - 173.3)^2 = 17{,}251$

$SSE = \sum (n_j - 1)s_j^2$ = (25 –1)(1,164) + (25 – 1)(1,720) + (25 – 1)(1,114) + (25 – 1)(1,658)

+ (25 – 1)(841.8) = 155,941

ANOVA table

Source	Degrees of Freedom	Sum of Squares	Mean Squares	F
Treatments	$k - 1 = 4$	SST = 17,251	MST = 4,312.6	F = 3.32
Error	$n - k = 120$	SSE = 155,941	MSE = 1,299.5	

F = 3.32, p-value = .0129. There is not enough evidence to allow the manufacturer to conclude that differences exist between the five lacquers.

b The times until first sign of corrosion for each lacquer must be normally distributed with a common variance.

c The histograms are approximately bell-shaped with similar sample variances.

© 2012 Cengage Learning. All Rights Reserved. May not be scanned, copied or duplicated, or posted to a publicly accessible website, in whole or in part.

14.14 $H_0: \mu_1 = \mu_2 = \mu_3$

H_1 : At least two means differ.

Rejection region: $F > F_{\alpha,k-1,n-k} = F_{.05,2,57} \approx 3.15$

Grand mean = 562.6

$SST = \sum n_j(\bar{x}_j - \bar{\bar{x}})^2 = 20(551.50 - 562.6)^2 + 20(576.75 - 562.6)^2 + 20(559.45 - 562.6)^2$

= 6,667

$SSE = \sum (n_j - 1)s_j^2 = (20-1)(2{,}741.95) + (20-1)(2{,}641.14) + (20-1)(3{,}129.31) = 161{,}736$

ANOVA table

Source	Degrees of Freedom	Sum of Squares	Mean Squares	F
Treatments	k − 1 = 2	SST = 6,667	MST = 3334	F = 1.17
Error	n − k = 57	SSE = 161,736	MSE = 2837	

F = 1.17, p-value = .3162. There is not enough evidence of a difference between fertilizers in terms of crop yields.

14.16 $H_0: \mu_1 = \mu_2 = \mu_3 = \mu_4$

H_1 : At least two means differ.

Rejection region: $F > F_{\alpha,k-1,n-k} = F_{.05,3,116} \approx 2.68$

Grand mean = 77.39

$SST = \sum n_j(\bar{x}_j - \bar{\bar{x}})^2 = 30(74.10 - 77.39)^2 + 30(75.67 - 77.39)^2 + 30(78.50 - 77.39)^2$

$+ 30(81.30 - 77.39)^2 = 909.42$

$SSE = \sum (n_j - 1)s_j^2 = (30-1)(249.96) + (30-1)(184.23) + (30-1)(233.36) + (30-1)(242.91)$

= 26,403

ANOVA table

Source	Degrees of Freedom	Sum of Squares	Mean Squares	F
Treatments	k − 1 = 3	SST = 909.4	MST = 303.1	F = 1.33
Error	n − k = 116	SSE = 26,403	MSE = 227.6	

F = 1.33, p-value = .2675. There is not enough evidence of a difference between the four groups of companies.

14.18 $H_0: \mu_1 = \mu_2 = \mu_3 = \mu_4$

H_1 : At least two means differ.

a Ages: Rejection region: $F > F_{\alpha,k-1,n-k} = F_{.05,3,291} \approx 2.61$

Grand mean = 36.23

© 2012 Cengage Learning. All Rights Reserved. May not be scanned, copied or duplicated, or posted to a publicly accessible website, in whole or in part.

$SST = \sum n_j(\bar{x}_j - \bar{\bar{x}})^2 = 63(31.30 - 36.23)^2 + 81(34.42 - 36.23)^2 + 40(37.38 - 36.23)^2$

$+ 111(39.93 - 36.23)^2 = 3{,}366$

$SSE = \sum (n_j - 1)s_j^2 = (63 - 1)(28.34) + (81 - 1)(23.20) + (40 - 1)(31.16) + (111 - 1)(72.03) =$

12,752

ANOVA table

Source	Degrees of Freedom	Sum of Squares	Mean Squares	F
Treatments	$k - 1 = 3$	SST =3,366	MST = 1122	F = 25.60
Error	$n - k = 291$	SSE = 12,752	MSE = 43.82	

F = 25.60, p-value = 0. There is sufficient evidence to infer that the ages of the four groups of cereal buyers differ.

b Incomes: Rejection region: $F > F_{\alpha,k-1,n-k} = F_{.05,3,291} \approx 2.61$

Grand mean = 39.97

$SST = \sum n_j(\bar{x}_j - \bar{\bar{x}})^2 = 63(37.22 - 39.97)^2 + 81(38.91 - 39.97)^2 + 40(41.48 - 39.97)^2$

$+ 111(41.75 - 39.97)^2 = 1{,}008$

$SSE = \sum (n_j - 1)s_j^2 = (63 - 1)(39.82) + (81 - 1)(40.85) + (40 - 1)(61.38) + (111 - 1)(46.59)$

= 13,256

ANOVA table

Source	Degrees of Freedom	Sum of Squares	Mean Squares	F
Treatments	$k - 1 = 3$	SST =1,008	MST = 336.0	F = 7.37
Error	$n - k = 291$	SSE = 13,256	MSE = 45.55	

F = 7.37, p-value = .0001. There is sufficient evidence to conclude that incomes differ between the four groups of cereal buyers.

c Education: Rejection region: $F > F_{\alpha,k-1,n-k} = F_{.05,3,291} \approx 2.61$

Grand mean = 11.98

$SST = \sum n_j(\bar{x}_j - \bar{\bar{x}})^2 = 63(11.75 - 11.98)^2 + 81(12.41 - 11.98)^2 + 40(11.73 - 11.98)^2$

$+ 111(11.89 - 11.98)^2 = 21.71$

$SSE = \sum (n_j - 1)s_j^2 = (63 - 1)(3.93) + (81 - 1)(3.39) + (40 - 1)(4.26) + (111 - 1)(4.30) = 1{,}154$

ANOVA table

Source	Degrees of Freedom	Sum of Squares	Mean Squares	F
Treatments	$k - 1 = 3$	SST =21.71	MST = 7.24	F = 1.82
Error	$n - k = 291$	SSE = 1,154	MSE = 3.97	

© 2012 Cengage Learning. All Rights Reserved. May not be scanned, copied or duplicated, or posted to a publicly accessible website, in whole or in part.

F = 1.82, p-value = .1428. There is not enough evidence to infer that education differs between the four groups of cereal buyers.

d Using the F-tests and the descriptive statistics we see that the mean ages and mean household incomes are in ascending order. For example, Sugar Smacks buyers are younger and earn less than the buyers of the other three cereals. Cheerio purchasers are older and earn the most.

14.20 $H_0: \mu_1 = \mu_2 = \mu_3$

H_1: At least two means differ.

Rejection region: $F > F_{\alpha,k-1,n-k} = F_{.05,2,232} \approx 3.07$

Grand mean = 19.50

$SST = \sum n_j(\bar{x}_j - \bar{\bar{x}})^2 = 61(18.54 - 19.50)^2 + 83(19.34 - 19.50)^2 + 91(20.29 - 19.50)^2 = 114.5$

$SSE = \sum (n_j - 1)s_j^2 = (61 - 1)(177.95) + (83 - 1)(171.42) + (91 - 1)(297.50) = 51{,}508$

ANOVA table

Source	Degrees of Freedom	Sum of Squares	Mean Squares	F
Treatments	$k - 1 = 2$	SST = 114.5	MST = 57.3	F = .26
Error	$n - k = 232$	SSE = 51,508	MSE = 222.0	

F = .26, p-value = .7730. There is not enough evidence of a difference between the three segments.

14.22 $H_0: \mu_1 = \mu_2 = \mu_3$

H_1: At least two means differ.

	A	B	C	D	E	F	G
1	Anova: Single Factor						
2							
3	SUMMARY						
4	*Groups*	*Count*	*Sum*	*Average*	*Variance*		
5	White	1014	2795	2.76	5.73		
6	Black	188	824	4.38	12.85		
7	Other	122	329	2.70	5.92		
8							
9							
10	ANOVA						
11	*Source of Variation*	*SS*	*df*	*MS*	*F*	*P-value*	*F crit*
12	Between Groups	430.5	2	215.26	31.86	3.06E-14	3.0025
13	Within Groups	8925.0	1321	6.76			
14							
15	Total	9355.6	1323				

F = 31.86, p-value ≈ 3.06E-140. There is enough evidence to infer that the amount of television differs by race.

© 2012 Cengage Learning. All Rights Reserved. May not be scanned, copied or duplicated, or posted to a publicly accessible website, in whole or in part.

14.24 $H_0: \mu_1 = \mu_2 = \mu_3 = \mu_4$

H_1: At least two means differ.

	A	B	C	D	E	F	G
1	Anova: Single Factor						
2							
3	SUMMARY						
4	*Groups*	*Count*	*Sum*	*Average*	*Variance*		
5	Year 2002	1729	72232	41.78	213.83		
6	Year 2004	1763	74509	42.26	225.65		
7	Year 2006	2739	115247	42.08	202.54		
8	Year 2008	1203	50530	42.00	209.67		
9							
10							
11	ANOVA						
12	*Source of Variation*	*SS*	*df*	*MS*	*F*	*P-value*	*F crit*
13	Between Groups	212.42	3	70.81	0.33	0.8005	2.6061
14	Within Groups	1573676	7430	211.80			
15							
16	Total	1573889	7433				

F = .33, p-value = .8005. There is not enough evidence to infer that the amount of time spent at work differs over the four years.

14.26 $H_0: \mu_1 = \mu_2 = \mu_3 = \mu_4$

H_1: At least two means differ.

	A	B	C	D	E	F	G
1	Anova: Single Factor						
2							
3	SUMMARY						
4	*Groups*	*Count*	*Sum*	*Average*	*Variance*		
5	Year 2002	905	2700	2.98	5.58		
6	Year 2004	899	2576	2.87	6.85		
7	Year 2006	1987	5833	2.94	5.23		
8	Year 2008	1324	3948	2.98	7.07		
9							
10							
11	ANOVA						
12	*Source of Variation*	*SS*	*df*	*MS*	*F*	*P-value*	*F crit*
13	Between Groups	9.00	3	3.00	0.496	0.6852	2.6066
14	Within Groups	30925	5111	6.05			
15							
16	Total	30934	5114				

© 2012 Cengage Learning. All Rights Reserved. May not be scanned, copied or duplicated, or posted to a publicly accessible website, in whole or in part.

F = .496, p-value = .6852. There is not enough evidence to infer that the amount of television differs by year.

14.28 H_0: $\mu_1 = \mu_2 = \mu_3$

H_1: At least two means differ.

	A	B	C	D	E	F	G
1	Anova: Single Factor						
2							
3	SUMMARY						
4	*Groups*	*Count*	*Sum*	*Average*	*Variance*		
5	Democrat	643	8414	13.09	7.75		
6	Republican	409	5662	13.84	5.93		
7	Independent	585	7780	13.30	4.97		
8							
9							
10	ANOVA						
11	*Source of Variation*	*SS*	*df*	*MS*	*F*	*P-value*	*F crit*
12	Between Groups	146.1	2	73.05	11.59	1.01E-05	3.0012
13	Within Groups	10301	1634	6.30			
14							
15	Total	10447	1636				

F = 11.59, p-value ≈ 0. There is enough evidence to infer that income differs between the three political affiliations.

© 2012 Cengage Learning. All Rights Reserved. May not be scanned, copied or duplicated, or posted to a publicly accessible website, in whole or in part.

14.30 H_0: $\mu_1 = \mu_2 = \mu_3 = \mu_4 = \mu_5 = \mu_6 = \mu_7 = \mu_8$

H_1: At least two means differ.

	A	B	C	D	E	F	G
1	Anova: Single Factor						
2							
3	SUMMARY						
4	*Groups*	*Count*	*Sum*	*Average*	*Variance*		
5	No degree	335	10,626,000	31,719	919,678,140		
6	Bachelor's	272	13,808,000	50,765	1,568,762,237		
7	Master's	100	5,655,000	56,550	1,538,104,798		
8	Ph.D.	13	1,203,000	92,538	3,274,394,231		
9	LLB	4	398,500	99,625	2,813,062,500		
10	MD	8	721,000	90,125	1,841,553,571		
11	JDC	1	175,000	175,000			
12	Associate's	201	8,888,500	44,221	1,299,251,990		
13							
14							
15	ANOVA						
16	*Source of Variation*	*SS*	*df*	*MS*	*F*	*P-value*	*F crit*
17	Between Groups	155,761,202,443	7	22,251,600,349	17.10	2.33E-21	2.0195
18	Within Groups	1,205,052,631,336	926	1,301,352,734			
19							
20	Total	1,360,813,833,779	933				

F = 17.10, p-value ≈ 0. There is enough evidence to infer that income differs between the completed degrees.

14.32 H_0: $\mu_1 = \mu_2 = \mu_3$

H_1: At least two means differ.

	A	B	C	D	E	F	G
1	Anova: Single Factor						
2							
3	SUMMARY						
4	*Groups*	*Count*	*Sum*	*Average*	*Variance*		
5	Democrat	645	5346	8.29	7.11		
6	Republican	411	3571	8.69	5.63		
7	Independent	585	4244	7.25	9.64		
8							
9							
10	ANOVA						
11	*Source of Variation*	*SS*	*df*	*MS*	*F*	*P-value*	*F crit*
12	Between Groups	572.8	2	286.39	37.47	1.22E-16	3.0012
13	Within Groups	12520	1638	7.64			
14							
15	Total	13092	1640				

F = 37.47, p-value ≈ 0. There is enough evidence to conclude that intention to vote differs by political affiliation.

© 2012 Cengage Learning. All Rights Reserved. May not be scanned, copied or duplicated, or posted to a publicly accessible website, in whole or in part.

14.34 a $\alpha = .05$: $t_{\alpha/2,n-k} = t_{.025,20} = 2.086$

$$LSD = t_{\alpha/2,n-k}\sqrt{MSE\left(\frac{1}{n_i}+\frac{1}{n_j}\right)} = 2.086\sqrt{125\left(\frac{1}{5}+\frac{1}{5}\right)} = 14.75$$

Treatment	Means		Difference
$i = 1, j = 2$	227	205	22
$i = 1, j = 3$	227	219	8
$i = 1, j = 4$	227	248	−21
$i = 1, j = 5$	227	202	25
$i = 2, j = 3$	205	219	−14
$i = 2, j = 4$	205	248	−43
$i = 2, j = 5$	205	202	3
$i = 3, j = 4$	219	248	−29
$i = 3, j = 5$	219	202	17
$i = 4, j = 5$	248	202	46

Conclusion: The following pairs of means differ. μ_1 and μ_2, μ_1 and μ_4, μ_1 and μ_5, μ_2 and μ_4, μ_3 and μ_4, μ_3 and μ_5, and μ_4 and μ_5.

b $C = 5(4)/2 = 10$, $\alpha_E = .05$, $\alpha = \alpha_E / C = .005$ $t_{\alpha/2,n-k} = t_{.0025,20} = 3.153$ (from Excel)

$$LSD = t_{\alpha/2,n-k}\sqrt{MSE\left(\frac{1}{n_i}+\frac{1}{n_j}\right)} = 3.153\sqrt{125\left(\frac{1}{5}+\frac{1}{5}\right)} = 22.30$$

Treatment	Means		Difference
$i = 1, j = 2$	227	205	22
$i = 1, j = 3$	227	219	8
$i = 1, j = 4$	227	248	−21
$i = 1, j = 5$	227	202	25
$i = 2, j = 3$	205	219	−14
$i = 2, j = 4$	205	248	−43
$i = 2, j = 5$	205	202	3
$i = 3, j = 4$	219	248	−29
$i = 3, j = 5$	219	202	17
$i = 4, j = 5$	248	202	46

Conclusion: The following pairs of means differ. μ_1 and μ_5, μ_2 and μ_4, μ_3 and μ_4, and μ_4 and μ_5.

© 2012 Cengage Learning. All Rights Reserved. May not be scanned, copied or duplicated, or posted to a publicly accessible website, in whole or in part.

c $q_\alpha(k,\nu) = q_{.05}(5, 20) = 4.23$ $\varpi = q_\alpha(k,\nu)\sqrt{\frac{MSE}{n_g}} = 4.23\sqrt{\frac{125}{5}} = 21.15$

Treatment	Means		Difference
i = 1, j = 2	227	205	22
i = 1, j = 3	227	219	8
i = 1, j = 4	227	248	−21
i = 1, j = 5	227	202	25
i = 2, j = 3	205	219	−14
i = 2, j = 4	205	248	−43
i = 2, j = 5	205	202	3
i = 3, j = 4	219	248	−29
i = 3, j = 5	219	202	17
i = 4, j = 5	248	202	46

Conclusion: The following pairs of means differ. μ_1 and μ_2, μ_1 and μ_5, μ_2 and μ_4, μ_3 and μ_4, and μ_4 and μ_5.

14.36 a $LSD = t_{\alpha/2,n-k}\sqrt{MSE\left(\frac{1}{n_i}+\frac{1}{n_j}\right)} = 1.782\sqrt{1.06\left(\frac{1}{5}+\frac{1}{5}\right)} = 1.16$

Treatment	Means		Difference
i = 1, j = 2	3.94	4.78	−.84
i = 1, j = 3	3.94	5.76	−1.82
i = 2, j = 3	4.78	5.76	−1.02

Means of BAs and BBAs differ.

b $C = 3(2)/2 = 3, \alpha_E = .10, \alpha = \alpha_E / C = .0333$: $t_{\alpha/2,n-k} = t_{.0167,12} = 2.404$ (from Excel)

$LSD = t_{\alpha/2,n-k}\sqrt{MSE\left(\frac{1}{n_i}+\frac{1}{n_j}\right)} = 2.404\sqrt{1.06\left(\frac{1}{5}+\frac{1}{5}\right)} = 1.57$

Treatment	Means		Difference
i = 1, j = 2	3.94	4.78	−.84
i = 1, j = 3	3.94	5.76	−1.82
i = 2, j = 3	4.78	5.76	−1.02

Means of BAs and BBAs differ.

14.38 Tukey's method: $q_\alpha(k,\nu) = q_{.05}(4, 116) \approx 3.68$ $\varpi = 3.68\sqrt{\frac{961.0}{30}} = 20.83$

LSD method with the Bonferroni adjustment: $C = 4(3)/2 = 6, \alpha_E = .05, \alpha = \alpha_E / C = .0083$

© 2012 Cengage Learning. All Rights Reserved. May not be scanned, copied or duplicated, or posted to a publicly accessible website, in whole or in part.

$$LSD = t_{\alpha/2,n-k}\sqrt{MSE\left(\frac{1}{n_i}+\frac{1}{n_j}\right)} = 2.64\sqrt{961.0\left(\frac{1}{30}+\frac{1}{30}\right)} = 21.13$$

Treatment	Means		Difference	Tukey	LSD
i = 1, j = 2	90.17	95.77	−5.60	20.83	21.13
i = 1, j = 3	90.17	106.8	−16.67	20.83	21.13
i = 1, j = 4	90.17	111.17	−21.00	20.83	21.13
i = 2, j = 3	95.77	106.8	−11.07	20.83	21.13
i = 2, j = 4	95.77	111.17	−15.40	20.83	21.13
i = 3, j = 4	106.8	111.17	−4.33	20.83	21.13

a The means for Forms 1 and 4 differ.

b No means differ.

14.40 a LSD method: $C = 5(4)/2 = 10, \alpha_E = .05,\ \alpha = \alpha_E / C = .005$

$t_{\alpha/2,n-k} = t_{.0025,120} = 2.860$ (from Excel)

$$LSD = t_{\alpha/2,n-k}\sqrt{MSE\left(\frac{1}{n_i}+\frac{1}{n_j}\right)} = 2.860\sqrt{1300\left(\frac{1}{25}+\frac{1}{25}\right)} = 29.17$$

b Tukey's method: $q_\alpha(k,\nu) = q_{.05}(5,120) = 3.92\quad \varpi = 3.92\sqrt{\frac{1300}{25}} = 28.27$

Treatment	Means		Difference
i = 1, j = 2	164.6	185.6	−21.0
i = 1, j = 3	164.6	154.8	9.8
i = 1, j = 4	164.6	182.6	−18.0
i = 1, j = 5	164.6	178.9	−14.3
i = 2, j = 3	185.6	154.8	30.8
i = 2, j = 4	185.6	182.6	3.0
i = 2, j = 5	185.6	178.9	6.7
i = 3, j = 4	154.8	182.6	−27.8
i = 3, j = 5	154.8	178.9	−24.1
i = 4, j = 5	182.6	178.9	3.7

a The means of lacquers 2 and 3 differ

b The means of lacquers 2 and 3 differ.

14.42 Tukey's method: $q_\alpha(k,\nu) = q_{.05}(3,57) \approx 3.40\quad \varpi = 3.40\sqrt{\frac{2,838}{20}} = 40.50$

LSD method: $C = 3(2)/2 = 3, \alpha_E = .05,\ \alpha = \alpha_E / C = .0167\ t_{\alpha/2,n-k} = t_{.0083,57} = 2.466$ (from Excel)

© 2012 Cengage Learning. All Rights Reserved. May not be scanned, copied or duplicated, or posted to a publicly accessible website, in whole or in part.

$$LSD = t_{\alpha/2,n-k}\sqrt{MSE\left(\frac{1}{n_i}+\frac{1}{n_j}\right)} = 2.466\sqrt{2{,}838\left(\frac{1}{20}+\frac{1}{20}\right)} = 41.54$$

Treatment	Means		Difference
$i = 1, j = 2$	551.5	576.8	−25.3
$i = 1, j = 3$	551.5	559.5	−8.0
$i = 2, j = 3$	576.8	559.5	17.3

a There are no differences.

b There are no differences.

14.44

	A	B	C	D	E
1	**Multiple Comparisons**				
2					
3				LSD	Omega
4	Treatment	Treatment	Difference	Alpha = 0.0167	Alpha = 0.05
5	White	Black	-1.627	0.495	0.598
6		Other	0.060	0.597	0.598
7	Black	Other	1.686	0.724	0.598

Blacks differ from Whites and from Other.

14.46

	A	B	C	D	E
1	**Multiple Comparisons**				
2					
3				LSD	Omega
4	Treatment	Treatment	Difference	Alpha = 0.005	Alpha = 0.05
5	Married	Widowed	11511	17111	15637
6		Divorced	5086	9400	15637
7		Separated	21574	16570	15637
8		Never married	17231	7229	15637
9	Widowed	Divorced	-6425	18487	15637
10		Separated	10063	22978	15637
11		Never married	5720	17484	15637
12	Divorced	Separated	16488	17988	15637
13		Never married	12145	10063	15637
14	Separated	Never married	-4343	16955	15637

Using Tukey's method the following pairs of means differ: Married and Separated, Married and Never married, and Divorced and Separated

© 2012 Cengage Learning. All Rights Reserved. May not be scanned, copied or duplicated, or posted to a publicly accessible website, in whole or in part.

14.48

	A	B	C	D	E
1	**Multiple Comparisons**				
2					
3				LSD	Omega
4	Treatment	Treatment	Difference	Alpha = 0.0167	Alpha = 0.05
5	Democrat	Republican	-0.758	0.380	0.363
6		Independent	-0.214	0.344	0.363
7	Republican	Independent	0.544	0.388	0.363

Using Tukey's method or the Bonferroni adjustment the following pairs of means differ: Democrat and Republican and Republican and Independent.

14.50

	A	B	C	D	E
1	**Multiple Comparisons**				
2					
3				LSD	Omega
4	Treatment	Treatment	Difference	Alpha = 0.0167	Alpha = 0.05
5	Democrat	Republican	-0.400	0.418	0.399
6		Independent	1.034	0.378	0.399
7	Republican	Independent	1.434	0.426	0.399

Using Tukey's method all three pairs of means differ. Using the Bonferroni adjustment Democrats and Independents and Republicans and Independents differ.

14.52 ANOVA Table

Source	Degrees of Freedom	Sum of Squares	Mean Squares	F
Treatments	4	1,500	375.0	16.50
Blocks	11	1,000	90.91	4.00
Error	44	1,000	22.73	
Total	59	3,500		

a Rejection region: $F > F_{\alpha,k-1,n-k-b+1} = F_{.01,4,44} \approx 3.83$

F = 16.50, p-value = 0. There is enough evidence to conclude that the treatment means differ.

b Rejection region: $F > F_{\alpha,b-1,n-k-b+1} = F_{.01,11,44} \approx 2.80$

Conclusion: F = 4.00, p-value = .0005. There is enough evidence to conclude that the block means differ.

14.54 Rejection region: $F > F_{\alpha,k-1,n-k-b+1} = F_{.05,2,14} = 3.74$

© 2012 Cengage Learning. All Rights Reserved. May not be scanned, copied or duplicated, or posted to a publicly accessible website, in whole or in part.

a ANOVA Table

Source	Degrees of Freedom	Sum of Squares	Mean Squares	F
Treatments	2	1,500	750.0	7.00
Blocks	7	500	71.43	.67
Error	14	1,500	107.1	
Total	23	3,500		

Conclusion: F = 7.00, p-value = .0078. There is enough evidence to conclude that the treatment means differ.

b ANOVA Table

Source	Degrees of Freedom	Sum of Squares	Mean Squares	F
Treatments	2	1,500	750.0	10.50
Blocks	7	1,000	142.86	2.00
Error	14	1,000	71.43	
Total	23	3,500		

Conclusion: F = 10.50, .0016. There is enough evidence to conclude that the treatment means differ

c ANOVA Table

Source	Degrees of Freedom	Sum of Squares	Mean Squares	F
Treatments	2	1,500	750	21.00
Blocks	7	1,500	214.3	6.00
Error	14	500	35.71	
Total	23	3,500		

Conclusion: F = 21.00, p-value = .0001. There is enough evidence to conclude that the treatment means differ

d The test statistic increases.

14.56 a k = 4, b = 3, Grand mean = 5.6

SS(Total) =

$$\sum_{j=1}^{k}\sum_{i=1}^{b}(x_{ij}-\bar{\bar{x}})^2 = (6-5.6)^2+(8-5.6)^2+(7-5.6)^2+(5-5.6)^2+(5-5.6)^2+(6-5.6)^2$$

$$+(4-5.6)^2+(5-5.6)^2+(5-5.6)^2+(4-5.6)^2+(6-5.6)^2+(6-5.6)^2 = 14.9$$

$$SST = \sum_{j=1}^{k} b(\bar{x}[T]_j-\bar{\bar{x}})^2 = 3[(7-5.6)^2+(5.3-5.6)^2+(4.7-5.6)^2+(5.3-5.6)^2] = 8.9$$

$$SSB = \sum_{i=1}^{b} k(\bar{x}[B]_i-\bar{\bar{x}})^2 = 4[(4.8-5.6)^2+(6-5.6)^2+(6-5.6)^2 = 4.2$$

© 2012 Cengage Learning. All Rights Reserved. May not be scanned, copied or duplicated, or posted to a publicly accessible website, in whole or in part.

SSE = SS(Total) – SST – SSB = 14.9– 8.9 – 4.2 = 1.8

b. SS(Total) =

$$\sum_{j=1}^{k}\sum_{i=1}^{b}(x_{ij}-\bar{\bar{x}})^2 = (6-5.6)^2+(8-5.6)^2+(7-5.6)^2+(5-5.6)^2+(5-5.6)^2+(6-5.6)^2$$

$$+(4-5.6)^2+(5-5.6)^2+(5-5.6)^2+(4-5.6)^2+(6-5.6)^2+(6-5.6)^2 = 14.9$$

$$SST = \sum_{j=1}^{k} b(\bar{x}[T]_j-\bar{\bar{x}})^2 = 3[(7-5.6)^2+(5.3-5.6)^2+(4.7-5.6)^2+(5.3-5.6)^2] = 8.9$$

SSE = SS(Total) – SST = 14.9 – 8.9 = 6.0

c The variation between all the data is the same for both designs.

d The variation between treatments is the same for both designs.

e Because the randomized block design divides the sum of squares for error in the one-way analysis of variance into two parts.

14.58 $H_0: \mu_1 = \mu_2 = \mu_3 = \mu_4$

H_1: At least two means differ.

Rejection region: $F > F_{\alpha,k-1,n-k-b+1} = F_{.01,3,12} = 5.95$

k = 4, b = 5, Grand mean = 8.3

$$SS(Total) = \sum_{j=1}^{k}\sum_{i=1}^{b}(x_{ij}-\bar{\bar{x}})^2$$

$$= (5-8.3)^2+(4-8.3)^2+(6-8.3)^2+(7-8.3)^2+(9-8.3)^2$$

$$+(2-8.3)^2+(7-8.3)^2+(12-8.3)^2+(11-8.3)^2+(8-8.3)^2$$

$$+(6-8.3)^2+(8-8.3)^2+(9-8.3)^2+(16-8.3)^2+(15-8.3)^2$$

$$+(8-8.3)^2+(10-8.3)^2+(2-8.3)^2+(7-8.3)^2+(14-8.3)^2 = 286.2$$

$$SST = \sum_{j=1}^{k} b(\bar{x}[T]_j-\bar{\bar{x}})^2 = 5[(6.2-8.3)^2+(8.0-8.3)^2+(10.8-8.3)^2+(8.2-8.3)^2] = 53.8$$

$$SSB = \sum_{i=1}^{b} k(\bar{x}[B]_i-\bar{\bar{x}})^2$$

$$= 4[(5.25-8.3)^2+(7.25-8.3)^2+(7.25-8.3)^2+(10.25-8.3)^2+(11.5-8.3)^2] = 102.2$$

SSE = SS(Total) – SST – SSB = 286.2 – 53.8 – 102.2 = 130.2

© 2012 Cengage Learning. All Rights Reserved. May not be scanned, copied or duplicated, or posted to a publicly accessible website, in whole or in part.

ANOVA Table

Source	Degrees of Freedom	Sum of Squares	Mean Squares	F
Treatments	3	53.8	17.93	1.65
Blocks	4	102.2	25.55	2.35
Error	12	130.2	10.85	
Total	19	286.2		

F = 1.65, p-value = .2296. There is not enough evidence to conclude there are differences between the four diets.

14.60 ANOVA Table

Source	Degrees of Freedom	Sum of Squares	Mean Squares	F
Treatments	2	7,131	3,566	123.36
Blocks	19	177,465	9,340	323.16
Error	38	1,098	28.90	

a $H_0: \mu_1 = \mu_2 = \mu_3$

H_1: At least two means differ.

Rejection region: $F > F_{\alpha,k-1,n-k-b+1} = F_{.05,2,38} \approx 3.23$

F = 123.36, p-value = 0. There is sufficient evidence to conclude that the three fertilizers differ with respect to crop yield.

b F = 323.16, p-value = 0. There is sufficient evidence to indicate that there are differences between the plots.

14.62 ANOVA Table

Source	Degrees of Freedom	Sum of Squares	Mean Squares	F
Treatments	3	4,206	1,402	21.16
Blocks	29	126,843	4,374	66.02
Error	87	5,764	66.25	

a $H_0: \mu_1 = \mu_2 = \mu_3 = \mu_4$

H_1: At least two means differ.

Rejection region: $F > F_{\alpha,k-1,n-k-b+1} = F_{.01,3,87} \approx 4.01$

F = 21.16, p-value = 0. There is sufficient evidence to conclude that differences in completion times exist between the four forms.

b $H_0: \mu_1 = \mu_2 = \ldots = \mu_{30}$

H_1: At least two means differ.

F = 66.02, p-value = 0. There is sufficient evidence to indicate that there are differences between the taxpayers, which tells us that this experimental design is recommended.

© 2012 Cengage Learning. All Rights Reserved. May not be scanned, copied or duplicated, or posted to a publicly accessible website, in whole or in part.

14.64 ANOVA Table

Source	Degrees of Freedom	Sum of Squares	Mean Squares	F
Treatments	4	1,406	351.6	10.72
Blocks	35	7,310	208.9	6.36
Error	140	4,594	32.81	

a $H_0: \mu_1 = \mu_2 = \mu_3 = \mu_4 = \mu_5$

H_1: At least two means differ.

F = 10.72, p-value = 0. There is enough evidence to infer differences between medical specialties.

b $H_0: \mu_1 = \mu_2 = \ldots = \mu_{36}$

H_1: At least two means differ.

F = 6.36, p-value = 0. There is sufficient evidence to indicate that there are differences between the physicians' ages, which tells us that this experimental design is recommended.

14.66 $H_0: \mu_1 = \mu_2 = \mu_3 = \mu_4$

H_1: At least two means differ.

	A	B	C	D	E	F	G
1	DAYS1	896	3183	3.55	7.71		
2	DAYS2	896	2852	3.18	7.33		
3	DAYS3	896	2266	2.53	7.04		
4	DAYS4	896	2243	2.50	7.44		
5							
6							
7	ANOVA						
8	*Source of Variation*	*SS*	*df*	*MS*	*F*	*P-value*	*F crit*
9	Rows	12193.9	895	13.62	2.57	1.78E-76	1.0927
10	Columns	711.2	3	237.06	44.74	3.3E-28	2.6082
11	Error	14226.8	2685	5.30			
12							
13	Total	27131.9	3583				

F = 44.74, p-value 3.30E-28 ≈ 0. There is enough evidence to conclude that the means differ.

14.68a ANOVA Table

Source	Degrees of Freedom	Sum of Squares	Mean Squares	F
Treatments	11	12,045	1095	8.23
Error	228	30,405	133	
Total	239	42,450		

b. Rejection region: $F > F_{\alpha,k-1,n-k} = F_{.01,11,228} \approx 2.25$

F = 8.53. There is enough evidence to conclude that the treatment means differ.

© 2012 Cengage Learning. All Rights Reserved. May not be scanned, copied or duplicated, or posted to a publicly accessible website, in whole or in part.

c. ANOVA Table

Source	Degrees of Freedom	Sum of Squares	Mean Squares	F
Factor A	2	1,560	780	5.86
Factor B	3	2,880	960	7.18
Interaction	6	7,605	1268	9.53
Error	228	30,405	133	
Total	239	42,450		

Interaction: Rejection region: $F > F_{\alpha,(a-1)(b-1),n-k} = F_{.01,6,228} \approx 2.80$

F = 9.53. There is enough evidence to infer that factors A and B interact.

14.70 ANOVA Table

	A	B	C	D	E	F	G
23	ANOVA						
24	*Source of Variation*	*SS*	*df*	*MS*	*F*	*P-value*	*F crit*
25	Sample	5.33	1	5.33	1.23	0.2995	5.32
26	Columns	56.33	1	56.33	13.00	0.0069	5.32
27	Interaction	1.33	1	1.33	0.31	0.5943	5.32
28	Within	34.67	8	4.33			
29							
30	Total	97.67	11				

a F = .31, p-value = .5943. There is not enough evidence to conclude that factors A and B interact.

b F = 1.23, p-value = .2995. There is not enough evidence to conclude that differences exist between the levels of factor A.

c F = 13.00, p-value = .0069. There is enough evidence to conclude that differences exist between the levels of factor B.

14.72 ANOVA Table

	A	B	C	D	E	F	G
35	ANOVA						
36	*Source of Variation*	*SS*	*df*	*MS*	*F*	*P-value*	*F crit*
37	Sample	135.85	3	45.28	4.49	0.0060	2.7318
38	Columns	151.25	1	151.25	15.00	0.0002	3.9739
39	Interaction	6.25	3	2.08	0.21	0.8915	2.7318
40	Within	726.20	72	10.09			
41							
42	Total	1019.55	79				

The test for interaction yields (F = .21, p-value = .8915) and the test for the differences between educational levels (F = 4.49, p-value = .0060) is the same as in Example 14.4. However, in this exercise there is evidence of a difference between men and women (F = 15.00, p-value = .0002).

14.74 a There are 12 treatments.

b There are two factors, tax form and income group.

© 2012 Cengage Learning. All Rights Reserved. May not be scanned, copied or duplicated, or posted to a publicly accessible website, in whole or in part.

c There are a = 4 forms and b = 3 income groups.

	A	B	C	D	E	F	G
28							
29	ANOVA						
30	*Source of Variation*	*SS*	*df*	*MS*	*F*	*P-value*	*F crit*
31	Sample	6719	2	3359.4	4.11	0.0190	3.08
32	Columns	6280	3	2093.3	2.56	0.0586	2.69
33	Interaction	5102	6	850.3	1.04	0.4030	2.18
34	Within	88217	108	816.8			
35							
36	Total	106317	119				

d F = 1.04, p-value = .4030. There is not enough evidence to conclude that forms and income groups interact

e F = 2.56, p-value = .0586. There is not enough evidence to conclude that differences exist between the forms.

f F = 4.11, p-value = .0190. There is enough evidence to conclude that differences exist between the three income groups.

14.76 a Factor A is the drug mixture and factor B is the schedule.

b The response variable is the improvement index.

c There are a = 4 drug mixtures and b = 2 schedules.

	A	B	C	D	E	F	G
23	ANOVA						
24	*Source of Variation*	*SS*	*df*	*MS*	*F*	*P-value*	*F crit*
25	Sample	14.40	1	14.40	0.57	0.4548	4.15
26	Columns	581.80	3	193.93	7.71	0.0005	2.90
27	Interaction	548.60	3	182.87	7.27	0.0007	2.90
28	Within	804.80	32	25.15			
29							
30	Total	1949.60	39				

d Test for interaction: F = 7.27, p-value = .0007. There is sufficient evidence to conclude that the schedules and drug mixtures interact. There is sufficient evidence to conclude that detergents and temperatures interact. The F-tests in Parts e and f are irrelevant.

14.78

	A	B	C	D	E	F	G
23	ANOVA						
24	*Source of Variation*	*SS*	*df*	*MS*	*F*	*P-value*	*F crit*
25	Sample	16.04	1	16.04	14.74	0.0005	4.11
26	Columns	6.77	1	6.77	6.22	0.0173	4.11
27	Interaction	0.025	1	0.025	0.023	0.8814	4.11
28	Within	39.17	36	1.09			
29							
30	Total	62.00	39				

© 2012 Cengage Learning. All Rights Reserved. May not be scanned, copied or duplicated, or posted to a publicly accessible website, in whole or in part.

The p-values for interaction, machines, and alloys are .8814, .0173, .0005, and, respectively. Both machines and alloys are sources of variation.

14.80

	A	B	C	D	E	F	G
29	ANOVA						
30	*Source of Variation*	*SS*	*df*	*MS*	*F*	*P-value*	*F crit*
31	Sample	211.78	2	105.89	21.04	0.0000	3.22
32	Columns	0.59	1	0.59	0.12	0.7348	4.07
33	Interaction	0.13	2	0.0640	0.0127	0.9874	3.22
34	Within	211.42	42	5.03			
35							
36	Total	423.91	47				

The p-values for interaction, methods, and skills are .9874, .7348, 0, and. The only source of variation is skill level.

14.82a $H_0: \mu_1 = \mu_2 = \mu_3 = \mu_4$

H_1: At least two means differ.

	A	B	C	D	E	F	G
11	ANOVA						
12	*Source of Variation*	*SS*	*df*	*MS*	*F*	*P-value*	*F crit*
13	Between Groups	9.90	3	3.30	7.67	0.0001	2.70
14	Within Groups	41.33	96	0.43			
15							
16	Total	51.23	99				

F = 7.67, p-value = .0001. There is sufficient evidence to infer that differences in productivity exist between the four groups of companies.

b

	A	B	C	D	E
1	**Multiple Comparisons**				
2					
3				LSD	Omega
4	Treatment	Treatment	Difference	Alpha = 0.0083	Alpha = 0.05
5	*Extensive*	*Some*	0.534	0.500	0.483
6		*Little*	0.722	0.500	0.483
7		*No*	0.811	0.500	0.483
8	*Some*	*Little*	0.188	0.500	0.483
9		*No*	0.277	0.500	0.483
10	*Little*	*No*	0.089	0.500	0.483

Using either the Bonferroni adjustment or Tukey's method we conclude that μ_1 differs from μ_2, μ_3 and μ_4. Companies that offered extensive training have productivity levels different from the other companies.

© 2012 Cengage Learning. All Rights Reserved. May not be scanned, copied or duplicated, or posted to a publicly accessible website, in whole or in part.

14.84 $H_0: \mu_1 = \mu_2 = \mu_3 = \mu_4$

H_1: At least two means differ.

	A	B	C	D	E	F	G
31	ANOVA						
32	*Source of Variation*	*SS*	*df*	*MS*	*F*	*P-value*	*F crit*
33	Rows	43980	19	2314.72	21.58	0.0000	1.77
34	Columns	4438	3	1479.21	13.79	0.0000	2.77
35	Error	6113	57	107.25			
36							
37	Total	54530	79				

F = 13.79, p-value = 0. There is sufficient evidence to conclude that the reading speeds differ between the four typefaces. The typeface that was read the fastest should be used.

14.86 $H_0: \mu_1 = \mu_2 = \mu_3$

H_1: At least two means differ

	A	B	C	D	E	F	G
17	ANOVA						
18	*Source of Variation*	*SS*	*df*	*MS*	*F*	*P-value*	*F crit*
19	Rows	195.33	6	32.56	11.55	0.0002	3.00
20	Columns	43.52	2	21.76	7.72	0.0070	3.89
21	Error	33.81	12	2.82			
22							
23	Total	272.67	20				

F = 7.72, p-value = .0070. There is enough evidence to infer that differences in attention span exist between the three products.

14.88a $H_0: \mu_1 = \mu_2 = \mu_3$

H_1: At least two means differ.

	A	B	C	D	E	F	G
10	ANOVA						
11	*Source of Variation*	*SS*	*df*	*MS*	*F*	*P-value*	*F crit*
12	Between Groups	1769.5	2	884.74	136.58	0.0000	3.02
13	Within Groups	2409.8	372	6.48			
14							
15	Total	4179.3	374				

F = 136.58, p-value = 0. There is sufficient evidence to infer that differences exist between the effects of the three teaching approaches.

© 2012 Cengage Learning. All Rights Reserved. May not be scanned, copied or duplicated, or posted to a publicly accessible website, in whole or in part.

b

	A	B	C	D	E
1	**Multiple Comparisons**				
2					
3				LSD	Omega
4	Treatment	Treatment	Difference	Alpha = 0.0167	Alpha = 0.05
5	*hole Langua*	*Embedded*	-0.856	0.774	0.754
6		*Pure*	-4.976	0.774	0.754
7	*Embedded*	*Pure*	-4.120	0.774	0.754

All three means differ from one another. From the sample means we may infer that the pure method is best, followed by embedded, and by whole-language.

14.90 $H_0: \mu_1 = \mu_2 = \mu_3 = \mu_4$

H_1: At least two means differ.

	A	B	C	D	E	F	G
11	ANOVA						
12	*Source of Variation*	*SS*	*df*	*MS*	*F*	*P-value*	*F crit*
13	Between Groups	5990284	3	1996761	14.47	0.0000	2.64
14	Within Groups	40024172	290	138014			
15							
16	Total	46014456	293				

F = 14.47, p-value = 0. There is enough evidence to infer differences in debt levels between the four types of degrees.

14.92 $H_0: \mu_1 = \mu_2 = \mu_3 = \mu_4$

H_1: At least two means differ.

	A	B	C	D	E	F	G
11	ANOVA						
12	*Source of Variation*	*SS*	*df*	*MS*	*F*	*P-value*	*F crit*
13	Between Groups	3007	3	1002.3	13.84	0.0000	2.67
14	Within Groups	10576	146	72.4			
15							
16	Total	13583	149				

F = 13.84, p-value = 0. There is enough evidence to infer that the length of time depends on the size of the party

14.94 $H_0: \mu_1 = \mu_2 = \mu_3$

H_1: At least two means differ.

© 2012 Cengage Learning. All Rights Reserved. May not be scanned, copied or duplicated, or posted to a publicly accessible website, in whole or in part.

	A	B	C	D	E	F	G
10	ANOVA						
11	*Source of Variation*	*SS*	*df*	*MS*	*F*	*P-value*	*F crit*
12	Between Groups	1.57	2	0.787	1.62	0.202233	3.09
13	Within Groups	46.98	97	0.484			
14							
15	Total	48.55	99				

F = 1.62, p-value = .2022. There is no evidence to infer that at least one buy indicator is useful.

14.96 $H_0: \mu_1 = \mu_2 = \mu_3$

H_1: At least two means differ.

	A	B	C	D	E	F	G
1	ANOVA						
2	*Source of Variation*	*SS*	*df*	*MS*	*F*	*P-value*	*F crit*
3	Between Groups	11374	2	5687	45.49	0.0000	3.00
4	Within Groups	229170	1833	125.0			
5							
6	Total	240544	1835				

F = 45.49, p-value = 0. There is enough evidence to infer that family incomes differ between the three market segments.

14.98 $H_0: \mu_1 = \mu_2 = \mu_3 = \mu_4$

H_1: At least two means differ.

	A	B	C	D	E	F	G
1	ANOVA						
2	*Source of Variation*	*SS*	*df*	*MS*	*F*	*P-value*	*F crit*
3	Between Groups	6636.1	3	2212.03	211.61	0.0000	2.63
4	Within Groups	3595.9	344	10.45			
5							
6	Total	10232.0	347				

F = 211.61, p-value = 0. There is enough evidence to conclude that there are differences in the age of the car between the four market segments.

© 2012 Cengage Learning. All Rights Reserved. May not be scanned, copied or duplicated, or posted to a publicly accessible website, in whole or in part.

Appendix 14

A14.2 t-test of μ_D

$H_0: \mu_D = 0$

$H_1: \mu_D < 0$

	A	B	C
1	t-Test: Paired Two Sample for Means		
2			
3		*Price shown*	*Price not shown*
4	Mean	56.15	60.31
5	Variance	243.68	467.71
6	Observations	100	100
7	Pearson Correlation	0.79	
8	Hypothesized Mean Difference	0	
9	df	99	
10	t Stat	-3.12	
11	P(T<=t) one-tail	0.0012	
12	t Critical one-tail	1.6604	
13	P(T<=t) two-tail	0.0024	
14	t Critical two-tail	1.9842	

$t = -3.12$, p-value = .0012. There is overwhelming evidence to conclude that ads with no price shown are more effective in generating interest than ads that show the price.

A14.4 a z-test of $p_1 - p_2$ (case 1)

$H_0: (p_1 - p_2) = 0$

$H_1: (p_1 - p_2) > 0$

	A	B	C	D
1	**z-Test: Two Proportions**			
2				
3			*Topiramate*	*Placebo*
4	Sample Proportions		0.2364	0.1042
5	Observations		55	48
6	Hypothesized Difference		0	
7	z Stat		1.76	
8	P(Z<=z) one tail		0.0390	
9	z Critical one-tail		1.6449	
10	P(Z<=z) two-tail		0.0780	
11	z Critical two-tail		1.96	

$z = 1.76$, p-value = .0390. There is enough evidence to conclude that topiramate is effective in causing abstinence for the first month.

© 2012 Cengage Learning. All Rights Reserved. May not be scanned, copied or duplicated, or posted to a publicly accessible website, in whole or in part.

b z-test of $p_1 - p_2$ (case 1)

$H_0: (p_1 - p_2) = 0$

$H_1: (p_1 - p_2) > 0$

	A	B	C	D
1	**z-Test: Two Proportions**			
2				
3			*Topiramate*	*Placebo*
4	Sample Proportions		0.5091	0.1667
5	Observations		55	48
6	Hypothesized Difference		0	
7	z Stat		3.64	
8	P(Z<=z) one tail		0.0001	
9	z Critical one-tail		1.6449	
10	P(Z<=z) two-tail		0.0002	
11	z Critical two-tail		1.96	

z = 3.64, p-value = .0001. There is enough evidence to conclude that topiramate is effective in causing alcoholics to refrain from binge drinking in the final month.

A14.6 a One-way analysis of variance

	A	B	C	D	E	F	G
11	ANOVA						
12	*Source of Variation*	*SS*	*df*	*MS*	*F*	*P-value*	*F crit*
13	Between Groups	25113	3	8371.2	85.98	0.0000	2.63
14	Within Groups	30766	316	97.36			
15							
16	Total	55880	319				

F = 85.98, p-value = 0.

Two-factor analysis of variance

	A	B	C	D	E	F	G
23	ANOVA						
24	*Source of Variation*	*SS*	*df*	*MS*	*F*	*P-value*	*F crit*
25	Sample	17024	1	17024	174.85	0.0000	3.87
26	Columns	7411	1	7411	76.12	0.0000	3.87
27	Interaction	679	1	678.6	6.97	0.0087	3.87
28	Within	30766	316	97.36			
29							
30	Total	55880	319				

Interaction: F = 6.97; p-value = .0087. There is enough evidence to infer that differences are caused by interaction. There is no need to conduct the other two tests.

© 2012 Cengage Learning. All Rights Reserved. May not be scanned, copied or duplicated, or posted to a publicly accessible website, in whole or in part.

A14.8 Two-way analysis of variance

$H_0: \mu_1 = \mu_2 = \mu_3$

H_1 : At least two means differ.

	A	B	C	D	E	F	G
35	ANOVA						
36	*Source of Variation*	*SS*	*df*	*MS*	*F*	*P-value*	*F crit*
37	Rows	31,154,590	24	1,298,108	15.05	5.20E-15	1.75
38	Columns	913,217	2	456,608	5.29	0.0084	3.19
39	Error	4,141,276	48	86,277			
40							
41	Total	36,209,083	74				

F = 5.29; p-value = .0084. There is sufficient evidence to infer that differences exist between the estimated repair costs from different appraisers.

A14.10 z-test of $p_1 - p_2$ (case 2)

H_0: $(p_1 - p_2) = -.15$

H_1: $(p_1 - p_2) < -.15$

	A	B	C
1	**z-Test: Two Proportions**		
2			
3		*Comm 1*	*Comm 2*
4	Sample Proportions	0.268	0.486
5	Observations	500	500
6	Hypothesized Difference	-0.15	
7	z Stat	-2.28	
8	P(Z<=z) one tail	0.0114	
9	z Critical one-tail	1.6449	
10	P(Z<=z) two-tail	0.0228	
11	z Critical two-tail	1.9600	

z = –2.28, p-value = .0114. There is evidence to indicate that the second commercial is viable.

A14.12 Two-factor analysis of variance

	A	B	C	D	E	F	G
29	ANOVA						
30	*Source of Variation*	*SS*	*df*	*MS*	*F*	*P-value*	*F crit*
31	Sample	427.61	2	213.81	39.97	0.0000	3.06
32	Columns	20.17	1	20.17	3.77	0.0541	3.91
33	Interaction	17.77	2	8.89	1.66	0.1935	3.06
34	Within	770.32	144	5.35			
35							
36	Total	1235.87	149				

Interaction: F = 1.66, p-value = .1935. There is no evidence of interaction.

© 2012 Cengage Learning. All Rights Reserved. May not be scanned, copied or duplicated, or posted to a publicly accessible website, in whole or in part.

Gender (Columns) : F = 3.77, p-value = .0541. There is not enough evidence of a difference between men and women.

Fitness (Sample): F = 39.97, p-value = 0. There is overwhelming evidence of differences among the three levels of fitness.

A14.14 One-way analysis of variance

	A	B	C	D	E	F	G
10	ANOVA						
11	*Source of Variation*	*SS*	*df*	*MS*	*F*	*P-value*	*F crit*
12	Between Groups	1813.7	2	906.87	6.46	0.0030	3.16
13	Within Groups	7998.0	57	140.32			
14							
15	Total	9811.7	59				

Multiple comparisons

	A	B	C	D	E
1	**Multiple Comparisons**				
2					
3				LSD	Omega
4	Treatment	Treatment	Difference	Alpha = 0.0167	Alpha = 0.05
5	*Price: $34*	*Price: $39*	-12.9	9.24	9.01
6		*Price: $44*	-3.1	9.24	9.01
7	*Price: $39*	*Price: $44*	9.8	9.24	9.01

Sales with $34 and $44 dollar prices do not differ. Sales with $39 differ from sales with $34 and $44 prices.

A14.16 Two-way analysis of variance

	A	B	C	D	E	F	G
24	ANOVA						
25	*Source of Variation*	*SS*	*df*	*MS*	*F*	*P-value*	*F crit*
26	Rows	335.17	13	25.78	16.86	0.0000	2.12
27	Columns	10.90	2	5.45	3.57	0.0428	3.37
28	Error	39.76	26	1.53			
29							
30	Total	385.83	41				

a $H_0 : \mu_1 = \mu_2 = \mu_3$

H_1 : At least two means differ.

F = 3.57, p-value = .0428. There is enough evidence to conclude that there are differences in waiting times between the three resorts.

b The waiting times are required to be normally distributed with the same variance at all three resorts.

c Histograms are used to check the normality requirement.

© 2012 Cengage Learning. All Rights Reserved. May not be scanned, copied or duplicated, or posted to a publicly accessible website, in whole or in part.

A14.18 a z-estimate of p

	A	B	C	D	E
1	**z-Estimate of a Proportion**				
2					
3	**Sample proportion**	0.3569	**Confidence Interval Estimate**		
4	**Sample size**	1328	**0.357**	±	**0.026**
5	**Confidence level**	0.95	**Lower confidence limit**		**0.331**
6			**Upper confidence limit**		**0.383**

Estimate of the number of households with at least one dog

LCL = 112 million × .331 = 37.072 million

UCL = 112 million × .383 = 42.896 million

b

	A	B	C	D	E
1	**z-Estimate of a Proportion**				
2					
3	**Sample proportion**	0.316	**Confidence Interval Estimate**		
4	**Sample size**	1328	**0.316**	±	**0.025**
5	**Confidence level**	0.95	**Lower confidence limit**		**0.291**
6			**Upper confidence limit**		**0.341**

Number of households with at least one cat

LCL = 112 million × .291 = 32.592 million

UCL = 112 million × .341 = 38.192million

c t-estimate of μ

	A	B	C	D
1	**t-Estimate: Mean**			
2				
3				*Dogs*
4	Mean			247.19
5	Standard Deviation			133.16
6	LCL			235.17
7	UCL			259.20

Estimate of the total amount spent on dogs

LCL = 40 million ×235.17 = $9.407 billion

UCL = 40 million ×259.29 = $10.368 billion,

d t-estimate of μ

© 2012 Cengage Learning. All Rights Reserved. May not be scanned, copied or duplicated, or posted to a publicly accessible website, in whole or in part.

	A	B	C	D
1	**t-Estimate: Mean**			
2				
3				*Cats*
4	Mean			158.07
5	Standard Deviation			88.94
6	LCL			149.53
7	UCL			166.61

Estimate of the total amount spent on cats

LCL = 35 million ×149.53 = \$5.234 billion

UCL = 35 million ×166.61 = \$5.831 billion

A14.20 H_0: $(p_1 - p_2) = 0$

H_1: $(p_1 - p_2) \neq 0$

	A	B	C
1	**z-Test: Two Proportions**		
2			
3		*Democrats*	*Republicans*
4	Sample Proportions	0.0396	0.0291
5	Observations	631	446
6	Hypothesized Difference	0	
7	z Stat	0.918	
8	P(Z<=z) one tail	0.1794	
9	z Critical one-tail	1.6449	
10	P(Z<=z) two-tail	0.3588	
11	z Critical two-tail	1.96	

z = .918, p-value = .3588. There is not enough evidence to conclude that Democrats and Republicans differ in their responses to the question about the use of any drugs.

A14.22 One-way Analysis of variance

$H_0: \mu_1 = \mu_2 = \mu_3$

H_1 : At least two means differ

© 2012 Cengage Learning. All Rights Reserved. May not be scanned, copied or duplicated, or posted to a publicly accessible website, in whole or in part.

	A	B	C	D	E	F	G
1	Anova: Single Factor						
2							
3	SUMMARY						
4	*Groups*	*Count*	*Sum*	*Average*	*Variance*		
5	White	904	38224	42.28	201.86		
6	Black	178	7248	40.72	245.16		
7	Other	121	5058	41.80	216.46		
8							
9							
10	ANOVA						
11	*Source of Variation*	*SS*	*df*	*MS*	*F*	*P-value*	*F crit*
12	Between Groups	369.29	2	184.64	0.88	0.4149	3.0032
13	Within Groups	251651	1200	209.71			
14							
15	Total	252020	1202				

F = .88, p-value = .4149. There is not enough evidence to conclude that the number of hours worked differ between the races.

A14.24 H_0: $(p_1 - p_2) = 0$

H_1: $(p_1 - p_2) \neq 0$

	A	B	C	D
1	**z-Test: Two Proportions**			
2				
3			*Democrats*	*Republicans*
4	Sample Proportions		0.6548	0.8127
5	Observations		646	411
6	Hypothesized Difference		0	
7	z Stat		-5.55	
8	P(Z<=z) one tail		0	
9	z Critical one-tail		1.6449	
10	P(Z<=z) two-tail		0	
11	z Critical two-tail		1.96	

z = -5.55, p-value = 0. There is sufficient evidence to infer that Democrats and Republicans differ in their access to the Internet.

© 2012 Cengage Learning. All Rights Reserved. May not be scanned, copied or duplicated, or posted to a publicly accessible website, in whole or in part.

Chapter 15

15.2 $H_0: p_1 = .1,\ p_2 = .2,\ p_3 = .3,\ p_4 = .2,\ p_5 = .2$

H_1: At least one p_i is not equal to its specified value.

Cell i	f_i	e_i	$(f_i - e_i)$	$(f_i - e_i)^2 / e_i$
1	12	150(.1) = 15	-3	.60
2	32	150(.2) = 30	2	.13
3	42	150(.3) = 45	-3	.20
4	36	150(.2) = 30	6	1.20
5	28	150(.2) = 30	-2	.13
Total	150	150		$\chi^2 = 2.26$

Rejection region: $\chi^2 > \chi^2_{\alpha,k-1} = \chi^2_{.01,4} = 13.3$

$\chi^2 = 2.26$, p-value = .6868. There is not enough evidence to infer that at least one p_i is not equal to its specified value.

15.4 The χ^2 statistic decreases.

15.6 $H_0: p_1 = .3,\ p_2 = .3,\ p_3 = .2,\ p_4 = .2$

H_1: At least one p_i is not equal to its specified value.

Cell i	f_i	e_i	$(f_i - e_i)$	$(f_i - e_i)^2 / e_i$
1	76	300(.3) = 90	-14	2.18
2	100	300(.3) = 90	10	1.11
3	76	300(.2) = 60	16	4.27
4	48	300(.2) = 60	-12	2.40
Total	300	300		$\chi^2 = 9.96$

Rejection region: $\chi^2 > \chi^2_{\alpha,k-1} = \chi^2_{.05,3} = 7.81$

$\chi^2 = 9.96$, p-value = .0189. There is enough evidence to infer that at least one p_i is not equal to its specified value.

15.8 $H_0: p_1 = .15,\ p_2 = .40,\ p_3 = .35,\ p_4 = .10$

H_1: At least one p_i is not equal to its specified value.

© 2012 Cengage Learning. All Rights Reserved. May not be scanned, copied or duplicated, or posted to a publicly accessible website, in whole or in part.

Cell i	f_i	e_i	$(f_i - e_i)$	$(f_i - e_i)^2 / e_i$
1	41	233(.15) = 34.95	6.05	1.05
2	107	233(.40) = 93.20	13.80	2.04
3	66	233(.35) = 81.55	-15.55	2.97
4	19	233(.10) = 23.30	-4.30	0.79
Total	233	233		$\chi^2 = 6.85$

Rejection region: $\chi^2 > \chi^2_{\alpha,k-1} = \chi^2_{.05,3} = 7.81$

$\chi^2 = 6.85$, p-value = .0769. There is not enough evidence to infer that at least one p_i is not equal to its specified value.

15.10 $H_0: p_1 = .05,\ p_2 = .25\ p_3 = .40,\ p_4 = .25\ p_5 = .05$

H_1 : At least one p_i is not equal to its specified value.

Cell i	f_i	e_i	$(f_i - e_i)$	$(f_i - e_i)^2 / e_i$
1	11	150(.05) = 7.5	3.5	1.63
2	32	150(.25) = 37.5	-5.5	0.81
3	62	150(.40) = 60.0	2.0	0.07
4	29	150(.25) = 37.5	-8.5	1.93
5	16	150(.05) = 7.5	8.5	9.63
Total	150	150		$\chi^2 = 14.07$

Rejection region: $\chi^2 > \chi^2_{\alpha,k-1} = \chi^2_{.10,4} = 7.78$

$\chi^2 = 14.07$, p-value = .0071. There is enough evidence to infer that grades are distributed differently from grades in the past.

15.12 $H_0: p_1 = .72,\ p_2 = .15,\ p_3 = .10,\ p_4 = .03$

H_1 : At least one p_i is not equal to its specified value.

Cell i	f_i	e_i	$(f_i - e_i)$	$(f_i - e_i)^2 / e_i$
1	159	250(.72) = 180.0	-21.0	2.45
2	28	250(.15) = 37.5	-9.5	2.41
3	47	250(.10) = 25.0	22.0	19.36
4	16	250(.03) = 7.5	8.5	9.63
Total	250	250		$\chi^2 = 33.85$

Rejection region: $\chi^2 > \chi^2_{\alpha,k-1} = \chi^2_{.05,3} = 7.81$

χ^2 =33.85, p-value = 0. There is enough evidence to infer that the aging schedule has changed.

© 2012 Cengage Learning. All Rights Reserved. May not be scanned, copied or duplicated, or posted to a publicly accessible website, in whole or in part.

15.14 $H_0: p_1 = .31,\ p_2 = .51,\ p_3 = .18$

H_1: At least one p_i is not equal to its specified value.

Cell i	f_i	e_i	$(f_i - e_i)$	$(f_i - e_i)^2 / e_i$
1	408	1200(.31) = 372	36	3.48
2	571	1200(.51) = 612	-41	2.75
3	221	1200(.18) = 216	5	0.12
Total	1200	1200		$\chi^2 = 6.35$

Rejection region: $\chi^2 > \chi^2_{\alpha,k-1} = \chi^2_{.10,2} = 4.61$

$\chi^2 = 6.35$, p-value = .0419. There is enough evidence to infer that voter support has changed since the election.

15.16 $H_0: p_1 = .23,\ p_2 = .40,\ p_3 = .15,\ p_4 = .22$

H_1: At least one p_i is not equal to its specified value.

Cell i	f_i	e_i	$(f_i - e_i)$	$(f_i - e_i)^2 / e_i$
1	63	320(.23) = 73.6	-10.6	1.53
2	125	320(.40) = 128.0	-3.0	0.07
3	45	320(.15) = 48.0	-3.0	0.19
4	87	320(.22) = 70.4	16.6	3.91
Total	320	320		$\chi^2 = 5.70$

Rejection region: $\chi^2 > \chi^2_{\alpha,k-1} = \chi^2_{.05,3} = 7.81$

$\chi^2 = 5.70$, p-value = .1272. There is not enough evidence to infer that there has been a change in proportions.

15.18 H_0: $p_1 = .79$, $p_2 = .13$, $p_3 = .08$

H_1: At least one p_i is not equal to its specified value.

Race	Observed	Expected
White	1559	.79(2023) = 1598.2
Black	281	.13(2023) = 263.0
Other	183	.08(2023) = 161.8
Total	2023	

$\chi^2 = 4.97$, p-value = .0833. There is not enough evidence to infer that the GSS in 2008 overrepresented at least one race.

© 2012 Cengage Learning. All Rights Reserved. May not be scanned, copied or duplicated, or posted to a publicly accessible website, in whole or in part.

15.20 H_0: $p_1 = .58$, $p_2 = .06$, $p_3 = .11$, $p_4 = .25$

H_1: At least one p_i is not equal to its specified value.

Marital status	Observed	Expected
Married & separated	972 + 70 = 1042	.58(2018) = 1170.4
Widowed	164	.06(2018) = 121.1
Divorced	281	.11(2018) = 222.0
Never married	531	.25(2018) = 504.5
Total	2018	

$\chi^2 = 46.36$, p-value = 4.76E-10 ≈ 0. There is sufficient evidence to conclude that the GSS in 2008 over represented at least one category of marital status.

15.22 H_0 : The two variables are independent

H_1 : The two variables are dependent

Cell i	f_i	e_i	$(f_i - e_i)$	$(f_i - e_i)^2 / e_i$
1	28	96(84)/188 = 42.89	-14.89	5.17
2	68	96(104)/188 = 53.11	14.89	4.17
3	56	92(84)/188 = 41.11	14.89	5.40
4	36	92(104)/188 = 50.89	-14.89	4.36
Total	188	188		$\chi^2 = 19.10$

Rejection region: $\chi^2 > \chi^2_{\alpha,(r-1)(c-1} = \chi^2_{.05,1} = 3.84$

$\chi^2 = 19.10$, p-value = 0. There is enough evidence to infer that the two variables are dependent.

15.24 H_0 : The two variables are independent

H_1 : The two variables are dependent

Cell i	f_i	e_i	$(f_i - e_i)$	$(f_i - e_i)^2 / e_i$
1	7	24(21)/188 = 10.72	-3.72	1.29
2	17	24(26)/188 = 13.28	3.72	1.04
3	14	23(21)/188 = 10.28	3.72	1.35
4	9	23(26)/188 = 12.72	-3.72	1.09
Total	47	47		$\chi^2 = 4.77$

Rejection region: $\chi^2 > \chi^2_{\alpha,(r-1)(c-1} = \chi^2_{.05,1} = 3.84$

$\chi^2 = 4.77$, p-value = .0289. There is enough evidence to infer that the two classifications L and M are dependent.

© 2012 Cengage Learning. All Rights Reserved. May not be scanned, copied or duplicated, or posted to a publicly accessible website, in whole or in part.

15.26 H_0 : The two variables are independent

H_1 : The two variables are dependent

Cell i	f_i	e_i	$(f_i - e_i)$	$(f_i - e_i)^2 / e_i$
1	40	120(70)/250 = 33.60	6.40	1.22
2	32	120(80)/250 = 38.40	- 6.40	1.07
3	48	120(100)/250 = 48.00	0	0.00
4	30	130(70)/250 = 36.40	-6.40	1.13
5	48	130(80)/250 = 41.60	6.40	0.99
6	52	130(100)/250 = 52.00	0	0.00
Total	250	250		$\chi^2 = 4.41$

Rejection region: $\chi^2 > \chi^2_{\alpha,(r-1)(c-1} = \chi^2_{.10,2} = 4.61$

$\chi^2 = 4.41$, p-value = .1110. There is not enough evidence to infer that the two classifications R and C are dependent.

15.28 H_0 : The two variables (shirt condition and shift) are independent

H_1 : The two variables are dependent

Cell i	f_i	e_i	$(f_i - e_i)$	$(f_i - e_i)^2 / e_i$
1	240	570(250)/600 = 237.5	2.5	.03
2	191	570(200)/600 = 190.0	1.0	.01
3	139	570(150)/600 = 142.5	-3.5	.09
4	10	30(250)/600 = 12.5	-2.5	.50
5	9	30(200)/600 = 10.0	-1.0	10
6	11	30(150)/600 = 7.5	3.5	1.63
Total	600	600		$\chi^2 = 2.36$

Rejection region: $\chi^2 > \chi^2_{\alpha,(r-1)(c-1} = \chi^2_{.05,2} = 5.99$

$\chi^2 = 2.36$, p-value = .3087. There is not enough evidence to infer that there are differences in quality among the three shifts.

15.30 H_0 : The two variables (inducement and return) are independent

H_1 : The two variables are dependent

© 2012 Cengage Learning. All Rights Reserved. May not be scanned, copied or duplicated, or posted to a publicly accessible website, in whole or in part.

Cell i	f_i	e_i	$(f_i - e_i)$	$(f_i - e_i)^2 / e_i$
1	80	300(200)/1000 = 60	20	6.67
2	100	300(300)/1000 = 90	10	1.11
3	120	300(500)/1000 = 150	-30	6.00
4	120	700(200)/1000 = 140	-20	2.86
5	200	700(300)/1000 = 210	-10	0.50
6	380	700(500)/1000 = 350	30	2.57
Total	1000	1000		$\chi^2 = 19.71$

Rejection region: $\chi^2 > \chi^2_{\alpha,(r-1)(c-1} = \chi^2_{.05,2} = 5.99$

$\chi^2 = 19.71$, p-value = .0001. There is sufficient evidence to infer that the return rates differ among the different inducements.

15.32 a H_0 : The two variables (predicted change and actual change) are independent

H_1 : The two variables are dependent

Cell i	f_i	e_i	$(f_i - e_i)$	$(f_i - e_i)^2 / e_i$
1	65	129(104)/216 = 62.11	2.89	.13
2	39	87(104)/216 = 41.89	-2.89	.20
3	64	129(112)/216 =66.89	-2.89	.12
4	48	87(112)/216 = 45.11	2.89	.19
Total	216	216		$\chi^2 = .64$

Rejection region: $\chi^2 > \chi^2_{\alpha,(r-1)(c-1} = \chi^2_{.10,1} = 2.71$

$\chi^2 = .64$, p-value = .4225. There is not enough evidence to infer that the predicted and actual directions of change are related.

b Ignore what the other investors are doing.

15.34 H_0 : The two variables (education and smoker) are independent

H_1 : The two variables are dependent

© 2012 Cengage Learning. All Rights Reserved. May not be scanned, copied or duplicated, or posted to a publicly accessible website, in whole or in part.

Cell i	f_i	e_i	$(f_i - e_i)$	$(f_i - e_i)^2 / e_i$
1	34	57(460)/1000 = 26.22	7.78	2.31
2	23	57(540)/1000 = 30.78	-7.78	1.97
3	251	463(460)/1000 = 212.98	38.02	6.79
4	212	463(540)/1000 = 250.02	-38.02	5.78
5	159	407(460)/1000 = 187.22	-28.22	4.25
6	248	407(540)/1000 = 219.78	28.22	3.62
7	16	73(460)/1000 = 33.58	-17.58	9.20
8	57	73(540)/1000 = 39.42	17.58	7.84
Total	1000	1000		$\chi^2 = 41.77$

Rejection region: $\chi^2 > \chi^2_{\alpha,(r-1)(c-1} = \chi^2_{.05,3} = 7.81$

$\chi^2 = 41.77$, p-value = 0. There is sufficient evidence to infer that the amount of education is a factor in determining whether a smoker will quit.

15.36 H_0 : The two variables (university and degree) are independent

H_1 : The two variables are dependent

Cell i	f_i	e_i	$(f_i - e_i)$	$(f_i - e_i)^2 / e_i$
1	44	100(167)/400=41.75	2.25	.12
2	11	100(64)/ 400=16.00	-5.00	1.56
3	34	100(121)/ 400=30.25	3.75	.46
4	11	100(48)/ 400=12.00	-1.00	.08
5	52	100(167)/ 400=41.75	10.25	2.52
6	14	100(64)/ 400=16.00	-2.00	.25
7	27	100(121)/ 400=30.25	-3.25	.35
8	7	100(48)/ 400=12.00	-5.00	2.08
9	31	100(167)/ 400=41.75	-10.75	2.77
10	27	100(64) 400=16.00	11.00	7.56
11	18	100(121) 400=/30.25	-12.25	4.96
12	24	100(48)/ 400=12.00	12.00	12.00
13	40	100(167)/ 400=41.75	-1.75	.07
14	12	100(64)/ 400=16.00	-4.00	1.00
15	42	100(121)/ 400=30.25	11.75	4.56
16	6	100(49)/ 400=12.00	-6.00	3.00
Total	400	400		$\chi^2 = 43.36$

© 2012 Cengage Learning. All Rights Reserved. May not be scanned, copied or duplicated, or posted to a publicly accessible website, in whole or in part.

Rejection region: $\chi^2 > \chi^2_{\alpha,(r-1)(c-1} = \chi^2_{.05,9} = 16.9$

$\chi^2 = 43.36$, p-value = 0. There is enough evidence to infer that undergraduate degree and the university applied to are related.

15.38 H_0: The two variables (degree and approach) are independent

H_1: The two variables are dependent

Cell i	f_i	e_i	$(f_i - e_i)$	$(f_i - e_i)^2 / e_i$
1	51	75(101)/195 = 38.85	12.15	3.80
2	8	75(31)/195 = 11.92	-3.92	1.29
3	5	75(36)/195 = 13.85	-8.85	5.65
4	11	752(27)/195 = 10.38	.62	.04
5	24	58(101)/195 = 30.04	-6.04	1.21
6	14	58(31)/195 = 9.22	4.78	2.48
7	12	58(36)/195 = 10.71	1.29	.16
8	8	58(27)/195 = 8.03	-.03	0
9	26	62(101)/195 =32.11	-6.11	1.16
10	9	62(31)/195 = 9.86	-.86	.07
11	19	62(36)/195 = 11.45	7.55	4.99
12	8	62(27)/195 = 8.58	-.58	.04
Total	195	195		$\chi^2 = 20.89$

Rejection region: $\chi^2 > \chi^2_{\alpha,(r-1)(c-1} = \chi^2_{.05,6} = 12.6$

$\chi^2 = 20.89$, p-value = .0019. There is sufficient evidence to infer that there are differences in teaching approach among the four types of degree. The editor can design books and sales campaigns based on the distribution of degrees.

15.40 H_0: The two variables are independent

H_1: The two variables are dependent

© 2012 Cengage Learning. All Rights Reserved. May not be scanned, copied or duplicated, or posted to a publicly accessible website, in whole or in part.

	A	B	C	D	E	F
1	**Contingency Table**					
2						
3		*Year 2002*	*Year 2004*	*Year 2006*	*Year 2008*	TOTAL
4	*Married*	1269	1479	2170	972	5890
5	*Widowed*	247	204	366	164	981
6	*Divorced*	445	415	732	281	1873
7	*Separated*	96	95	156	70	417
8	*Never married*	708	619	1080	531	2938
9	TOTAL	2765	2812	4504	2018	12099
10						
11	chi-squared Stat			36.57		
12	df			12		
13	p-value			0.0003		
14	chi-squared Critical			21.03		

$\chi^2 = 36.57$, p-value = .0003. There is enough evidence to infer that marital status varied from year to year.

15.42 H_0: The two variables are independent

H_1: The two variables are dependent

	A	B	C	D	E
1	**Contingency Table**				
2					
3		*PARTYID3*			
4	*CAPPUN*		1	2	TOTAL
5		1	372	318	690
6		2	457	222	679
7		3	406	82	488
8		TOTAL	1235	622	1857
9					
10					
11		chi-squared Stat			110.35
12		df			2
13		p-value			0
14		chi-squared Critical			5.99

$\chi^2 = 110.35$, p-value = 0. There is enough evidence to infer that support for gun laws is related to political affiliation.

15.44 H_0: The two variables are independent

H_1: The two variables are dependent

© 2012 Cengage Learning. All Rights Reserved. May not be scanned, copied or duplicated, or posted to a publicly accessible website, in whole or in part.

	A	B	C	D	E
1	**Contingency Table**				
2					
3		*PARTY3*			
4	*READ*		1	5	TOTAL
5		1	145	65	210
6		2	114	37	151
7		3	136	78	214
8		TOTAL	395	180	575
9					
10					
11		chi-squared Stat			5.89
12		df			2
13		p-value			0.0525
14		chi-squared Critical			5.99

χ^2 = 5.89, p-value = .0525. There is not enough evidence to infer that there are differences between the three party affiliations with respect to reading about campaign.

15.46 H_0: The two variables are independent

H_1: The two variables are dependent

	A	B	C	D	E
1	**Contingency Table**				
2					
3		*PARTY3*			
4	*ACCESS*		1	5	TOTAL
5		1	423	223	646
6		2	334	77	411
7		3	445	142	587
8		TOTAL	1202	442	1644
9					
10					
11		chi-squared Stat			35.21
12		df			2
13		p-value			0
14		chi-squared Critical			5.99

χ^2 = 35.21, p-value = 0. There is enough evidence to infer that there are differences between the three party affiliations with respect to access to the Internet.

15.48 H_0 : The data are normally distributed

H_1 : The data are not normally distributed

© 2012 Cengage Learning. All Rights Reserved. May not be scanned, copied or duplicated, or posted to a publicly accessible website, in whole or in part.

Interval	Probability	Expected Value e_i	Observed Value f_i	$f_i - e_i$	$(f_i - e_i)^2 / e_i$
$Z \le -1$	.1587	7.94	6	-1.94	0.47
$-1 < Z \le 0$	.3413	17.07	27	9.93	5.78
$0 < Z \le 1$	.3413	17.07	14	-3.07	0.55
$Z > 1$	.1587	7.94	3	-4.94	3.07
Total	1	50	50		$\chi^2 = 9.87$

Rejection region: $\chi^2 > \chi^2_{\alpha,k-3} = \chi^2_{.10,1} = 2.71$

$\chi^2 = 9.87$, p-value = .0017. There is sufficient evidence to infer that the data are not normally distributed.

15.50 H_0 : Costs are normally distributed

H_1 : Costs are not normally distributed

	A	B	C	D
1	**Chi-Squared Test of Normality**			
2				
3		*Drug Cost*		
4	Mean	29.69		
5	Standard deviation	27.53		
6	Observations	900		
7				
8	Intervals	Probability	Expected	Observed
9	(z <= -2)	0.0228	20.48	0
10	(-2 < z <= -1)	0.1359	122.31	9
11	(-1 < z <= 0)	0.3413	307.21	599
12	(0 < z <= 1)	0.3413	307.21	248
13	(1 < z <= 2)	0.1359	122.31	17
14	(z > 2)	0.0228	20.48	27
15				
16	chi-squared Stat	506.76		
17	df	3		
18	p-value	0		
19	chi-squared Critical	7.8147		

$\chi^2 = 506.76$, p-value = 0. There is sufficient evidence to infer that drug costs are not normally distributed.

15.52 H_0 : Reaction times are normally distributed

H_1 : Reaction times re not normally distributed

© 2012 Cengage Learning. All Rights Reserved. May not be scanned, copied or duplicated, or posted to a publicly accessible website, in whole or in part.

Phone

	A	B	C	D
1	**Chi-Squared Test of Normality**			
2				
3		*Phone*		
4	Mean	0.646		
5	Standard deviation	0.045		
6	Observations	125		
7				
8	Intervals	Probability	Expected	Observed
9	(z <= -1.5)	0.0668	8.35	8
10	(-1.5 < z <= -0.5)	0.2417	30.22	32
11	(-0.5 < z <= 0.5)	0.3829	47.87	47
12	(0.5 < z <= 1.5)	0.2417	30.22	29
13	(z > 1.5)	0.0668	8.35	9
14				
15				
16	chi-squared Stat	0.2351		
17	df	2		
18	p-value	0.8891		
19	chi-squared Critical	5.9915		

$\chi^2 = .2351$, p-value = .8891. There is not enough evidence to infer that reaction times of those using the cell phone are not normally distributed.

Not on phone

	A	B	C	D
1	**Chi-Squared Test of Normality**			
2				
3		*Not*		
4	Mean	0.601		
5	Standard deviation	0.053		
6	Observations	145		
7				
8	Intervals	Probability	Expected	Observed
9	(z <= -1.5)	0.0668	9.69	8
10	(-1.5 < z <= -0.5)	0.2417	35.05	40
11	(-0.5 < z <= 0.5)	0.3829	55.52	55
12	(0.5 < z <= 1.5)	0.2417	35.05	29
13	(z > 1.5)	0.0668	9.69	13
14				
15				
16	chi-squared Stat	3.1752		
17	df	2		
18	p-value	0.2044		
19	chi-squared Critical	5.9915		

$\chi^2 = 3.1752$, p-value = .2044. There is not enough evidence to infer that reaction times of those not using the cell phone are not normally distributed.

© 2012 Cengage Learning. All Rights Reserved. May not be scanned, copied or duplicated, or posted to a publicly accessible website, in whole or in part.

15.54 $H_0: p_1 = 1/3,\ p_2 = 1/3,\ p_3 = 1/3$

H_1 : At least one p_i is not equal to its specified value.

Cell i	f_i	e_i	$(f_i - e_i)$	$(f_i - e_i)^2 / e_i$
1	14	30(1/3) = 10	4	1.60
2	10	30(1/3) = 10	0	0.00
3	6	30(1/3) = 10	-4	1.60
Total	30	30		$\chi^2 = 3.20$

Rejection region: $\chi^2 > \chi^2_{\alpha,k-1} = \chi^2_{.10,2} = 4.61$

$\chi^2 = 3.20$, p-value = .2019. There is not enough evidence to infer that the game is unfair.

15.56 H_0 : The two variables (shift and day) are independent

H_1 : The two variables are dependent

Cell i	f_i	e_i	$(f_i - e_i)$	$(f_i - e_i)^2 / e_i$
1	52	181(87)/362 = 43.50	8.50	1.66
2	28	181(62)/362 = 31.00	-3.00	0.29
3	37	181(71)/362 = 35.50	-1.50	0.06
4	31	181(68)/362 = 34.00	-3.00	0.27
5	33	181(74)/362 = 37.00	-4.00	0.43
6	35	181(87)/362 = 43.50	-8.50	1.66
7	34	181(62)/362 = 31.00	3.00	0.29
8	34	181(71)/362 = 35.50	-1.50	0.06
9	37	181(68)/362 = 34.00	3.00	0.26
10	41	181(74)/362 = 37.00	4.00	0.43
Total	362	362		$\chi^2 = 5.41$

Rejection region: $\chi^2 > \chi^2_{\alpha,(r-1)(c-1} = \chi^2_{.10,4} = 7.78$

$\chi^2 = 5.41$, p-value = .2465. There is not enough evidence to infer that there is a relationship between the days an employee is absent and the shift on which the employee works.

15.58 H_0 : The two variables (Country and stress) are independent

H_1 : The two variables are dependent

© 2012 Cengage Learning. All Rights Reserved. May not be scanned, copied or duplicated, or posted to a publicly accessible website, in whole or in part.

	A	B	C	D	E
1	**Contingency Table**				
2					
3		*Stress*			
4	*Country*		1	2	TOTAL
5		1	266	315	581
6		2	347	276	623
7		3	153	187	340
8		4	164	128	292
9		5	92	79	171
10		TOTAL	1022	985	2007
11					
12					
13		chi-squared Stat			20.3755
14		df			4
15		p-value			0.0004
16		chi-squared Critical			9.4877

$\chi^2 = 20.3755$, p-value = .0004. There is enough evidence to infer that Americans and Canadians differ in their sources of stress.

15.60 H_0 : The two variables (education and section) are independent

H_1 : The two variables are dependent

	A	B	C	D	E	F	G
1	**Contingency Table**						
2							
3		*Section*					
4	*Education*		1	2	3	4	TOTAL
5		1	4	21	31	14	70
6		2	27	32	18	2	79
7		3	1	20	42	22	85
8		4	10	44	22	3	79
9		TOTAL	42	117	113	41	313
10							
11							
12		chi-squared Stat			86.6154		
13		df			9		
14		p-value			0		
15		chi-squared Critical			16.919		

$\chi^2 = 86.6154$, p-value = 0. There is sufficient evidence to infer that educational level affects the way adults read the newspaper.

© 2012 Cengage Learning. All Rights Reserved. May not be scanned, copied or duplicated, or posted to a publicly accessible website, in whole or in part.

15.62 Binomial probabilities with n = 5 and p = .5: P(X = 0) = .0313, P(X = 1) = .1563, P(X = 2) = .3125, P(X = 3) = .3125, P(X = 4) = .1563, P(X = 5) = .0313

$H_0: p_0 = .0313, p_1 = .1563,\ p_2 = .3125,\ p_3 = .3125,\ p_4 = .1563,\ p_5 = .0313$

H_1 : At least one p_i is not equal to its specified value.

Cell i	f_i	e_i	$(f_i - e_i)$	$(f_i - e_i)^2 / e_i$
0	8	200(.0313) = 6.26	1.74	0.48
1	35	200(.1563) = 31.26	3.74	0.45
2	57	200(.3125) = 62.50	-5.50	0.48
3	69	200(.3125) = 62.50	6.50	0.68
4	28	200(.1563) = 31.26	-3.26	0.34
5	3	200(.0313) = 6.26	-3.26	1.70
Total	200	200		$\chi^2 = 4.13$

Rejection region: $\chi^2 > \chi^2_{\alpha,6-1} = \chi^2_{.05,5} = 11.1$

$\chi^2 = 4.13$, p-value = .5310. There is not enough evidence to infer that at the number of boys in families with 5 children is not a binomial random variable with p =.5.

15.64 H_0 : The two variables (faculty and retire) are independent

H_1 : The two variables are dependent

	A	B	C	D	E	F	G	H
1	**Contingency Table**							
2								
3		*Retire*						
4	*Faculty*		1	2	3	4	5	TOTAL
5		1	174	51	113	42	86	466
6		2	13	7	22	7	6	55
7		TOTAL	187	58	135	49	92	521
8								
9								
10		chi-squared Stat			9.732			
11		df			4			
12		p-value			0.0452			
13		chi-squared Critical			9.4877			

$\chi^2 = 9.732$, p-value = .0452. There is enough evidence to infer that whether a professor wishes to retire is related to the faculty.

© 2012 Cengage Learning. All Rights Reserved. May not be scanned, copied or duplicated, or posted to a publicly accessible website, in whole or in part.

15.66 H_0 : The two variables (network and ask) are independent

H_1 : The two variables are dependent

	A	B	C	D	E	F
1	**Contingency Table**					
2						
3		*Ask*				
4	*Network*		1	2	3	TOTAL
5		1	19	30	43	92
6		2	104	107	123	334
7		TOTAL	123	137	166	426
8						
9						
10		chi-squared Stat			4.573	
11		df			2	
12		p-value			0.1016	
13		chi-squared Critical			5.9915	

$\chi^2 = 4.573$, p-value = .1016. There is not enough evidence to conclude that there are differences in responses between the three network news shows.

15.68 a H_0 : The two variables (gender and vote) are independent

H_1 : The two variables are dependent

	A	B	C	D	E
1	**Contingency Table**				
2					
3		*Votes*			
4	*Gender*		1	2	TOTAL
5		1	189	169	358
6		2	203	204	407
7		TOTAL	392	373	765
8					
9					
10		chi-squared Stat			0.6483
11		df			1
12		p-value			0.4207
13		chi-squared Critical			3.8415

$\chi^2 = .6483$, p-value = .4207. There is not enough evidence to infer that voting and gender are related.

b H_0 : The two variables (education and vote) are independent

H_1 : The two variables are dependent

© 2012 Cengage Learning. All Rights Reserved. May not be scanned, copied or duplicated, or posted to a publicly accessible website, in whole or in part.

	A	B	C	D	E	F	G
1	**Contingency Table**						
2							
3		*Votes*					
4	*Educ*		1	2	3	4	TOTAL
5		1	48	164	107	39	358
6		2	34	178	134	61	407
7		TOTAL	82	342	241	100	765
8							
9							
10		chi-squared Stat			7.7214		
11		df			3		
12		p-value			0.0521		
13		chi-squared Critical			7.8147		

$\chi^2 = 7.7214$, p-value = .0521. There is not enough evidence to infer that voting and educational level are related.

c H_0 : The two variables (income category and vote) are independent

H_1 : The two variables are dependent

	A	B	C	D	E	F	G
1	**Contingency Table**						
2							
3		*Votes*					
4	*Income*		1	2	3	4	TOTAL
5		1	38	186	105	29	358
6		2	21	185	128	73	407
7		TOTAL	59	371	233	102	765
8							
9							
10		chi-squared Stat			23.108		
11		df			3		
12		p-value			0		
13		chi-squared Critical			7.8147		

$\chi^2 = 23.108$, p-value = 0. There is enough evidence to infer that voting and income are related.

© 2012 Cengage Learning. All Rights Reserved. May not be scanned, copied or duplicated, or posted to a publicly accessible website, in whole or in part.

15.70 H_0 : The two variables (value and segment) are independent

H_1 : The two variables are dependent

	A	B	C	D	E	F
1	**Contingency Table**					
2						
3		*Segment*				
4	*Value*		1	2	3	TOTAL
5		1	147	135	136	418
6		2	221	155	160	536
7		3	339	254	289	882
8		TOTAL	707	544	585	1836
9						
10						
11		chi-squared Stat			4.5122	
12		df			4	
13		p-value			0.3411	
14		chi-squared Critical			9.4877	

$\chi^2 = 4.5122$, p-value = .3411. There is not enough evidence to infer that there are differences in the definition of value between the three market segments.

© 2012 Cengage Learning. All Rights Reserved. May not be scanned, copied or duplicated, or posted to a publicly accessible website, in whole or in part.

Appendix 15

A15.2 t-test of μ_D

$H_0: \mu_D = 0$

$H_1: \mu_D < 0$

	A	B	C
1	t-Test: Paired Two Sample for Means		
2			
3		*First Sat*	*Second SAT*
4	Mean	1175	1190
5	Variance	28422	35392
6	Observations	40	40
7	Pearson Correlation	0.91	
8	Hypothesized Mean Difference	0	
9	df	39	
10	t Stat	-1.20	
11	P(T<=t) one-tail	0.1182	
12	t Critical one-tail	1.6849	
13	P(T<=t) two-tail	0.2365	
14	t Critical two-tail	2.0227	

t = –1.20, p-value = .1182. There is not enough evidence to indicate that repeating the SAT produces higher exam scores.

A15.4 a t-estimator of μ

	A	B	C	D
1	**t-Estimate: Mean**			
2				
3				*Overdue*
4	Mean			7.09
5	Standard Deviation			6.97
6	LCL			6.40
7	UCL			7.77

LCL = 6.40, UCL = 7.77

b LCL = 50,000($.25)(6.40) = $80,000

UCL = 50,000($.25)(7.77) = $97,125

It does appear that not all fines are collected

© 2012 Cengage Learning. All Rights Reserved. May not be scanned, copied or duplicated, or posted to a publicly accessible website, in whole or in part.

A15.6 Chi-squared test of a contingency table

H_0 : The two variables (income category and mutual fund ownership) are independent

H_1 : The two variables are dependent

	A	B	C	D	E
1	**Contingency Table**				
2					
3		*Income category*			
4	*Mutual fund*		1	2	TOTAL
5		1	71	13	84
6		2	59	28	87
7		3	86	55	141
8		4	87	157	244
9		5	32	145	177
10		6	58	205	263
11		TOTAL	393	603	996
12					
13					
14		chi-squared Stat			196.77
15		df			5
16		p-value			0
17		chi-squared Critical			11.0705

$\chi^2 = 196.77$, p-value = 0. There is overwhelming evidence to infer that household income and ownership of mutual funds are related

A15.8 z-test of $p_1 - p_2$ (case 1) Code 3 results were omitted.

$H_0: (p_1 - p_2) = 0$

$H_1: (p_1 - p_2) < 0$

	A	B	C	D
1	**z-Test: Two Proportions**			
2				
3			*Folic acid*	*Placebo*
4	Sample Proportions		0.0101	0.0343
5	Observations		597	612
6	Hypothesized Difference		0	
7	z Stat		-2.85	
8	P(Z<=z) one tail		0.0022	
9	z Critical one-tail		1.6449	
10	P(Z<=z) two-tail		0.0044	
11	z Critical two-tail		1.9600	

z = –2.85, p-value = .0022. There is overwhelming evidence to conclude that folic acid reduces the incidence of spina bifida.

© 2012 Cengage Learning. All Rights Reserved. May not be scanned, copied or duplicated, or posted to a publicly accessible website, in whole or in part.

A15.10 one-way analysis of variance

$H_0: \mu_1 = \mu_2 = \mu_3$

H_1: At least two means differ

	A	B	C	D	E	F	G
10	ANOVA						
11	*Source of Variation*	*SS*	*df*	*MS*	*F*	*P-value*	*F crit*
12	Between Groups	626046	2	313023	58.37	0.0000	3.03
13	Within Groups	1523047	284	5363			
14							
15	Total	2149093	286				

F = 58.37, p-value = 0. There is enough evidence to conclude that there are differences between the three groups.

Multiple Comparisons

	A	B	C	D	E
1	**Multiple Comparisons**				
2					
3				LSD	Omega
4	Treatment	Treatment	Difference	Alpha = 0.0167	Alpha = 0.05
5	*Before 1976*	*After 1986*	122.62	28.03	25.46
6		*Canadian*	78.04	24.67	25.46
7	*After 1986*	*Canadian*	-44.58	25.75	25.46

All three groups differ from each other.

A15.12 t-estimator of μ

	A	B	C	D
1	**t-Estimate: Mean**			
2				
3				*Cars*
4	Mean			165.79
5	Standard Deviation			51.59
6	LCL			157.17
7	UCL			174.41

Five minute interval: LCL = 157.17, UCL = 174.41

Twenty-four hour day (12 5-minute intervals, 24 hours per day):

$$LCL = 12 \times 24 \times 157.17 = 45{,}265$$

$$UCL = 12 \times 24 \times 174.41 = 50{,}230$$

© 2012 Cengage Learning. All Rights Reserved. May not be scanned, copied or duplicated, or posted to a publicly accessible website, in whole or in part.

A15.14 Equal-variances t-test of $\mu_1 - \mu_2$

$$H_0: (\mu_1 - \mu_2) = 0$$

$$H_1: (\mu_1 - \mu_2) < 0$$

Two-tail F test: F = 1.37, p-value = .1986; use equal-variances t-test

	A	B	C
1	t-Test: Two-Sample Assuming Equal Variances		
2			
3		*Activity*	*Usual*
4	Mean	57.06	87.28
5	Variance	296.18	215.42
6	Observations	67	67
7	Pooled Variance	255.80	
8	Hypothesized Mean Difference	0.00	
9	df	132	
10	t Stat	-10.94	
11	P(T<=t) one-tail	0.0000	
12	t Critical one-tail	1,6565	
13	P(T<=t) two-tail	0.0000	
14	t Critical two-tail	1.9781	

t = –10.94, p-value = 0. There is enough evidence to indicate to infer that graded activity is effective.

A15.16 z-estimator of p

	A	B	C	D	E
1	**z-Estimate of a Proportion**				
2					
3	**Sample proportion**	0.774	**Confidence Interval Estimate**		
4	**Sample size**	780	**0.774**	±	**0.0294**
5	**Confidence level**	0.95	**Lower confidence limit**		**0.7446**
6			**Upper confidence limit**		**0.8034**

Total number of on-time departures:

LCL = 7,140,596(.7446) = 5,316,888

UCL = 7,140,596(.8034) = 5,736,755

A15.18 Chi-squared test of a contingency table

H_0: The two variables (party and support for capital punishment) are independent

H_1: The two variables are dependent

© 2012 Cengage Learning. All Rights Reserved. May not be scanned, copied or duplicated, or posted to a publicly accessible website, in whole or in part.

	A	B	C	D	E
1	**Contingency Table**				
2					
3		*PARTYID3*			
4	*CAPPUN*		1	2	TOTAL
5		1	372	318	690
6		2	457	222	679
7		3	406	82	488
8		TOTAL	1235	622	1857
9					
10					
11		chi-squared Stat			110.35
12		df			2
13		p-value			0
14		chi-squared Critical			5.99

$\chi^2 = 110.35$, p-value = 0. There is enough evidence to conclude that Democrats, Republicans, and Independents differ in their support for capital punishment.

A15.20 Chi-squared test of a contingency table

H_0 : The two variables (PARTYID and SEX) are independent

H_1 : The two variables are dependent

	A	B	C	D	E	F	G	H	I	J	K
1	**Contingency Table**										
2											
3		*SEX*									
4	*PARTYID*		*Code 0*	*Code 1*	*Code 2*	*Code 3*	*Code 4*	*Code 5*	*Code 6*	*Code 7*	*TOTAL*
5		*Code 1*	150	149	128	139	98	140	92	30	926
6		*Code 2*	240	182	134	183	64	163	110	8	1084
7		*TOTAL*	390	331	262	322	162	303	202	38	2010
8											
9											
10		Chi-Squared Statistic		41.27							
11		Degrees Of Freedom		7							
12		P-Value		0							
13		Chi-Squared Critical		14.1							

$\chi^2 = 41.27$, p-value = 0. There is sufficient evidence to conclude that men and women differ in their political affiliation.

A15.22 one-way analysis of variance

$H_0: \mu_1 = \mu_2 = \mu_3 = \mu_4$

H_1 : At least two means differ

© 2012 Cengage Learning. All Rights Reserved. May not be scanned, copied or duplicated, or posted to a publicly accessible website, in whole or in part.

	A	B	C	D	E	F	G
1	Anova: Single Factor						
2							
3	SUMMARY						
4	*Groups*	*Count*	*Sum*	*Average*	*Variance*		
5	CONRINC:2002	1780	66482390	37350	2028031586		
6	CONRINC:2004	1688	63486328	37610	1237881866		
7	CONRINC:2006	2608	84745434	32494	798558066		
8							
9							
10	ANOVA						
11	*Source of Variation*	*SS*	*df*	*MS*	*F*	*P-value*	*F crit*
12	Between Groups	37007841927	2	18503920964	14.45	5.5E-07	2.9972
13	Within Groups	7778015777735	6073	1280753462			
14							
15	Total	7815023619662	6075				

F = 14.45, p-value = 5.5E-07 ≈ 0. There is enough evidence to infer that inflation-adjusted incomes differ between 2002, 2004, and 2006.

A15.24 Chi-squared test of a contingency table

H_0 : The two variables (PARTYID3 and UNEMP) are independent

H_1 : The two variables are dependent

	A	B	C	D	E
1	**Contingency Table**				
2					
3		*PARTYID3*			
4	*UNEMP*		1	2	TOTAL
5		1	167	335	502
6		2	184	305	489
7		3	85	255	340
8		TOTAL	436	895	1331
9					
10					
11		chi-squared Stat			14.61
12		df			2
13		p-value			0.0007
14		chi-squared Critical			5.99

χ^2 = 14.61, p-value = .0007. There is sufficient evidence to conclude that Americans who have been unemployed in the last ten years have different party affiliations.

© 2012 Cengage Learning. All Rights Reserved. May not be scanned, copied or duplicated, or posted to a publicly accessible website, in whole or in part.

A15.26 Chi-squared test of a contingency table

H_0 : The two variables (Year and EMPLOY) are independent

H_1 : The two variables are dependent

	A	B	C	D	E	F	G	H	I	J	K
1	**Contingency Table**										
2											
3		*Year*									
4	*EMPLOY*		1	2	3	4	5	6	7	8	TOTAL
5		2004	807	15	0	35	205	35	85	28	1210
6		2008	5	48	257	563	888	0	0	0	1761
7		TOTAL	812	63	257	598	1093	35	85	28	2971
8											
9											
10		chi-squared Stat			2077						
11		df			7						
12		p-value			0						
13		chi-squared Critical			14.1						

$\chi^2 = 2077$, p-value = 0. There is sufficient evidence to conclude that employment status changed between 2004 and 2008.

© 2012 Cengage Learning. All Rights Reserved. May not be scanned, copied or duplicated, or posted to a publicly accessible website, in whole or in part.

Chapter 16

16.2 a

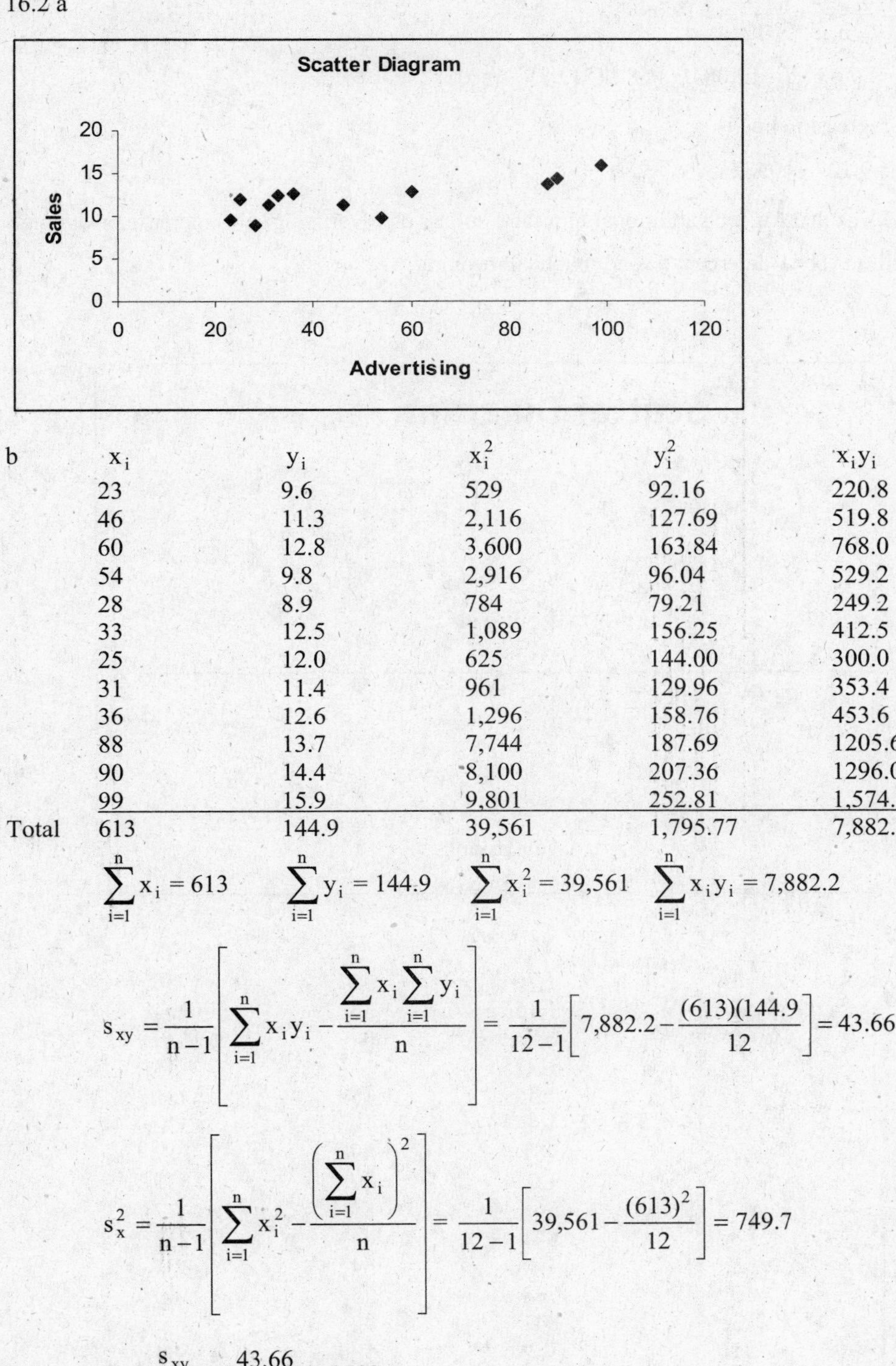

b

	x_i	y_i	x_i^2	y_i^2	$x_i y_i$
	23	9.6	529	92.16	220.8
	46	11.3	2,116	127.69	519.8
	60	12.8	3,600	163.84	768.0
	54	9.8	2,916	96.04	529.2
	28	8.9	784	79.21	249.2
	33	12.5	1,089	156.25	412.5
	25	12.0	625	144.00	300.0
	31	11.4	961	129.96	353.4
	36	12.6	1,296	158.76	453.6
	88	13.7	7,744	187.69	1205.6
	90	14.4	8,100	207.36	1296.0
	99	15.9	9,801	252.81	1,574.1
Total	613	144.9	39,561	1,795.77	7,882.2

$\sum_{i=1}^{n} x_i = 613 \qquad \sum_{i=1}^{n} y_i = 144.9 \qquad \sum_{i=1}^{n} x_i^2 = 39,561 \qquad \sum_{i=1}^{n} x_i y_i = 7,882.2$

$$s_{xy} = \frac{1}{n-1}\left[\sum_{i=1}^{n} x_i y_i - \frac{\sum_{i=1}^{n} x_i \sum_{i=1}^{n} y_i}{n}\right] = \frac{1}{12-1}\left[7,882.2 - \frac{(613)(144.9}{12}\right] = 43.66$$

$$s_x^2 = \frac{1}{n-1}\left[\sum_{i=1}^{n} x_i^2 - \frac{\left(\sum_{i=1}^{n} x_i\right)^2}{n}\right] = \frac{1}{12-1}\left[39,561 - \frac{(613)^2}{12}\right] = 749.7$$

$$b_1 = \frac{s_{xy}}{s_x^2} = \frac{43.66}{749.7} = .0582$$

© 2012 Cengage Learning. All Rights Reserved. May not be scanned, copied or duplicated, or posted to a publicly accessible website, in whole or in part.

$$\bar{x} = \frac{\sum x_i}{n} = \frac{613}{12} = 51.08$$

$$\bar{y} = \frac{\sum y_i}{n} = \frac{144.9}{12} = 12.08$$

$$b_0 = \bar{y} - b_1\bar{x} = 12.08 - (.0582)(51.08) = 9.107$$

The sample regression line is

$$\hat{y} = 9.107 + .0582x$$

The slope tells us that for each additional thousand dollars of advertising sales increase on average by .0582 million. The y-intercept has no practical meaning.

16.4a

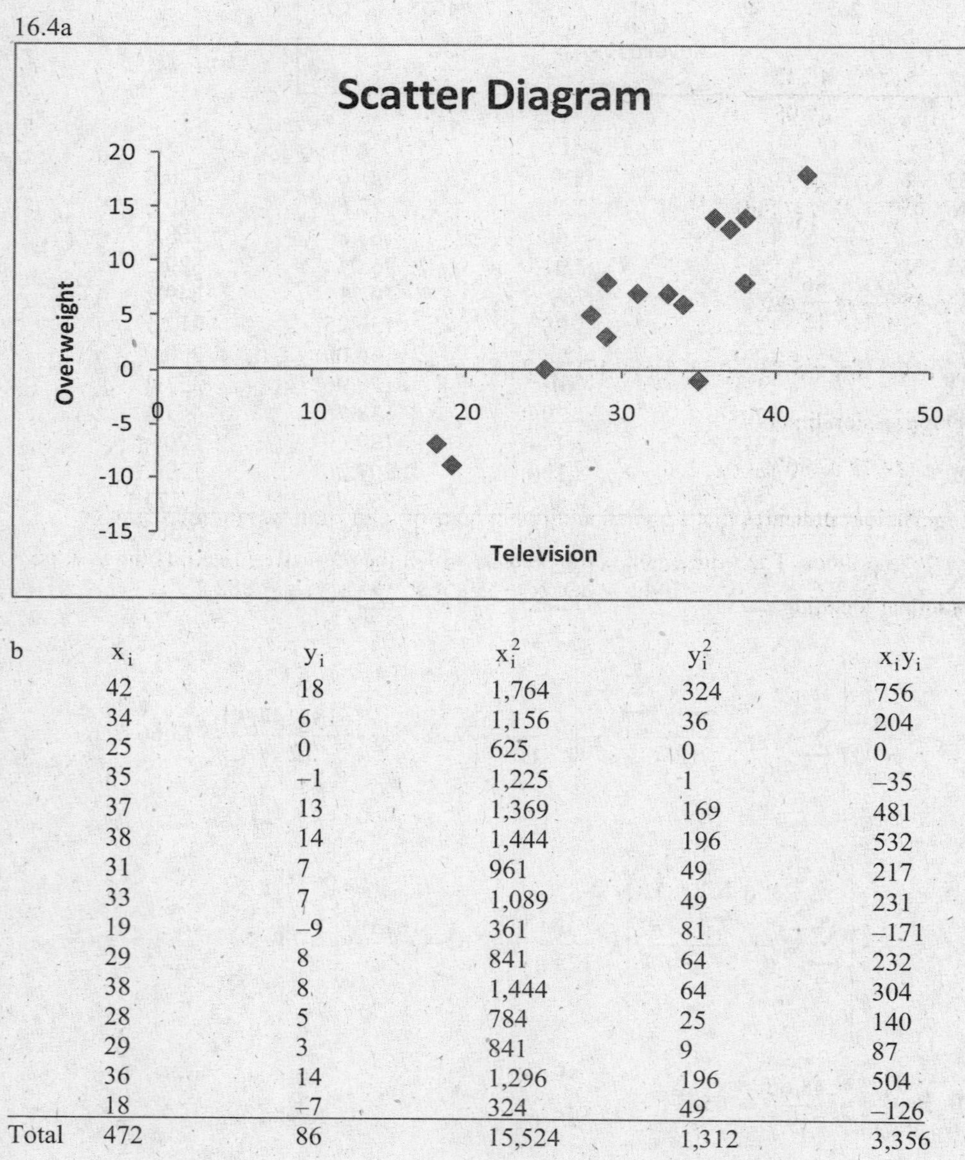

b

	x_i	y_i	x_i^2	y_i^2	x_iy_i
	42	18	1,764	324	756
	34	6	1,156	36	204
	25	0	625	0	0
	35	–1	1,225	1	–35
	37	13	1,369	169	481
	38	14	1,444	196	532
	31	7	961	49	217
	33	7	1,089	49	231
	19	–9	361	81	–171
	29	8	841	64	232
	38	8	1,444	64	304
	28	5	784	25	140
	29	3	841	9	87
	36	14	1,296	196	504
	18	–7	324	49	–126
Total	472	86	15,524	1,312	3,356

© 2012 Cengage Learning. All Rights Reserved. May not be scanned, copied or duplicated, or posted to a publicly accessible website, in whole or in part.

$$\sum_{i=1}^{n} x_i = 472 \qquad \sum_{i=1}^{n} y_i = 86 \qquad \sum_{i=1}^{n} x_i^2 = 15{,}524 \quad \sum_{i=1}^{n} x_i y_i = 3{,}356$$

$$s_{xy} = \frac{1}{n-1}\left[\sum_{i=1}^{n} x_i y_i - \frac{\sum_{i=1}^{n} x_i \sum_{i=1}^{n} y_i}{n}\right] = \frac{1}{15-1}\left[3{,}356 - \frac{(472)(86}{15}\right] = 46.42$$

$$s_x^2 = \frac{1}{n-1}\left[\sum_{i=1}^{n} x_i^2 - \frac{\left(\sum_{i=1}^{n} x_i\right)^2}{n}\right] = \frac{1}{15-1}\left[15{,}524 - \frac{(472)^2}{15}\right] = 47.98$$

$$b_1 = \frac{s_{xy}}{s_x^2} = \frac{46.42}{47.98} = .9675$$

$$\bar{x} = \frac{\sum x_i}{n} = \frac{472}{15} = 31.47$$

$$\bar{y} = \frac{\sum y_i}{n} = \frac{86}{15} = 5.73$$

$$b_0 = \bar{y} - b_1\bar{x} = 5.73 - (.9675)(31.47) = -24.72$$

The sample regression line is

$$\hat{y} = -24.72 + .9675x$$

The slope coefficient indicates that for each additional hour of television weight increases on average by .9675 pounds. The y-intercept is the point at which the regression line hits the y–axis; it has no practical meaning.

© 2012 Cengage Learning. All Rights Reserved. May not be scanned, copied or duplicated, or posted to a publicly accessible website, in whole or in part.

16.6 a

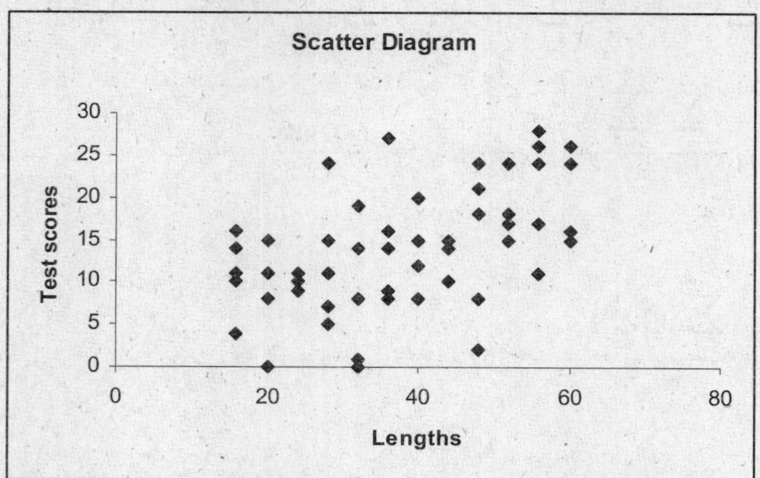

b $b_1 = \frac{s_{xy}}{s_x^2} = \frac{51.86}{193.9} = .2675$, $b_0 = \bar{y} - b_1\bar{x} = 13.80 - .2675(38.00) = 3.635$

Regression line: $\hat{y} = 3.635 + .2675x$ (Excel: $\hat{y} = 3.636 + .2675x$)

c $b_1 = .2675$; for each additional second of commercial, the memory test score increases on average by .2675. $b_0 = 3.64$ is the y-intercept.

16.8 $b_1 = \frac{s_{xy}}{s_x^2} = \frac{9.67}{107.51} = .0899$, $b_0 = \bar{y} - b_1\bar{x} = 11.55 - .0899(45.49) = 7.460$.

Regression line: $\hat{y} = 7.460 + .0899x$ (Excel: $\hat{y} = 7.462 + .0900x$)

The slope coefficient tells us that for each additional year of age time increases on average by .0899 minutes. The y-intercept has no meaning.

16.10a $b_1 = \frac{s_{xy}}{s_x^2} = \frac{20.55}{108.3} = .1898$, $b_0 = \bar{y} - b_1\bar{x} = 14.43 - .1898(37.64) = 7.286$.

Regression line: $\hat{y} = 7.286 + .1898x$ (Excel: $\hat{y} = 7.287 + .1897x$)

b For each additional cigarette the number of days absent from work increases on average by .1898. The y-intercept has no meaning.

16.12a $b_1 = \frac{s_{xy}}{s_x^2} = \frac{30,945}{688.2} = 44.97$, $b_0 = \bar{y} - b_1\bar{x} = 6,465 - 44.97(53.93) = 4040$.

Regression line: $\hat{y} = 4040 + 44.97x$ (Excel: $\hat{y} = 4040 + 44.97x$)

© 2012 Cengage Learning. All Rights Reserved. May not be scanned, copied or duplicated, or posted to a publicly accessible website, in whole or in part.

b. For each additional thousand square feet the price increases on average by $44.97 thousand.

16.14 $b_1 = \frac{s_{xy}}{s_x^2} = \frac{310.0}{4.84} = 64.05,\ b_0 = \bar{y} - b_1\bar{x} = 762.6 - 64.05(4.75) = 458.4.$

Regression line: $\hat{y} = 458.4 + 64.05x$ (Excel: $\hat{y} = 458.9 + 64.00x$)

For each additional occupant the electrical use increases on average by 64.05.

16.16 a $b_1 = \frac{s_{xy}}{s_x^2} = \frac{-10.78}{35.47} = -.3039,\ b_0 = \bar{y} - b_1\bar{x} = 17.20 - (-.3039)(11.33) = 20.64.$

Regression line: $\hat{y} = 20.64 - .3039x$ (Excel: $\hat{y} = 20.64 - .3038x$)

b The slope indicates that for each additional one percentage point increase in the vacancy rate rents on average decrease by $.3039.

16.18 $b_1 = \frac{s_{xy}}{s_x^2} = \frac{.8258}{16.07} = .0514,\ b_0 = \bar{y} - b_1\bar{x} = 93.89 - .0514(79.47) = 89.81.$

Regression line: $\hat{y} = 89.81 + .0514x$ (Excel: $\hat{y} = 89.81 + .0514x$)

For each additional mark on the test the number of non-defective products increases on average by .0514.

16.20 For each number of years of education incomes are normally distributed with constant variance and a mean that is a linear function of the number of years of education.

16.22 b

	x_i	y_i	x_i^2	y_i^2	x_iy_i
	1	1	1	1	1
	3	8	9	64	24
	4	15	16	225	60
	6	33	36	1089	198
	9	75	81	5625	675
	8	70	64	4900	560
	10	95	100	9025	950
Total	41	297	307	20,929	2,468

$\sum_{i=1}^{n} x_i = 41 \quad \sum_{i=1}^{n} y_i = 297 \quad \sum_{i=1}^{n} x_i^2 = 307 \quad \sum_{i=1}^{n} y_i^2 = 20,929 \quad \sum_{i=1}^{n} x_iy_i = 2,468$

$$s_{xy} = \frac{1}{n-1}\left[\sum_{i=1}^{n} x_iy_i - \frac{\sum_{i=1}^{n} x_i \sum_{i=1}^{n} y_i}{n}\right] = \frac{1}{7-1}\left[2,468 - \frac{(41)(297}{7}\right] = 121.4$$

© 2012 Cengage Learning. All Rights Reserved. May not be scanned, copied or duplicated, or posted to a publicly accessible website, in whole or in part.

$$s_x^2 = \frac{1}{n-1}\left[\sum_{i=1}^{n} x_i^2 - \frac{\left(\sum_{i=1}^{n} x_i\right)^2}{n}\right] = \frac{1}{7-1}\left[307 - \frac{(41)^2}{7}\right] = 11.14$$

$$s_y^2 = \frac{1}{n-1}\left[\sum_{i=1}^{n} y_i^2 - \frac{\left(\sum_{i=1}^{n} y_i\right)^2}{n}\right] = \frac{1}{7-1}\left[20{,}929 - \frac{(297)^2}{7}\right] = 1{,}388.0$$

$$b_1 = \frac{s_{xy}}{s_x^2} = \frac{121.4}{11.14} = 10.90$$

$$SSE = (n-1)\left(s_y^2 - \frac{s_{xy}^2}{s_x^2}\right) = (7-1)\left(1{,}388.0 - \frac{(121.4)^2}{11.14}\right) = 390.1$$

$$s_\varepsilon = \sqrt{\frac{SSE}{n-2}} = \sqrt{\frac{390.1}{7-2}} = 8.83 \text{ (Excel: } s_\varepsilon = 8.85)$$

$$H_0 : \beta_1 = 0$$

$$H_1 : \beta_1 \neq 0$$

Rejection region: $t > t_{\alpha/2,n-2} = t_{.025,5} = 2.571$ or $t < -t_{\alpha/2,n-2} = -t_{.025,5} = -2.571$

$$s_{b_1} = \frac{s_\varepsilon}{\sqrt{(n-1)s_x^2}} = \frac{8.83}{\sqrt{(7-1)(11.14)}} = 1.08$$

$t = \dfrac{b_1 - \beta_1}{s_{b_1}} = \dfrac{10.90 - 0}{1.08} = 10.09$ (Excel: t = 10.07, p–value = .0002. There is enough evidence to infer a linear relationship.

© 2012 Cengage Learning. All Rights Reserved. May not be scanned, copied or duplicated, or posted to a publicly accessible website, in whole or in part.

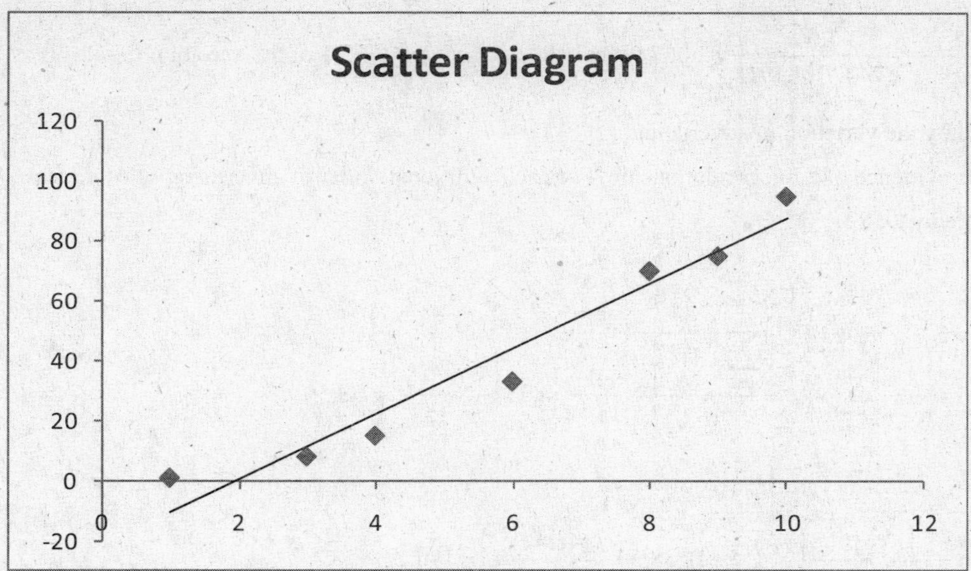

There does appear to be a linear relationship.

16.24 a $s_y^2 = \frac{1}{n-1}\left[\sum_{i=1}^{n} y_i^2 - \frac{\left(\sum_{i=1}^{n} y_i\right)^2}{n}\right] = \frac{1}{12-1}\left[1{,}795.77 - \frac{(144.9)^2}{12}\right] = 4.191$

$SSE = (n-1)\left(s_y^2 - \frac{s_{xy}^2}{s_x^2}\right) = (12-1)\left(4.191 - \frac{(43.66)^2}{749.7}\right) = 18.13$

$s_\varepsilon = \sqrt{\frac{SSE}{n-2}} = \sqrt{\frac{18.13}{12-2}} = 1.347$ (Excel: $s_\varepsilon = 1.347$)

b $H_0: \beta_1 = 0$

$H_1: \beta_1 \neq 0$

Rejection region: $t > t_{\alpha/2,n-2} = t_{.025,10} = 2.228$ or $t < -t_{\alpha/2,n-2} = -t_{.025,10} = -2.228$

$s_{b_1} = \frac{s_\varepsilon}{\sqrt{(n-1)s_x^2}} = \frac{1.347}{\sqrt{(12-1)(749.7)}} = .0148$

$t = \frac{b_1 - \beta_1}{s_{b_1}} = \frac{.0582 - 0}{.0148} = 3.93$ (Excel: t = 3.93, p–value = .0028. There is enough evidence to infer a linear relationship between advertising and sales.

c $b_1 \pm t_{\alpha/2,n-2} s_{b_1} = .0582 \pm 2.228(.0148) = .0582 \pm .0330$ LCL = .0252, UCL = .0912

© 2012 Cengage Learning. All Rights Reserved. May not be scanned, copied or duplicated, or posted to a publicly accessible website, in whole or in part.

d $R^2 = \frac{s_{xy}^2}{s_x^2 s_y^2} = \frac{(43.66)^2}{(749.7)(4.191)} = .6067$ (Excel: $R^2 = .6066$). 60.67% of the variation in sales is explained by the variation in advertising.

e There is evidence of a linear relationship. For each additional dollar of advertising sales increase on average by .0582.

16.26 $s_y^2 = \frac{1}{n-1}\left[\sum_{i=1}^{n} y_i^2 - \frac{\left(\sum_{i=1}^{n} y_i\right)^2}{n}\right] = \frac{1}{15-1}\left[1{,}312 - \frac{(86)^2}{15}\right] = 58.50$

$$SSE = (n-1)\left(s_y^2 - \frac{s_{xy}^2}{s_x^2}\right) = (15-1)\left(58.50 - \frac{(46.42)^2}{47.98}\right) = 190.2$$

$$s_\varepsilon = \sqrt{\frac{SSE}{n-2}} = \sqrt{\frac{190.2}{15-2}} = 3.825$$

$H_0: \beta_1 = 0$

$H_1: \beta_1 \neq 0$

Rejection region: $t > t_{\alpha/2,n-2} = t_{.025,13} = 2.160$ or $t < -t_{\alpha/2,n-2} = -t_{.025,13} = -2.160$

$$s_{b_1} = \frac{s_\varepsilon}{\sqrt{(n-1)s_x^2}} = \frac{3.825}{\sqrt{(15-1)(47.98)}} = .1476$$

$t = \frac{b_1 - \beta_1}{s_{b_1}} = \frac{.9675 - 0}{.1476} = 6.55$ (Excel: $t = 6.55$, p–value = 0.) There is enough evidence to conclude that there is a linear relationship between hours of television viewing and how overweight the child is.

16.28 a $SSE = (n-1)\left(s_y^2 - \frac{s_{xy}^2}{s_x^2}\right) = (60-1)\left(47.96 - \frac{(51.86)^2}{193.9}\right) = 2{,}011$

$s_\varepsilon = \sqrt{\frac{SSE}{n-2}} = \sqrt{\frac{2{,}011}{60-2}} = 5.888$ (Excel: $s_\varepsilon = 5.888$). Relative to the values of the dependent variable the standard error of estimate appears to be large indicating a weak linear relationship.

b $R^2 = \frac{s_{xy}^2}{s_x^2 s_y^2} = \frac{(51.86)^2}{(193.9)(47.96)} = .2892$ (Excel: $R^2 = .2893$).

c $H_0: \beta_1 = 0$

$H_1: \beta_1 \neq 0$

© 2012 Cengage Learning. All Rights Reserved. May not be scanned, copied or duplicated, or posted to a publicly accessible website, in whole or in part.

Rejection region: $t > t_{\alpha/2,n-2} = t_{.025,58} \approx 2.000$ or $t < -t_{\alpha/2,n-2} = -t_{.025,58} = -2.000$

$$s_{b_1} = \frac{s_\varepsilon}{\sqrt{(n-1)s_x^2}} = \frac{5.888}{\sqrt{(60-1)(193.9)}} = .0550$$

$t = \frac{b_1 - \beta_1}{s_{b_1}} = \frac{.2675 - 0}{.0550} = 4.86$ (Excel: t = 4.86, p–value = 0). There is enough evidence to infer a linear relationship between memory test scores and length of commercial.

d $b_1 \pm t_{\alpha/2,n-2} s_{b_1} = .2675 \pm 1.671(.0550) = .2675 \pm .0919$ LCL = .1756, UCL = .3594

16.30 $SSE = (n-1)\left(s_y^2 - \frac{s_{xy}^2}{s_x^2}\right) = (229-1)\left(42.54 - \frac{(9.67)^2}{107.51}\right) = 9500.8$

$$s_\varepsilon = \sqrt{\frac{SSE}{n-2}} = \sqrt{\frac{9500.8}{229-2}} = 6.47$$

$H_0 : \beta_1 = 0$

$H_1 : \beta_1 \neq 0$

Rejection region: $t > t_{\alpha/2,n-2} = t_{.025,227} \approx 1.96$ or $t < -t_{\alpha/2,n-2} = -t_{.025,227} = -1.96$

$$s_{b_1} = \frac{s_\varepsilon}{\sqrt{(n-1)s_x^2}} = \frac{6.47}{\sqrt{(229-1)(107.51)}} = .0413$$

$t = \frac{b_1 - \beta_1}{s_{b_1}} = \frac{.0899 - 0}{.0413} = 2.17$ (Excel: t =2.18, p–value = .0305.) There is evidence of a linear relationship between age and time to complete census.

16.32 $SSE = (n-1)\left(s_y^2 - \frac{s_{xy}^2}{s_x^2}\right) = (231-1)\left(19.80 - \frac{(20.55)^2}{108.3}\right) = 3657$

$$s_\varepsilon = \sqrt{\frac{SSE}{n-2}} = \sqrt{\frac{3657}{231-2}} = 3.996$$

$H_0 : \beta_1 = 0$

$H_1 : \beta_1 > 0$

Rejection region: $t > t_{\alpha/2,n-2} = t_{.025,229} \approx 1.960$ or $t < -t_{\alpha/2,n-2} = -t_{.025,229} \approx -1.960$

$$s_{b_1} = \frac{s_\varepsilon}{\sqrt{(n-1)s_x^2}} = \frac{3.996}{\sqrt{(231-1)(108.3)}} = .02532$$

$t = \frac{b_1 - \beta_1}{s_{b_1}} = \frac{.1898 - 0}{.02532} = 7.50$ (Excel: t =7.49, p–value = 0.) There is evidence of a positive linear relationship between cigarettes smoked and the number of sick days.

© 2012 Cengage Learning. All Rights Reserved. May not be scanned, copied or duplicated, or posted to a publicly accessible website, in whole or in part.

16.34 $SSE = (n-1)\left(s_y^2 - \frac{s_{xy}^2}{s_x^2}\right) = (40-1)\left(11{,}918{,}489 - \frac{(30{,}945)^2}{688.2}\right) = 410{,}554{,}683$

a $s_\varepsilon = \sqrt{\frac{SSE}{n-2}} = \sqrt{\frac{410{,}554{,}683}{40-2}} = 3{,}287$ (Excel: $s_\varepsilon = 3{,}287$). There is a weak linear relationship.

b $H_0: \beta_1 = 0$

$H_1: \beta_1 \neq 0$

Rejection region: $t > t_{\alpha/2,n-2} = t_{.025,38} \approx 2.021$ or $t < -t_{\alpha/2,n-2} = -t_{.025,38} \approx -2.021$

$s_{b_1} = \frac{s_\varepsilon}{\sqrt{(n-1)s_x^2}} = \frac{3{,}287}{\sqrt{(40-1)(688.2)}} = 20.06$

$t = \frac{b_1 - \beta_1}{s_{b_1}} = \frac{44.97 - 0}{20.06} = 2.24$ (Excel: $t = 2.24$, p–value = .0309.) There is enough evidence of a linear relationship.

c $R^2 = \frac{s_{xy}^2}{s_x^2 s_y^2} = \frac{(30{,}945)^2}{(688.2)(11{,}918{,}489)} = .1167$ (Excel: $R^2 = .1168$) 11.67% of the variation in percent damage is explained by the variation in distance to the fire station.

16.36 $SSE = (n-1)\left(s_y^2 - \frac{s_{xy}^2}{s_x^2}\right) = (200-1)\left(56{,}725 - \frac{(310.0)^2}{4.84}\right) = 7{,}337{,}056$

$s_\varepsilon = \sqrt{\frac{SSE}{n-2}} = \sqrt{\frac{7{,}337{,}056}{200-2}} = 191.1$ (Excel: $s_\varepsilon = 192.5$).

$R^2 = \frac{s_{xy}^2}{s_x^2 s_y^2} = \frac{(310.0)^2}{(4.84)(56{,}725)} = .3500$ (Excel: $R^2 = .3496$) 35.00% of the variation in the electricity use is explained by the variation in the number of occupants.

$H_0: \beta_1 = 0$

$H_1: \beta_1 \neq 0$

Rejection region: $t > t_{\alpha/2,n-2} = t_{.025,198} \approx 1.972$ or $t < -t_{\alpha/2,n-2} = -t_{.025,198} \approx -1.972$

$s_{b_1} = \frac{s_\varepsilon}{\sqrt{(n-1)s_x^2}} = \frac{191.1}{\sqrt{(200-1)(4.84)}} = 6.16$

$t = \frac{b_1 - \beta_1}{s_{b_1}} = \frac{64.05 - 0}{6.16} = 10.39$ (Excel: $t = 10.32$, p–value = 0.) There is enough evidence of a linear relationship.

© 2012 Cengage Learning. All Rights Reserved. May not be scanned, copied or duplicated, or posted to a publicly accessible website, in whole or in part.

16.38 $SSE = (n-1)\left(s_y^2 - \frac{s_{xy}^2}{s_x^2}\right) = (30-1)\left(11.24 - \frac{(-10.78)^2}{35.47}\right) = 230.9$

$s_\varepsilon = \sqrt{\frac{SSE}{n-2}} = \sqrt{\frac{230.9}{30-2}} = 2.872$ (Excel: $s_\varepsilon = 2.873$).

$H_0: \beta_1 = 0$

$H_1: \beta_1 \neq 0$

Rejection region: $t > t_{\alpha/2,n-2} = t_{.025,28} = 2.048$ or $t < -t_{\alpha/2,n-2} = -t_{.025,28} = -2.048$

$s_{b_1} = \frac{s_\varepsilon}{\sqrt{(n-1)s_x^2}} = \frac{2.872}{\sqrt{(30-1)(35.47)}} = .08955$

$t = \frac{b_1 - \beta_1}{s_{b_1}} = \frac{-.3039 - 0}{.08955} = -3.39$ (Excel: t = –3.39, p–value = .0021.) There is sufficient evidence to conclude that office rents and vacancy rates are linearly related.

16.40 a $R^2 = \frac{s_{xy}^2}{s_x^2 s_y^2} = \frac{(.8258)^2}{(16.07)(1.283)} = .0331$ (Excel: $R^2 = .0331$) 3.31% of the variation in percentage of defectives is explained by the variation in aptitude test scores.

b. $SSE = (n-1)\left(s_y^2 - \frac{s_{xy}^2}{s_x^2}\right) = (45-1)\left(1.283 - \frac{(.8258)^2}{16.07}\right) = 54.58$

$s_\varepsilon = \sqrt{\frac{SSE}{n-2}} = \sqrt{\frac{54.58}{45-2}} = 1.127$ (Excel: $s_\varepsilon = 1.127$).

$H_0: \beta_1 = 0$

$H_1: \beta_1 \neq 0$

Rejection region: $t > t_{\alpha/2,n-2} = t_{.025,43} \approx 2.014$ or $t < -t_{\alpha/2,n-2} = -t_{.025,43} \approx -2.014$

$s_{b_1} = \frac{s_\varepsilon}{\sqrt{(n-1)s_x^2}} = \frac{1.127}{\sqrt{(45-1)(16.07)}} = .04238$

$t = \frac{b_1 - \beta_1}{s_{b_1}} = \frac{.0516 - 0}{.04238} = 1.22$ (Excel: t = 1.21, p–value = .2319) There is not enough evidence to conclude that aptitude test scores and percentage of defectives are linearly related.

16.42 $H_0: \rho = 0$

$H_1: \rho \neq 0$

Rejection region: $t > t_{\alpha/2,n-2} = t_{.025,58} \approx 2.000$ or $t < -t_{\alpha/2,n-2} = -t_{.025,58} = -2.000$

© 2012 Cengage Learning. All Rights Reserved. May not be scanned, copied or duplicated, or posted to a publicly accessible website, in whole or in part.

$$r = \frac{s_{xy}}{s_x s_y} = \frac{51.86}{\sqrt{(193.9)(47.96)}} = .5378$$

$t = r\sqrt{\frac{n-2}{1-r^2}} = (.5378)\sqrt{\frac{60-2}{1-(.5378)^2}} = 4.86$ (Excel: t = 4.86, p–value = 0) This result is identical to the one produced in Exercise 16.6.

16.44 $H_0: \rho = 0$

$H_1: \rho > 0$

Rejection region: $t > t_{\alpha,n-2} = t_{.05,229} \approx 1.645$

$$r = \frac{s_{xy}}{s_x s_y} = \frac{20.55}{\sqrt{(108.3)(19.80)}} = .4438$$

$t = r\sqrt{\frac{n-2}{1-r^2}} = (.4438)\sqrt{\frac{231-2}{1-(.4438)^2}} = 7.49$ (Excel: t = 7.49, p–value = 0.) There is evidence of a positive linear relationship between cigarettes smoked and the number of sick days.

16.46

	A	B	C	D	E	F
1	SUMMARY OUTPUT					
2						
3	*Regression Statistics*					
4	Multiple R	0.3512				
5	R Square	0.1234				
6	Adjusted R Square	0.1229				
7	Standard Error	32684				
8	Observations	1681				
9						
10	ANOVA					
11		*df*	*SS*	*MS*	*F*	*Significance F*
12	Regression	1	252,422,349,567	252,422,349,567	236.30	5.43E-50
13	Residual	1679	1,793,584,958,955	1,068,245,955		
14	Total	1680	2,046,007,308,522			
15						
16		*Coefficients*	*Standard Error*	*t Stat*	*P-value*	
17	Intercept	-29984	4321	-6.94	5.62E-12	
18	EDUC	4905	319	15.37	5.43E-50	

t = 15.37, p-value = 5.43E-50 ≈ 0. There is enough evidence to infer that there is a positive linear relationship between income and education.

© 2012 Cengage Learning. All Rights Reserved. May not be scanned, copied or duplicated, or posted to a publicly accessible website, in whole or in part.

16.48

	A	B	C	D	E	F
1	SUMMARY OUTPUT					
2						
3	*Regression Statistics*					
4	Multiple R	0.1545				
5	R Square	0.0239				
6	Adjusted R Square	0.0233				
7	Standard Error	2.95				
8	Observations	1774				
9						
10	ANOVA					
11		*df*	*SS*	*MS*	*F*	*Significance F*
12	Regression	1	376.19	376.19	43.33	6.06E-11
13	Residual	1772	15383	8.68		
14	Total	1773	15759			
15						
16		*Coefficients*	*Standard Error*	*t Stat*	*P-value*	
17	Intercept	6.56	0.204	32.11	1.19E-178	
18	AGE	0.0265	0.0040	6.58	6.062E-11	

t = 6.58, p-value = 6.06E-11 ≈ 0. There is enough evidence to infer that Age and intention to vote are linearly related.

16.50

	A	B	C	D	E	F
1	SUMMARY OUTPUT					
2						
3	*Regression Statistics*					
4	Multiple R	0.2665				
5	R Square	0.0710				
6	Adjusted R Square	0.0698				
7	Standard Error	1.91				
8	Observations	797				
9						
10	ANOVA					
11		*df*	*SS*	*MS*	*F*	*Significance F*
12	Regression	1	220.58	220.58	60.77	2.01E-14
13	Residual	795	2885.47	3.63		
14	Total	796	3106.05			
15						
16		*Coefficients*	*Standard Error*	*t Stat*	*P-value*	
17	Intercept	2.98	0.100	29.72	3.8E-131	
18	INCOME	0.0000142	0.0000018	7.80	2.01E-14	

t = 7.80, p-value = 2.01E-14 ≈ 0. There is enough evidence to infer that there is a linear relationship between income and position on the question should the government reduce income differences between rich and poor.

© 2012 Cengage Learning. All Rights Reserved. May not be scanned, copied or duplicated, or posted to a publicly accessible website, in whole or in part.

16.52

	A	B	C	D	E	F
1	SUMMARY OUTPUT					
2						
3	*Regression Statistics*					
4	Multiple R	0.2392				
5	R Square	0.0572				
6	Adjusted R Square	0.0565				
7	Standard Error	2.59				
8	Observations	1321				
9						
10	ANOVA					
11		*df*	*SS*	*MS*	*F*	*Significance F*
12	Regression	1	535.0	534.98	80.05	1.21E-18
13	Residual	1319	8814.6	6.68		
14	Total	1320	9349.6			
15						
16		*Coefficients*	*Standard Error*	*t Stat*	*P-value*	
17	Intercept	5.79	0.322	17.98	7.70E-65	
18	EDUC	-0.210	0.0235	-8.95	1.21E-18	

$t = -8.95$, p-value = 1.21E-18 ≈ 0. There is enough evidence to conclude that more educated people watch less television.

16.54 The prediction interval provides a prediction for a value of y. The confidence interval estimator of the expected value of y is an estimator of the population mean for a given x.

16.56 $\hat{y} = b_0 + b_1 x_g = 475.2 - 39.17(8) = 161.8$

Confidence interval estimate: $\hat{y} \pm t_{\alpha/2,n-2} s_\varepsilon \sqrt{\frac{1}{n} + \frac{(x_g - \bar{x})^2}{(n-1)s_x^2}}$ (where $t_{\alpha/2,n-2} = t_{.05,8} = 1.860$)

$$= 161.8 \pm 1.860(31.35)\sqrt{\frac{1}{10} + \frac{(8-8.20)^2}{(10-1)(.24)}} = 161.8 \pm 20.01$$

LCL = 141.8, UCL = 181.8 (Excel: 141.7, 182.0)

© 2012 Cengage Learning. All Rights Reserved. May not be scanned, copied or duplicated, or posted to a publicly accessible website, in whole or in part.

16.58 $\hat{y} = b_0 + b_1 x_g = -100{,}652 + 1{,}513(80) = 20{,}388$

Prediction interval: $\hat{y} \pm t_{\alpha/2,n-2} s_\varepsilon \sqrt{1 + \frac{1}{n} + \frac{(x_g - \bar{x})^2}{(n-1)s_x^2}}$ (where $t_{\alpha/2,n-2} = t_{.05,8} = 1.860$)

$$= 20{,}388 \pm 1.860(3{,}522)\sqrt{1 + \frac{1}{10} + \frac{(80 - 80.5)^2}{(10-1)(48.50)}} = 20{,}388 \pm 6{,}872$$

Lower prediction limit = 13,516, Upper prediction limit = 27,260 (Excel: 13,518, 27,258)

16.60 $\hat{y} = b_0 + b_1 x_g = 190.4 + 1.465(25) = 227.0$

a Prediction interval: $\hat{y} \pm t_{\alpha/2,n-2} s_\varepsilon \sqrt{1 + \frac{1}{n} + \frac{(x_g - \bar{x})^2}{(n-1)s_x^2}}$ (where $t_{\alpha/2,n-2} = t_{.025,48} \approx 2.009$)

$$= 227.0 \pm 2.009(19.41)\sqrt{1 + \frac{1}{50} + \frac{(25 - 13.68)^2}{(50-1)(59.32)}} = 227.0 \pm 40.22$$

Lower prediction limit = 186.8, Upper prediction limit = 267.2 (Excel: 186.8, 267.3)

b $\hat{y} = b_0 + b_1 x_g = 190.4 + 1.465(12) = 208.0$

Confidence interval estimate: $\hat{y} \pm t_{\alpha/2,n-2} s_\varepsilon \sqrt{\frac{1}{n} + \frac{(x_g - \bar{x})^2}{(n-1)s_x^2}}$ (where $t_{\alpha/2,n-2} = t_{.005,48} = 2.678$)

$$= 208.0 \pm 2.678(19.41)\sqrt{\frac{1}{50} + \frac{(12 - 13.68)^2}{(50-1)(59.32)}} = 208.0 \pm 7.527$$

LCL = 200.5, UCL = 215.5 (Excel: 200.4, 215.5)

16.62 $\hat{y} = b_0 + b_1 x_g = 30.64 - .1169(25) = 27.72$

Prediction interval: $\hat{y} \pm t_{\alpha/2,n-2} s_\varepsilon \sqrt{1 + \frac{1}{n} + \frac{(x_g - \bar{x})^2}{(n-1)s_x^2}}$ (where $t_{\alpha/2,n-2} = t_{.025,78} \approx 1.990$)

$$= 27.72 \pm 1.990(1.813)\sqrt{1 + \frac{1}{80} + \frac{(25 - 37.29)^2}{(80-1)(55.11)}} = 27.72 \pm 3.707$$

Lower prediction limit = 24.01, Upper prediction limit = 31.43 (Excel: 24.02, 31.40)

16.64 $\hat{y} = b_0 + b_1 x_g = 23.10 + 5.347(5) = 49.84$

a Prediction interval: $\hat{y} \pm t_{\alpha/2,n-2} s_\varepsilon \sqrt{1 + \frac{1}{n} + \frac{(x_g - \bar{x})^2}{(n-1)s_x^2}}$ (where $t_{\alpha/2,n-2} = t_{.025,83} \approx 1.990$)

© 2012 Cengage Learning. All Rights Reserved. May not be scanned, copied or duplicated, or posted to a publicly accessible website, in whole or in part.

$$= 49.84 \pm 1.990(11.10)\sqrt{1 + \frac{1}{85} + \frac{(5 - 4.885)^2}{(85-1)(4.270)}} = 49.84 \pm 22.22$$

Lower prediction limit = 27.62, Upper prediction limit = 72.06 (Excel:27.62, 72.06)

b $\hat{y} = b_0 + b_1 x_g = 23.10 + 5.347(2) = 33.79$

Confidence interval estimate: $\hat{y} \pm t_{\alpha/2, n-2} s_\varepsilon \sqrt{\frac{1}{n} + \frac{(x_g - \bar{x})^2}{(n-1)s_x^2}}$

$$= 33.79 \pm 1.990(11.10)\sqrt{\frac{1}{85} + \frac{(2 - 4.885)^2}{(85-1)(4.270)}} = 33.79 \pm 4.131$$

LCL = 29.66, UCL = 37.92 (Excel: 29.67, 37.93)

16.66 $\hat{y} = b_0 + b_1 x_g = 29.39 - .00138(500) = 28.70$

Prediction interval: $\hat{y} \pm t_{\alpha/2, n-2} s_\varepsilon \sqrt{1 + \frac{1}{n} + \frac{(x_g - \bar{x})^2}{(n-1)s_x^2}}$ (where $t_{\alpha/2, n-2} = t_{.005, 58} \approx 2.660$)

$$= 28.70 \pm 2.660(1.889)\sqrt{1 + \frac{1}{60} + \frac{(500 - 1{,}199)^2}{(60-1)(59{,}153)}} = 28.70 \pm 5.404$$

Lower prediction limit = 23.30, Upper prediction limit = 34.10 (Excel: 23.29, 34.11)

16.68 $\hat{y} = b_0 + b_1 x_g = 153.9 + 1.959(50) = 251.9$

Prediction interval: $\hat{y} \pm t_{\alpha/2, n-2} s_\varepsilon \sqrt{1 + \frac{1}{n} + \frac{(x_g - \bar{x})^2}{(n-1)s_x^2}}$ (where $t_{\alpha/2, n-2} = t_{.05, 148} \approx 1.656$)

$$= 251.9 \pm 1.656(36.93)\sqrt{1 + \frac{1}{150} + \frac{(50 - 59.42)^2}{(150-1)(115.2)}} = 251.9 \pm 61.52$$

Lower prediction limit = 190.4, Upper prediction limit = 313.4 (Excel: 190.3, 313.3)

16.70 a $\hat{y} = b_0 + b_1 x_g = 17.94 + .604(72) = 61.43$

Confidence interval: $\hat{y} \pm t_{\alpha/2, n-2} s_\varepsilon \sqrt{\frac{1}{n} + \frac{(x_g - \bar{x})^2}{(n-1)s_x^2}}$ (where $t_{\alpha/2, n-2} = t_{.025, 248} \approx 1.96$)

$$= 61.43 \pm 1.96(8.28\sqrt{\frac{1}{250} + \frac{(72 - 68.95)^2}{(250-1)(9.966)}} = 61.43 \pm 1.43$$

Lower confidence limit = 60.00, Upper confidence limit = 62.86 (Excel: 59.99, 62.86)

b $\hat{y} = b_0 + b_1 x_g = 17.94 + .604(66) = 57.80$

© 2012 Cengage Learning. All Rights Reserved. May not be scanned, copied or duplicated, or posted to a publicly accessible website, in whole or in part.

Prediction interval: $\hat{y} \pm t_{\alpha/2,n-2} s_\varepsilon \sqrt{1+\frac{1}{n}+\frac{(x_g-\bar{x})^2}{(n-1)s_x^2}}$ (where $t_{\alpha/2,n-2} = t_{.025,248} \approx 1.96$)

$$= 57.80 \pm 1.96(8.28\sqrt{1+\frac{1}{250}+\frac{(66-68.95)^2}{(250-1)(9.966)}} = 57.80 \pm 16.29$$

Lower prediction limit = 41.51, Upper prediction limit = 74.09 (Excel: 41.43, 74.18)

16.72 16.71 $\hat{y} = b_0 + b_1 x_g = 89.81 + .0514(80) = 93.92$

Prediction interval: $\hat{y} \pm t_{\alpha/2,n-2} s_\varepsilon \sqrt{1+\frac{1}{n}+\frac{(x_g-\bar{x})^2}{(n-1)s_x^2}}$ where $t_{\alpha/2,n-2} = t_{.05,43} \approx 1.679$

$$= 93.92 \pm 1.679(1.127)\sqrt{1+\frac{1}{45}+\frac{(80-79.47)^2}{(45-1)(16.07)}} = 93.92 \pm 1.91$$

Lower prediction limit = 92.01, Upper prediction limit = 95.83 (Excel: 92.00, 95.83)

16.74

	A	B
1	**Prediction Interval**	
2		
3		
4		INCOME
5	Predicted Value	19,062
6		
7	Prediction Interval	
8	Lower Limit	(45,097)
9	Upper Limit	83,220
10		
11	Interval Estimate of Expected Value	
12	Lower Limit	16,466
13	Upper Limit	21,657

LCL = 16,466, UCL = 21,657

© 2012 Cengage Learning. All Rights Reserved. May not be scanned, copied or duplicated, or posted to a publicly accessible website, in whole or in part.

16.76

	A	B
1	**Prediction Interval**	
2		
3		
4		TIME4
5	Predicted Value	60.41
6		
7	Prediction Interval	
8	Lower Limit	-83.99
9	Upper Limit	204.81
10		
11	Interval Estimate of Expected Value	
12	Lower Limit	53.27
13	Upper Limit	67.55

Lower prediction limit = 0 (increased from -83.09), Upper prediction limit = 204.81

16.78

	A	B
1	**Prediction Interval**	
2		
3		
4		TVHOURS
5	Predicted Value	3.27
6		
7	Prediction Interval	
8	Lower Limit	-0.98
9	Upper Limit	7.53
10		
11	Interval Estimate of Expected Value	
12	Lower Limit	3.15
13	Upper Limit	3.40

LCL = 3.15, UCL = 3.40

© 2012 Cengage Learning. All Rights Reserved. May not be scanned, copied or duplicated, or posted to a publicly accessible website, in whole or in part.

16.80

	A	B
1	**Prediction Interval**	
2		
3		
4		TVHOURS
5	Predicted Value	4.11
6		
7	Prediction Interval	
8	Lower Limit	-0.15
9	Upper Limit	8.38
10		
11	Interval Estimate of Expected Value	
12	Lower Limit	3.88
13	Upper Limit	4.35

Lower prediction limit = 0 (increased from -.15), Upper prediction limit = 8.38

16.82

x_i	y_i	$\hat{y}_i = 9.107 - .0582x$	$e_i = y_i - \hat{y}_i$
23	9.6	10.45	–.85
46	11.3	11.78	–.48
60	12.8	12.60	.20
54	9.8	12.25	–2.45
28	8.9	10.74	–1.84
33	12.5	11.03	1.47
25	12.0	10.56	1.44
31	11.4	10.91	.49
36	12.6	11.20	1.40
88	13.7	14.23	–.53
90	14.4	14.35	.06
99	15.9	14.87	1.03

16.84 a & b

x_i	y_i	$\hat{y} = -24.72 + .9675x$	$e_i = y_i - \hat{y}_i$
42	18	15.92	2.09
34	6	8.18	–2.18
25	0	–.53	.53
35	–1	9.14	–10.14
37	13	11.08	1.92
38	14	12.05	1.96
31	7	5.27	1.73
33	7	7.21	–.21
19	–9	–6.34	–2.66
29	8	3.34	4.66
38	8	12.05	–4.05
28	5	2.37	2.63
29	3	3.34	–.34
36	14	10.11	3.89
18	–7	–7.31	.31

c

© 2012 Cengage Learning. All Rights Reserved. May not be scanned, copied or duplicated, or posted to a publicly accessible website, in whole or in part.

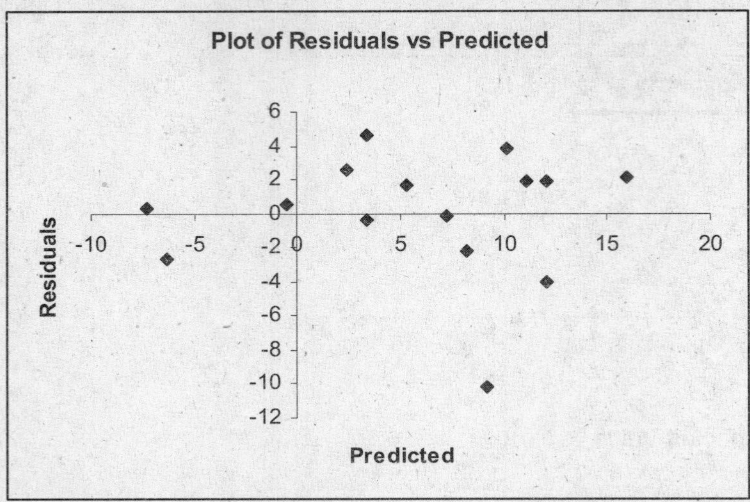

The histograms drawn below are of the standardized residuals, which make it easier to see whether the shape is extremely nonnormal. It also makes it easier to identify outliers. The shape of the resulting histogram is identical to the histogram of the residuals using the equivalent class limits.

16.86 b & c

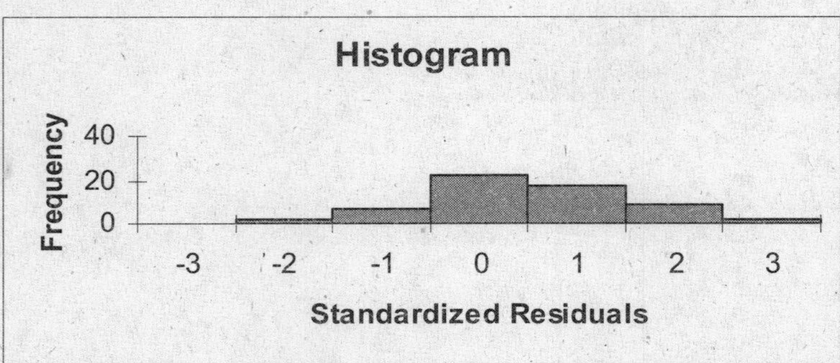

Because the histogram is approximately bell shaped the errors appear to be normally distributed. There are two residuals whose absolute value exceeds 2.0.

© 2012 Cengage Learning. All Rights Reserved. May not be scanned, copied or duplicated, or posted to a publicly accessible website, in whole or in part.

d

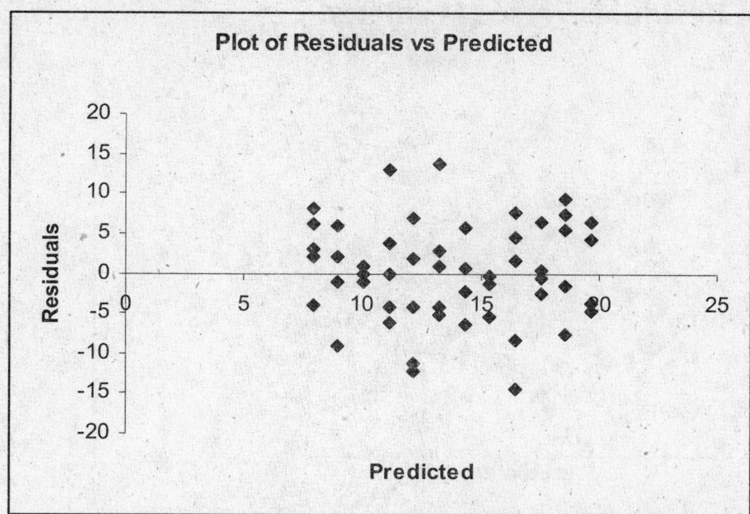

There is no indication of heteroscedasticity.

16.88

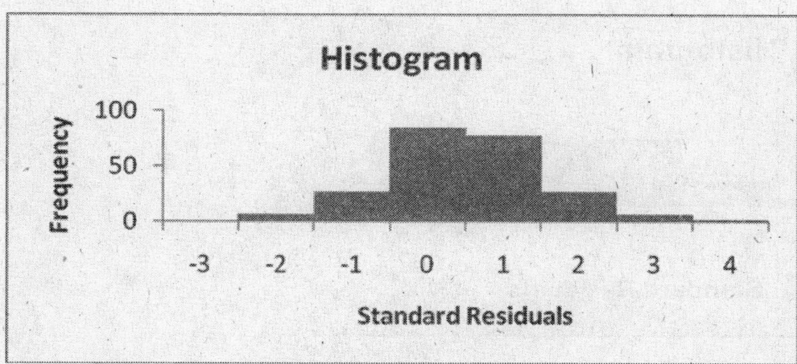

The error variable appears to be normally distributed.

© 2012 Cengage Learning. All Rights Reserved. May not be scanned, copied or duplicated, or posted to a publicly accessible website, in whole or in part.

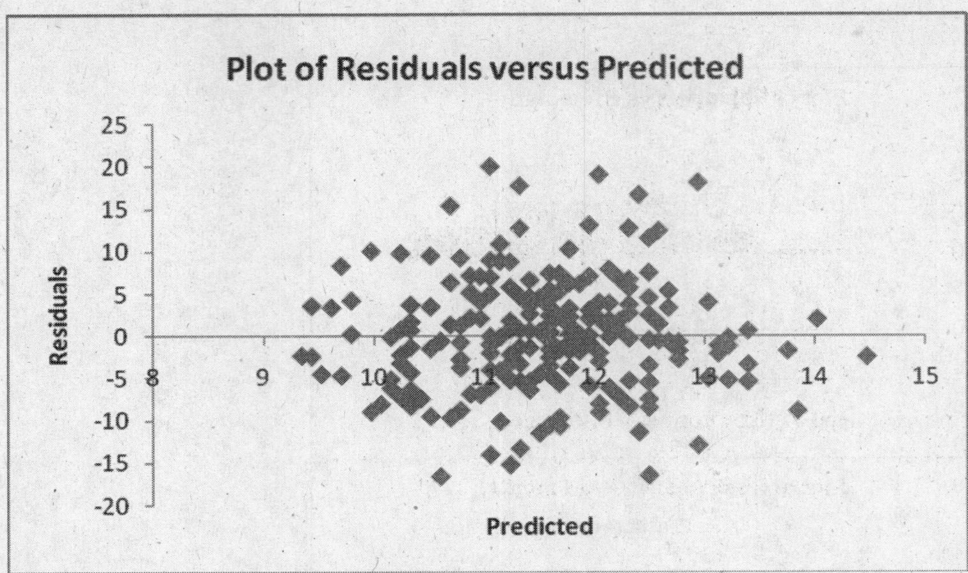

The variance of the error variable is constant.

16.90

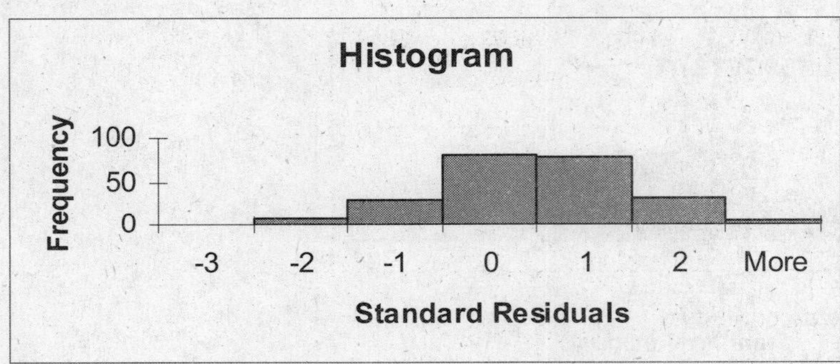

The error variable appears to be normally distributed.

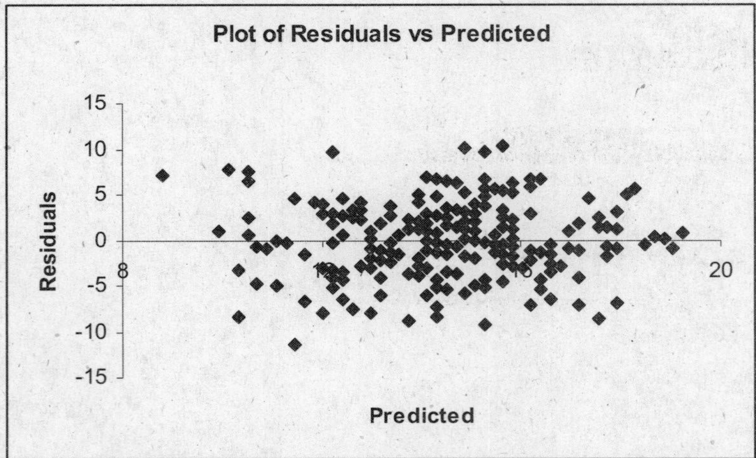

The variance of the error variable is constant.

© 2012 Cengage Learning. All Rights Reserved. May not be scanned, copied or duplicated, or posted to a publicly accessible website, in whole or in part.

16.92

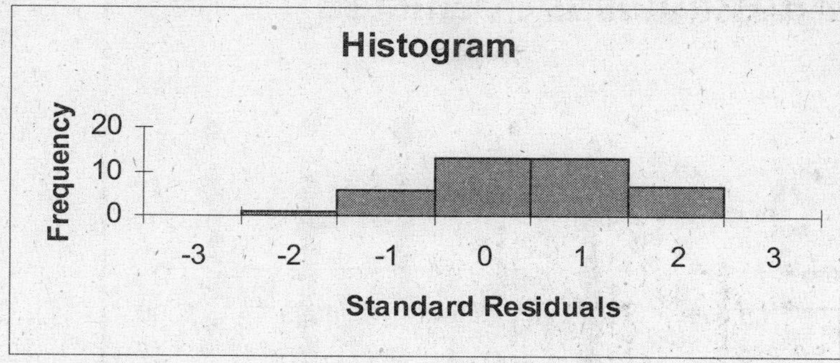

The error variable appears to be normally distributed.

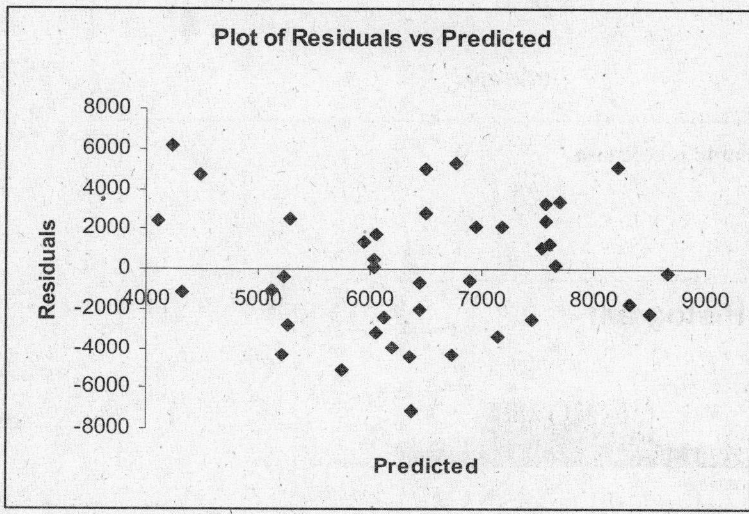

There is no clear sign of heteroscedasticity.

16.94

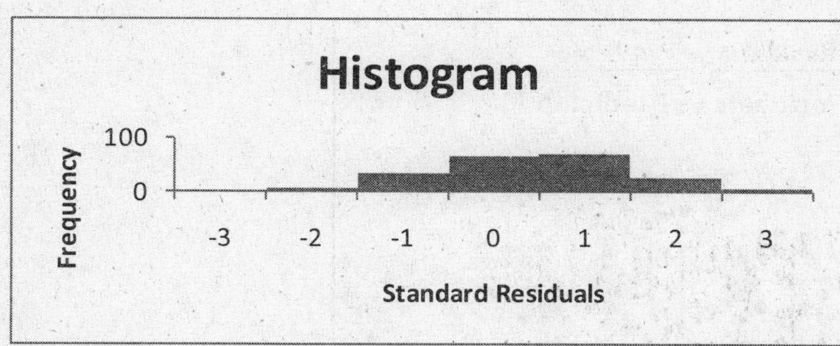

The error variable appears to be normal.

© 2012 Cengage Learning. All Rights Reserved. May not be scanned, copied or duplicated, or posted to a publicly accessible website, in whole or in part.

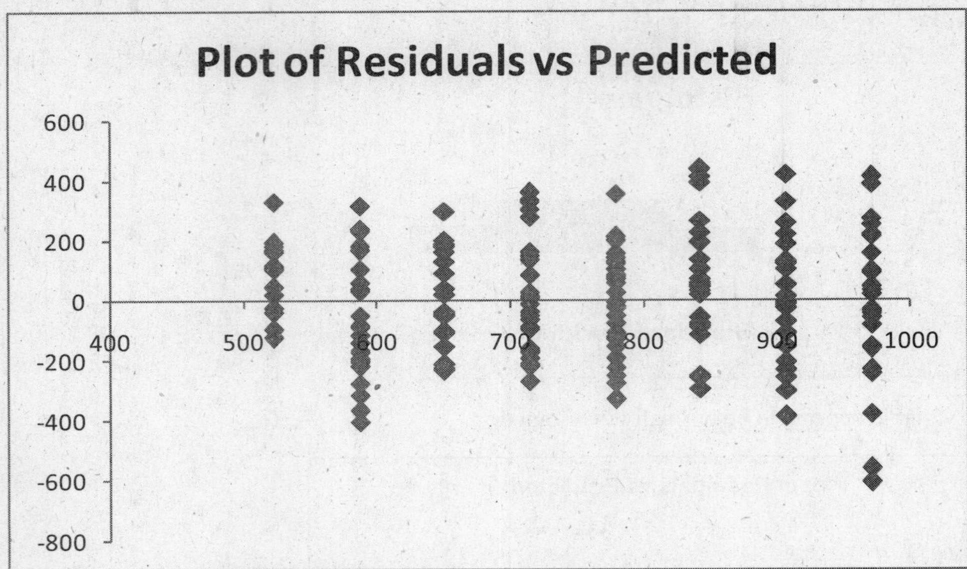

The variance of the error variable is constant.

16.96

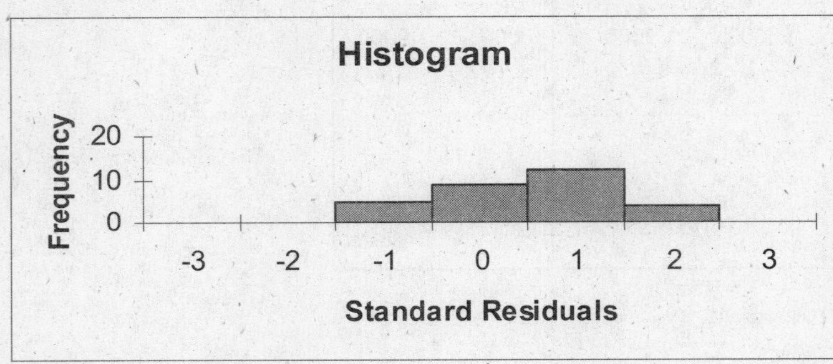

The error variable appears to be normal.

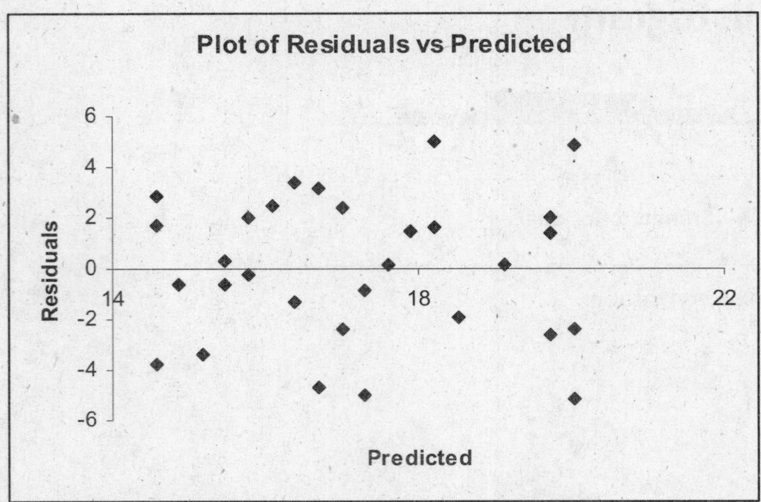

© 2012 Cengage Learning. All Rights Reserved. May not be scanned, copied or duplicated, or posted to a publicly accessible website, in whole or in part.

The variance of the error variable is constant.

16.98

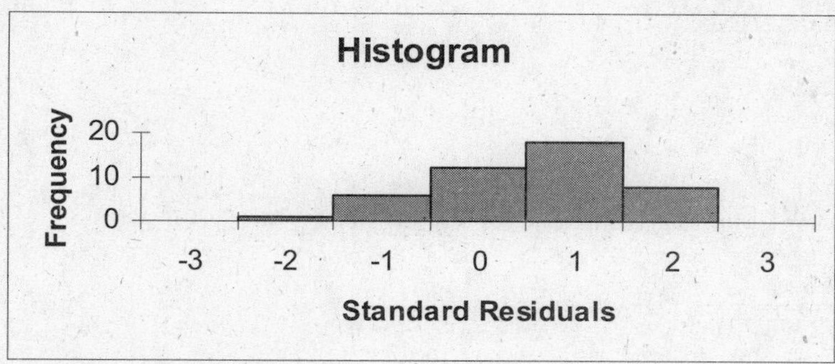

The error variable appears to be normal.

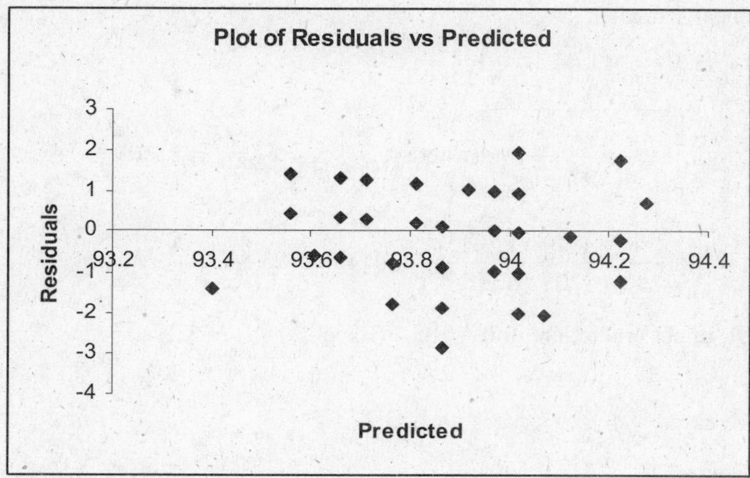

The variance of the error variable is constant.

16.100 a $b_1 = \frac{s_{xy}}{s_x^2} = \frac{936.82}{378.77} = 2.47$ $b_0 = \bar{y} - b_1\bar{x} = 395.21 - 2.47(113.35) = 115.24.$

Regression line: $\hat{y} = 115.24 + 2.47x$ (Excel: $\hat{y} = 114.85 + 2.47x$)

b $b_1 = 2.47$; for each additional month of age, repair costs increase on average by \$2.47.

$b_0 = 114.85$ is the y-intercept.

c $R^2 = \frac{s_{xy}^2}{s_x^2 s_y^2} = \frac{(936.82)^2}{(378.77)(4{,}094.79)} = .5659$ (Excel: $R^2 = .5659$) 56.59% of the variation in repair

costs s explained by the variation in ages.

© 2012 Cengage Learning. All Rights Reserved. May not be scanned, copied or duplicated, or posted to a publicly accessible website, in whole or in part.

d $SSE = (n-1)\left(s_y^2 - \frac{s_{xy}^2}{s_x^2}\right) = (20-1)\left(4{,}094.79 - \frac{(936.82)^2}{378.77}\right) = 33{,}777$

$s_\varepsilon = \sqrt{\frac{SSE}{n-2}} = \sqrt{\frac{33{,}777}{20-2}} = 43.32$ (Excel: $s_\varepsilon = 43.32$).

$H_0: \beta_1 = 0$

$H_1: \beta_1 \neq 0$

Rejection region: $t > t_{\alpha/2,n-2} = t_{.025,18} = 2.101$ or $t < -t_{\alpha/2,n-2} = -t_{.025,18} = -2.101$

$s_{b_1} = \frac{s_\varepsilon}{\sqrt{(n-1)s_x^2}} = \frac{43.32}{\sqrt{(20-1)(378.77)}} = .511$

$t = \frac{b_1 - \beta_1}{s_{b_1}} = \frac{2.47 - 0}{.511} = 4.84$ (Excel: t = 4.84, p–value = .0001. There is enough evidence to infer

that repair costs and age are linearly related.

e $\hat{y} = b_0 + b_1 x_g = 115.24 + 2.47(120) = 411.64$

Prediction interval: $\hat{y} \pm t_{\alpha/2,n-2} s_\varepsilon \sqrt{1 + \frac{1}{n} + \frac{(x_g - \bar{x})^2}{(n-1)s_x^2}}$ (where $t_{\alpha/2,n-2} = t_{.025,18} = 2.101$)

$= 411.64 \pm 2.101(43.32)\sqrt{1 + \frac{1}{20} + \frac{(120 - 113.35)^2}{(20-1)(378.77)}} = 411.64 \pm 93.54$

Lower prediction limit = 318.1, upper prediction limit = 505.2 (Excel: 318.1, 505.2)

16.102a $H_0: \rho = 0$

$H_1: \rho \neq 0$

	A	B
1	**Correlation**	
2		
3	*Tar and Nicotine*	
4	Pearson Coefficient of Correlation	0.9766
5	t Stat	21.78
6	df	23
7	P(T<=t) one tail	0
8	t Critical one tail	1.7139
9	P(T<=t) two tail	0
10	t Critical two tail	2.0687

r = .9766, t = 21.78, p–value = 0. There is sufficient evidence to infer that levels of tar and nicotine are linearly related.

b $H_0: \rho = 0$

$H_1: \rho \neq 0$

© 2012 Cengage Learning. All Rights Reserved. May not be scanned, copied or duplicated, or posted to a publicly accessible website, in whole or in part.

	A	B
1	**Correlation**	
2		
3	*Nicotine and CO*	
4	Pearson Coefficient of Correlation	0.9259
5	t Stat	11.76
6	df	23
7	P(T<=t) one tail	0
8	t Critical one tail	1.7139
9	P(T<=t) two tail	0
10	t Critical two tail	2.0687

r = .9259, t = 11.76, p–value = 0. There is sufficient evidence to infer that levels of nicotine and carbon monoxide are linearly related.

16.104 $H_0 : \rho = 0$

$H_1 : \rho \neq 0$

Rejection region: $t > t_{\alpha/2,n-2} = t_{.025,48} \approx 2.009$ or $t < -t_{\alpha/2,n-2} = -t_{.025,48} = -2.009$

$$r = \frac{s_{xy}}{s_x s_y} = \frac{13.08}{\sqrt{(90.97)(11.84)}} = .3985 \text{ (Excel: .3984)}$$

$t = r\sqrt{\frac{n-2}{1-r^2}} = (.3985)\sqrt{\frac{50-2}{1-(.3985)^2}} = 3.01$ (Excel: t = 3.01, p–value = .0042). There is enough evidence of a linear relationship. The theory appears to be valid.

16.106 $H_0 : \rho = 0$

$H_1 : \rho > 0$

	A	B	C	D
1	**Correlation**			
2				
3	*Time and Sales*			
4	Pearson Coefficient of Correlation			0.2791
5	t Stat			1.67
6	df			33
7	P(T<=t) one tail			0.0522
8	t Critical one tail			1.6924
9	P(T<=t) two tail			0.1044
10	t Critical two tail			2.0345

t = 1.67, p-value = .0522. There is not enough evidence to infer that when the times between movies increase so do sales.

© 2012 Cengage Learning. All Rights Reserved. May not be scanned, copied or duplicated, or posted to a publicly accessible website, in whole or in part.

16.108 $H_0: \rho = 0$

$H_1: \rho \neq 0$

	A	B
1	**Correlation**	
2		
3	*Hours and GPA*	
4	Pearson Coefficient of Correlation	-0.5748
5	t Stat	-9.88
6	df	198
7	P(T<=t) one tail	0
8	t Critical one tail	1.6526
9	P(T<=t) two tail	0
10	t Critical two tail	1.9720

r = t = –9.88, p–value = 0. There is enough evidence of a linear relationship between time spent at part time jobs and grade point average.

© 2012 Cengage Learning. All Rights Reserved. May not be scanned, copied or duplicated, or posted to a publicly accessible website, in whole or in part.

Appendix 16

A16.2 Two-way analysis of variance

$H_0: \mu_1 = \mu_2 = \mu_3 = \mu_4$

H_1 : At least two means differ

	A	B	C	D	E	F	G
40	ANOVA						
41	*Source of Variation*	*SS*	*df*	*MS*	*F*	*P-value*	*F crit*
42	Rows	3708.8	28	132.46	8.63	6.52E-15	1.61
43	Columns	997.0	3	332.33	21.64	1.77E-10	2.71
44	Error	1289.8	84	15.35			
45							
46	Total	5995.5	115				

F = 21.64; p-value = 0. There is enough evidence to conclude that there are differences in the decrease in test scores between the four types of breakfast meals.

A16.4 t-test of ρ or t-test of β_1

$H_0: \rho = 0$

$H_1: \rho > 0$

	A	B	C	D
1	**Correlation**			
2				
3	*Age and Duration*			
4	Pearson Coefficient of Correlation			0.558
5	t Stat			7.90
6	df			138
7	P(T<=t) one tail			0
8	t Critical one tail			1.6560
9	P(T<=t) two tail			0
10	t Critical two tail			1.9773

t = 7.90; p-value = 0. There is overwhelming evidence to infer that the older the patient the longer it takes for the symptoms to disappear?

A16.6 Question 1: Equal-variances t-test of $\mu_1 - \mu_2$

$H_0: (\mu_1 - \mu_2) = 0$

$H_1: (\mu_1 - \mu_2) < 0$

Two-tail F test: F = .984, p-value = .8887; use equal-variances t-test

© 2012 Cengage Learning. All Rights Reserved. May not be scanned, copied or duplicated, or posted to a publicly accessible website, in whole or in part.

	A	B	C
1	t-Test: Two-Sample Assuming Equal Variances		
2			
3		*US Days*	*Canada Days*
4	Mean	26.98	29.44
5	Variance	55.90	56.82
6	Observations	300	300
7	Pooled Variance	56.36	
8	Hypothesized Mean Difference	0	
9	df	598	
10	t Stat	-4.00	
11	P(T<=t) one-tail	0.0000	
12	t Critical one-tail	1.6474	
13	P(T<=t) two-tail	0.0001	
14	t Critical two-tail	1.9639	

t = –4.00, p-value = 0. There is enough evidence to indicate that recovery is faster in the United States.

Question 2: z-tests of $p_1 - p_2$ (case 1)

$H_0: (p_1 - p_2) = 0$

$H_1: (p_1 - p_2) < 0$

	A	B	C	D
1	**z-Test: Two Proportions**			
2				
3			*U.S.*	*Canada*
4	Sample Proportions		0.6267	0.6867
5	Observations		300	300
6	Hypothesized Difference		0	
7	z Stat		-1.55	
8	P(Z<=z) one tail		0.0609	
9	z Critical one-tail		1.6449	
10	P(Z<=z) two-tail		0.1218	
11	z Critical two-tail		1.9600	

z = –1.55, p-value = .0609. There is not enough evidence to infer that recovery is faster in the United States.

© 2012 Cengage Learning. All Rights Reserved. May not be scanned, copied or duplicated, or posted to a publicly accessible website, in whole or in part.

6 months after heart attack:

	A	B	C	D
1	**z-Test: Two Proportions**			
2				
3			*U.S.*	*Canada*
4	Sample Proportions		0.1867	0.1733
5	Observations		300	300
6	Hypothesized Difference		0	
7	z Stat		0.43	
8	P(Z<=z) one tail		0.3354	
9	z Critical one-tail		1.6449	
10	P(Z<=z) two-tail		0.6708	
11	z Critical two-tail		1.9600	

z = .43, p-value = 1 - .3354 = .6646. There is no evidence to infer that recovery is faster in the United States.

12 months after heart attack

	A	B	C	D
1	**z-Test: Two Proportions**			
2				
3			*U.S.*	*Canada*
4	Sample Proportions		0.1167	0.1100
5	Observations		300	300
6	Hypothesized Difference		0	
7	z Stat		0.26	
8	P(Z<=z) one tail		0.3984	
9	z Critical one-tail		1.6449	
10	P(Z<=z) two-tail		0.7968	
11	z Critical two-tail		1.9600	

z = .26, p-value = 1 – .3984 = .6016. There is no evidence to infer that recovery is faster in the United States.

A16.8 t-test of μ_D

$$H_0: \mu_D = 0$$

$$H_1: \mu_D < 0$$

© 2012 Cengage Learning. All Rights Reserved. May not be scanned, copied or duplicated, or posted to a publicly accessible website, in whole or in part.

	A	B	C
1	t-Test: Paired Two Sample for Means		
2			
3		*No-Slide*	*Slide*
4	Mean	3.73	3.78
5	Variance	0.0653	0.0727
6	Observations	25	25
7	Pearson Correlation	0.96	
8	Hypothesized Mean Difference	0	
9	df	24	
10	t Stat	-3.04	
11	P(T<=t) one-tail	0.0028	
12	t Critical one-tail	1.7109	
13	P(T<=t) two-tail	0.0057	
14	t Critical two-tail	2.0639	

t = –3.04, p-value = .0028. There is overwhelming evidence to indicate that sliding is slower.

A16.10 Simple linear regression with cholesterol reduction (Before – After) as the dependent variable

a t-test of β_1 or test of ρ

$$H_0: \beta_1 = 0$$

$$H_1: \beta_1 \neq 0$$

We used the t-test of β_1 because parts (b) and (c) use the regression equation to predict and estimate.

	A	B	C	D	E	F
1	SUMMARY OUTPUT					
2						
3	*Regression Statistics*					
4	Multiple R	0.7138				
5	R Square	0.5095				
6	Adjusted R Square	0.4993				
7	Standard Error	10.53				
8	Observations	50				
9						
10	ANOVA					
11		*df*	*SS*	*MS*	*F*	*Significance F*
12	Regression	1	5528	5528.5	49.87	5.92E-09
13	Residual	48	5322	110.9		
14	Total	49	10850			
15						
16		*Coefficients*	*Standard Error*	*t Stat*	*P-value*	
17	Intercept	2.05	3.94	0.52	0.6051	
18	Exercise	0.0909	0.0129	7.06	5.92E-09	

t = 7.06; p-value = 0. There is overwhelming evidence to infer that exercise and cholesterol reduction are related.

© 2012 Cengage Learning. All Rights Reserved. May not be scanned, copied or duplicated, or posted to a publicly accessible website, in whole or in part.

b Prediction interval

	A	B	C
1	**Prediction Interval**		
2			
3			Reduction
4			
5	Predicted value		11.14
6			
7	Prediction Interval		
8	Lower limit		-10.76
9	Upper limit		33.05
10			
11	Interval Estimate of Expected Valu		
12	Lower limit		5.54
13	Upper limit		16.75

The cholesterol reduction is predicted to fall between −10.76 and 33.05.

c Confidence interval estimator of the expected value of y

	A	B	C
1	**Prediction Interval**		
2			
3			Reduction
4			
5	Predicted value		12.96
6			
7	Prediction Interval		
8	Lower limit		-8.83
9	Upper limit		34.76
10			
11	Interval Estimate of Expected Valu		
12	Lower limit		7.79
13	Upper limit		18.14

We estimate that the mean reduction in cholesterol lies between 7.79 and 18.14.

A16.12 a One-way analysis of variance

$H_0: \mu_1 = \mu_2 = \mu_3$

H_1 : At least two means differ

	A	B	C	D	E	F	G
10	ANOVA						
11	*Source of Variation*	*SS*	*df*	*MS*	*F*	*P-value*	*F crit*
12	Between Groups	1.65	2	0.823	0.1332	0.8753	3.0259
13	Within Groups	1847.2	299	6.18			
14							
15	Total	1848.9	301				

© 2012 Cengage Learning. All Rights Reserved. May not be scanned, copied or duplicated, or posted to a publicly accessible website, in whole or in part.

F = .1332; p-value = .8753. There is no evidence to infer that there are differences between the three groups of patients.

b One-way analysis of variance

$H_0: \mu_1 = \mu_2 = \mu_3$

H_1: At least two means differ

	A	B	C	D	E	F	G
10	ANOVA						
11	*Source of Variation*	*SS*	*df*	*MS*	*F*	*P-value*	*F crit*
12	Between Groups	247.0	2	123.48	15.81	2.96E-07	3.03
13	Within Groups	2334.6	299	7.81			
14							
15	Total	2581.6	301				

F = 15.81; p-value = 0. There is overwhelming evidence to conclude that there are differences between the three groups of patients.

Multiple comparisons

	A	B	C	D	E
1	**Multiple Comparisons**				
2					
3				LSD	Omega
4	Treatment	Treatment	Difference	Alpha = 0.0167	Alpha = 0.05
5	*Group 1 After*	*Group 2 After*	0.099	0.949	0.922
6		*Group 3 After*	-1.867	0.942	0.922
7	*Group 2 After*	*Group 3 After*	-1.965	0.954	0.922

Group 3 differs from both group 1 and group 2. Groups 1 and 2 do not differ.

c. The test assures researchers that the three groups of patients were very similar prior to treatments.

A16.14 a Chi-squared test of a contingency table

H_0: The two variables (year and party) are independent

H_1: The two variables are dependent

© 2012 Cengage Learning. All Rights Reserved. May not be scanned, copied or duplicated, or posted to a publicly accessible website, in whole or in part.

	A	B	C	D	E	F
1	**Contingency Table**					
2						
3		*1990*	*1996*	*2000*	*2004*	TOTAL
4	*Democrats*	154	161	159	152	626
5	*Republicar*	99	100	97	87	383
6	*Other*	22	42	56	60	180
7	TOTAL	275	303	312	299	1189
8						
9	chi-squared Stat			19.27		
10	df			6		
11	p-value			0.0037		
12	chi-squared Critical			12.5916		

$\chi^2 = 19.27$; p-value = .0037. There is overwhelming evidence to infer that party affiliation in Broward County changed over the four years.

b Chi-squared test of a contingency table

H_0 : The two variables (year and party) are independent

H_1 : The two variables are dependent

	A	B	C	D	E	F
1	**Contingency Table**					
2						
3		*1990*	*1996*	*2000*	*2004*	TOTAL
4	*Democrats*	173	157	136	146	612
5	*Republicar*	117	128	117	122	484
6	*Other*	25	43	56	63	187
7	TOTAL	315	328	309	331	1283
8						
9	chi-squared Stat			22.65		
10	df			6		
11	p-value			0.0009		
12	chi-squared Critical			12.5916		

$\chi^2 = 22.65$; p-value = .0009. There is overwhelming evidence to infer that party affiliation in Miami-Dade changed over the four years.

c Chi-squared test of a contingency table

H_0 : The two variables (County and party in 2004) are independent

H_1 : The two variables are dependent

© 2012 Cengage Learning. All Rights Reserved. May not be scanned, copied or duplicated, or posted to a publicly accessible website, in whole or in part.

	A	B	C	D
1	**Contingency Table**			
2				
3		*Broward*	*Miami-Dade*	TOTAL
4	*Democrats*	152	146	298
5	*Republicans*	87	122	209
6	*Other*	60	63	123
7	TOTAL	299	331	630
8				
9	chi-squared Stat			4.44
10	df			2
11	p-value			0.1085
12	chi-squared Critical			5.9915

$\chi^2 = 4.44$; p-value = 1095. There is not enough evidence to infer that party affiliation differ between Broward County and Miami-Dade County.

A16.16 t-estimator of μ

	A	B	C	D
1	**t-Estimate: Mean**			
2				
3				*Commute*
4	Mean			24.54
5	Standard Deviation			11.63
6	LCL			23.64
7	UCL			25.45

Total time spent commuting by all workers:

LCL = 129,142,000 (23.64) = 3,052,916,880 minutes

UCL = 129,142,000 (25.45) = 3,286,663,900 minutes

A16.18 $H_0: (\mu_1 - \mu_2) = 0$

$H_1: (\mu_1 - \mu_2) \neq 0$

Two-tail F test: F = .814, p-value = .0383; Use unequal-variances t-test.

© 2012 Cengage Learning. All Rights Reserved. May not be scanned, copied or duplicated, or posted to a publicly accessible website, in whole or in part.

	A	B	C
1	t-Test: Two-Sample Assuming Unequal Variances		
2			
3		*Democrats*	*Republicans*
4	Mean	2.87	4.60
5	Variance	3.11	3.82
6	Observations	497	337
7	Hypothesized Mean Difference	0	
8	df	671	
9	t Stat	-12.98	
10	P(T<=t) one-tail	7.59E-35	
11	t Critical one-tail	1.6471	
12	P(T<=t) two-tail	1.52E-34	
13	t Critical two-tail	1.9635	

t = -12.98, p-value = 1.52E-34 ≈ 0. There is sufficient evidence to infer that Democrats and Republicans differ In their positions on whether the government should reduce income differences between rich and poor.

A16.20 $H_0: \mu_1 = \mu_2 = \mu_3 = \mu_4$

H_1: At least two means differ

	A	B	C	D	E	F	G
1	Anova: Single Factor						
2							
3	SUMMARY						
4	*Groups*	*Count*	*Sum*	*Average*	*Variance*		
5	Respondent belongs	118	335	2.84	1.54		
6	Spouse belongs	53	154	2.91	1.59		
7	Both belong	23	68	2.96	1.32		
8	Neither belongs	1132	3197	2.82	1.46		
9							
10							
11	ANOVA						
12	*Source of Variation*	*SS*	*df*	*MS*	*F*	*P-value*	*F crit*
13	Between Groups	0.718	3	0.239	0.162	0.9217	2.6116
14	Within Groups	1947.44	1322	1.47			
15							
16	Total	1948.16	1325				

F = .162, p-value = .9217. There is not enough evidence to conclude that there are differences between union households with respect to their position on whether the government should improve the living conditions of poor people.

A16.22 $H_0: \rho = 0$

$H_1: \rho > 0$

© 2012 Cengage Learning. All Rights Reserved. May not be scanned, copied or duplicated, or posted to a publicly accessible website, in whole or in part.

	A	B
1	**Correlation**	
2		
3	*NUMORG and INCOME*	
4	Pearson Coefficient of Correlation	0.0522
5	t Stat	1.87
6	df	1283
7	P(T<=t) one tail	0.0308
8	t Critical one tail	1.646
9	P(T<=t) two tail	0.0616
10	t Critical two tail	1.9618

t = 1.87, p-value = .0308. There is enough evidence to infer that there is a positive linear relationship between income and the number of people working for the company.

A16.24 H_0: $\rho = 0$

H_1: $\rho > 0$

	A	B
1	**Correlation**	
2		
3	*HRS and INCOME*	
4	Pearson Coefficient of Correlation	0.2842
5	t Stat	9.35
6	df	995
7	P(T<=t) one tail	0
8	t Critical one tail	1.6464
9	P(T<=t) two tail	0
10	t Critical two tail	1.9624

t = 9.35, p-value = 0. There is sufficient evidence to infer that the more one works the greater the income.

A16.26 H_0: $\rho = 0$

H_1: $\rho > 0$

© 2012 Cengage Learning. All Rights Reserved. May not be scanned, copied or duplicated, or posted to a publicly accessible website, in whole or in part.

	A	B
1	**Correlation**	
2		
3	*EDUC and PRESTG80*	
4	Pearson Coefficient of Correlation	0.5259
5	t Stat	27.05
6	df	1914
7	P(T<=t) one tail	0
8	t Critical one tail	1.6457
9	P(T<=t) two tail	0
10	t Critical two tail	1.9612

t = 27.05, p-value = 0. There is enough evidence to conclude that there is a positive linear relationship between education and occupation prestige score.

A16.28 H_0: $\rho = 0$

H_1: $\rho \neq 0$

	A	B
1	**Correlation**	
2		
3	*DAYS1 and DAYS2*	
4	Pearson Coefficient of Correlation	0.4820
5	t Stat	16.45
6	df	894
7	P(T<=t) one tail	0
8	t Critical one tail	1.6466
9	P(T<=t) two tail	0
10	t Critical two tail	1.9626

t = 16.45, p-value 0. There is enough evidence to conclude that the number of days watching national news is linearly related to the number of days watching local news in the late afternoon or early evening.

© 2012 Cengage Learning. All Rights Reserved. May not be scanned, copied or duplicated, or posted to a publicly accessible website, in whole or in part.

Chapter 17

17.2

	A	B	C	D	E	F
1	SUMMARY OUTPUT					
2						
3	*Regression Statistics*					
4	Multiple R	0.8734				
5	R Square	0.7629				
6	Adjusted R Square	0.7453				
7	Standard Error	3.75				
8	Observations	30				
9						
10	ANOVA					
11		*df*	*SS*	*MS*	*F*	*Significance F*
12	Regression	2	1223.2	611.59	43.43	0.0000
13	Residual	27	380.2	14.08		
14	Total	29	1603.4			
15						
16		*Coefficients*	*Standard Error*	*t Stat*	*P-value*	
17	Intercept	13.01	3.53	3.69	0.0010	
18	Assignment	0.194	0.200	0.97	0.3417	
19	Midterm	1.11	0.122	9.12	0.0000	

a $\hat{y} = 13.01 + .194x_1 + 1.11x_2$

b The standard error of estimate is $s_\varepsilon = 3.75$. It is an estimate of the standard deviation of the error variable.

c The coefficient of determination is $R^2 = .7629$; 76.29% of the variation in final exam marks is explained by the model.

d H_0: $\beta_1 = \beta_2 = 0$

H_1: At least one β_i is not equal to zero

F = 43.43, p-value = 0. There is enough evidence to conclude that the model is valid.

e $b_1 = .194$; for each addition mark on assignments the final exam mark on average increases by .194 provided that the other variable remains constant.

$b_2 = 1.112$; for each addition midterm mark the final exam mark on average increases by 1.112 provided that the other variable remains constant.

f $H_0 : \beta_1 = 0$

$H_1 : \beta_1 \neq 0$

t = .97, p-value = .3417. There is not enough evidence to infer that assignment marks and final exam marks are linearly related.

© 2012 Cengage Learning. All Rights Reserved. May not be scanned, copied or duplicated, or posted to a publicly accessible website, in whole or in part.

g $H_0 : \beta_2 = 0$

$H_1 : \beta_2 \neq 0$

t = 9.12, p-value = 0. There is sufficient evidence to infer that midterm marks and final exam marks are linearly related.

h

	A	B	C	D
1	**Prediction Interval**			
2				
3			Final	
4				
5	Predicted value		31	
6				
7	Prediction Interval			
8	Lower limit		23	
9	Upper limit		39	
10				
11	Interval Estimate of Expected Value			
12	Lower limit		29	
13	Upper limit		33	

Pat's final exam mark is predicted to lie between 23 and 39

i Pat's predicted final grade: LCL = 12 + 14 + 23 = 49, UCL = 12 + 14 + 39 = 65

17.4 a

	A	B	C	D	E	F
1	SUMMARY OUTPUT					
2						
3	*Regression Statistics*					
4	Multiple R	0.5926				
5	R Square	0.3511				
6	Adjusted R Square	0.3352				
7	Standard Error	6.99				
8	Observations	126				
9						
10	ANOVA					
11		*df*	*SS*	*MS*	*F*	*Significance F*
12	Regression	3	3228	1075.87	22.01	0.0000
13	Residual	122	5965	48.89		
14	Total	125	9192			
15						
16		*Coefficients*	*Standard Error*	*t Stat*	*P-value*	
17	Intercept	-1.97	9.55	-0.21	0.8369	
18	Minor HR	0.666	0.087	7.64	0.0000	
19	Age	0.136	0.524	0.26	0.7961	
20	Years Pro	1.18	0.671	1.75	0.0819	

b b_1 = .666; for each additional minor league home run the number of major league home runs increases on average by .666 provided that the other variables remain constant.

© 2012 Cengage Learning. All Rights Reserved. May not be scanned, copied or duplicated, or posted to a publicly accessible website, in whole or in part.

$b_2 = .136$; for each additional year of age the number of major league home runs increases on average by .14 provided that the other variables remain constant.

$b_3 = 1.18$; for each additional year as a professional the number of major league home runs increases on average by 1.18 provided that the other variables remain constant.

c $s_\varepsilon = 6.99$ and $R^2 = .3511$; the model's fit is not very good.

d $H_0: \beta_1 = \beta_2 = \beta_3 = 0$

H_1: At least one β_i is not equal to zero

F = 22.01, p-value = 0. There is enough evidence to conclude that the model is valid.

e $H_0 : \beta_i = 0$

$H_1 : \beta_i \neq 0$

Minor league home runs: t = 7.64, p-value = 0

Age: t = .26, p-value = .7961

Years professional: t = 1.75, p-value = .0819

At the 5% significance level only the number of minor league home runs is linearly related to the number of major league home runs.

f

	A	B	C	D
1	**Prediction Interval**			
2				
3			Major HR	
4				
5	Predicted value		24.31	
6				
7	Prediction Interval			
8	Lower limit		9.86	
9	Upper limit		38.76	
10				
11	Interval Estimate of Expected Value			
12	Lower limit		20.16	
13	Upper limit		28.45	

We predict that the player will hit between 9.86 (rounded to 10) and 38.76 (rounded to 39) home runs.

© 2012 Cengage Learning. All Rights Reserved. May not be scanned, copied or duplicated, or posted to a publicly accessible website, in whole or in part.

g

	A	B	C	D
1	**Prediction Interval**			
2				
3			Major HR	
4				
5	Predicted value		19.56	
6				
7	Prediction Interval			
8	Lower limit		4.88	
9	Upper limit		34.25	
10				
11	Interval Estimate of Expected Value			
12	Lower limit		14.66	
13	Upper limit		24.47	

It is estimated that the average player will hit between 14.66 and 24.47 home runs.

17.6

	A	B	C	D	E	F
1	SUMMARY OUTPUT					
2						
3	*Regression Statistics*					
4	Multiple R	0.5369				
5	R Square	0.2882				
6	Adjusted R Square	0.2660				
7	Standard Error	2.0302				
8	Observations	100				
9						
10	ANOVA					
11		*df*	*SS*	*MS*	*F*	*Significance F*
12	Regression	3	160.23	53.41	12.96	0.0000
13	Residual	96	395.70	4.12		
14	Total	99	555.93			
15						
16		*Coefficients*	*Standard Error*	*t Stat*	*P-value*	
17	Intercept	0.721	1.87	0.39	0.7006	
18	HS GPA	0.611	0.101	6.06	0.0000	
19	SAT	0.00135	0.00144	0.94	0.3485	
20	Activities	0.0462	0.0641	0.72	0.4720	

b The coefficient of determination is $R^2 = .2882$; 28.82% of the variation in university GPAs is explained by the model.

c H_0: $\beta_1 = \beta_2 = \beta_3 = 0$

H_1: At least one β_i is not equal to zero

F = 12.96, p-value = 0. There is enough evidence to conclude that the model is valid.

© 2012 Cengage Learning. All Rights Reserved. May not be scanned, copied or duplicated, or posted to a publicly accessible website, in whole or in part.

d $H_0 : \beta_i = 0$

$H_1 : \beta_i \neq 0$

High school GPA: t = 6.06, p-value = 0

SAT: t = .94, p-value = .3485

Activities: t = .72, p-value = .4720

At the 5% significance level only the high school GPA is linearly related to the university GPA

e

	A	B	C	D
1	**Prediction Interval**			
2				
3			Univ GPA	
4				
5	Predicted value		8.55	
6				
7	Prediction Interval			
8	Lower limit		4.45	
9	Upper limit		12.65	
10				
11	Interval Estimate of Expected Value			
12	Lower limit		7.79	
13	Upper limit		9.31	

We predict that the student's GPA will fall between 4.45 and 12.00 (12 is the maximum).

f

	A	B	C	D
1	**Prediction Interval**			
2				
3			Univ GPA	
4				
5	Predicted value		7.56	
6				
7	Prediction Interval			
8	Lower limit		4.12	
9	Upper limit		10.99	
10				
11	Interval Estimate of Expected Value			
12	Lower limit		6.90	
13	Upper limit		8.22	

The mean GPA is estimated to lie between 6.90 and 8.22.

© 2012 Cengage Learning. All Rights Reserved. May not be scanned, copied or duplicated, or posted to a publicly accessible website, in whole or in part.

17.8 a

	A	B	C	D	E	F
1	SUMMARY OUTPUT					
2						
3	*Regression Statistics*					
4	Multiple R	0.4125				
5	R Square	0.1702				
6	Adjusted R Square	0.1645				
7	Standard Error	3.67				
8	Observations	440				
9						
10	ANOVA					
11		*df*	*SS*	*MS*	*F*	*Significance F*
12	Regression	3	1205.93	401.98	29.80	1.52E-17
13	Residual	436	5880.39	13.49		
14	Total	439	7086.32			
15						
16		*Coefficients*	*Standard Error*	*t Stat*	*P-value*	
17	Intercept	7.19	1.09	6.59	1.30E-10	
18	HSize	0.0019	0.0006	3.21	0.0014	
19	Children	1.10	0.14	7.84	3.58E-14	
20	Adults	1.04	0.23	4.48	9.58E-06	

b H_0: $\beta_1 = \beta_2 = \beta_3 = 0$

H_1: At least one β_i is not equal to zero

F = 29.80, p-value = 0. There is enough evidence to conclude that the model is valid.

c b_1= .0019; for each additional square foot the amount of garbage increases on average by .0019 pounds holding the other variables constant.

b_2= 1.10; for each additional child in the home the amount of garbage increases on average by 1.10 pounds holding the other variables constant.

b_3= 1.04; for each additional adult at home during the day the amount of garbage increases on average by 1.04 holding the other variables constant.

d $H_0 : \beta_i = 0$

$H_1 : \beta_i \neq 0$

House size : t = 3.21, p-value = .0014

Number of children: t = 7.84 p-value = 0

Number of adults at home: t = 4.48, p-value = 0

All three independent variable are linearly related to the amount of garbage.

© 2012 Cengage Learning. All Rights Reserved. May not be scanned, copied or duplicated, or posted to a publicly accessible website, in whole or in part.

17.10 a

	A	B	C	D	E	F
1	SUMMARY OUTPUT					
2						
3	*Regression Statistics*					
4	Multiple R	0.8608				
5	R Square	0.7411				
6	Adjusted R Square	0.7301				
7	Standard Error	2.66				
8	Observations	100				
9						
10	ANOVA					
11		*df*	*SS*	*MS*	*F*	*Significance F*
12	Regression	4	1930	482.38	67.97	0.0000
13	Residual	95	674	7.10		
14	Total	99	2604			
15						
16		*Coefficients*	*Standard Error*	*t Stat*	*P-value*	
17	Intercept	3.24	5.42	0.60	0.5512	
18	Mother	0.451	0.0545	8.27	0.0000	
19	Father	0.411	0.0498	8.26	0.0000	
20	Gmothers	0.0166	0.0661	0.25	0.8028	
21	Gfathers	0.0869	0.0657	1.32	0.1890	

b $H_0: \beta_1 = \beta_2 = \beta_3 = \beta_4 = 0$

H_1: At least one β_i is not equal to zero

F = 67.97, p-value = 0. There is enough evidence to conclude that the model is valid.

c b_1 = .451; for each one year increase in the mother's age the customer's age increases on average by .451 provided the other variables are constant (which may not be possible because of the multicollinearity).

b_2 = .411; for each one year increase in the father's age the customer's age increases on average by .411 provided the other variables are constant.

b_3= .0166; for each one year increase in the grandmothers' mean age the customer's age increases on average by .0166 provided the other variables are constant.

b_4 = .0869; for each one year increase in the grandfathers' mean age the customer's age increases on average by .0869 provided the other variables are constant.

$H_0 : \beta_i = 0$

$H_1 : \beta_i \neq 0$

Mothers: t = 8.27, p-value = 0

Fathers: t = 8.26, p-value = 0

Grandmothers: t = .25, p-value .8028

Grandfathers: t = 1.32, p-value = .1890

© 2012 Cengage Learning. All Rights Reserved. May not be scanned, copied or duplicated, or posted to a publicly accessible website, in whole or in part.

The ages of mothers and fathers are linearly related to the ages of their children. The other two variables are not.

d

	A	B	C	D
1	**Prediction Interval**			
2				
3			Longvity	
4				
5	Predicted value		71.43	
6				
7	Prediction Interval			
8	Lower limit		65.54	
9	Upper limit		77.31	
10				
11	Interval Estimate of Expected Value			
12	Lower limit		68.85	
13	Upper limit		74.00	

The man is predicted to live to an age between 65.54 and 77.31

e

	A	B	C	D
1	**Prediction Interval**			
2				
3			Longvity	
4				
5	Predicted value		71.71	
6				
7	Prediction Interval			
8	Lower limit		65.65	
9	Upper limit		77.77	
10				
11	Interval Estimate of Expected Value			
12	Lower limit		68.75	
13	Upper limit		74.66	

The mean longevity is estimated to fall between 68.75 and 74.66.

© 2012 Cengage Learning. All Rights Reserved. May not be scanned, copied or duplicated, or posted to a publicly accessible website, in whole or in part.

17.12

	A	B	C	D	E	F
1	SUMMARY OUTPUT					
2						
3	*Regression Statistics*					
4	Multiple R	0.8984				
5	R Square	0.8072				
6	Adjusted R Square	0.7990				
7	Standard Error	7.07				
8	Observations	50				
9						
10	ANOVA					
11		*df*	*SS*	*MS*	*F*	*Significance F*
12	Regression	2	9,832	4,916	98.37	0.0000
13	Residual	47	2,349	49.97		
14	Total	49	12,181			
15						
16		*Coefficients*	*Standard Error*	*t Stat*	*P-value*	
17	Intercept	-28.43	6.89	-4.13	0.0001	
18	Boxes	0.604	0.0557	10.85	0.0000	
19	Weight	0.374	0.0847	4.42	0.0001	

a $\hat{y} = -28.43 + .604x_1 + .374x_2$

b $s_\varepsilon = 7.07$ and $R^2 = .8072$; the model fits well.

c $b_1 = .604$; for each one additional box, the amount of time to unload increases on average by .604 minutes provided the weight is constant.

$b_2 = .374$; for each additional hundred pounds the amount of time to unload increases on average by .374 minutes provided the number of boxes is constant.

$$H_0 : \beta_i = 0$$

$$H_1 : \beta_i \neq 0$$

Boxes: t = 10.85, p-value = 0

Weight: t = 4.42, p-value = .0001

Both variables are linearly related to time to unload.

© 2012 Cengage Learning. All Rights Reserved. May not be scanned, copied or duplicated, or posted to a publicly accessible website, in whole or in part.

d & e

	A	B	C	D
1	**Prediction Interval**			
2				
3			Time	
4				
5	Predicted value		50.70	
6				
7	Prediction Interval			
8	Lower limit		35.16	
9	Upper limit		66.24	
10				
11	Interval Estimate of Expected Value			
12	Lower limit		44.43	
13	Upper limit		56.96	

d It is predicted that the truck will be unloaded in a time between 35.16 and 66.24 minutes.

e The mean time to unload the trucks is estimated to lie between 44.43 and 56.96 minutes.

17.14 a

	A	B	C	D	E	F
1	SUMMARY OUTPUT					
2						
3	*Regression Statistics*					
4	Multiple R	0.6808				
5	R Square	0.4635				
6	Adjusted R Square	0.4446				
7	Standard Error	0.7879				
8	Observations	89				
9						
10	ANOVA					
11		*df*	*SS*	*MS*	*F*	*Significance F*
12	Regression	3	45.60	15.20	24.48	1.64E-11
13	Residual	85	52.77	0.621		
14	Total	88	98.37			
15						
16		*Coefficients*	*Standard Error*	*t Stat*	*P-value*	
17	Intercept	0.466	1.51	0.310	0.7576	
18	UnderGPA	0.0628	0.120	0.524	0.6017	
19	GMAT	0.01128	0.00138	8.16	2.71E-12	
20	Work	0.09259	0.03091	3.00	0.0036	

b H_0: $\beta_1 = \beta_2 = \beta_3 = 0$

H_1: At least one β_i is not equal to zero

F = 24.48, p-value = 1.64E-11 $\approx$ 0. There is sufficient evidence to conclude that the model is valid.

© 2012 Cengage Learning. All Rights Reserved. May not be scanned, copied or duplicated, or posted to a publicly accessible website, in whole or in part.

c $H_0 : \beta_i = 0$

$H_1 : \beta_i \neq 0$

Undergraduate GPA: t = .524, p-value = .6017

GMAT: t = 8.16, p-value = 2.71E-12 ≈ 0

Work experience: t = 3.00, p-value = .0036

Both the GMAT and work experience are linearly related to MBA GPA

7.16

	A	B	C	D	E	F
1	SUMMARY OUTPUT					
2						
3	*Regression Statistics*					
4	Multiple R	0.5024				
5	R Square	0.2524				
6	Adjusted R Square	0.2513				
7	Standard Error	2.60				
8	Observations	1395				
9						
10	ANOVA					
11		*df*	*SS*	*MS*	*F*	*Significance F*
12	Regression	2	3165.4	1582.7	234.93	1.23E-88
13	Residual	1392	9377.6	6.74		
14	Total	1394	12543.0			
15						
16		*Coefficients*	*Standard Error*	*t Stat*	*P-value*	
17	Intercept	9.09	0.236	38.50	2.16E-221	
18	PAEDUC	0.219	0.0225	9.73	1.11E-21	
19	MAEDUC	0.197	0.0256	7.69	2.78E-14	

b $H_0 : \beta_1 = \beta_2 = 0$

H_1 : At least one β_i is not equal to zero

F = 234.93, p-value = 1.23E-88 .≈ 0. There is sufficient evidence to conclude that the model is valid.

c $H_0 : \beta_i = 0$

$H_1 : \beta_i \neq 0$

PAEDUC: t = 9.73, p-value = 1.11E-11 ≈ 0

MAEDUC: t = 7.69, p-value = 2.78E-14 ≈ 0

Both variables are linearly related to EDUC.

d For each additional year of the father's education the offspring's education increases on average by .219 years. For each additional year of the mother's education the offspring's education increases on average by .197 years.

© 2012 Cengage Learning. All Rights Reserved. May not be scanned, copied or duplicated, or posted to a publicly accessible website, in whole or in part.

7.18

	A	B	C	D	E	F
1	SUMMARY OUTPUT					
2						
3	*Regression Statistics*					
4	Multiple R	0.25669				
5	R Square	0.06589				
6	Adjusted R Square	0.05864				
7	Standard Error	1.94				
8	Observations	780				
9						
10	ANOVA					
11		*df*	*SS*	*MS*	*F*	*Significance F*
12	Regression	6	205.4	34.23	9.09	1.27E-09
13	Residual	773	2911.6	3.77		
14	Total	779	3117.0			
15						
16		*Coefficients*	*Standard Error*	*t Stat*	*P-value*	
17	Intercept	4.72	0.484	9.75	2.90E-21	
18	AGE	0.0136	0.0058	2.34	0.01943	
19	EDUC	-0.0913	0.0293	-3.11	0.00192	
20	HRS	-0.0115	0.0049	-2.35	0.01894	
21	PRESTG80	-0.0209	0.0060	-3.47	0.00055	
22	CHILDS	-0.0427	0.0509	-0.84	0.40214	
23	EARNRS	-0.0796	0.0816	-0.98	0.32985	

a $H_0: \beta_1 = \beta_2 = \beta_3 = \beta_4 = \beta_5 = \beta_6 = 0$

H_1: At least one β_i is not equal to zero

F = 9.09, p-value = 1.27E-09 ≈ 0. There is enough evidence to infer that the model is valid.

b $H_0: \beta_i = 0$

$H_1: \beta_i \neq 0$

Variable	t-statistic	p-value
AGE	2.34	.0194
EDUC	-3.11	.0019
HRS	-2.35	.0189
PRESTG80	-3.47	.0006
CHILDS	-.84	.4021
EARNRS	-.98	.3296

Only CHILDS and EARNRS are not linearly related to TVHOURS.

c $R^2 = .0659$, 6.59% of the variation in TVHOURS is explained by the independent variables.

© 2012 Cengage Learning. All Rights Reserved. May not be scanned, copied or duplicated, or posted to a publicly accessible website, in whole or in part.

17.20

	A	B	C	D	E	F
1	SUMMARY OUTPUT					
2						
3	*Regression Statistics*					
4	Multiple R	0.5069				
5	R Square	0.2570				
6	Adjusted R Square	0.2497				
7	Standard Error	29636.9939				
8	Observations	820				
9						
10	ANOVA					
11		*df*	*SS*	*MS*	*F*	*Significance F*
12	Regression	8	246,387,013,867	30,798,376,733	35.06	9.53E-48
13	Residual	811	712,342,991,078	878,351,407		
14	Total	819	958,730,004,945			
15						
16		*Coefficients*	*Standard Error*	*t Stat*	*P-value*	
17	Intercept	-68028	8388	-8.11	1.86E-15	
18	AGE	40.8	101.0	0.40	0.6864	
19	EDUC	3376	428	7.89	9.74E-15	
20	HRS	570	80	7.10	2.75E-12	
21	CHILDS	1561	972	1.61	0.1084	
22	AGEKDBRN	1007	205	4.90	1.14E-06	
23	YEARSJOB	790	135	5.85	7.06E-09	
24	MOREDAYS	197	145	1.36	0.1754	
25	NUMORG	0.303	0.221	1.37	0.1713	

a $H_0: \beta_1 = \beta_2 = \beta_3 = \beta_4 = \beta_5 = \beta_6 = \beta_7 = 0$

H_1: At least one β_i is not equal to zero

F = 35.06, p-value = 9.53E-48 ≈ 0. There is enough evidence to infer that the model is valid.

b $H_0: \beta_i = 0$

$H_1: \beta_i \neq 0$

Variable	t-statistic	p-value
AGE	.40	.6864
EDUC	7.89	9.74E-15≈ 0
HRS	7.10	2.75E-12≈ 0
CHILDS	1.61	.1084
AGEKDBRN	4.90	1.14E-06≈ 0
YEARSJOB	5.85	7.06E-09≈ 0
MOREDAYS	1.36	.1754
NUMORG	1.37	.1713

EDUC, HRS, AGEKDBRN, and YEARSJOB are linearly related to INCOME.

© 2012 Cengage Learning. All Rights Reserved. May not be scanned, copied or duplicated, or posted to a publicly accessible website, in whole or in part.

17.22

	A	B	C	D	E	F
1	SUMMARY OUTPUT					
2						
3	*Regression Statistics*					
4	Multiple R	0.2713				
5	R Square	0.0736				
6	Adjusted R Square	0.0673				
7	Standard Error	2.86				
8	Observations	892				
9						
10	ANOVA					
11		*df*	*SS*	*MS*	*F*	*Significance F*
12	Regression	6	574.6	95.77	11.72	1.16E-12
13	Residual	885	7234.2	8.17		
14	Total	891	7808.8			
15						
16		*Coefficients*	*Standard Error*	*t Stat*	*P-value*	
17	Intercept	6.36	0.204656129	31.10	4.42E-144	
18	DAYS1	0.135	0.040	3.33	0.0009	
19	DAYS2	0.036	0.045	0.81	0.4183	
20	DAYS3	0.060	0.043	1.41	0.1582	
21	DAYS4	0.107	0.036	3.00	0.0027	
22	DAYS5	0.142	0.047	3.05	0.0024	
23	DAYS6	0.134	0.036	3.71	0.0002	

b H_0: $\beta_1 = \beta_2 = \beta_3 = \beta_4 = \beta_5 = \beta_6 = 0$

H_1: At least one β_i is not equal to zero

F = 11.72, p-value = 1.16E-12 ≈ 0. There is enough evidence to infer that the model is valid.

c H_0: $\beta_i = 0$

H_1: $\beta_i \neq 0$

Variable	t-statistic	p-value
DAYS1	3.33	.0009
DAYS2	.81	.4183
DAYS3	1.41	.1582
DAYS4	3.00	.0027
DAYS5	3.05	.0024
DAYS6	3.71	.0002

Only DAYS2 and DAYS3 are not linearly related to DEFINITE.

© 2012 Cengage Learning. All Rights Reserved. May not be scanned, copied or duplicated, or posted to a publicly accessible website, in whole or in part.

17.24

	A	B	C	D
1		*Lot size*	*Trees*	*Distance*
2	Lot size	1		
3	Trees	0.2857	1	
4	Distance	-0.1895	0.0794	1

There does not appear to be a multicollinearity problem. The t–tests are valid.

17.26 a

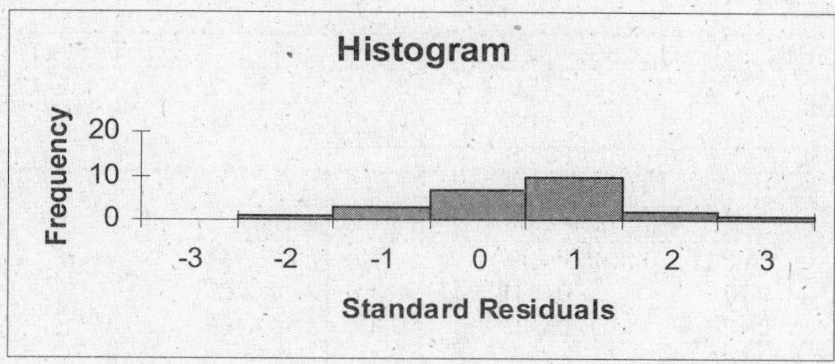

The error variable may be normally distributed.

b

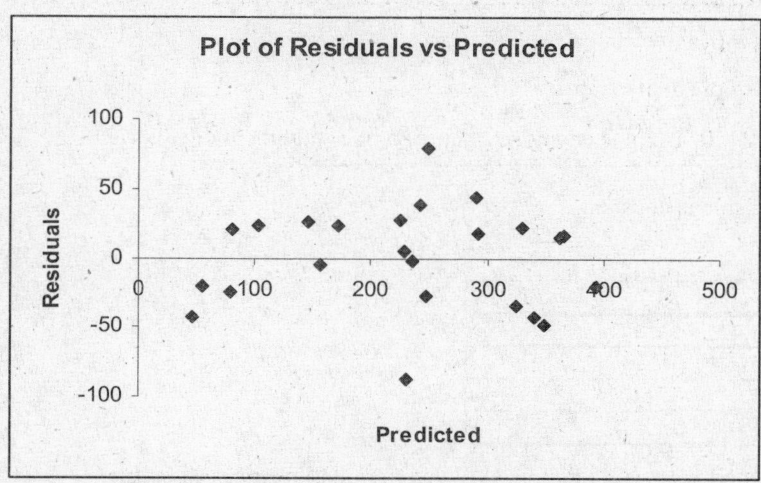

The variance of the error variable is constant.

c

	A	B	C	D	E
1		*Permits*	*Mortgage*	*A Vacancy*	*O Vacancy*
2	Permits	1			
3	Mortgage	0.0047	1		
4	A Vacancy	-0.1505	-0.0399	1	
5	O Vacancy	-0.1027	-0.0332	0.0652	1

Multicollinearity is not a problem.

© 2012 Cengage Learning. All Rights Reserved. May not be scanned, copied or duplicated, or posted to a publicly accessible website, in whole or in part.

17.28 a

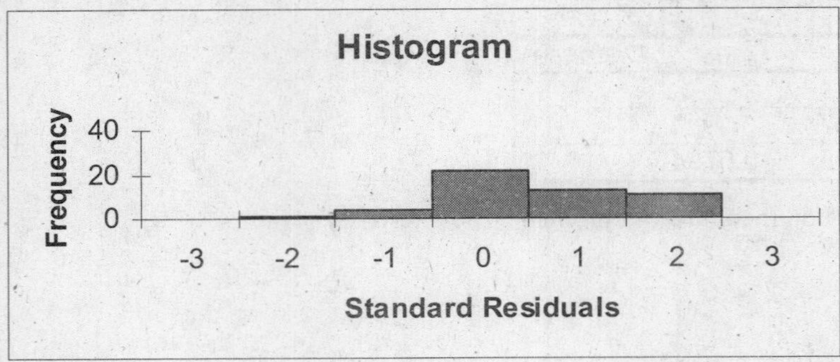

The error variable is approximately normally distributed.

b

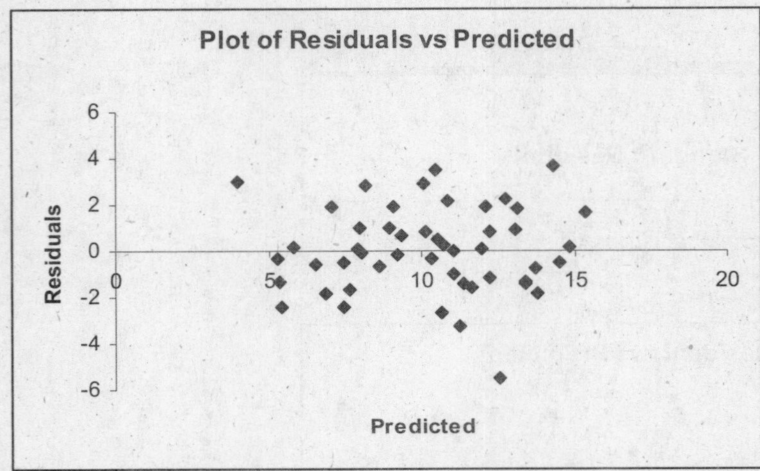

The variance of the error variable is constant.

c

	A	B	C	D
1		*Age*	*Years*	*Pay*
2	Age	1		
3	Years	0.8080	1	
4	Pay	0.1725	0.2610	1

The correlation between age and years is high indicating that multicollinearity is a problem.

© 2012 Cengage Learning. All Rights Reserved. May not be scanned, copied or duplicated, or posted to a publicly accessible website, in whole or in part.

17.30 a

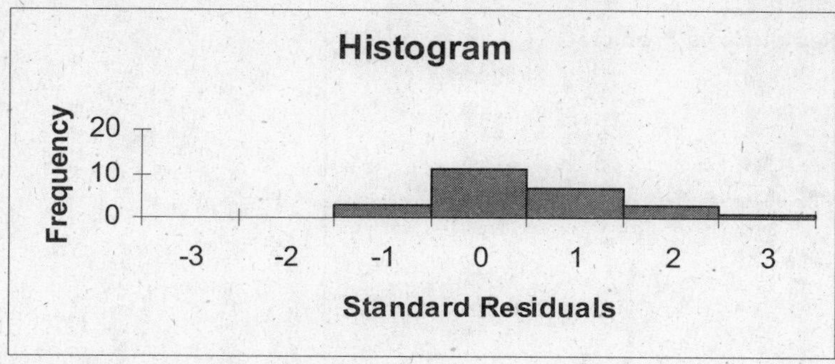

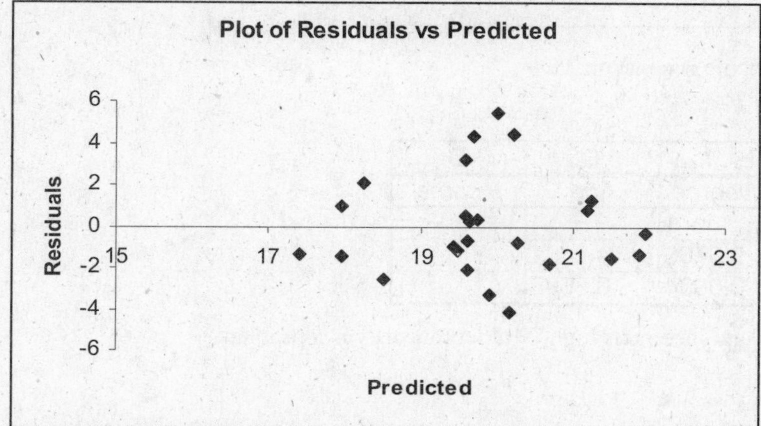

The error variable is approximately normal. However, the variance is not constant.

b

	A	B	C	D
1		*Direct*	*Newspaper*	*Television*
2	Direct	1		
3	Newspaper	-0.1376	1	
4	Television	-0.1246	0.1468	1

Multicollinearity is not a problem.

c There is one observation whose standardized residual exceeds 2.0 that should be checked

17.32 a

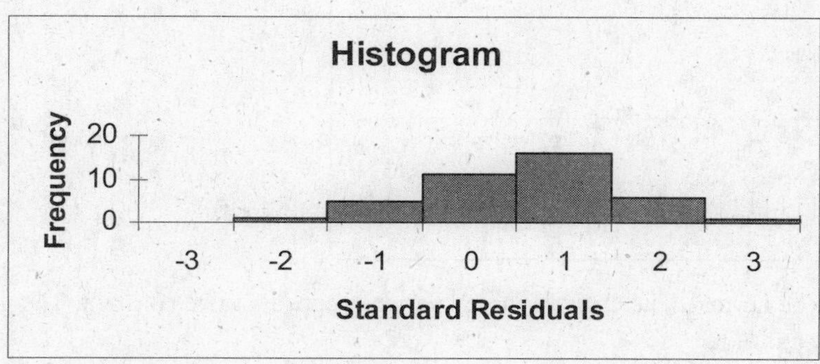

© 2012 Cengage Learning. All Rights Reserved. May not be scanned, copied or duplicated, or posted to a publicly accessible website, in whole or in part.

The normality requirement is satisfied.

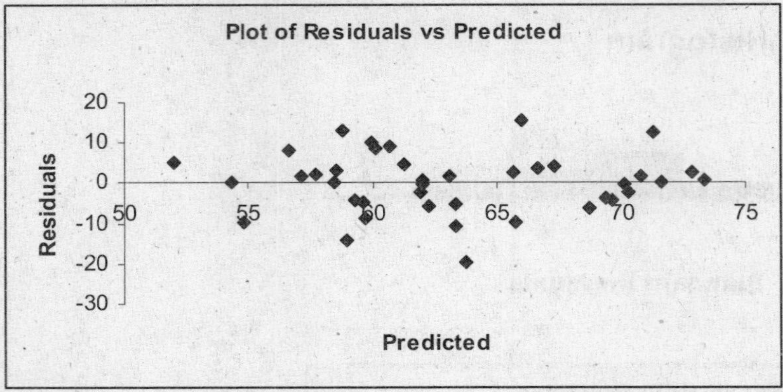

The variance of the error variable is constant.

c

	A	B	C	D
1		*Math Degree*	*Age*	*Income*
2	Math Degree	1		
3	Age	0.0766	1	
4	Income	0.0994	0.5698	1

The correlation between age and income is high. Multicollinearity is a problem.

17.34

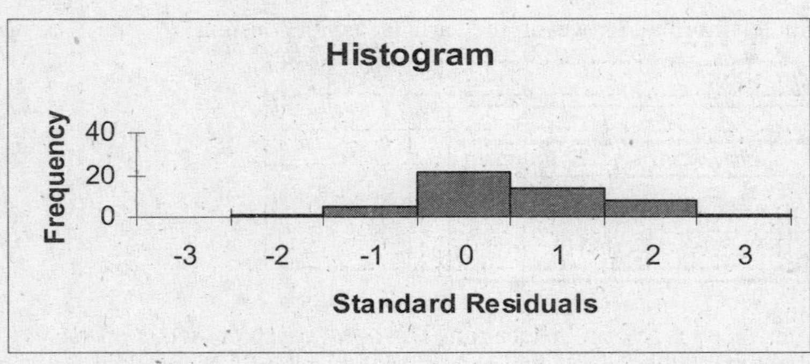

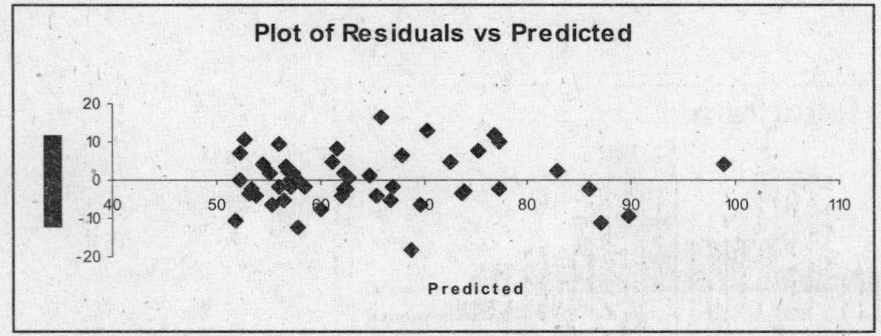

The error variable appears to be normal. The error variable's variance appears to be constant. The required conditions are satisfied.

© 2012 Cengage Learning. All Rights Reserved. May not be scanned, copied or duplicated, or posted to a publicly accessible website, in whole or in part.

17.36 a

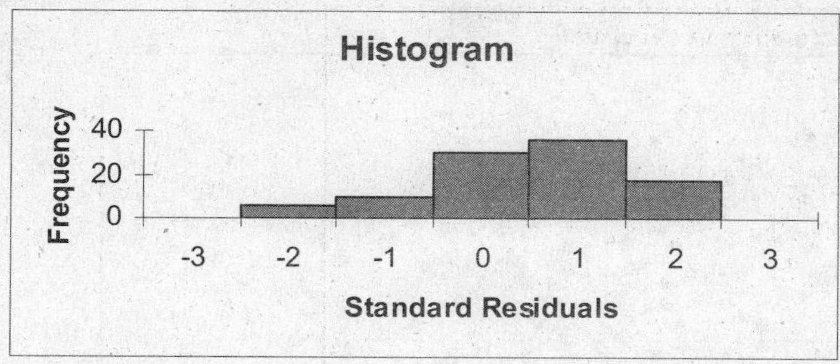

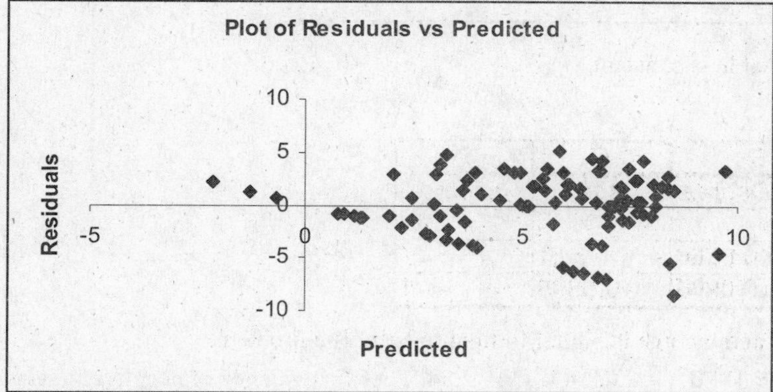

The errors appear to be normally distributed. The variance of the errors is not constant.

b

	Lottery	*Education*	*Age*	*Children*	*Income*
Lottery	1				
Education	-0.6202	1			
Age	0.1767	-0.1782	1		
Children	-0.0230	0.1073	0.1072	1	
Income	-0.5891	0.7339	-0.0418	0.0801	1

There is a strong correlation between income and education. The t–tests of these two coefficients may be distorted.

17.38

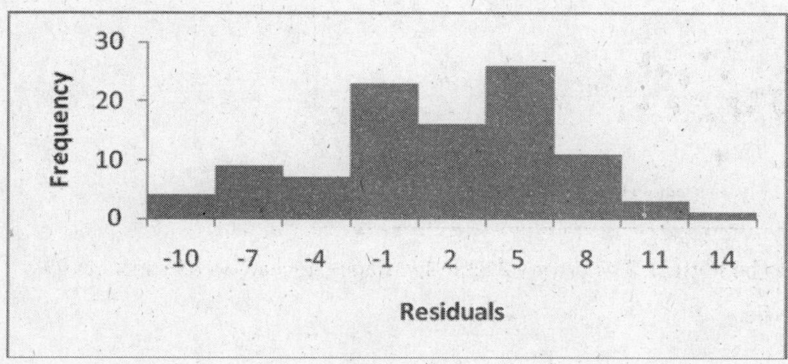

© 2012 Cengage Learning. All Rights Reserved. May not be scanned, copied or duplicated, or posted to a publicly accessible website, in whole or in part.

The histograms is somewhat bimodal. There residuals may not be normally distributed.

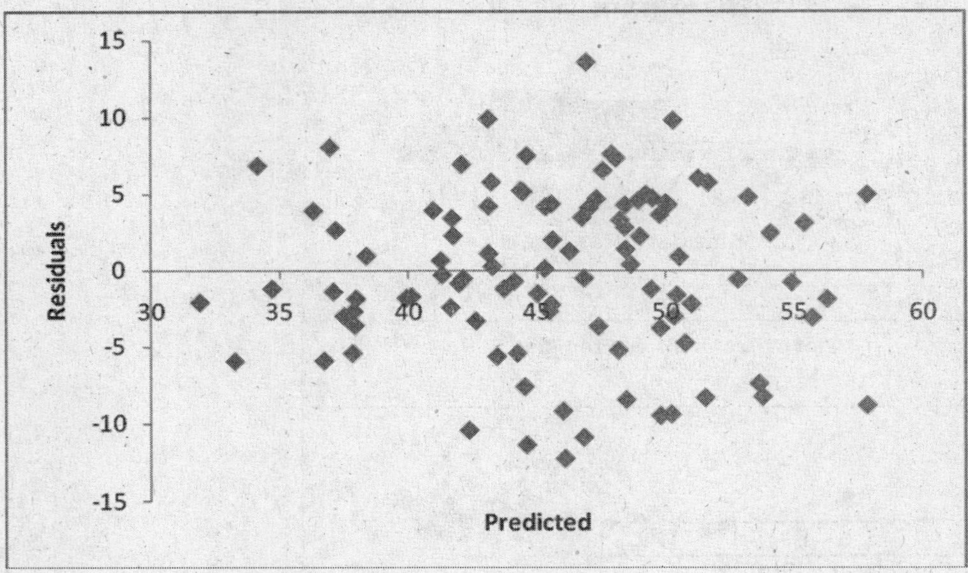

There is no evidence of heteroscedasticity.

17.40 $d_L = 1.16$, $d_U = 1.59$, $4 - d_U = 2.41$, $4 - d_L = 2.84$. There is evidence of negative first–order autocorrelation.

17.42 $d_L = 1.46$, $d_U = 1.63$. There is evidence of positive first–order autocorrelation.

17.44 $4 - d_U = 4 - 1.73 = 2.27$, $4 - d_L = 4 - 1.19 = 2.81$. There is no evidence of negative first–order autocorrelation.

17.46 a The regression equation is $\hat{y} = 2260 + .423x$

© 2012 Cengage Learning. All Rights Reserved. May not be scanned, copied or duplicated, or posted to a publicly accessible website, in whole or in part.

b

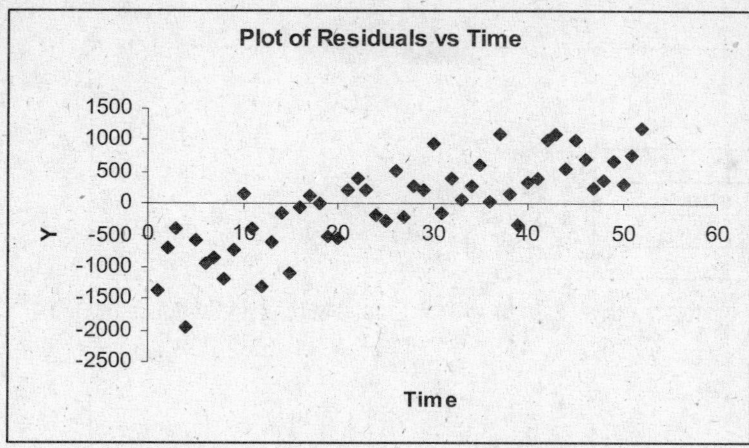

There appears to be a strong autocorrelation.

c

	A	B	C
1	**Durbin-Watson Statistic**		
2			
3	d = 0.7859		

$d_L \approx 1.50$, $d_U \approx 1.59$, $4 - d_U \approx 2.41$, $4 - d_L \approx$ ≈ 2.50. There is evidence of first–order autocorrelation.

d The model is $y = \beta_0 + \beta_1 x + \beta_2 t + \varepsilon$

The regression equation is $\hat{y} = 446.2 + 1.10x + 38.92t$

e

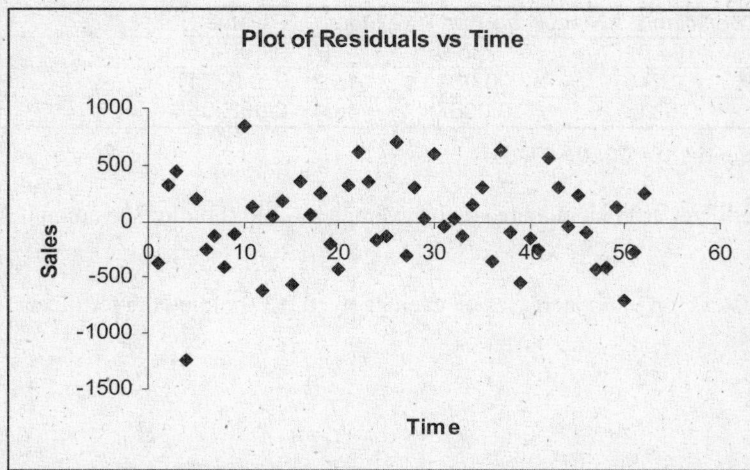

	A	B	C
1	**Durbin-Watson Statistic**		
2			
3	d = 2.2631		

There is no evidence of autocorrelation.

© 2012 Cengage Learning. All Rights Reserved. May not be scanned, copied or duplicated, or posted to a publicly accessible website, in whole or in part.

First model: $s_\varepsilon = 709.7$ and $R^2 = .0146$. Second model: $s_\varepsilon = 413.7$ and $R^2 = .6718$.

The second model fits better.

17.48

	A	B	C
1	**Durbin-Watson Statistic**		
2			
3	d = 2.2003		

$d = 2.2003$; $d_L = 1.30$, $d_U = 1.46$, $4 - d_U = 2.70$, $4 - d_L = 2.54$. There is no evidence of first–order autocorrelation.

17.50 a

	A	B	C	D	E	F
1	SUMMARY OUTPUT					
2						
3	*Regression Statistics*					
4	Multiple R	0.6894				
5	R Square	0.4752				
6	Adjusted R Square	0.4363				
7	Standard Error	63.08				
8	Observations	30				
9						
10	ANOVA					
11		*df*	*SS*	*MS*	*F*	*Significance F*
12	Regression	2	97283	48641	12.23	0.0002
13	Residual	27	107428	3979		
14	Total	29	204711			
15						
16		*Coefficients*	*Standard Error*	*t Stat*	*P-value*	
17	Intercept	164.01	35.9	4.57	9.60E-05	
18	Fetilizer	0.140	0.081	1.72	0.0974	
19	Water	0.0313	0.0067	4.64	8.08E-05	

a $\hat{y} = 164.01 + .140x_1 + .0313x_2$

For each additional unit of fertilizer crop yield increases on average by .140 (holding the amount of water constant).

For each additional unit of water crop yield increases on average by .0313 (holding the fertilizer constant).

b $H_0: \beta_1 = 0$

$H_1: \beta_1 \neq 0$

$t = 1.72$, p-value = .0974. There is not enough evidence to conclude that there is a linear relationship between crop yield and amount of fertilizer.

© 2012 Cengage Learning. All Rights Reserved. May not be scanned, copied or duplicated, or posted to a publicly accessible website, in whole or in part.

c $H_0 : \beta_2 = 0$

$H_1 : \beta_2 \neq 0$

t = 4.64, p-value = .0001. There is enough evidence to conclude that there is a linear relationship between crop yield and amount of water.

d $s_\varepsilon = 63.08$ and $R^2 = .4752$; the model fits moderately well.

e

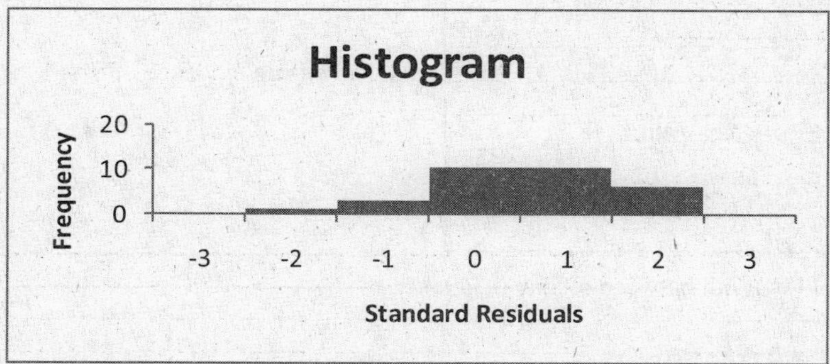

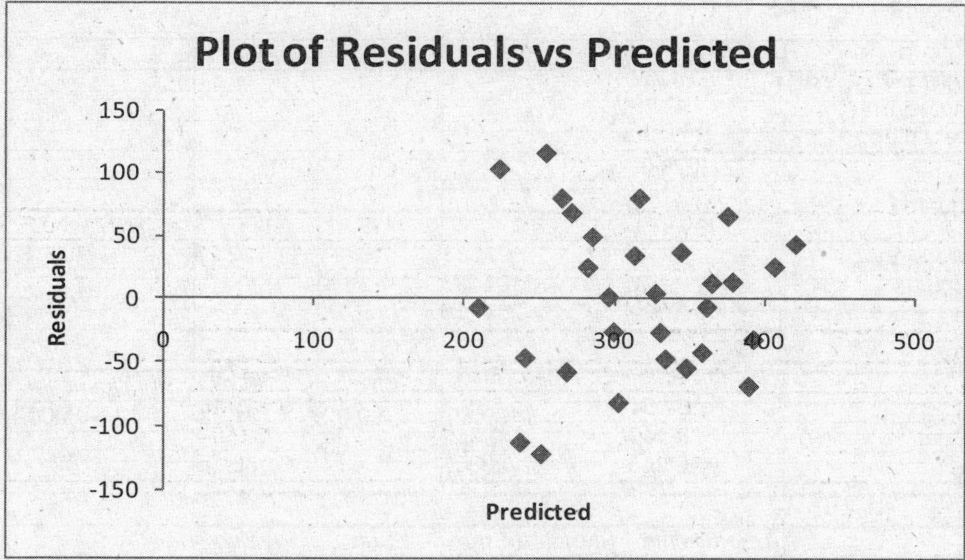

The errors appear to be normal, but the plot of residuals vs predicted aeems to indicate a problem.

© 2012 Cengage Learning. All Rights Reserved. May not be scanned, copied or duplicated, or posted to a publicly accessible website, in whole or in part.

f

	A	B
1	**Prediction Interval**	
2		
3		Yield
4		
5	Predicted value	209.3
6		
7	Prediction Interval	
8	Lower limit	69.2
9	Upper limit	349.3
10		
11	Interval Estimate of Expected Value	
12	Lower limit	155.7
13	Upper limit	262.8
14		

We predict that the crop yield will fall between 69.2 and 349.3.

17.52 a $\hat{y} = 29.60 - .309x_1 - 1.11x_2$

	A	B	C	D	E	F
1	SUMMARY OUTPUT					
2						
3	*Regression Statistics*					
4	Multiple R	0.7825				
5	R Square	0.6123				
6	Adjusted R Square	0.5835				
7	Standard Error	2.16				
8	Observations	30				
9						
10	ANOVA					
11		*df*	*SS*	*MS*	*F*	*Significance F*
12	Regression	2	199.65	99.82	21.32	0.0000
13	Residual	27	126.44	4.68		
14	Total	29	326.09			
15						
16		*Coefficients*	*Standard Error*	*t Stat*	*P-value*	
17	Intercept	29.60	2.08	14.22	0.0000	
18	Vacancy	-0.309	0.067	-4.58	0.0001	
19	Unemployment	-1.11	0.24	-4.73	0.0001	

b $R^2 = .6123$; 61.23 % of the variation in rents is explained by the independent variables.

c $H_0: \beta_1 = \beta_2 = 0$

H_1: At least one β_i is not equal to zero

F = 21.32, p-value = 0. There is enough evidence to conclude that the model is valid.

d $H_0: \beta_i = 0$

$H_1: \beta_i \neq 0$

© 2012 Cengage Learning. All Rights Reserved. May not be scanned, copied or duplicated, or posted to a publicly accessible website, in whole or in part.

Vacancy rate: t = –4.58, p-value = .0001

Unemployment rate: t = –4.73, p-value = .0001

Both vacancy and unemployment rates are linearly related to rents.

e

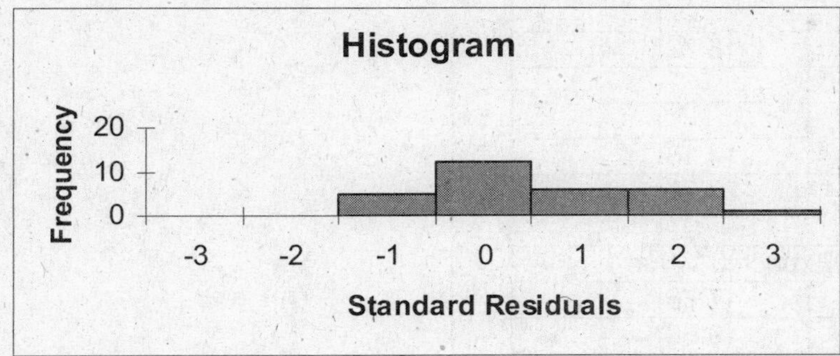

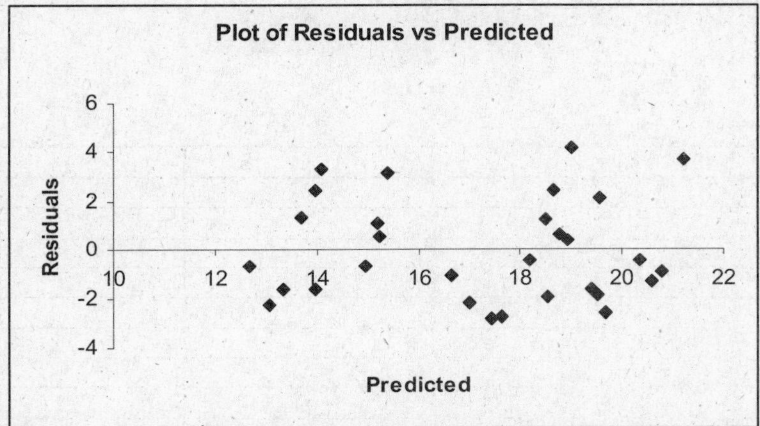

The error is approximately normally distributed with a constant variance.

f

	A	B	C
1	**Durbin-Watson Statistic**		
2			
3	d = 2.0687		

d_L = 1.28, d_U = 1.57, 4 – d_U = 2.72, 4 – d_L = 2.43. There is no evidence of first–order autocorrelation.

© 2012 Cengage Learning. All Rights Reserved. May not be scanned, copied or duplicated, or posted to a publicly accessible website, in whole or in part.

g

	A	B	C	D
1	**Prediction Interval**			
2				
3			Rent	
4				
5	Predicted value		18.72	
6				
7	Prediction Interval			
8	Lower limit		14.18	
9	Upper limit		23.27	
10				
11	Interval Estimate of Expected Value			
12	Lower limit		17.76	
13	Upper limit		19.68	

The city's office rent is predicted to lie between $14.18 and $23.27.

© 2012 Cengage Learning. All Rights Reserved. May not be scanned, copied or duplicated, or posted to a publicly accessible website, in whole or in part.

Appendix 17

A17.2 t-test of μ_D

H_0: $\mu_D = 0$

H_1: $\mu_D > 0$

	A	B	C
1	t-Test: Paired Two Sample for Means		
2			
3		*Eye-level*	*Lower shelf*
4	Mean	302.4	290.8
5	Variance	2482.2	6262.7
6	Observations	40	40
7	Pearson Correlation	0.7334	
8	Hypothesized Mean Difference	0	
9	df	39	
10	t Stat	1.35	
11	P(T<=t) one-tail	0.0922	
12	t Critical one-tail	1.6849	
13	P(T<=t) two-tail	0.1845	
14	t Critical two-tail	2.0227	

t = 1.35; p-value = .0922. There is not enough evidence to conclude that placement of the product at eye level significantly increases sales?

A17.4 Chi-squared test of a contingency table

H_0 : The two variables are independent

H_1 : The two variables are dependent

	A	B	C	D	E
1	**Contingency Table**				
2					
3		*Group*			
4	*Choice*		1	2	TOTAL
5		1	7	19	26
6		2	8	17	25
7		3	11	14	25
8		TOTAL	26	50	76
9					
10					
11		chi-squared Stat			1.73
12		df			2
13		p-value			0.4206
14		chi-squared Critical			5.9915

© 2012 Cengage Learning. All Rights Reserved. May not be scanned, copied or duplicated, or posted to a publicly accessible website, in whole or in part.

$\chi^2 = 1.73$, p-value = .4206. There is not enough evidence to infer that there is a relationship between choices students make and their level of intoxication.

A17.6 z-estimator of p

	A	B
1	**z-Estimate: Proportion**	
2		*Photography*
3	Sample Proportion	0.124
4	Observations	283
5	LCL	0.085
6	UCL	0.162

Confidence interval estimate of the total number of American adults who participate in photography

LCL = 205.8 million (.085) = 17.493 million

UCL = 205.8 million (.162) = 33.396 million

17.8 Ch-squared test of a contingency table

H_0 : The two variables are independent

H_1 : The two variables are dependent

	A	B	C	D	E
1	**Contingency Table**				
2					
3		*Age category*			
4	*Mutual fund*		1	2	TOTAL
5		1	19	6	25
6		2	75	57	132
7		3	92	123	215
8		4	89	109	198
9		5	63	77	140
10		6	73	43	116
11		TOTAL	411	415	826
12					
13					
14		chi-squared Stat			24.84
15		df			5
16		p-value			0.0001
17		chi-squared Critical			11.0705

$\chi^2 = 24.84$; p-value = .0001. There is enough evidence to infer that the age of the head of the household is related to whether he or she owns mutual funds.

© 2012 Cengage Learning. All Rights Reserved. May not be scanned, copied or duplicated, or posted to a publicly accessible website, in whole or in part.

A17.10 Chi-squared test of a contingency table.

H_0 : The two variables are independent

H_1 : The two variables are dependent

	A	B	C	D	E
1	**Contingency Table**				
2					
3		*Weight category*			
4	*Hip/Knee*		1	2	TOTAL
5		1	9	6	15
6		2	113	60	173
7		3	184	166	350
8		4	165	272	437
9		TOTAL	471	504	975
10					
11					
12		chi-squared Stat			42.89
13		df			3
14		p-value			0
15		chi-squared Critical			7.8147

$\chi^2 = 42.89$; p-value = 0. There is enough evidence to conclude that weight and the joint needing replacement are related.

A17.12

	A	B	C	D	E	F
1	SUMMARY OUTPUT					
2						
3	*Regression Statistics*					
4	Multiple R	0.8415				
5	R Square	0.7081				
6	Adjusted R Square	0.7021				
7	Standard Error	213.7				
8	Observations	100				
9						
10	ANOVA					
11		*df*	*SS*	*MS*	*F*	*Significance F*
12	Regression	2	10,744,454	5,372,227	117.6	0.0000
13	Residual	97	4,429,664	45,667		
14	Total	99	15,174,118			
15						
16		*Coefficients*	*Standard Error*	*t Stat*	*P-value*	
17	Intercept	576.8	514.0	1.12	0.2646	
18	Space	90.61	6.48	13.99	0.0000	
19	Water	9.66	2.41	4.00	0.0001	

a The regression equation is $\hat{y} = 576.8 + 90.61x_1 + 9.66x_2$

ing. All Rights Reserved. May not be scanned, copied or duplicated, or posted to a publicly accessible website, in whole or in part.

b The coefficient of determination is $R^2 = .7081$; 70.81% of the variation in electricity consumption is explained by the model. The model fits reasonably well.

c $H_0: \beta_1 = \beta_2 = 0$

H_1 : At least one β_i is not equal to zero

F = 117.6, p-value = 0. There is enough evidence to conclude that the model is valid.

d & e

	A	B	C	D
1	**Prediction Interval**			
2				
3			Consumption	
4				
5	Predicted value		8175	
6				
7	Prediction Interval			
8	Lower limit		7748	
9	Upper limit		8601	
10				
11	Interval Estimate of Expected Value			
12	Lower limit		8127	
13	Upper limit		8222	

e We predict that the house will consume between 7748 and 8601 units of electricity.

f We estimate that the average house will consume between 8127 and 8222 units of electricity.

A17.14 Multiple regression, test of coefficients

$$t = \frac{b_i - \beta_i}{s_{b_i}}$$

The ordinary multiple regression model fit quite well. The coefficient of determination is .7042 and the p-value of the F-test is 0. However, no independent variable is linearly related to salary. This is a clear sign of multicollinearity. Stepwise regression was used with the outcome shown below.

The only independent variables that are linearly related to salary are assists in 1992-93 and goals in 1992-93. It appears that players' salaries are most strongly related to the number of goals and the number of assists in the previous season.

© 2012 Cengage Learning. All Rights Reserved. May not be scanned, copied or duplicated, or posted to a publicly accessible website, in whole or in part.

	M	N	O	P	Q	R	S
1	**Results of stepwise regression**						
2							
3	**Step 1 - Entering variable: Ast92_93**						
4							
5	Summary measures						
6		Multiple R	0.7725				
7		R-Square	0.5967				
8		Adj R-Square	0.5883				
9		StErr of Est	380046.1250				
10							
11	ANOVA Table						
12		Source	df	SS	MS	F	p-value
13		Explained	1	10258242603399.2000	10258242603399.2000	71.0232	0.0000
14		Unexplained	48	6932882522112.0000	144435052544.0000		
15							
16	Regression coefficients						
17			Coefficient	Std Err	t-value	p-value	
18		Constant	38325.8711	82112.9297	0.4667	0.6428	
19		Ast92_93	25746.7754	3055.0806	8.4275	0.0000	
20							
21	**Step 2 - Entering variable: Goal92_93**						
22							
23	Summary measures			Change	% Change		
24		Multiple R	0.8086	0.0361	%4.7		
25		R-Square	0.6538	0.0571	%9.6		
26		Adj R-Square	0.6390	0.0507	%8.6		
27		StErr of Est	355859.9375	-24186.1875	-%6.4		
28							
29	ANOVA Table						
30		Source	df	SS	MS	F	p-value
31		Explained	2	11239219530119.2000	5619609765059.6100	44.3760	0.0000
32		Unexplained	47	5951905595392.0000	126636289263.6600		
33							
34	Regression coefficients						
35			Coefficient	Std Err	t-value	p-value	
36		Constant	65924.4297	77524.0313	0.8504	0.3994	
37		Ast92_93	14124.2783	5061.7593	2.7904	0.0076	
38		Goal92_93	18523.1426	6655.2490	2.7832	0.0077	

A17.16 t-estimator of μ

	A	B	C	D
1	**t-Estimate: Mean**			
2				
3				*Acres*
4	Mean			676.1
5	Standard Deviation			140.5
6	LCL			664.1
7	UCL			688.2

Estimate of total farmland:

LCL = 229,373(664.1) = 152,326,609 acres

UCL = 229,373(688.2) = 157,854,499 acres

© 2012 Cengage Learning. All Rights Reserved. May not be scanned, copied or duplicated, or posted to a publicly accessible website, in whole or in part.

A17.18

	A	B
1	**z-Estimate: Proportion**	
2		*DIVORCE*
3	Sample Proportion	0.2438
4	Observations	1136
5	LCL	0.2189
6	UCL	0.2688

LCL = .2189, UCL = .2688

A17.20

	A	B
1	**t-Estimate: Mean**	
2		
3		*CUREMPYR*
4	Mean	8.51
5	Standard Deviation	8.61
6	LCL	7.93
7	UCL	9.10

LCL = 7.93, UCL = 9.10

A17.22 t-test of ρ

$H_0: \rho = 0$

$H_1: \rho > 0$

	A	B
1	**Correlation**	
2		
3	*AGE and TVHOURS*	
4	Pearson Coefficient of Correlation	0.1511
5	t Stat	5.54
6	df	1314
7	P(T<=t) one tail	0
8	t Critical one tail	1.646
9	P(T<=t) two tail	0
10	t Critical two tail	1.9618

t = 5.54, p-value = 0. There is enough evidence to infer that older people watch more television.

A17.24 Unequal-variances t-test of $\mu_1 - \mu_2$

$H_0: \mu_1 - \mu_2 = 0$

$H_1: \mu_1 - \mu_2 < 0$

Two-tail F test: F = 1.58, p-value = .0080; use unequal-variances t-test

© 2012 Cengage Learning. All Rights Reserved. May not be scanned, copied or duplicated, or posted to a publicly accessible website, in whole or in part.

	A	B	C
1	t-Test: Two-Sample Assuming Unequal Variances		
2			
3		*Disabled*	*Not disabled*
4	Mean	2.33	2.39
5	Variance	2.29	1.45
6	Observations	61	846
7	Hypothesized Mean Difference	0	
8	df	66	
9	t Stat	-0.290	
10	P(T<=t) one-tail	0.3863	
11	t Critical one-tail	1.6683	
12	P(T<=t) two-tail	0.7727	
13	t Critical two-tail	1.9966	

t = -.290, p-value = .3863. There is not enough evidence to conclude that people with vision problems are more likely to believe that it is the government's responsibility to help pay for doctor and hospital bills.

A17.26 t-test of ρ

$H_0 : \rho = 0$

$H_1 : \rho \neq 0$

	A	B
1	**Correlation**	
2		
3	*HRS and SPHRS*	
4	Pearson Coefficient of Correlation	-0.1371
5	t Stat	-2.88
6	df	433
7	P(T<=t) one tail	0.0021
8	t Critical one tail	1.6484
9	P(T<=t) two tail	0.0042
10	t Critical two tail	1.9655

t = -2.88, p-value = .0021. There is enough evidence to infer that there is a relationship between the number of hours husbands and their wives work.

A17.28 t-test of ρ

$H_0 : \rho = 0$

$H_1 : \rho \neq 0$

© 2012 Cengage Learning. All Rights Reserved. May not be scanned, copied or duplicated, or posted to a publicly accessible website, in whole or in part.

	A	B
1	**Correlation**	
2		
3	*EDUC and TIME2*	
4	Pearson Coefficient of Correlation	-0.0228
5	t Stat	-0.647
6	df	803
7	P(T<=t) one tail	0.2589
8	t Critical one tail	1.6468
9	P(T<=t) two tail	0.5178
10	t Critical two tail	1.9629

t = -.647, p-value = .5178. There is not enough evidence to infer that education and amount of time spent watching television news are related.

© 2012 Cengage Learning. All Rights Reserved. May not be scanned, copied or duplicated, or posted to a publicly accessible website, in whole or in part.

Chapter 18

18.2 a

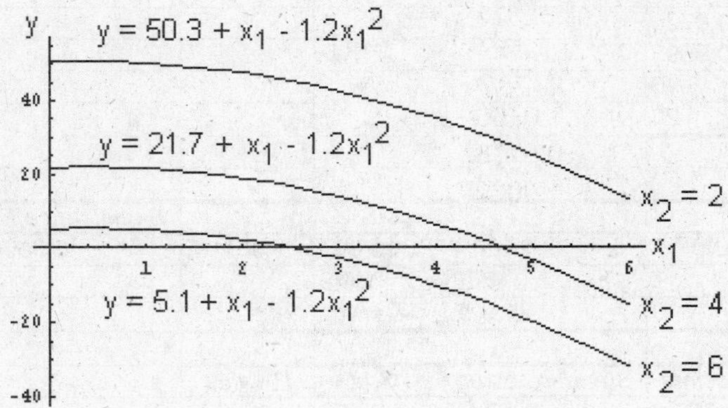

18.4a First–order model: a Demand = $\beta_0 + \beta_1$ Price+ ε

Second–order model: a Demand = $\beta_0 + \beta_1$ Price + β_2 Price $^2 + \varepsilon$

First–order model:

	A	B	C	D	E	F
1	SUMMARY OUTPUT					
2						
3	*Regression Statistics*					
4	Multiple R	0.9249				
5	R Square	0.8553				
6	Adjusted R Square	0.8473				
7	Standard Error	13.29				
8	Observations	20				
9						
10	ANOVA					
11		*df*	*SS*	*MS*	*F*	*Significance F*
12	Regression	1	18,798	18,798	106.44	0.0000
13	Residual	18	3,179	176.6		
14	Total	19	21,977			
15						
16		*Coefficients*	*Standard Error*	*t Stat*	*P-value*	
17	Intercept	453.6	15.18	29.87	0.0000	
18	Price	-68.91	6.68	-10.32	0.0000	

© 2012 Cengage Learning. All Rights Reserved. May not be scanned, copied or duplicated, or posted to a publicly accessible website, in whole or in part.

Second–order model:

	A	B	C	D	E	F
1	SUMMARY OUTPUT					
2						
3	*Regression Statistics*					
4	Multiple R	0.9862				
5	R Square	0.9726				
6	Adjusted R Square	0.9693				
7	Standard Error	5.96				
8	Observations	20				
9						
10	ANOVA					
11		*df*	*SS*	*MS*	*F*	*Significance F*
12	Regression	2	21,374	10,687	301.15	0.0000
13	Residual	17	603	35.49		
14	Total	19	21,977			
15						
16		*Coefficients*	*Standard Error*	*t Stat*	*P-value*	
17	Intercept	766.9	37.40	20.50	0.0000	
18	Price	-359.1	34.19	-10.50	0.0000	
19	Price-sq	64.55	7.58	8.52	0.0000	

c The second order model fits better because its standard error of estimate is 5.96, whereas that of the first–order models is 13.29

d $\hat{y} = 766.9 - 359.1(2.95) + 64.55(2.95)^2 = 269.3$

18.6a MBA GPA= $\beta_0 + \beta_1$ UnderGPA + β_2 GMAT + β_3 Work + β_4 UnderGPA$\times$GMAT + ε

© 2012 Cengage Learning. All Rights Reserved. May not be scanned, copied or duplicated, or posted to a publicly accessible website, in whole or in part.

b

	A	B	C	D	E	F
1	SUMMARY OUTPUT					
2						
3	*Regression Statistics*					
4	Multiple R	0.6836				
5	R Square	0.4674				
6	Adjusted R Square	0.4420				
7	Standard Error	0.790				
8	Observations	89				
9						
10	ANOVA					
11		*df*	*SS*	*MS*	*F*	*Significance F*
12	Regression	4	45.97	11.49	18.43	0.0000
13	Residual	84	52.40	0.62		
14	Total	88	98.37			
15						
16		*Coefficients*	*Standard Error*	*t Stat*	*P-value*	
17	Intercept	-11.11	14.97	-0.74	0.4601	
18	UnderGPA	1.19	1.46	0.82	0.4159	
19	GMAT	0.0311	0.0255	1.22	0.2265	
20	Work	0.0956	0.0312	3.06	0.0030	
21	UGPA-GMAT	-0.0019	0.0025	-0.78	0.4392	

F = 18.43, p-value = 0; s_ε = .790 and R^2 = .4674. The model is valid, but the fit is relatively poor.

c MBA example s_ε = .788 and R^2 = .4635. There is little difference between the fits of the two models.

© 2012 Cengage Learning. All Rights Reserved. May not be scanned, copied or duplicated, or posted to a publicly accessible website, in whole or in part.

18.8 a

	A	B	C	D	E	F
1	SUMMARY OUTPUT					
2						
3	*Regression Statistics*					
4	Multiple R	0.9255				
5	R Square	0.8566				
6	Adjusted R Square	0.8362				
7	Standard Error	5.20				
8	Observations	25				
9						
10	ANOVA					
11		*df*	*SS*	*MS*	*F*	*Significance F*
12	Regression	3	3398.7	1132.9	41.83	0.0000
13	Residual	21	568.8	27.08		
14	Total	24	3967.4			
15						
16		*Coefficients*	*Standard Error*	*t Stat*	*P-value*	
17	Intercept	260.7	162.3	1.61	0.1230	
18	Temperature	-3.32	2.09	-1.59	0.1270	
19	Currency	-164.3	667.1	-0.25	0.8078	
20	Temp-Curr	3.64	8.54	0.43	0.6741	

b

	A	B	C	D	E	F
1	SUMMARY OUTPUT					
2						
3	*Regression Statistics*					
4	Multiple R	0.9312				
5	R Square	0.8671				
6	Adjusted R Square	0.8322				
7	Standard Error	5.27				
8	Observations	25				
9						
10	ANOVA					
11		*df*	*SS*	*MS*	*F*	*Significance F*
12	Regression	5	3440.3	688.1	24.80	0.0000
13	Residual	19	527.1	27.74		
14	Total	24	3967.4			
15						
16		*Coefficients*	*Standard Error*	*t Stat*	*P-value*	
17	Intercept	274.8	283.8	0.97	0.3449	
18	Temperature	-1.72	6.88	-0.25	0.8053	
19	Currency	-828.6	888.5	-0.93	0.3627	
20	Temp-sq	-0.0024	0.0475	-0.05	0.9608	
21	Curr-sq	2054.0	1718.5	1.20	0.2467	
22	Temp-Curr	-0.870	10.57	-0.08	0.9353	

c Both models fit equally well. The standard errors of estimate and coefficients of determination are quite similar.

© 2012 Cengage Learning. All Rights Reserved. May not be scanned, copied or duplicated, or posted to a publicly accessible website, in whole or in part.

18.10 a Yield = $\beta_0 + \beta_1$ Pressure + β_2 Temperature + β_3 Pressure^2

$+ \beta_4$ Temperature^2 + β_5 Pressure Temperature + ε

b

	A	B	C	D	E	F
1	SUMMARY OUTPUT					
2						
3	*Regression Statistics*					
4	Multiple R	0.8290				
5	R Square	0.6872				
6	Adjusted R Square	0.6661				
7	Standard Error	512				
8	Observations	80				
9						
10	ANOVA					
11		*df*	*SS*	*MS*	*F*	*Significance F*
12	Regression	5	42,657,846	8,531,569	32.52	0.0000
13	Residual	74	19,413,277	262,342		
14	Total	79	62,071,123			
15						
16		*Coefficients*	*Standard Error*	*t Stat*	*P-value*	
17	Intercept	74462	7526	9.89	0.0000	
18	Pressure	14.40	5.92	2.43	0.0174	
19	Temperature	-613.3	59.95	-10.23	0.0000	
20	Press-sq	-0.0159	0.0032	-5.04	0.0000	
21	Temp-sq	1.23	0.12	9.86	0.0000	
22	Press-temp	0.0381	0.0174	2.19	0.0316	

c $s_\varepsilon = 512$ and $R^2 = .6872$. The model's fit is good.

18.12 a $I_1 = 1$ if Catholic

$I_1 = 0$ otherwise

$I_2 = 1$ if Protestant

$I_2 = 0$ otherwise

b $I_1 = 1$ if 8:00 A.M. to 4:00 P.M.

$I_1 = 0$ otherwise

$I_2 = 1$ if 4:00 P.M. to midnight

$I_2 = 0$ otherwise

© 2012 Cengage Learning. All Rights Reserved. May not be scanned, copied or duplicated, or posted to a publicly accessible website, in whole or in part.

c $I_1 = 1$ if Jack Jones

$I_1 = 0$ otherwise

$I_2 = 1$ if Mary Brown

$I_2 = 0$ otherwise

$I_3 = 1$ if George Fosse

$I_3 = 0$ otherwise

18.14 $I_1 = 1$ if B.A.

$= 0$ otherwise

$I_2 = 1$ if B.B.A.

$= 0$ otherwise

$I_3 = 1$ if B.Sc. or B.Eng.

$= 0$ otherwise

	A	B	C	D	E	F
1	SUMMARY OUTPUT					
2						
3	*Regression Statistics*					
4	Multiple R	0.7461				
5	R Square	0.5566				
6	Adjusted R Square	0.5242				
7	Standard Error	0.7293				
8	Observations	89				
9						
10	ANOVA					
11		*df*	*SS*	*MS*	*F*	*Significance F*
12	Regression	6	54.75	9.13	17.16	9.59E-13
13	Residual	82	43.62	0.532		
14	Total	88	98.37			
15						
16		*Coefficients*	*Standard Error*	*t Stat*	*P-value*	
17	Intercept	0.190	1.41	0.135	0.8930	
18	UnderGPA	-0.0061	0.114	-0.053	0.9577	
19	GMAT	0.0128	0.0014	9.43	9.92E-15	
20	Work	0.0982	0.0303	3.24	0.0017	
21	I1	-0.345	0.224	-1.54	0.1269	
22	I2	0.706	0.241	2.93	0.0043	
23	I3	0.0348	0.209	0.166	0.8684	

I_1: t = -1.54, p-value = .1269

I_2: t = 2.93, p-value = .0043

I_3: t = .166, p-value = .8684

Only I_2 is statistically significant. However, this allows us to answer the question affirmatively.

© 2012 Cengage Learning. All Rights Reserved. May not be scanned, copied or duplicated, or posted to a publicly accessible website, in whole or in part.

18.16 a

	A	B	C	D	E	F
1	SUMMARY OUTPUT					
2						
3	*Regression Statistics*					
4	Multiple R	0.8973				
5	R Square	0.8051				
6	Adjusted R Square	0.7947				
7	Standard Error	2.32				
8	Observations	100				
9						
10	ANOVA					
11		*df*	*SS*	*MS*	*F*	*Significance F*
12	Regression	5	2096.3	419.26	77.66	0.0000
13	Residual	94	507.5	5.40		
14	Total	99	2603.8			
15						
16		*Coefficients*	*Standard Error*	*t Stat*	*P-value*	
17	Intercept	23.57	5.98	3.94	0.0002	
18	Mother	0.306	0.0542	5.65	0.0000	
19	Father	0.303	0.0476	6.37	0.0000	
20	Gmothers	0.0316	0.0577	0.55	0.5853	
21	Gfathers	0.0778	0.0573	1.36	0.1777	
22	Smoker	-3.72	0.669	-5.56	0.0000	

b Exercise 18.10: $\hat{y} = 3.24 + .451\text{Mother} + .411\text{Father} + .0166\text{Gmothers} + .0869\text{Gfathers}$

There are large differences to all the coefficients.

c $H_0 : \beta_5 = 0$

$H_1 : \beta_5 \neq 0$

t = –5.56, p-value = 0. There is enough evidence to infer that smoking affects longevity.

© 2012 Cengage Learning. All Rights Reserved. May not be scanned, copied or duplicated, or posted to a publicly accessible website, in whole or in part.

18.18 a

	A	B	C	D	E	F
1	SUMMARY OUTPUT					
2						
3	*Regression Statistics*					
4	Multiple R	0.5602				
5	R Square	0.3138				
6	Adjusted R Square	0.2897				
7	Standard Error	5.84				
8	Observations	60				
9						
10	ANOVA					
11		*df*	*SS*	*MS*	*F*	*Significance F*
12	Regression	2	887.9	443.95	13.03	0.0000
13	Residual	57	1941.7	34.06		
14	Total	59	2829.6			
15						
16		*Coefficients*	*Standard Error*	*t Stat*	*P-value*	
17	Intercept	7.02	3.24	2.17	0.0344	
18	Length	0.250	0.056	4.46	0.0000	
19	Type	-1.35	0.947	-1.43	0.1589	

b $H_0 : \beta_2 = 0$

$H_1 : \beta_2 \neq 0$

$t = -1.43$, p-value = .1589. There is not enough evidence to infer that the type of commercial affects memory test scores.

c Let

$I_1 = 1$ if humorous

$I_1 = 0$ otherwise

$I_2 = 1$ if musical

$I_2 = 0$ otherwise

See Excel output below.

d $H_0 : \beta_i = 0$

$H_1 : \beta_i \neq 0$

I1: t = 1.61, p-value = .1130

I2: t = 3.01, p-value = .0039

There is enough evidence to infer that there is a difference in memory test scores between watchers of humorous and serious commercials.

e The variable type of commercial in parts (a) and (b) is nominal. It is usually meaningless to conduct a regression analysis with such variables without converting them to indicator variables.

© 2012 Cengage Learning. All Rights Reserved. May not be scanned, copied or duplicated, or posted to a publicly accessible website, in whole or in part.

	A	B	C	D	E	F
1	SUMMARY OUTPUT					
2						
3	*Regression Statistics*					
4	Multiple R	0.6231				
5	R Square	0.3882				
6	Adjusted R Square	0.3554				
7	Standard Error	5.56				
8	Observations	60				
9						
10	ANOVA					
11		*df*	*SS*	*MS*	*F*	*Significance F*
12	Regression	3	1099	366.17	11.85	0.0000
13	Residual	56	1731	30.91		
14	Total	59	2830			
15						
16		*Coefficients*	*Standard Error*	*t Stat*	*P-value*	
17	Intercept	2.53	2.15	1.18	0.2445	
18	Length	0.223	0.054	4.10	0.0001	
19	I1	2.91	1.81	1.61	0.1130	
20	I2	5.50	1.83	3.01	0.0039	

18.20 a Let

$I_1 = 1$ if no scorecard

$I_1 = 0$ otherwise

$I_2 = 1$ if scorecard overturned more than 10% of the time

$I_2 = 0$ otherwise

© 2012 Cengage Learning. All Rights Reserved. May not be scanned, copied or duplicated, or posted to a publicly accessible website, in whole or in part.

b

	A	B	C	D	E	F
1	SUMMARY OUTPUT					
2						
3	*Regression Statistics*					
4	Multiple R	0.7299				
5	R Square	0.5327				
6	Adjusted R Square	0.5181				
7	Standard Error	4.20				
8	Observations	100				
9						
10	ANOVA					
11		*df*	*SS*	*MS*	*F*	*Significance F*
12	Regression	3	1933	644.46	36.48	0.0000
13	Residual	96	1696	17.67		
14	Total	99	3629			
15						
16		*Coefficients*	*Standard Error*	*t Stat*	*P-value*	
17	Intercept	4.65	2.06	2.26	0.0260	
18	Loan Size	0.00012	0.00015	0.83	0.4084	
19	I1	4.08	1.14	3.57	0.0006	
20	I2	10.18	1.01	10.08	0.0000	

c $s_\varepsilon = 4.20$ and $R^2 = .5327$. The model's fit is mediocre.

d

	A	B	C	D	E
1		*Pct Bad*	*Loan Size*	*I1*	*I2*
2	Pct Bad	1			
3	Loan Size	0.1099	1		
4	I1	-0.1653	-0.0346	1	
5	I2	0.6835	0.0737	-0.5471	1

There is a high correlation between I_1 and I_2 that may distort the t–tests.

e $b_1 = .00012$; in this sample for each additional dollar lent the default rate increases by .00012 provided the other variables remain the same.

$b_2 = 4.08$; In this sample banks that don't use scorecards on average have default rates 4.08 percentage points higher than banks that overturn their scorecards less than 10% of the time.

$b_3 = 10.18$; In this sample banks that overturn their scorecards more than 10% of the time on average have default rates 10.18 percentage points higher than banks that overturn their scorecards less than 10% of the time.

© 2012 Cengage Learning. All Rights Reserved. May not be scanned, copied or duplicated, or posted to a publicly accessible website, in whole or in part.

f

	A	B	C	D
1	**Prediction Interval**			
2				
3			Pct Bad	
4				
5	Predicted value		9.94	
6				
7	Prediction Interval			
8	Lower limit		1.39	
9	Upper limit		18.49	
10				
11	Interval Estimate of Expected Value			
12	Lower limit		8.08	
13	Upper limit		11.81	

We predict that the bank's default rate will fall between 1.39 and 18.49%.

18.22

	A	B	C	D	E	F
1	SUMMARY OUTPUT					
2						
3	*Regression Statistics*					
4	Multiple R	0.7991				
5	R Square	0.6385				
6	Adjusted R Square	0.6324				
7	Standard Error	5.90				
8	Observations	121				
9						
10	ANOVA					
11		*df*	*SS*	*MS*	*F*	*Significance F*
12	Regression	2	7255.3	3627.6	104.22	8.45E-27
13	Residual	118	4107.4	34.81		
14	Total	120	11362.7			
15						
16		*Coefficients*	*Standard Error*	*t Stat*	*P-value*	
17	Intercept	137.7	5.47	25.19	2.66E-49	
18	Index finger length (cm)	3.78	0.787	4.80	4.75E-06	
19	Gender	12.16	1.21	10.08	1.26E-17	

a. The coefficient of determination in Exercise 16.107 was .3270. In this model the coefficient of determination is .6385. This model is better.

© 2012 Cengage Learning. All Rights Reserved. May not be scanned, copied or duplicated, or posted to a publicly accessible website, in whole or in part.

b

	A	B
1	**Prediction Interval**	
2		
3		
4		Height (cm)
5	Predicted Value	162.3
6		
7	Prediction Interval	
8	Lower Limit	150.5
9	Upper Limit	174.1
10		
11	Interval Estimate of Expected Value	
12	Lower Limit	160.6
13	Upper Limit	164.0

Lower prediction limit = 150.5, upper prediction limit = 174.1

c

	A	B
1	**Prediction Interval**	
2		
3		
4		Height (cm)
5	Predicted Value	174.4
6		
7	Prediction Interval	
8	Lower Limit	162.6
9	Upper Limit	186.3
10		
11	Interval Estimate of Expected Value	
12	Lower Limit	172.3
13	Upper Limit	176.6

Lower prediction limit = 162.6, upper prediction limit = 186.3

d No, because the width of the prediction intervals are far too wide.

© 2012 Cengage Learning. All Rights Reserved. May not be scanned, copied or duplicated, or posted to a publicly accessible website, in whole or in part.

18.24a.

	A	B	C	D	E	F
1	SUMMARY OUTPUT					
2						
3	*Regression Statistics*					
4	Multiple R	0.4136				
5	R Square	0.1711				
6	Adjusted R Square	0.1690				
7	Standard Error	35,401				
8	Observations	1186				
9						
10	ANOVA					
11		*df*	*SS*	*MS*	*F*	*Significance F*
12	Regression	3	305,696,067,736	101,898,689,245	81.31	8.00E-48
13	Residual	1182	1,481,344,206,716	1,253,252,290		
14	Total	1185	1,787,040,274,452			
15						
16		*Coefficients*	*Standard Error*	*t Stat*	*P-value*	
17	Intercept	-23472	8482	-2.77	0.0057	
18	AGE	368.5	75.3	4.89	1.12E-06	
19	EDUC	4998.0	357.2	13.99	2.83E-41	
20	WRKSLF	-10589	3036	-3.49	0.0005	

b t = -3.49, p-value = .0005. There is sufficient evidence to infer that people with similar education and age who work for themselves earn lower incomes.

18.26 $I_1 = 1$ if male

$I_1 = 0$ otherwise (i.e. female)

© 2012 Cengage Learning. All Rights Reserved. May not be scanned, copied or duplicated, or posted to a publicly accessible website, in whole or in part.

	A	B	C	D	E	F
1	SUMMARY OUTPUT					
2						
3	*Regression Statistics*					
4	Multiple R	0.2520				
5	R Square	0.0635				
6	Adjusted R Square	0.0540				
7	Standard Error	1.83				
8	Observations	698				
9						
10	ANOVA					
11		*df*	*SS*	*MS*	*F*	*Significance F*
12	Regression	7	157.3	22.47	6.68	1.13E-07
13	Residual	690	2320.8	3.36		
14	Total	697	2478.2			
15						
16		*Coefficients*	*Standard Error*	*t Stat*	*P-value*	
17	Intercept	4.44	0.493945339	8.99	2.42E-18	
18	AGE	0.015	0.006	2.51	0.0124	
19	EDUC	-0.094	0.030	-3.16	0.0016	
20	HRS	-0.010	0.005	-1.90	0.0585	
21	CHILDS	-0.050	0.070	-0.72	0.4744	
22	PRESTG80	-0.018	0.006	-3.08	0.0022	
23	EARNRS	-0.054	0.084	-0.64	0.5200	
24	I1	0.075	0.145	0.52	0.6067	

t = .52, p-value = .6067. There is not enough evidence to conclude that men and women with the same age, education, etc. differ in the amount of television watched.

© 2012 Cengage Learning. All Rights Reserved. May not be scanned, copied or duplicated, or posted to a publicly accessible website, in whole or in part.

18.28

	A	B	C	D	E	F
1	SUMMARY OUTPUT					
2						
3	*Regression Statistics*					
4	Multiple R	0.9737				
5	R Square	0.9482				
6	Adjusted R Square	0.9454				
7	Standard Error	3015				
8	Observations	100				
9						
10	ANOVA					
11		*df*	*SS*	*MS*	*F*	*Significance F*
12	Regression	5	15,636,303,318	3,127,260,664	344.04	0.0000
13	Residual	94	854,451,113	9,089,905		
14	Total	99	16,490,754,431			
15						
16		*Coefficients*	*Standard Error*	*t Stat*	*P-value*	
17	Intercept	-5916	3141	-1.88	0.0627	
18	Years	1022	48.93	20.88	0.0000	
19	PhD	725.7	961.5	0.75	0.4523	
20	Evaluation	3729	619.8	6.02	0.0000	
21	Articles	439.1	80.7	5.44	0.0000	
22	Gender	1090	632.0	1.72	0.0879	

a $H_0 : \beta_1 = \beta_2 = \beta_3 = \beta_4 = \beta_5 = 0$

H_1 : At least on β_i is not equal to 0

F = 344.04, p-value = 0. There is enough evidence to infer that the model is valid.

b $H_0 : \beta_5 = 0$

$H_1 : \beta_5 > 0$

t = 1.72, p-value = .0879/2 = .0440. There is evidence that male professors are better paid than female professors with the same qualifications.

© 2012 Cengage Learning. All Rights Reserved. May not be scanned, copied or duplicated, or posted to a publicly accessible website, in whole or in part.

18.30 All weights = .2

	A	B	C	D	E	F
1	SUMMARY OUTPUT					
2						
3	*Regression Statistics*					
4	Multiple R	0.7623				
5	R Square	0.5812				
6	Adjusted R Square	0.4136				
7	Standard Error	2.16				
8	Observations	8				
9						
10	ANOVA					
11		*df*	*SS*	*MS*	*F*	*Significance F*
12	Regression	2	32.37	16.19	3.47	0.1135
13	Residual	5	23.33	4.67		
14	Total	7	55.70			
15						
16		*Coefficients*	*Standard Error*	*t Stat*	*P-value*	
17	Intercept	4.70	4.07	1.15	0.3011	
18	Score	2.57	1.01	2.55	0.0514	
19	Gender	0.26	1.56	0.16	0.8761	

In this case male–dominated jobs are paid on average $.26 (26 cents) more than female–dominated jobs after adjusting for the value of each job.

18.32 a

23	**Step 2 - Entering Variable: PRESTG80**					
24						
25	Summary Measures		Change	% Change		
26	Multiple R	0.1742	0.0459	35.80%		
27	R-Square	0.0304	0.0139	84.40%		
28	Adj R-Square	0.0279	0.0127	83.40%		
29	StErr of Est	2.0004	-0.013	-0.60%		
30						
31	ANOVA Table					
32	Source	df	SS	MS	F	p-Value
33	Explained	2	98.2011	49.1005	12.27	0
34	Unexplained	784	3137.3084	4.0017		
35						
36	Regression Coefficients					
37		Coefficient	Std Err	t-value	p-value	
38	Constant	2.0411	0.3169	6.4406	0	
39	AGE	0.0152	0.0042	3.6136	0.0003	
40	PRESTG80	0.0172	0.0051	3.3517	0.0008	

b. In this model only AGE and PRESTG80 are included. EDUC was excluded because it is highly correlated with PRESTG80.

© 2012 Cengage Learning. All Rights Reserved. May not be scanned, copied or duplicated, or posted to a publicly accessible website, in whole or in part.

18.34

23	Step 2 - Entering Variable: AGE					
24						
25	Summary Measures		Change	% Change		
26	Multiple R	0.1716	0.053	44.70%		
27	R-Square	0.0294	0.0154	109.30%		
28	Adj R-Square	0.0279	0.0146	110%		
29	StErr of Est	1.1895	-0.0089	-0.70%		
30						
31	ANOVA Table					
32	Source	df	SS	MS	F	p-Value
33	Explained	2	53.5983	26.7991	18.941	0
34	Unexplained	1249	1767.1773	1.4149		
35						
36	Regression Coefficients					
37		Coefficient	Std Err	t-value	p-value	
38	Constant	1.737	0.1849	9.3957	0	
39	EDUC	0.0499	0.011	4.5237	0	
40	AGE	0.0088	0.002	4.4474	0	

18.36

	A	B	C	D	E	F	G
60	Step 4 - Entering variable: DAYS5						
61							
62	Summary measures			Change	% Change		
63		Multiple R	0.2628	0.0182	%7.4		
64		R-Square	0.0690	0.0092	%15.4		
65		Adj R-Square	0.0648	0.0082	%14.5		
66		StErr of Est	2.8628	-0.0125	-%0.4		
67							
68	ANOVA Table						
69		Source	df	SS	MS	F	p-value
70		Explained	4	539.0999	134.7750	16.4444	0.0000
71		Unexplained	887	7269.6748	8.1958		
72							
73	Regression coefficients						
74			Coefficient	Std Err	t-value	p-value	
75		Constant	6.5176	0.1897	34.3510	0.0000	
76		DAYS1	0.1729	0.0352	4.9077	0.0000	
77		DAYS6	0.1272	0.0360	3.5359	0.0004	
78		DAYS4	0.1075	0.0357	3.0084	0.0027	
79		DAYS5	0.1375	0.0464	2.9637	0.0031	

18.38a Apply a first–order model with interaction.

© 2012 Cengage Learning. All Rights Reserved. May not be scanned, copied or duplicated, or posted to a publicly accessible website, in whole or in part.

b

	A	B	C	D	E	F
1	SUMMARY OUTPUT					
2						
3	*Regression Statistics*					
4	Multiple R	0.8623				
5	R Square	0.7436				
6	Adjusted R Square	0.7299				
7	Standard Error	1.27				
8	Observations	60				
9						
10	ANOVA					
11		*df*	*SS*	*MS*	*F*	*Significance F*
12	Regression	3	260.2	86.74	54.14	0.0000
13	Residual	56	89.72	1.60		
14	Total	59	349.9			
15						
16		*Coefficients*	*Standard Error*	*t Stat*	*P-value*	
17	Intercept	640.8	53.80	11.91	0.0000	
18	Cars	-64.17	5.27	-12.19	0.0000	
19	Speed	-10.63	0.897	-11.85	0.0000	
20	Cars-Speed	1.08	0.088	12.26	0.0000	

c: $H_0 : \beta_1 = \beta_2 = \beta_3 = 0$

H_1 : At least on β_i is not equal to 0

F = 54.14, p-value = 0. There is enough evidence to infer that the model is valid.

18.40 a Let

$I_1 = 1$ if ad was in newspaper

$I_1 = 0$ otherwise

$I_2 = 1$ if ad was on radio

$I_2 = 0$ otherwise

© 2012 Cengage Learning. All Rights Reserved. May not be scanned, copied or duplicated, or posted to a publicly accessible website, in whole or in part.

b

	A	B	C	D	E	F
1	SUMMARY OUTPUT					
2						
3	*Regression Statistics*					
4	Multiple R	0.6946				
5	R Square	0.4824				
6	Adjusted R Square	0.4501				
7	Standard Error	44.87				
8	Observations	52				
9						
10	ANOVA					
11		*df*	*SS*	*MS*	*F*	*Significance F*
12	Regression	3	90057	30019	14.91	0.0000
13	Residual	48	96627	2013		
14	Total	51	186684			
15						
16		*Coefficients*	*Standard Error*	*t Stat*	*P-value*	
17	Intercept	282.6	17.46	16.19	0.0000	
18	Ads	25.23	3.98	6.34	0.0000	
19	I1	-23.36	15.83	-1.48	0.1467	
20	I2	-46.59	16.44	-2.83	0.0067	

b $H_0: \beta_1 = \beta_2 = \beta_3 = 0$

H_1 : At least on β_i is not equal to 0

F = 14.91, p-value = 0. There is enough evidence to infer that the model is valid.

c $H_0: \beta_i = 0$

$H_1: \beta_i \neq 0$

I–1: t = –1.48, p-value = .1467

I–2: t = –2.83, p-value = .0067

There is enough evidence to infer that the advertising medium makes a difference.

18.42a Units = $\beta_0 + \beta_1$ Years $+ \beta_2$ Years^2 + ε

© 2012 Cengage Learning. All Rights Reserved. May not be scanned, copied or duplicated, or posted to a publicly accessible website, in whole or in part.

b

	A	B	C	D	E	F
1	SUMMARY OUTPUT					
2						
3	*Regression Statistics*					
4	Multiple R	0.4351				
5	R Square	0.1893				
6	Adjusted R Square	0.1726				
7	Standard Error	87.98				
8	Observations	100				
9						
10	ANOVA					
11		*df*	*SS*	*MS*	*F*	*Significance F*
12	Regression	2	175,291	87,646	11.32	0.0000
13	Residual	97	750,764	7,740		
14	Total	99	926,056			
15						
16		*Coefficients*	*Standard Error*	*t Stat*	*P-value*	
17	Intercept	331.2	17.55	18.87	0.0000	
18	Years	21.45	5.50	3.90	0.0002	
19	Years-sq	-0.848	0.325	-2.61	0.0105	

c $s_\varepsilon = 87.98$ and $R^2 = .1893$. The model fits poorly.

© 2012 Cengage Learning. All Rights Reserved. May not be scanned, copied or duplicated, or posted to a publicly accessible website, in whole or in part.

Chapter 19

19.2 H_0 : The two population locations are the same

H_1 : The location of population 1 is to the right of the location of population 2

Rejection region: $z > z_\alpha = z_{.05} = 1.645$

$$E(T) = \frac{n_1(n_1 + n_2 + 1)}{2} = \frac{30(30+40+1)}{2} = 1{,}065$$

$$\sigma_T = \sqrt{\frac{n_1 n_2 (n_1 + n_2 + 1)}{12}} = \sqrt{\frac{(30)(40)(30+40+1)}{12}} = 84.26$$

a $z = \frac{T - E(T)}{\sigma_T} = \frac{1{,}205 - 1{,}065}{84.26} = 1.66$, p-value $P(Z > 1.66) = 1 - .9515 = .0485$. There is enough evidence to infer that the location of population 1 is to the right of the location of population 2.

b $z = \frac{T - E(T)}{\sigma_T} = \frac{1{,}065 - 1{,}065}{84.26} = 0$, p-value $= P(Z > 0) = .5$. There is not enough evidence to infer that the location of population 1 is to the right of the location of population 2.

c The value of the test statistic decreases and the p-value increases.

19.4 H_0 : The two population locations are the same

H_1 : The location of population 1 is different from the location of population 2

Rejection region: $T \geq T_U = 127$ or $T \leq T_L = 83$

Sample 1	Rank	Sample 2	Rank
15	4.0	8	2.0
7	1.0	27	18.0
22	14.0	17	7.0
20	.5	25	16.0
32	20.0	20	11.5
18	9.5	16	5.0
26	17.0	21	13.0
17	7.0	17	7.0
23	15.0	10	3.0
30	19.0	18	9.5
	$T_1 = 118$		$T_2 = 92$

There is not enough evidence to infer that the location of population 1 is different from the location of population 2.

19.6 H_0 : The two population locations are the same

H_1 : The location of population 1 is different from the location of population 2

© 2012 Cengage Learning. All Rights Reserved. May not be scanned, copied or duplicated, or posted to a publicly accessible website, in whole or in part.

	A	B	C	D	E
1	**Wilcoxon Rank Sum Test**				
2					
3			Rank Sum	Observations	
4	*Business*		4004	40	
5	*Economy*		8086	115	
6	z Stat		3.6149		
7	P(Z<=z) one-tail		0.0002		
8	z Critical one-tail		1.6449		
9	P(Z<=z) two-tail		0.0004		
10	z Critical two-tail		1.96		

a $z = 3.61$, p-value = .0004. There is enough evidence to infer that the business and economy class differ in their degree of satisfaction.

b The printout is identical to that of part a.

c All codes that preserve the order produce the same results.

19.8 H_0 : The two population locations are the same

H_1 : The location of population 1 is to the right of the location of population 2

Rejection region: $z > z_{\alpha} = z_{.05} = 1.645$

$$E(T) = \frac{n_1(n_1 + n_2 + 1)}{2} = \frac{82(82 + 75 + 1)}{2} = 6478$$

$$\sigma_T = \sqrt{\frac{n_1 n_2(n_1 + n_2 + 1)}{12}} = \sqrt{\frac{(82)(75)(82 + 75 + 1)}{12}} = 284.6$$

$z = \frac{T - E(T)}{\sigma_T} = \frac{6{,}807 - 6{,}478}{284.6} = 1.16$, p-value $P(Z > 1.16) = 1 - .8770 = .1230$. There is not enough evidence to infer that members of the Mathematics department rate nonparametric techniques as more important than do members of other departments.

19.10 H_0 : The two population locations are the same

H_1 : The location of population 1 is to the left of the location of population 2

Rejection region: $z < -z_{\alpha} = -z_{.05} = -1.645$

$$E(T) = \frac{n_1(n_1 + n_2 + 1)}{2} = \frac{125(125 + 125 + 1)}{2} = 15{,}687.5$$

$$\sigma_T = \sqrt{\frac{n_1 n_2(n_1 + n_2 + 1)}{12}} = \sqrt{\frac{(125)(125)(125 + 125 + 1)}{12}} = 571.7$$

$z = \frac{T - E(T)}{\sigma_T} = \frac{14{,}873 - 15{,}687.5}{571.7} = -1.42$, p-value $P(Z < -1.42) = .0778$. There is not enough evidence to infer that women are doing less housework today than last year.

© 2012 Cengage Learning. All Rights Reserved. May not be scanned, copied or duplicated, or posted to a publicly accessible website, in whole or in part.

19.12 H_0 : The two population locations are the same

H_1 : The location of population 1 is different from the location of population 2

Rejection region: $z < -z_{\alpha/2} = -z_{.025} = -1.96$ or $z > z_{\alpha/2} = z_{.025} = 1.96$

$$E(T) = \frac{n_1(n_1+n_2+1)}{2} = \frac{50(50+50+1)}{2} = 2525$$

$$\sigma_T = \sqrt{\frac{n_1 n_2(n_1+n_2+1)}{12}} = \sqrt{\frac{(50)(50)(50+50+1)}{12}} = 145.1$$

$z = \frac{T - E(T)}{\sigma_T} = \frac{2810 - 2525}{145.1} = 1.964$, p-value = 2P(Z > 1.964), which is slightly less than 2P(Z > 1.96) = 2(1 – .9750) = .05. There is enough evidence to infer that men and women experience different levels of stomach upset.

19.14 H_0 : The two population locations are the same

H_1 : The location of population 1 is to the right of the location of population 2

Rejection region: $z > z_{\alpha} = z_{.05} = 1.645$

$$E(T) = \frac{n_1(n_1+n_2+1)}{2} = \frac{20(20+20+1)}{2} = 410,$$

$$\sigma_T = \sqrt{\frac{n_1 n_2(n_1+n_2+1)}{12}} = \sqrt{\frac{(20)(20)(20+20+1)}{12}} = 37.0$$

$z = \frac{T - E(T)}{\sigma_T} = \frac{439.5 - 410}{37.0} = .80$, p-value = P(Z > .80) = 1 – .7881 = .2119. There is not enough evidence to infer that women perceive another woman wearing a size 6 dress as more professional than one wearing a size 14 dress.

19.16 H_0 : The two population locations are the same

H_1 : The location of population 1 is different from the location of population 2

Rejection region: $z < -z_{\alpha/2} = -z_{.025} = -1.96$ or $z > z_{\alpha/2} = z_{.025} = 1.96$

$$E(T) = \frac{n_1(n_1+n_2+1)}{2} = \frac{182(182+163+1)}{2} = 31{,}486$$

$$\sigma_T = \sqrt{\frac{n_1 n_2(n_1+n_2+1)}{12}} = \sqrt{\frac{(182)(163)(182+163+1)}{12}} = 924.9$$

$z = \frac{T - E(T)}{\sigma_T} = \frac{32{,}225.5 - 31{,}486}{924.9} = .80$, p-value = 2P(Z > .80) = 2(1 – .7881) = .4238. There is not enough evidence to infer that the night and day shifts rate the service differently.

© 2012 Cengage Learning. All Rights Reserved. May not be scanned, copied or duplicated, or posted to a publicly accessible website, in whole or in part.

19.18 H_0 :The two population locations are the same

H_1:The location of population 1 is different from the location of population 2

	A	B	C	D
1	**Wilcoxon Rank Sum Test**			
2				
3				
4			Rank Sum	Observations
5	Democrats		119,358.5	366
6	Republicans		74,394.5	256
7				
8	z-Statistic		2.43	
9	P(Z<=z) one-tail		0.0076	
10	z Critical one-tail		1.6449	
11	P(Z<=z) two-tail		0.0153	
12	z Critical two-tail		1.96	

z = 2.43, p-value = .0153. There is enough evidence to infer that Democrats and Republicans differ in their views about taxes for rich people.

19.20 H_0: The two population locations are the same

H_1: The location of population 1 (men) is to the left of the location of population 2 (women)

	A	B	C	D
1	**Wilcoxon Rank Sum Test**			
2				
3			Rank Sum	Observations
4	*Men*		187,417	442
5	*Women*		163,287	395
6	z Stat		0.635	
7	P(Z<=z) one-tail		0.2626	
8	z Critical one-tail		1.6449	
9	P(Z<=z) two-tail		0.5252	
10	z Critical two-tail		1.96	

z = .635. There is not enough evidence to infer that men are more likely than women to lose their jobs.

19.22 H_0: The two population locations are the same

H_1: The location of population 1 is different from the location of population 2

© 2012 Cengage Learning. All Rights Reserved. May not be scanned, copied or duplicated, or posted to a publicly accessible website, in whole or in part.

	A	B	C
1	**Wilcoxon Rank Sum Test**		
2			
3		Rank Sum	Observations
4	*Democrat*	50348.5	262
5	*Republican*	36804.5	155
6	z Stat	-3.71	
7	P(Z<=z) one-tail	0.0001	
8	z Critical one-tail	1.6449	
9	P(Z<=z) two-tail	0.0002	
10	z Critical two-tail	1.96	

z = -3.71, p-value = .0001. There is enough evidence to conclude that Democrats and Republicans differ in the attention paid to local news on television about the campaign for president.

19.24 H_0: The two population locations are the same

H_1: The location of population 1 (voted for Obama) is to the right of the location of population 2(voted for McCain)

	A	B	C	D
1	**Wilcoxon Rank Sum Test**			
2				
3			Rank Sum	Observations
4	*Obama*		443,168	689
5	*McCain*		259,537	496
6	z Stat		5.95	
7	P(Z<=z) one-tail		0	
8	z Critical one-tail		1.6449	
9	P(Z<=z) two-tail		0	
10	z Critical two-tail		1.96	

z = 5.95, p-value = 0. There is sufficient evidence to conclude that those who voted for Obama are more likely to believe that the economy has gotten worse in the year prior to the election.

19.26 H_0 : The two population locations are the same

H_1 : The location of population 1 is to the left of the location of population 2

Rejection region: $z < -z_{\alpha} = -z_{.10} = -1.28$

$z = \frac{x - .5n}{.5\sqrt{n}} = \frac{28 - .5(69)}{.5\sqrt{69}} = -1.57$, p-value = P(Z < −1.57) = .0582. There is enough evidence to infer that the location of population 1 is to the left of the location of population 2.

19.28 H_0 : The two population locations are the same

H_1 : The location of population 1 is to the right of the location of population 2

© 2012 Cengage Learning. All Rights Reserved. May not be scanned, copied or duplicated, or posted to a publicly accessible website, in whole or in part.

Pair	A	B	Sign of Difference
1	5	3	+
2	3	2	+
3	4	4	0
4	2	3	–
5	3	3	0
6	4	1	+
7	3	3	0
8	5	4	+
9	4	2	+
10	3	5	–
11	4	1	+
12	5	2	+
13	4	2	+
14	5	3	+
15	3	2	+
16	2	2	0

Rejection region: $z > z_\alpha = z_{.05} = 1.645$

$x = 10, n = 12,\ z = \frac{x - .5n}{.5\sqrt{n}} = \frac{10 - .5(12)}{.5\sqrt{12}} = 2.31$, p-value = P(Z > 2.31) = 1 – .9896 = .0104

There is enough evidence to infer that the population 1 is located to the right of population 2.

19.30 H_0 : The two population locations are the same

H_1 : The location of population 1 is to the right of the location of population 2

Rejection region: $z > z_\alpha = z_{.01} = 2.33$

$E(T) = \frac{n(n+1)}{4} = \frac{108(109)}{4} = 2943$; $\sigma_T = \sqrt{\frac{n(n+1)(2n+1)}{24}} = \sqrt{\frac{108(109)(217)}{24}} = 326.25$

$z = \frac{T - E(T)}{\sigma_T} = \frac{3457 - 2943}{326.25} = 1.58$, p-value = P(Z > 1.58) = 1 – .9429 = .0571. There is not enough evidence to conclude that population 1 is located to the right of the location of population 2.

19.32 H_0 : The two population locations are the same

H_1 : The location of population 1 is different from the location of population 2

Rejection region: $T \geq T_U = 39$ or $T \leq T_L = 6$

© 2012 Cengage Learning. All Rights Reserved. May not be scanned, copied or duplicated, or posted to a publicly accessible website, in whole or in part.

Pair	Sample 1	Sample 2	Difference	|Difference|	Ranks	
1	18.2	18.2	0	0		
2	14.1	14.1	0	0		
3	24.5	23.6	.9	.9	6.5	
4	11.9	12.1	–.2	.2		2
5	9.5	9.5	0	0		
6	12.1	11.3	.8	.8	5	
7	10.9	9.7	1.2	1.2	8	
8	16.7	17.6	–.9	.9		6.5
9	19.6	19.4	.2	.2	2	
10	8.4	8.1	.3	.3	4	
11	21.7	21.9	–.2	.2		2
12	23.4	21.6	1.8	1.8	9	
					$T^+ = 34.5$	$T^- = 10.5$

T = 34.5. There is not enough evidence to conclude that the population locations differ.

19.34 H_0 : H_0 : The two population locations are the same

H_1 : The location of population 1 is to the right of the location of population 2

	A	B	C	D	E
1	**Sign Test**				
2					
3	Difference			*Brand A - Brand B*	
4					
5	Positive Differences			21	
6	Negative Differences			15	
7	Zero Differences			14	
8	z Stat			1.00	
9	P(Z<=z) one-tail			0.1587	
10	z Critical one-tail			1.6449	
11	P(Z<=z) two-tail			0.3174	
12	z Critical two-tail			1.96	

a z = 1.00, p-value = .1587. There is no evidence to infer that Brand A is preferred.

b The printout is identical to that of part a.

c All codes that preserve the order produce the same results.

19.36 H_0 : The two population locations are the same

H_1 : The location of population 1 is different from the location of population 2

© 2012 Cengage Learning. All Rights Reserved. May not be scanned, copied or duplicated, or posted to a publicly accessible website, in whole or in part.

	A	B	C	D	E
1	**Sign Test**				
2					
3	Difference			*Sample 1 - Sample 2*	
4					
5	Positive Differences			51	
6	Negative Differences			74	
7	Zero Differences			0	
8	z Stat			-2.06	
9	P(Z<=z) one-tail			0.0198	
10	z Critical one-tail			1.6449	
11	P(Z<=z) two-tail			0.0396	
12	z Critical two-tail			1.96	

a. $z = -2.06$, p-value = .0396. There is enough evidence to infer that the population locations differ.

b

	A	B	C	D	E
1	**Wilcoxon Signed Rank Sum Test**				
2					
3	Difference		*Sample 1 - Sample 2*		
4					
5	T+		3726.5		
6	T-		4148.5		
7	Observations (for test)		125		
8	z Stat		-0.52		
9	P(Z<=z) one-tail		0.3016		
10	z Critical one-tail		1.6449		
11	P(Z<=z) two-tail		0.6032		
12	z Critical two-tail		1.96		

$z = -.52$, p-value = .6032. There is not enough evidence to infer that the population locations differ.

c The sign test ignores the magnitudes of the paired differences whereas the Wilcoxon signed rank sum test does not.

19.38 H_0 : The two population locations are the same

H_1 : The location of population 1 is to the left of the location of population 2

Rejection region: $z < -z_\alpha = -z_{.05} = -1.645$

$$E(T) = \frac{n(n+1)}{4} = \frac{72(72+1)}{4} = 1314 \; ; \; \sigma_T = \sqrt{\frac{n(n+1)(2n+1)}{24}} = \sqrt{\frac{72(72+1)(2[72]+1)}{24}} = 178.2$$

$z = \dfrac{T - E(T)}{\sigma_T} = \dfrac{378.5 - 1314}{178.2} = -5.25$, p-value = $P(Z < -5.25) = 0$. There is enough evidence to infer that the drug is effective.

© 2012 Cengage Learning. All Rights Reserved. May not be scanned, copied or duplicated, or posted to a publicly accessible website, in whole or in part.

19.40 H_0 : The two population locations are the same

H_1 : The location of population 1 is to the right of the location of population 2

Rejection region: $z > z_\alpha = z_{.05} = 1.645$

$z = \frac{x - .5n}{.5\sqrt{n}} = \frac{60 - .5(98)}{.5\sqrt{98}} = 2.22$, p-value = P(Z > 2.22) = 1 – .9868 = .0132. There is enough evidence to conclude that concern about a gasoline shortage exceeded concern about an electricity shortage.

19.42 H_0 : The two population locations are the same

H_1 : The location of population 1 is to the left of the location of population 2

Rejection region: $T \le T_L = 110$

T = 111. There is not enough evidence to infer that the swimming department has higher gross sales.

19.44 H_0 : The two population locations are the same

H_1 : The location of population 1 is to the left of the location of population 2

Rejection region: $z < -z_\alpha = -z_{.01} = -2.33$

$z = \frac{x - .5n}{.5\sqrt{n}} = \frac{5 - .5(20)}{.5\sqrt{20}} = -2.24$, p-value = P(Z < –2.24) = .0125. There is not enough evidence to conclude that children feel less pain.

19.46 H_0 : The two population locations are the same

H_1 : The location of population 1 is to the right of the location of population 2

Rejection region: $z > z_\alpha = z_{.05} = 1.645$

$z = \frac{x - .5n}{.5\sqrt{n}} = \frac{32 - .5(53)}{.5\sqrt{53}} = 1.51$, p-value = P(Z > 1.51) = 1 – .9345 = .0655. There is not enough evidence to infer that preference should be given to students for high school 1.

19.48 H_0: The two population locations are the same

H_1: The location of population 1 is different from the location of population 2

© 2012 Cengage Learning. All Rights Reserved. May not be scanned, copied or duplicated, or posted to a publicly accessible website, in whole or in part.

	A	B
1	**Sign Test**	
2		
3	Difference	*ATTN1 - ATTN2*
4		
5	Positive Differences	91
6	Negative Differences	222
7	Zero Differences	299
8	z Stat	-7.40
9	P(Z<=z) one-tail	0
10	z Critical one-tail	1.6449
11	P(Z<=z) two-tail	0
12	z Critical two-tail	1.96

z = -7.40, p-value = 0. There is enough evidence to conclude that attention paid to national network news about the presidential campaign differs from the attention paid to local news on television about the presidential campaign.

19.50 H_0 : The locations of all 3 populations are the same.

H_1: At least two population locations differ.

Rejection region: $H > \chi^2_{\alpha,k-1} = \chi^2_{.05,2} = 5.99$

$H = \left[\frac{12}{n(n+1)}\sum\frac{T_j^2}{n_j}\right] - 3(n+1) = \left[\frac{12}{88(88+1)}\left(\frac{984^2}{23}+\frac{1502^2}{36}+\frac{1430^2}{29}\right)\right] - 3(88+1) = 1.56$. There is not enough evidence to conclude that the population locations differ.

19.52 H_0 : The locations of all 3 populations are the same.

H_1 : At least two population locations differ.

Rejection region: $H > \chi^2_{\alpha,k-1} = \chi^2_{.10,2} = 4.61$

$$H = \left[\frac{12}{n(n+1)}\sum\frac{T_j^2}{n_j}\right] - 3(n+1) = \left[\frac{12}{143(143+1)}\left(\frac{3741^2}{47}+\frac{1610^2}{29}+\frac{4945^2}{67}\right)\right] - 3(143+1) = 6.30.$$

There is enough evidence to conclude that the population locations differ.

19.54 H_0 : The locations of all 3 populations are the same.

H_1 : At least two population locations differ.

Rejection region: $H > \chi^2_{\alpha,k-1} = \chi^2_{.05,2} = 5.99$

© 2012 Cengage Learning. All Rights Reserved. May not be scanned, copied or duplicated, or posted to a publicly accessible website, in whole or in part.

1	Rank	2	Rank	3	Rank
25	10.5	19	2	27	12
15	1	21	4	25	10.5
20	3	23	8.5	22	6
22	6	22	6	29	15
23	8.5	28	13.5	28	13.5
$T_1 = 29$		$T_2 = 34$		$T_3 = 57$	

$$H = \left[\frac{12}{n(n+1)}\sum\frac{T_j^2}{n_j}\right] - 3(n+1) = \left[\frac{12}{15(15+1)}\left(\frac{29^2}{5}+\frac{34^2}{5}+\frac{57^2}{5}\right)\right] - 3(15+1) = 4.46, \text{ p-value} = .1075.$$

There is not enough evidence to conclude that at least two population locations differ.

19.56 H_0 : The locations of all 4 populations are the same.

H_1 : At least two population locations differ.

Rejection region: $F_r > \chi^2_{\alpha,k-1} = \chi^2_{.10,3} = 6.25$

	Treatment							
Block	1	Rank	2	Rank	3	Rank	4	Rank
1	10	2	12	3	15	4	9	1
2	8	2	10	3	11	4	6	1
3	13	2	14	3	16	4	11	1
4	9	1.5	9	1.5	12	3	13	4
5	7	1	8	2	14	4	10	3
		$T_1 = 8.5$		$T_2 = 12.5$		$T_3 = 19$		$T_4 = 10$

$$F_r = \left[\frac{12}{b(k)(k+1)}\sum_{j=1}^{k} T_j^2\right] - 3b(k+1) = \left[\frac{12}{(5)(4)(5)}(8.5^2 + 12.5^2 + 19^2 + 10^2\right] - 3(5)(5) = 7.74, \text{ p-}$$

value = .0517. There is enough evidence to infer that at least two population locations differ.

19.58 H_0 : The locations of all 4 populations are the same.

H_1 : At least two population locations differ.

	A	B	C
1	**Friedman Test**		
2			
3	Group		Rank Sum
4	*Brand A*		65
5	*Brand B*		65
6	*Brand C*		85
7	*Brand D*		85
8			
9	Fr Stat		8.00
10	df		3
11	p-value		0.0460
12	chi-squared Critical		7.8147

© 2012 Cengage Learning. All Rights Reserved. May not be scanned, copied or duplicated, or posted to a publicly accessible website, in whole or in part.

a $F_r = 8.00$, p-value = .0460. There is enough evidence to infer that differences exist between the ratings of the four brands of coffee.

b Printout is identical to that of part a.

c Different codes produce identical results provided the codes are in order.

19.60 H_0 : The locations of all 3 populations are the same.

H_1 : At least two population locations differ.

Rejection region: $H > \chi^2_{\alpha,k-1} = \chi^2_{.05,2} = 5.99$

$$H = \left[\frac{12}{n(n+1)}\sum_{j=1}^{k}\frac{T_j^2}{n_j}\right] - 3(n+1) = \frac{12}{75(75+1)}\left(\frac{767.5^2}{25}+\frac{917^2}{25}+\frac{1165^2}{25}\right) - 3(75+1) = 6.81,$$ p-value = .0333. There is enough evidence to infer that there are differences in student satisfaction between the teaching methods.

19.62 H_0 : The locations of all 4 populations are the same.

H_1 : At least two population locations differ.

Rejection region: $F_r > \chi^2_{\alpha,k-1} = \chi^2_{.05,3} = 7.81$

	Orange Juice Brand							
Judge	1	Rank	2	Rank	3	Rank	4	Rank
1	3	1.5	5	4	4	3	3	1.5
2	2	1	3	2	5	4	4	3
3	4	3	4	3	3	1	4	3
4	3	2	4	3	5	4	2	1
5	2	1	4	3.5	4	3.5	3	2
6	4	2	5	3.5	5	3.5	3	1
7	3	1.5	3	1.5	4	3.5	4	3.5
8	2	1	3	3	3	3	3	3
9	4	2.5	3	1	5	4	4	2.5
10	2	1	4	3	5	4	3	2
		$T_1 = 16.5$		$T_2 = 27.5$		$T_3 = 33.5$		$T_4 = 22.5$

$$F_r = \left[\frac{12}{b(k)(k+1)}\sum_{j=1}^{k}T_j^2\right] - 3b(k+1) = \left[\frac{12}{(10)(4)(5)}(16.5^2+27.5^2+33.5^2+22.5^2)\right] - 3(10)(5)$$

= 9.42, p-value = .0242. There is enough evidence to infer that differences in sensory perception exist between the four brands of orange juice.

© 2012 Cengage Learning. All Rights Reserved. May not be scanned, copied or duplicated, or posted to a publicly accessible website, in whole or in part.

19.64 H_0 : The locations of all 3 populations are the same.

H_1 : At least two population locations differ.

Rejection region: $F_r > \chi^2_{\alpha,k-1} = \chi^2_{.05,2} = 5.99$

$$F_r = \left[\frac{12}{b(k)(k+1)}\sum_{j=1}^{k} T_j^2\right] - 3b(k+1) = \left[\frac{12}{(12)(3)(4)}(28.5^2 + 22.5^2 + 21^2\right] - 3(12)(4) = 2.63,$$ p-value

= .2691. There is not enough evidence to infer that there are differences in delivery times between the three couriers.

19.66 H_0 : The locations of all 4 populations are the same.

H_1 : At least two population locations differ.

Rejection region: $H > \chi^2_{\alpha,k-1} = \chi^2_{.05,3} = 7.81$

$$H = \left[\frac{12}{n(n+1)}\sum_{j=1}^{k}\frac{T_j^2}{n_j}\right] - 3(n+1)$$

$$= \frac{12}{132(132+1)}\left(\frac{2195^2}{33} + \frac{1650.5^2}{34} + \frac{2830^2}{34} + \frac{2102.5^2}{31}\right) - 3(132+1)$$

= 14.04, p-value = .0029. There is enough evidence to conclude that there are differences in grading standards between the four high schools.

19.68 H_0 : The locations of all 3 populations are the same.

H_1 : At least two population locations differ.

Rejection region: $F_r > \chi^2_{\alpha,k-1} = \chi^2_{.05,2} = 5.99$

$$F_r = \left[\frac{12}{b(k)(k+1)}\sum_{j=1}^{k} T_j^2\right] - 3b(k+1) = \left[\frac{12}{(20)(3)(4)}(33^2 + 39.5^2 + 47.5^2\right] - 3(20)(4) = 5.28,$$ p-

value = .0715. There is not enough evidence to infer that there are differences in the ratings of the three recipes.

19.70a The one-way analysis of variance and the Kruskal-Wallis test should be considered.

b H_0 : The locations of all 4 populations are the same.

H_1 : At least two population locations differ.

Rejection region: $H > \chi^2_{\alpha,k-1} = \chi^2_{.05,3} = 7.81$

© 2012 Cengage Learning. All Rights Reserved. May not be scanned, copied or duplicated, or posted to a publicly accessible website, in whole or in part.

$$H = \left[\frac{12}{n(n+1)}\sum_{j=1}^{k}\frac{T_j^2}{n_j}\right] - 3(n+1) = \frac{12}{200(200+1)}\left(\frac{4180^2}{50}+\frac{5262^2}{50}+\frac{5653^2}{50}+\frac{5005^2}{50}\right) - 3(200+1)$$

= 6.96, p-value = .0733. There is not enough evidence to infer that differences exist between the speeds at which the four brands perform.

19.72 H_0 : The locations of all 4 populations are the same.

H_1 : At least two population locations differ.

Rejection region: $H > \chi^2_{\alpha,k-1} = \chi^2_{.05,3} = 7.81$

$$H = \left[\frac{12}{n(n+1)}\sum_{j=1}^{k}\frac{T_j^2}{n_j}\right] - 3(n+1)$$

$$= \frac{12}{400(400+1)}\left(\frac{21{,}246^2}{100}+\frac{19{,}784^2}{100}+\frac{20{,}976}{100}+\frac{18{,}194^2}{100}\right) - 3(400+1) = 4.34, \text{ p-value} = .2269.$$

There is not enough evidence to infer that differences in believability exist between the four ads.

19.74 H_0: The locations of all 5 populations are the same.

H_1: At least two population locations differ.

Rejection region: $H > \chi^2_{\alpha,k-1} = \chi^2_{.05,4} = 9.49$

$$H = \left[\frac{12}{n(n+1)}\sum_{j=1}^{k}\frac{T_j^2}{n_j}\right] - 3(n+1)$$

$$= \frac{12}{133(133+1)}\left(\frac{638.5^2}{18}+\frac{1233.5^2}{14}+\frac{1814.5^2}{26}+\frac{3159.5^2}{42}+\frac{2065^2}{33}\right) - 3(133+1) = 18.73, \text{ p-value} =$$

.0009. There is enough evidence to infer that differences in perceived ease of use between the five brands of scanners.

19.76 H_0: The locations of all 5 populations are the same.

H_1: At least two population locations differ.

© 2012 Cengage Learning. All Rights Reserved. May not be scanned, copied or duplicated, or posted to a publicly accessible website, in whole or in part.

	A	B	C
1	**Kruskal-Wallis Test**		
2			
3	Group	Rank Sum	Observations
4	*Married*	427,653.5	652
5	*Widowed*	89,318.0	108
6	*Divorced*	124,560.0	173
7	*Single*	34,094.5	46
8	*Never married*	232,252.0	368
9			
10	H Stat		26.39
11	df		4
12	p-value		0
13	chi-squared Critical		9.49

H = 26.39, p-value = 0. There is enough evidence to conclude that there are differences in health between the five categories of marital status.

19.78 H_0: The locations of all 5 populations are the same.

H_1: At least two population locations differ.

	A	B	C
1	**Kruskal-Wallis Test**		
2			
3	Group	Rank Sum	Observations
4	*Democrat*	580,540.5	646
5	*Republican*	299,780.0	409
6	*Independent*	462,020.5	583
7			
8	H Stat		33.69
9	df		2
10	p-value		0
11	chi-squared Critical		5.99

H = 33.69, p-value = 0. There is enough evidence to infer that Democrats, Independents, and Conservatives differ in their perception about whether the economy has gotten better or worse in the previous year.

19.80 Rejection region: $z < -z_{\alpha/2} = -z_{.025} = -1.96$ or $z > z_{\alpha/2} = z_{.025} = 1.96$

$z = r_S\sqrt{n-1} = (.23)\sqrt{50-1} = 1.61$, p-value = 2P(Z > 1.61) = 2(1 – .9463) = .1074 There is not enough evidence to reject the null hypothesis.

© 2012 Cengage Learning. All Rights Reserved. May not be scanned, copied or duplicated, or posted to a publicly accessible website, in whole or in part.

19.82 $H_0: \rho_S = 0$

$H_1: \rho_S \neq 0$

Mathematics	a	Economics	b	a^2	b^2	ab
4	5.5	5	6.5	30.25	42.25	35.75
2	3	2	1.5	9	2.25	4.5
5	7	3	4	49	16	28
4	5.5	5	6.5	30.25	42.25	35.75
2	3	3	4	9	16	12
2	3	3	4	9	16	12
1	1	2	1.5	1	2.25	1.5
Totals	28		28	137.5	137.0	129.5

$$\sum_{i=1}^{n} a_i = 28 \quad \sum_{i=1}^{n} b_i = 28 \quad \sum_{i=1}^{n} a_i^2 = 137.5 \quad \sum_{i=1}^{n} b_i^2 = 137.0 \quad \sum_{i=1}^{n} a_i b_i = 129.5$$

$$s_{ab} = \frac{1}{n-1}\left[\sum_{i=1}^{n} a_i b_i - \frac{\sum_{i=1}^{n} a_i \sum_{i=1}^{n} b_i}{n}\right] = \frac{1}{7-1}\left[129.5 - \frac{(28)(28}{7}\right] = 2.917$$

$$s_a^2 = \frac{1}{n-1}\left[\sum_{i=1}^{n} a_i^2 - \frac{\left(\sum_{i=1}^{n} a_i\right)^2}{n}\right] = \frac{1}{7-1}\left[137.5 - \frac{(28)^2}{7}\right] = 4.250,\ s_a = \sqrt{s_a^2} = \sqrt{4.250} = 2.062$$

$$s_b^2 = \frac{1}{n-1}\left[\sum_{i=1}^{n} b_i^2 - \frac{\left(\sum_{i=1}^{n} b_i\right)^2}{n}\right] = \frac{1}{7-1}\left[137.0 - \frac{(28)^2}{7}\right] = 4.167,\ s_b = \sqrt{s_b^2} = \sqrt{4.167} = 2.041$$

$$r_S = \frac{s_{ab}}{s_b s_b} = \frac{2.917}{(2.062)(2.041)} = .6931$$

$H_0: \rho_S = 0$

$H_1: \rho_S \neq 0$

Rejection region: $r_S > .786$ or $r_S < -.786$

There is not enough evidence to infer a relationship between the grades in the two courses.

19.84 $H_0: \rho_S = 0$

$H_1: \rho_S \neq 0$

© 2012 Cengage Learning. All Rights Reserved. May not be scanned, copied or duplicated, or posted to a publicly accessible website, in whole or in part.

Stock 1	a	Stock 2	b	a^2	b^2	ab
–7	4.5	6	8.5	20.25	72.25	38.25
–4	6.5	6	8.5	42.25	72.25	55.25
–7	4.5	–4	2	20.25	4	9
–3	8	9	12.5	64	156.25	100
2	10.5	3	5	110.25	25	52.5
–10	2.5	–3	3.5	6.25	12.25	8.75
–10	2.5	7	10.5	6.25	110.25	26.25
5	12	–3	3.5	144	12.25	42
1	9	4	6	81	36	54
–4	6.5	7	10.5	42.25	110.25	68.25
2	10.5	9	12.5	110.25	156.25	131.25
6	13	5	7	169	49	91
–13	1	–7	1	1	1	1
Totals	91		91	817	817	677.5

$$\sum_{i=1}^{n} a_i = 91 \quad \sum_{i=1}^{n} b_i = 91 \quad \sum_{i=1}^{n} a_i^2 = 817 \sum_{i=1}^{n} b_i^2 = 817 \sum_{i=1}^{n} a_i b_i = 677.5$$

$$s_{ab} = \frac{1}{n-1}\left[\sum_{i=1}^{n} a_i b_i - \frac{\sum_{i=1}^{n} a_i \sum_{i=1}^{n} b_i}{n}\right] = \frac{1}{13-1}\left[677.5 - \frac{(91)(91}{13}\right] = 3.375$$

$$s_a^2 = \frac{1}{n-1}\left[\sum_{i=1}^{n} a_i^2 - \frac{\left(\sum_{i=1}^{n} a_i\right)^2}{n}\right] = \frac{1}{13-1}\left[817 - \frac{(91)^2}{13}\right] = 15.00,\ s_a = \sqrt{s_a^2} = \sqrt{15.00} = 3.873$$

$$s_b^2 = \frac{1}{n-1}\left[\sum_{i=1}^{n} b_i^2 - \frac{\left(\sum_{i=1}^{n} b_i\right)^2}{n}\right] = \frac{1}{13-1}\left[817 - \frac{(91)^2}{13}\right] = 15.00,\ s_b = \sqrt{s_b^2} = \sqrt{15.00} = 3.873$$

$$r_S = \frac{s_{ab}}{s_b s_b} = \frac{3.375}{(3.873)(3.873)} = .2250$$

$H_0: \rho_S = 0$

$H_1: \rho_S \neq 0$

Rejection region: $r_S > .566$ or $r_S < -.566$

There is not enough evidence to infer a relationship between the two stock returns.

19.86 $H_0: \rho_S = 0$

$H_1: \rho_S \neq 0$

© 2012 Cengage Learning. All Rights Reserved. May not be scanned, copied or duplicated, or posted to a publicly accessible website, in whole or in part.

	A	B	C	D
1	**Spearman Rank Correlation**			
2				
3	*Price and Odometer*			
4	Spearman Rank Correlation			-0.0201
5	z Stat			-0.20
6	P(Z<=z) one tail			0.4206
7	z Critical one tail			1.6449
8	P(Z<=z) two tail			0.8412
9	z Critical two tail			1.96

z = –.20, p-value = .8412. There is not enough evidence to infer that odometer reading and price are related.

19.88 $H_0: \rho_S = 0$

$H_1: \rho_S > 0$

	A	B	C	D
1	**Spearman Rank Correlation**			
2				
3	*Age and Heartburn*			
4	Spearman Rank Correlation			0.0302
5	z Stat			0.54
6	P(Z<=z) one tail			0.2931
7	z Critical one tail			1.6449
8	P(Z<=z) two tail			0.5862
9	z Critical two tail			1.96

z = .54, p-value = .2931. There is not enough evidence to conclude that age and severity of heartburn are positively related.

19.90 $H_0: \rho_S = 0$

$H_1: \rho_S > 0$

	A	B	C	D
1	**Spearman Rank Correlation**			
2				
3	*Floor and Price*			
4	Spearman Rank Correlation			0.553
5	z Stat			3.87
6	P(Z<=z) one tail			0.0001
7	z Critical one tail			1.6449
8	P(Z<=z) two tail			0.0002
9	z Critical two tail			1.96

z = 3.87, p-value = .0001. There is sufficient evidence to conclude that price and floor number are positively related.

© 2012 Cengage Learning. All Rights Reserved. May not be scanned, copied or duplicated, or posted to a publicly accessible website, in whole or in part.

19.92 H_0: $\rho_s = 0$

H_1: $\rho_s > 0$

	A	B	C	D
1	**Spearman Rank Correlation**			
2				
3	*Wager and Enjoyment*			
4	Spearman Rank Correlation			0.3912
5	z Stat			5.52
6	P(Z<=z) one tail			0
7	z Critical one tail			1.6449
8	P(Z<=z) two tail			0
9	z Critical two tail			1.96

z = 5.52, p-value = 0. There is enough evidence to infer that the greater the wager the more enjoyable the game is.

19.94 H_0: $\rho_s = 0$

H_1: $\rho_s < 0$

	A	B
1	**Spearman Rank Correlation**	
2		
3	*EDUC and PARSOL*	
4	Spearman Rank Correlation	-0.0582
5	z Stat	-2.13
6	P(Z<=z) one tail	0.0166
7	z Critical one tail	1.6449
8	P(Z<=z) two tail	0.0332
9	z Critical two tail	1.96

z = -2.13, p-value = .0166. There is enough evidence to conclude that more educated people are more likely to believe that compared to their parents their standard of living is better.

19.96 H_0: $\rho_s = 0$

H_1: $\rho_s < 0$

© 2012 Cengage Learning. All Rights Reserved. May not be scanned, copied or duplicated, or posted to a publicly accessible website, in whole or in part.

	A	B
1	**Spearman Rank Correlation**	
2		
3	*AGE and INTB*	
4	Spearman Rank Correlation	-0.1799
5	z Stat	-5.25
6	P(Z<=z) one tail	0
7	z Critical one tail	1.6449
8	P(Z<=z) two tail	0
9	z Critical two tail	1.96

z = -5.25, p-value = 0. There is enough evidence to conclude that older people are more interested in information about government and politics.

19.98 $H_0: \rho_S = 0$

$H_1: \rho_S > 0$

	A	B	C	D
1	**Spearman Rank Correlation**			
2				
3	*Education and Income*			
4	Spearman Rank Correlation			0.5742
5	z Stat			9.64
6	P(Z<=z) one tail			0
7	z Critical one tail			1.6449
8	P(Z<=z) two tail			0
9	z Critical two tail			1.96

z = 9.64, p-value = 0. There is sufficient evidence to conclude that more education and higher incomes are linked.

19.100 H_0 : The two population locations are the same

H_1 : The location of population 1 is left of the location of population 2

	A	B	C	D	E
1	**Wilcoxon Rank Sum Test**				
2					
3			Rank Sum	Observations	
4	*New*		207.5	15	
5	*Existing*		257.5	15	
6	z Stat		-1.04		
7	P(Z<=z) one-tail		0.1499		
8	z Critical one-tail		1.6449		
9	P(Z<=z) two-tail		0.2998		
10	z Critical two-tail		1.96		

z = –1.04, p-value = .1499. There is not enough evidence to infer that the new method is better.

© 2012 Cengage Learning. All Rights Reserved. May not be scanned, copied or duplicated, or posted to a publicly accessible website, in whole or in part.

19.102 H_0 : The two population locations are the same

H_1 : The location of population 1 is to the left of the location of population 2

	A	B	C	D	E
1	**Sign Test**				
2					
3	Difference			*Drug A - Drug B*	
4					
5	Positive Differences			2	
6	Negative Differences			18	
7	Zero Differences			10	
8	z Stat			-3.58	
9	P(Z<=z) one-tail			0.0002	
10	z Critical one-tail			1.6449	
11	P(Z<=z) two-tail			0.0004	
12	z Critical two-tail			1.96	

z = –3.58, p-value = .0002. There is enough evidence to conclude that drug B is more effective.

19.104a The one-way analysis of variance and the Kruskal-Wallis test should be considered. If the data are normal apply the analysis of variance, otherwise use the Kruskal-Wallis test.

b H_0 : The locations of all 3 populations are the same.

H_1 : At least two population locations differ.

	A	B	C	D
1	**Kruskal-Wallis Test**			
2				
3	Group	Rank Sum	Observations	
4	*Binding 1*	827	25	
5	*Binding 2*	1110	25	
6	*Binding 3*	913	25	
7				
8	H Stat		3.55	
9	df		2	
10	p-value		0.1699	
11	chi-squared Critical		5.9915	

H = 3.55, p-value = .1699. There is not enough evidence to infer that there are differences between bindings.

19.106 H_0 : The locations of all 7 populations are the same.

H_1 : At least two population locations differ.

© 2012 Cengage Learning. All Rights Reserved. May not be scanned, copied or duplicated, or posted to a publicly accessible website, in whole or in part.

	A	B	C	D
1	**Kruskal-Wallis Test**			
2				
3	Group	Rank Sum	Observations	
4	*Sunday*	10060	63	
5	*Monday*	2977	26	
6	*Tuesday*	2932.5	29	
7	*Wednesda*	3834.5	31	
8	*Thursday*	4060.5	30	
9	*Friday*	6045	42	
10	*Saturday*	6405.5	48	
11				
12	H Stat		14.87	
13	df		6	
14	p-value		0.0213	
15	chi-squared Critical		12.5916	

H = 14.87, p-value = .0213. There is enough evidence to infer that there are differences in the perceptions of speed of service between the days of the week.

19.108 H_0 : The two population locations are the same

H_1 : The location of population 1 is to the right of the location of population 2

	A	B	C	D
1	**Wilcoxon Signed Rank Sum Test**			
2				
3	Difference		*Men - Women*	
4				
5	T+		324	
6	T-		204	
7	Observations (for test)		32	
8	z Stat		1.12	
9	P(Z<=z) one-tail		0.1309	
10	z Critical one-tail		1.6449	
11	P(Z<=z) two-tail		0.2618	
12	z Critical two-tail		1.96	

z = 1.12, p-value = .1309. There is not enough evidence to conclude that men lose a greater percentage of their hearing than women.

19.110 $H_0 : \rho_S = 0$

$H_1 : \rho_S \neq 0$

© 2012 Cengage Learning. All Rights Reserved. May not be scanned, copied or duplicated, or posted to a publicly accessible website, in whole or in part.

	A	B	C	D
1	**Spearman Rank Correlation**			
2				
3	*Reference and GPA*			
4	Spearman Rank Correlation			0.0775
5	z Stat			1.05
6	P(Z<=z) one tail			0.148
7	z Critical one tail			1.6449
8	P(Z<=z) two tail			0.296
9	z Critical two tail			1.96

z = 1.05, p-value = .2960. There is not enough evidence to infer that the letter of reference and MBA GPA are related.

19.112 H_0 : The two population locations are the same

H_1 : The location of population 1 is to the right of the location of population 2

	A	B	C	D	E
1	**Sign Test**				
2					
3	Difference			*Before - After*	
4					
5	Positive Differences			19	
6	Negative Differences			5	
7	Zero Differences			16	
8	z Stat			2.86	
9	P(Z<=z) one-tail			0.0021	
10	z Critical one-tail			1.6449	
11	P(Z<=z) two-tail			0.0042	
12	z Critical two-tail			1.96	

z = 2.86, p-value = .0021. There is enough evidence to infer that the midterm test negatively influences student opinion.

19.114 H_0 : The two population locations are the same

H_1 : The location of population 1 is to the left of the location of population 2

	A	B	C	D	E
1	**Wilcoxon Rank Sum Test**				
2					
3			Rank Sum	Observations	
4	*Low*		9055	100	
5	*High*		11045	100	
6	z Stat		-2.43		
7	P(Z<=z) one-tail		0.0075		
8	z Critical one-tail		1.6449		
9	P(Z<=z) two-tail		0.015		
10	z Critical two-tail		1.96		

© 2012 Cengage Learning. All Rights Reserved. May not be scanned, copied or duplicated, or posted to a publicly accessible website, in whole or in part.

z = –2.43, p-value = .0075. There is enough evidence to conclude that boys with high levels of lead are more aggressive than boys with low levels.

19.116 H_0 : The locations of all 3 populations are the same.

H_1 : At least two population locations differ.

	A	B	C	D
1	**Kruskal-Wallis Test**			
2				
3	Group	Rank Sum	Observations	
4	*Unattractiv*	16844.5	134	
5	*Neutral*	13313	68	
6	*Attractive*	26122.5	133	
7				
8	H Stat		42.59	
9	df		2	
10	p-value		0	
11	chi-squared Critical		5.9915	

H = 42.59, p-value = 0. There is enough evidence to conclude that incomes of lawyers are affected by physical attractiveness.

19.118 H_0 : The two population locations are the same

H_1 : The location of population 1 is to the left of the location of population 2

	A	B	C	D	E
1	**Wilcoxon Rank Sum Test**				
2					
3			Rank Sum	Observations	
4	*3 Hours Before*		22553.5	180	
5	*Closing*		42426.5	180	
6	z Stat		-10.06		
7	P(Z<=z) one-tail		0		
8	z Critical one-tail		1.6449		
9	P(Z<=z) two-tail		0		
10	z Critical two-tail		1.96		

z = –10.06, p-value = 0. There is enough evidence to conclude that alcohol impairs judgment.

© 2012 Cengage Learning. All Rights Reserved. May not be scanned, copied or duplicated, or posted to a publicly accessible website, in whole or in part.

Appendix 19

A19.2 Spearman rank correlation coefficient test

H_0: $\rho_S = 0$

H_1: $\rho_S > 0$

	A	B	C	D
1	**Spearman Rank Correlation**			
2				
3	*Satisfaction and Time*			
4	Spearman Rank Correlation			0.541
5	z Stat			8.984
6	P(Z<=z) one tail			0
7	z Critical one tail			1.6449
8	P(Z<=z) two tail			0
9	z Critical two tail			1.96

z = 8.98; p-value = 0. There is enough evidence to infer that those who do more research are more satisfied with their choice.

A19.4 Histograms (not shown) are approximately bell shaped

Unequal-variances t-test of $\mu_1 - \mu_2$

$H_0: (\mu_1 - \mu_2) = 0$

$H_1: (\mu_1 - \mu_2) < 0$

Two-tail F test: F = 2.89, p-value = .0045; use unequal-variances t-test

	A	B	C
1	t-Test: Two-Sample Assuming Unequal Variances		
2			
3		*British*	*American*
4	Mean	7137	9304
5	Variance	38051	110151
6	Observations	28	33
7	Hypothesized Mean Difference	0	
8	df	53	
9	t Stat	-31.61	
10	P(T<=t) one-tail	2.26E-36	
11	t Critical one-tail	1.6741	
12	P(T<=t) two-tail	4.51E-36	
13	t Critical two-tail	2.0057	

t = −31.61; p-value = 0. There is overwhelming evidence to conclude that the total distance of American golf courses is greater than that of British courses.

© 2012 Cengage Learning. All Rights Reserved. May not be scanned, copied or duplicated, or posted to a publicly accessible website, in whole or in part.

A19.6 t-test of ρ or β_1

$$H_0: \rho = 0$$

$$H_1: \rho > 0$$

	A	B
1	**Correlation**	
2		
3	*Visits and Income*	
4	Pearson Coefficient of Correlation	0.1747
5	t Stat	2.48
6	df	195
7	P(T<=t) one tail	0.0071
8	t Critical one tail	1.6527
9	P(T<=t) two tail	0.0142
10	t Critical two tail	1.9722

t = 2.48; p-value = .0071. There is enough evidence to infer that more affluent people shop more downtown than poorer people.

A19.8 All histograms (not shown) are somewhat bell shaped.

One-way analysis of variance

$$H_0: \mu_1 = \mu_2 = \mu_3$$

H_1: At least two means differ

Miami-Dade

	A	B	C	D	E	F	G
10	ANOVA						
11	*Source of Variation*	*SS*	*df*	*MS*	*F*	*P-value*	*F crit*
12	Between Groups	6,409,467,776	2	3,204,733,888	231.37	1.1E-57	3.03
13	Within Groups	3,476,645,492	251	13,851,177			
14							
15	Total	9,886,113,268	253				

F = 231.37; p-value – 0. There is overwhelming evidence to infer that there are differences between the three groups of Americans residing in Miami-Dade.

Florida

	A	B	C	D	E	F	G
10	ANOVA						
11	*Source of Variation*	*SS*	*df*	*MS*	*F*	*P-value*	*F crit*
12	Between Groups	4,160,159,751	2	2,080,079,875	99.21	7.62E-34	3.03
13	Within Groups	6,331,923,528	302	20,966,634			
14							
15	Total	10,492,083,279	304				

F = 99.21; p-value – 0. There is overwhelming evidence to infer that there are differences between the three groups of Americans residing in the state of Florida.

© 2012 Cengage Learning. All Rights Reserved. May not be scanned, copied or duplicated, or posted to a publicly accessible website, in whole or in part.

United States

	A	B	C	D	E	F	G
10	ANOVA						
11	*Source of Variation*	*SS*	*df*	*MS*	*F*	*P-value*	*F crit*
12	Between Groups	5,742,495,149	2	2,871,247,574	110.48	9.27E-41	3.01
13	Within Groups	13,618,559,386	524	25,989,617			
14							
15	Total	19,361,054,535	526				

F = 110.48; p-value – 0. There is overwhelming evidence to infer that there are differences between the three groups of Americans residing in the United States.

A19.10 All three histograms (not shown) are bell shaped.

One-way analysis of variance

$H_0 : \mu_1 = \mu_2 = \mu_3$

H_1: At least two means differ

	A	B	C	D	E	F	G
10	ANOVA						
11	*Source of Variation*	*SS*	*df*	*MS*	*F*	*P-value*	*F crit*
12	Between Groups	1116.46	2	558.23	73.45	3.90E-29	3.01
13	Within Groups	4369.92	575	7.60			
14							
15	Total	5486.38	577				

F = 73.45; p-value = 0. There is overwhelming evidence to infer that there are differences in distance driven between cars, buses, and vans, pickups, and SUV's.

A19.12 Both histograms (not shown) are positively skewed but not sufficiently so to violate the normality requirement of the t-test of $\mu_1 - \mu_2$.

Equal-variances t-test of $\mu_1 - \mu_2$

H_0: $(\mu_1 - \mu_2) = 0$

H_1: $(\mu_1 - \mu_2) < 0$

Two-tail F test: F = 1.45, p-value = .0884; use equal-variances t-test

© 2012 Cengage Learning. All Rights Reserved. May not be scanned, copied or duplicated, or posted to a publicly accessible website, in whole or in part.

	A	B	C
1	t-Test: Two-Sample Assuming Equal Variances		
2			
3		*5 years ago*	*This year*
4	Mean	7.14	7.81
5	Variance	12.87	18.64
6	Observations	84	91
7	Pooled Variance	15.87	
8	Hypothesized Mean Difference	0	
9	df	173	
10	t Stat	-1.11	
11	P(T<=t) one-tail	0.1338	
12	t Critical one-tail	1.6537	
13	P(T<=t) two-tail	0.2677	
14	t Critical two-tail	1.9738	

t = − 1.11; p-value = .1338. There is not enough evidence to allow us to infer that investors' portfolios are becoming more diverse.

A19.14 Chi-squared test of a contingency table

H_0 : The two variables are independent

H_1 : The two variables are dependent

	A	B	C	D	E	F	G	H
1	**Contingency Table**							
2								
3		*Group*						
4	*Side Effect*		1	2	3	4	5	TOTAL
5		1	11	10	10	30	106	167
6		2	126	61	54	101	440	782
7		3	111	55	41	78	473	758
8		TOTAL	248	126	105	209	1019	1707
9								
10								
11		chi-squared Stat			20.6415			
12		df			8			
13		p-value			0.0082			
14		chi-squared Critical			15.5073			

$\chi^2 = 20.64$; p-value = .0082. There is not enough evidence to conclude that there are differences in side effects between the three groups.

© 2012 Cengage Learning. All Rights Reserved. May not be scanned, copied or duplicated, or posted to a publicly accessible website, in whole or in part.

A19.16 a t-test of μ

$H_0: \mu = 0$

$H_1: \mu > 0$

	A	B	C	D
1	**t-Test: Mean**			
2				
3				*Decrease*
4	Mean			24.73
5	Standard Deviation			17.92
6	Hypothesized Mean			0
7	df			222
8	t Stat			20.61
9	P(T<=t) one-tail			0
10	t Critical one-tail			1.6517
11	P(T<=t) two-tail			0
12	t Critical two-tail			1.9707

t = 20.61; p-value = 0. There is overwhelming evidence to infer that there is a decrease in metabolism when children watch television.

b Both histograms (not shown) are roughly bell shaped.

Unequal-variances t-test of $\mu_1 - \mu_2$

$H_0: (\mu_1 - \mu_2) = 0$

$H_1: (\mu_1 - \mu_2) > 0$

Two-tail F test: F = 3.18, p-value = 0; use unequal-variances t-test

	A	B	C
1	t-Test: Two-Sample Assuming Unequal Variances		
2			
3		*Obese*	*Nonobese*
4	Mean	30.86	23.35
5	Variance	112.85	358.58
6	Observations	41	182
7	Hypothesized Mean Difference	0	
8	df	106	
9	t Stat	3.46	
10	P(T<=t) one-tail	0.0004	
11	t Critical one-tail	1.6594	
12	P(T<=t) two-tail	0.0008	
13	t Critical two-tail	1.9826	

t = 3.46; p-value = .0004. There is enough evidence to conclude that the decrease in metabolism is greater among obese children.

A19.18a Histograms (not shown) are bell shaped.

Equal-variances t-test of $\mu_1 - \mu_2$

© 2012 Cengage Learning. All Rights Reserved. May not be scanned, copied or duplicated, or posted to a publicly accessible website, in whole or in part.

$H_0: (\mu_1 - \mu_2) = 0$

$H_1: (\mu_1 - \mu_2) < 0$

Two-tail F test: F = 1.53, p-value = .0349; use unequal-variances t-test

	A	B	C
1	t-Test: Two-Sample Assuming Unequal Variances		
2			
3		*4 or more*	*Less than 4*
4	Mean	6.00	7.40
5	Variance	5.62	8.61
6	Observations	100	100
7	Hypothesized Mean Difference	0	
8	df	190	
9	t Stat	-3.71	
10	P(T<=t) one-tail	0.0001	
11	t Critical one-tail	1.6529	
12	P(T<=t) two-tail	0.0003	
13	t Critical two-tail	1.9725	

t = –3.71; p-value = .0001. There is enough evidence to infer that children who wash their hands four or more times per day have less sick days due to cold and flu.

b Histograms (not shown) are bell shaped.

Unequal-variances t-test of $\mu_1 - \mu_2$

$H_0: (\mu_1 - \mu_2) = 0$

$H_1: (\mu_1 - \mu_2) < 0$

Two-tail F test: F = 2.16, p-value = .0002; use unequal-variances t-test

	A	B	C
1	t-Test: Two-Sample Assuming Unequal Variances		
2			
3		*Four or more*	*Less*
4	Mean	1.76	3.17
5	Variance	1.48	3.19
6	Observations	100	100
7	Hypothesized Mean Difference	0	
8	df	174	
9	t Stat	-6.52	
10	P(T<=t) one-tail	0.0000	
11	t Critical one-tail	1.6537	
12	P(T<=t) two-tail	0.0000	
13	t Critical two-tail	1.9737	

t = –6.52; p-value = 0. There is enough evidence to infer that children who wash their hands four or more times per day have less sick days due to stomach illness.

© 2012 Cengage Learning. All Rights Reserved. May not be scanned, copied or duplicated, or posted to a publicly accessible website, in whole or in part.

A19.20 a Histograms (not shown) of sick days are bell shaped.

Unequal-variances t-test of $\mu_1 - \mu_2$

$$H_0 : (\mu_1 - \mu_2) = 0$$

$$H_1 : (\mu_1 - \mu_2) < 0$$

Two-tail F test: F = 1.66, p-value = .0022; use unequal-variances t-test

	A	B	C
1	t-Test: Two-Sample Assuming Unequal Variances		
2			
3		*Days flu shot*	*Days placebo*
4	Mean	2.82	3.22
5	Variance	1.25	2.07
6	Observations	150	150
7	Hypothesized Mean Difference	0	
8	df	281	
9	t Stat	-2.69	
10	P(T<=t) one-tail	0.0038	
11	t Critical one-tail	1.6503	
12	P(T<=t) two-tail	0.0076	
13	t Critical two-tail	1.9684	

t = –2.69; p-value = .0038. There is overwhelming evidence to indicate that the number of sick days is less for those who take the flu shots.

b The number of visits is extremely nonnormal.

Wilcoxon rank sum test

H_0: The two population locations are the same

H_1: The location of population 1 is to the left of the location of population 2

	A	B	C	D
1	**Wilcoxon Rank Sum Test**			
2				
3			Rank Sum	Observations
4	*Visits flu shot*		19152	150
5	*Visits placebo*		25998	150
6	z Stat		-4.56	
7	P(Z<=z) one-tail		0	
8	z Critical one-tail		1.6449	
9	P(Z<=z) two-tail		0	
10	z Critical two-tail		1.9600	

z = –4.56; p-value = 0. There is overwhelming evidence to indicate that those who take the flu shots visit their doctors less frequently

A19.22 Chi-squared test of a contingency table

H_0 : The two variables are independent

H_1 : The two variables are dependent

© 2012 Cengage Learning. All Rights Reserved. May not be scanned, copied or duplicated, or posted to a publicly accessible website, in whole or in part.

	A	B	C	D	E
1	**Contingency Table**				
2					
3		*City*			
4	*Outcome*		1	2	TOTAL
5		1	503	201	704
6		2	536	215	751
7		3	308	83	391
8		TOTAL	1347	499	1846
9					
10					
11		chi-squared Stat			8.47
12		df			2
13		p-value			0.0145
14		chi-squared Critical			5.9915

$\chi^2 = 8.47$; p-value = .0145. There is enough evidence to conclude that there are differences in the death rate between the three cities. Recommendation: Spend less time at accident scene and get patient to the hospital as soon as possible.

A19.24 Chi-squared test of a contingency table

H_0 : The two variables are independent

H_1 : The two variables are dependent

	A	B	C	D	E
1	**Contingency Table**				
2					
3		*Income*			
4	*University?*		1	2	TOTAL
5		1	101	29	130
6		2	261	87	348
7		3	40	25	65
8		TOTAL	402	141	543
9					
10					
11		chi-squared Stat			6.35
12		df			2
13		p-value			0.0417
14		chi-squared Critical			5.9915

$\chi^2 = 6.35$; p-value = .0417. There is enough evidence to conclude that family income affects whether children attend university.

© 2012 Cengage Learning. All Rights Reserved. May not be scanned, copied or duplicated, or posted to a publicly accessible website, in whole or in part.

A19.26 Spearman rank correlation coefficient test

H_0: $\rho_S = 0$

H_1: $\rho_S > 0$

	A	B
1	**Spearman Rank Correlation**	
2		
3	*AGE and TAXSHARE*	
4	Spearman Rank Correlation	-0.0483
5	z Stat	-1.53
6	P(Z<=z) one tail	0.0624
7	z Critical one tail	1.6449
8	P(Z<=z) two tail	0.1248
9	z Critical two tail	1.96

z = -1.53. There is no evidence to conclude that younger people believe that that the rich should pay a bigger share of taxes. In fact, there is some evidence to the contrary.

A19.28 t-test of ρ

$H_0: \rho = 0$

$H_1: \rho \neq 0$

	A	B
1	**Correlation**	
2		
3	*INCOME and CUREMPYR*	
4	Pearson Coefficient of Correlation	0.2017
5	t Stat	5.53
6	df	722
7	P(T<=t) one tail	0
8	t Critical one tail	1.6470
9	P(T<=t) two tail	0
10	t Critical two tail	1.9633

t = 5.53, p-value = 0. There is enough evidence to conclude that income and job tenure are linearly related.

A19.30 H_0 : The locations of all 4 populations are the same.

H_1 : At least two population locations differ.

Histograms reveal that CUREMPYR is not normally distributed. The appropriate technique is the Kruskal-Wallis test.

© 2012 Cengage Learning. All Rights Reserved. May not be scanned, copied or duplicated, or posted to a publicly accessible website, in whole or in part.

	A	B	C
1	**Kruskal-Wallis Test**		
2			
3	Group	Rank Sum	Observations
4	*Class 1*	8087.5	30
5	*Class 2*	181119.5	448
6	*Class 3*	154075.5	341
7	*Class 4*	9097.5	20
8			
9	H Stat		19.74
10	df		3
11	p-value		0.0002
12	chi-squared Critical		7.81

H = 19.74, p-value = .0002. There is enough evidence to infer that there are differences in job tenure between the four classes.

A19.32 H_0 : The locations of all 4 populations are the same.

H_1 : At least two population locations differ.

	A	B	C
1	**Kruskal-Wallis Test**		
2			
3	Group	Rank Sum	Observations
4	*White*	716069	1024
5	*Black*	102240.5	182
6	*Other*	60165.5	119
7			
8	H Stat		42.09
9	df		2
10	p-value		0
11	chi-squared Critical		5.99

H = 42.09, p-value = 0. There is enough evidence to conclude that there are differences between the races with respect to the question about their children's standard of living.

A19.34 t-test of ρ

$H_0 : \rho = 0$

$H_1 : \rho > 0$

© 2012 Cengage Learning. All Rights Reserved. May not be scanned, copied or duplicated, or posted to a publicly accessible website, in whole or in part.

	A	B
1	**Correlation**	
2		
3	*AGE and HELPSICK*	
4	Pearson Coefficient of Correlation	0.1269
5	t Stat	4.65
6	df	1321
7	P(T<=t) one tail	0
8	t Critical one tail	1.646
9	P(T<=t) two tail	0
10	t Critical two tail	1.9618

$z = 4.65$. There is no evidence to support the hypothesis that older people are more likely to agree. In fact, there is evidence to the contrary.

A19.36 t-test of ρ

$$H_0: \rho = 0$$

$$H_1: \rho > 0$$

	A	B
1	**Correlation**	
2		
3	*PRESTG80 and SPPRES80*	
4	Pearson Coefficient of Correlation	0.2638
5	t Stat	8.11
6	df	878
7	P(T<=t) one tail	0
8	t Critical one tail	1.6466
9	P(T<=t) two tail	0
10	t Critical two tail	1.9627

$t = 8.11$, p-value = 0. There is enough evidence to conclude that there is a positive linear relationship between occupation prestige scores of married couples.

A19.38 Equal-variances t-test of $\mu_1 - \mu_2$

$$H_0: (\mu_1 - \mu_2) = 0$$

$$H_1: (\mu_1 - \mu_2) < 0$$

Two-tail F test: $F = 1.43$, p-value = .0864; use equal-variances t-test

© 2012 Cengage Learning. All Rights Reserved. May not be scanned, copied or duplicated, or posted to a publicly accessible website, in whole or in part.

	A	B	C
1	t-Test: Two-Sample Assuming Equal Variances		
2			
3		*Disabled*	*Not disabled*
4	Mean	2.17	2.39
5	Variance	2.10	1.47
6	Observations	41	868
7	Pooled Variance	1.50	
8	Hypothesized Mean Difference	0	
9	df	907	
10	t Stat	-1.13	
11	P(T<=t) one-tail	0.1295	
12	t Critical one-tail	1.6465	
13	P(T<=t) two-tail	0.2589	
14	t Critical two-tail	1.9626	

t = -1.13, p-value = .1295. There is not enough evidence to conclude that hearing disabled people are likely to believe that it is the government's responsibility to help pay for doctor and hospital bills.

A19.40 $H_0 : (p_1 - p_2) = 0$

$H_1 : (p_1 - p_2) < 0$

1 = Success

	A	B	C
1	**z-Test: Two Proportions**		
2			
3		*Victim*	*Not victim*
4	Sample Proportions	0.697	0.800
5	Observations	33	855
6	Hypothesized Difference	0	
7	z Stat	-1.44	
8	P(Z<=z) one tail	0.0747	
9	z Critical one-tail	1.6449	
10	P(Z<=z) two-tail	0.1494	
11	z Critical two-tail	1.96	

z = -1.44, p-value = .0747. There is not enough evidence to conclude that victims of a personal assault are less likely to favor requiring a police permit to buy a gun.

A19.42 H_0 : The locations of all 4 populations are the same.

H_1 : At least two population locations differ.

© 2012 Cengage Learning. All Rights Reserved. May not be scanned, copied or duplicated, or posted to a publicly accessible website, in whole or in part.

	A	B	C
1	**Kruskal-Wallis Test**		
2			
3	Group	Rank Sum	Observations
4	*Liberal*	113233	258
5	*Moderate*	173057	377
6	*Conservative*	186588	337
7			
8	H Stat		30.32
9	df		2
10	p-value		0
11	chi-squared Critical		5.99

H = 30.32, p-value = 0. There is enough evidence to infer that liberals, moderates, and conservatives differ in their belief that the rich should pay bigger share of taxes.

A19.44 Simple linear regression

	A	B	C	D	E	F
1	SUMMARY OUTPUT					
2						
3	*Regression Statistics*					
4	Multiple R	0.4138				
5	R Square	0.1712				
6	Adjusted R Square	0.1705				
7	Standard Error	28927				
8	Observations	1100				
9						
10	ANOVA					
11		*df*	*SS*	*MS*	*F*	*Significance F*
12	Regression	1	189,824,516,194	189,824,516,194	226.86	9.6104E-47
13	Residual	1098	918,760,406,306	836,758,111		
14	Total	1099	1,108,584,922,500			
15						
16		*Coefficients*	*Standard Error*	*t Stat*	*P-value*	
17	Intercept	-37938	4933	-7.69	3.25033E-14	
18	EDUC	5318	353	15.06	9.6104E-47	

t = 15.06, p-value = 9.61E-47. There is evidence of a linear relationship. For each additional year of education, income increases on average by $5318.

A19.46 H_0 : The locations of all 4 populations are the same.

H_1 : At least two population locations differ.

© 2012 Cengage Learning. All Rights Reserved. May not be scanned, copied or duplicated, or posted to a publicly accessible website, in whole or in part.

	A	B	C
1	**Kruskal-Wallis Test**		
2			
3	Group	Rank Sum	Observations
4	*Liberal*	270602	375
5	*Moderate*	263967	395
6	*Conservative*	305887	526
7			
8	H Stat		32.25
9	df		2
10	p-value		0
11	chi-squared Critical		5.99

H = 32.25, p-value = 0. There is enough evidence to infer that liberals, moderates, and conservatives differ in their perception about the level of unemployment in the previous year.

A19.48 H_0 : The locations of all 4 populations are the same.

H_1 : At least two population locations differ.

	A	B	C
1	**Kruskal-Wallis Test**		
2			
3	Group	Rank Sum	Observations
4	*Liberal*	256774.5	373
5	*Moderate*	265012.5	395
6	*Conservative*	314784	525
7			
8	H Stat		14.67
9	df		2
10	p-value		0.0007
11	chi-squared Critical		5.99

H = 14.67, p-value = .0007. There is enough evidence to infer that liberals, moderates, and conservatives differ in their perception about the level of inflation in the previous year.

A19.50 Wilcoxon rank sum test

H_0: The two population locations are the same

H_1: The location of population 1 is different from the location of population 2

© 2012 Cengage Learning. All Rights Reserved. May not be scanned, copied or duplicated, or posted to a publicly accessible website, in whole or in part.

	A	B	C
1	**Wilcoxon Rank Sum Test**		
2			
3		Rank Sum	Observations
4	*Democrat*	74124	297
5	*Republican*	51627	204
6	z Stat	-0.266	
7	P(Z<=z) one-tail	0.3952	
8	z Critical one-tail	1.6449	
9	P(Z<=z) two-tail	0.7904	
10	z Critical two-tail	1.96	

z = -.266, p-value = .7904. There is not enough evidence to conclude that Democrats and Republicans differ in their interest in information about what's going on in government and politics.

© 2012 Cengage Learning. All Rights Reserved. May not be scanned, copied or duplicated, or posted to a publicly accessible website, in whole or in part.

Chapter 20

20.2

Time series	Moving average
48	
41	
37	(48 +41+37+32+36)/5 = 38.8
32	(41+37+32+36+31)/5 = 35.4
36	(37+32+36+31+43)/5 = 35.8
31	(32+36+31+43+52)/5 = 38.8
43	(36+31+43+52+60)/5 = 44.4
52	(31+43+52+60+48)/5 = 46.8
60	(43+52+60+48+41)/5 = 48.8
48	(52+60+48+41+30)/5 = 46.2
41	
30	

20.4

Time series	Moving average
16	
22	(16+22+19)/3 = 19.00
19	(22+19+24)/3 = 21.67
24	(19+24+30)/3 = 24.33
30	(24+30+26)/3 = 26.67
26	(30+26+24)/3 = 26.67
24	(26+24+29)/3 = 26.33
29	(24+29+21)/3 = 24.67
21	(29+21+23)/3 = 24.33
23	(21+23+19)/3 = 21.00
19	(23+19+15)/3 = 19.00
15	

20.6

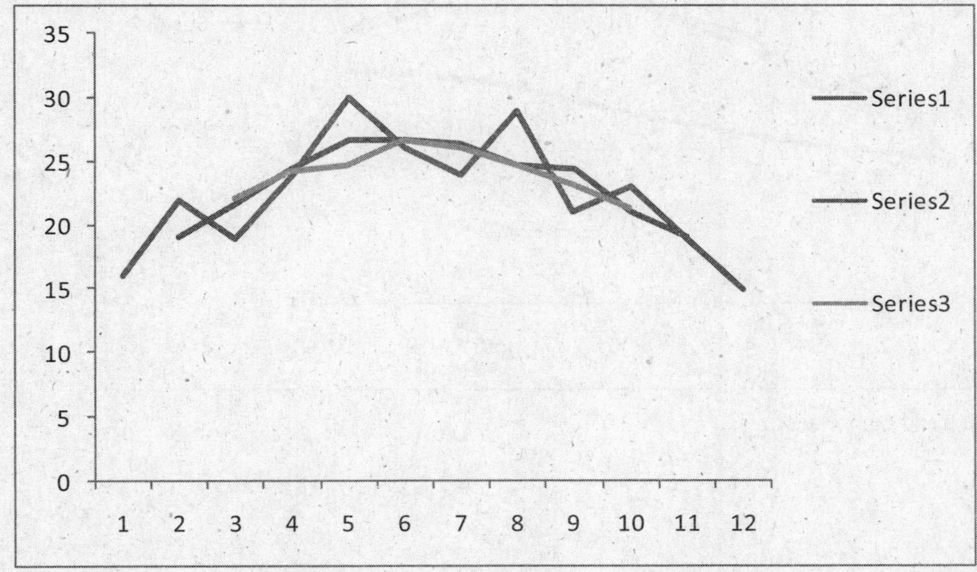

© 2012 Cengage Learning. All Rights Reserved. May not be scanned, copied or duplicated, or posted to a publicly accessible website, in whole or in part.

20.8 Time series	Exponentially smoothed time series
12	12.00
18	.8(18) +..2(12) = 16.80
16	.8(16) +. 2(16.80) = 16.16
24	.8(24) +. 2(16.16) = 22.43
17	.8(17) +. 2(22.43) = 18.09
16	.8(16) +. 2(18.09) = 16.42
25	.8(25) +. 2(16.42) = 23.28
21	.8(21) +. 2(23.28) = 21.46
23	.8(23) + .2(21.46) = 22.69
14	.8(14) + .2(22.69) = 15.74

20.10 Time series	Exponentially smoothed time series
38	38.00
43	.1(43) +. 9(38) = 38.50
42	.1(42) +. 9(38.50) = 38.85
45	.1(45) +. 9(38.85) = 39.47
46	.1(46) +. 9(39.47) = 40.12
48	.1(48) +. 9(40.12) = 40.91
50	.1(50) +. 9(40.91) = 41.82
49	.1(49) +. 9(41.82) = 42.53
46	.1(46) + .9(42.53) = 42.88
45	.1(45) + .9(42.88) = 43.09

There appears to be a gradual upward trend.

20.12

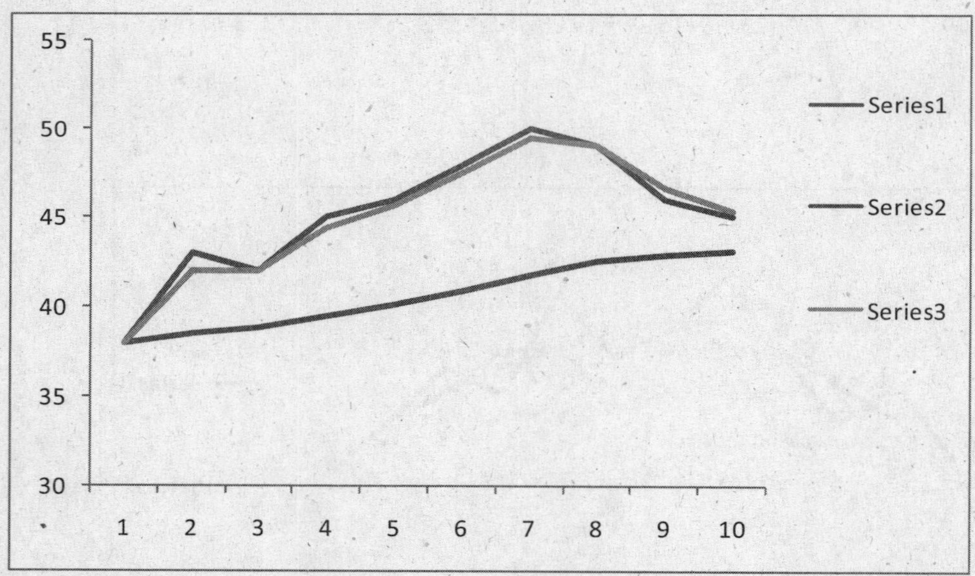

There is a trend component.

© 2012 Cengage Learning. All Rights Reserved. May not be scanned, copied or duplicated, or posted to a publicly accessible website, in whole or in part.

20.14

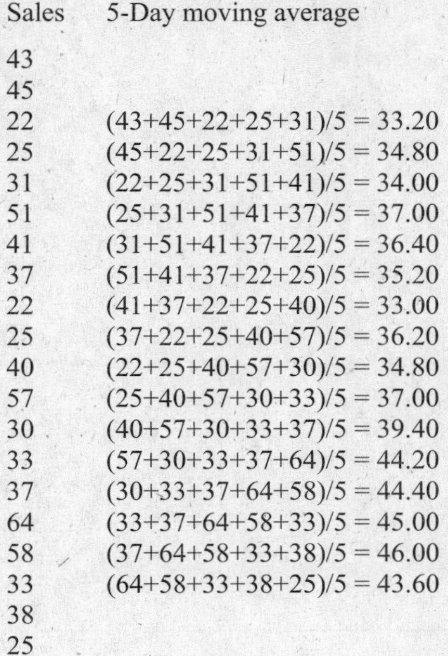

Sales	5-Day moving average
43	
45	
22	(43+45+22+25+31)/5 = 33.20
25	(45+22+25+31+51)/5 = 34.80
31	(22+25+31+51+41)/5 = 34.00
51	(25+31+51+41+37)/5 = 37.00
41	(31+51+41+37+22)/5 = 36.40
37	(51+41+37+22+25)/5 = 35.20
22	(41+37+22+25+40)/5 = 33.00
25	(37+22+25+40+57)/5 = 36.20
40	(22+25+40+57+30)/5 = 34.80
57	(25+40+57+30+33)/5 = 37.00
30	(40+57+30+33+37)/5 = 39.40
33	(57+30+33+37+64)/5 = 44.20
37	(30+33+37+64+58)/5 = 44.40
64	(33+37+64+58+33)/5 = 45.00
58	(37+64+58+33+38)/5 = 46.00
33	(64+58+33+38+25)/5 = 43.60
38	
25	

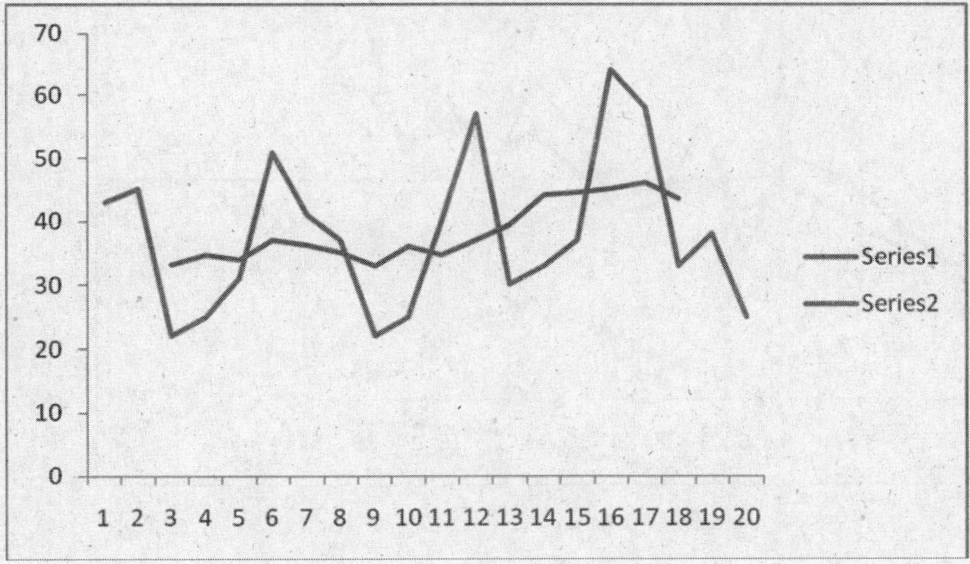

c There appears to be a seasonal (weekly) pattern.

© 2012 Cengage Learning. All Rights Reserved. May not be scanned, copied or duplicated, or posted to a publicly accessible website, in whole or in part.

20.16

Sales	Exponentially smoothed w = .4
18	18.00
22	.4(22)+.6(18) = 19.60
27	.4(27)+.6(19.6) = 22.56
31	.4(31)+.6(22.56) = 25.94
33	.4(33)+.6(25.94) = 28.76
20	.4(20)+.6(28.76) = 25.26
38	.4(38)+.6(25.26) = 30.35
26	.4(26)+.6(30.35) = 28.61
25	.4(25)+.6(28.61) = 27.17
36	.4(36)+.6(27.17) = 30.70
44	.4(44)+.6(30.70) = 36.02
29	.4(29)+.6(36.02) = 33.21
41	.4(41)+.6(33.21) = 36.33
33	.4(33)+.6(36.33) = 35.00
52	.4(52)+.6(35.00) = 41.80
45	.4(45)+.6(41.80) = 43.08

20.16 b

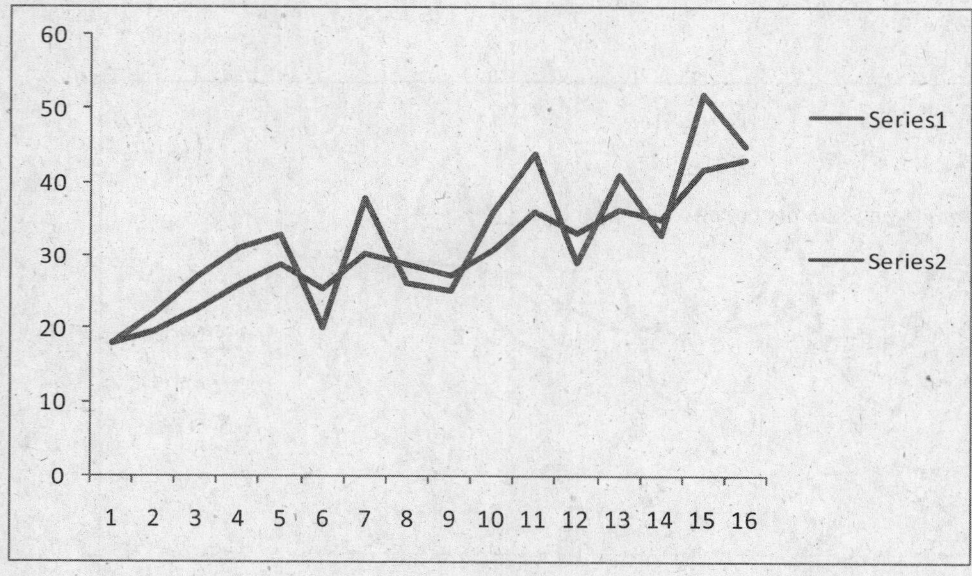

© 2012 Cengage Learning. All Rights Reserved. May not be scanned, copied or duplicated, or posted to a publicly accessible website, in whole or in part.

20.18

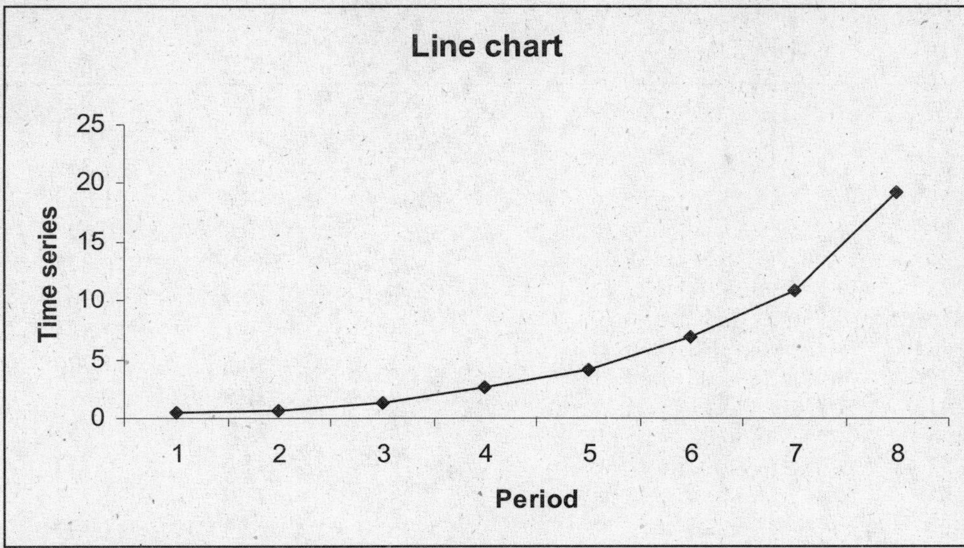

The quadratic model would appear to be the best model.

20.20

$\hat{y} = -4.96 + 2.38t$ $(R^2 = .81)$

$\hat{y} = 3.14 - 2.48t + .54t^2$ $(R^2 = .98)$

The quadratic trend line fits better.

© 2012 Cengage Learning. All Rights Reserved. May not be scanned, copied or duplicated, or posted to a publicly accessible website, in whole or in part.

20.22

Week	Day	Period t	y	$\hat{y}$	$y/\hat{y}$
1	1	1	12	17.2	0.699
	2	2	18	17.5	1.027
	3	3	16	17.9	0.894
	4	4	25	18.3	1.369
	5	5	31	18.6	1.664
2	1	6	11	19.0	0.579
	2	7	17	19.4	0.878
	3	8	19	19.7	0.963
	4	9	24	20.1	1.194
	5	10	27	20.5	1.320
3	1	11	14	20.8	0.672
	2	12	16	21.2	0.755
	3	13	16	21.6	0.742
	4	14	28	21.9	1.277
	5	15	25	22.3	1.122
4	1	16	17	22.7	0.750
	2	17	21	23.0	0.912
	3	18	20	23.4	0.855
	4	19	24	23.8	1.010
	5	20	32	24.1	1.327

	Day					
Week	Monday	Tuesday	Wednesday	Thursday	Friday	Total
1	.699	1.027	.894	1.369	1.664	
2	.579	.878	.963	1.194	1.320	
3	.672	.755	.742	1.277	1.122	
4	.750	.912	.855	1.010	1.327	
Average	.675	.893	.864	1.213	1.358	5.003
Seasonal Index	.675	.892	.864	1.212	1.357	5.000

© 2012 Cengage Learning. All Rights Reserved. May not be scanned, copied or duplicated, or posted to a publicly accessible website, in whole or in part.

20.24

Year	Quarter	Period t	y	$\hat{y}$	$y/\hat{y}$
2001	1	1	52	62.9	0.827
	2	2	67	64.1	1.045
	3	3	85	65.3	1.302
	4	4	54	66.5	0.812
2002	1	5	57	67.7	0.842
	2	6	75	68.8	1.090
	3	7	90	70.0	1.286
	4	8	61	71.2	0.857
2003	1	9	60	72.4	0.829
	2	10	77	73.6	1.046
	3	11	94	74.7	1.258
	4	12	63	75.9	0.830
2004	1	13	66	77.1	0.856
	2	14	82	78.3	1.047
	3	15	98	79.5	1.233
	4	16	67	80.6	0.831

	Quarter				
Year	1	2	3	4	Total
2001	.827	1.045	1.302	.812	
2002	.842	1.090	1.286	.857	
2003	.829	1.046	1.258	.830	
2004	.856	1.047	1.233	.831	
Average	.838	1.057	1.270	.833	3.998
Seasonal Index	.839	1.058	1.270	.833	4.000

20.26 a

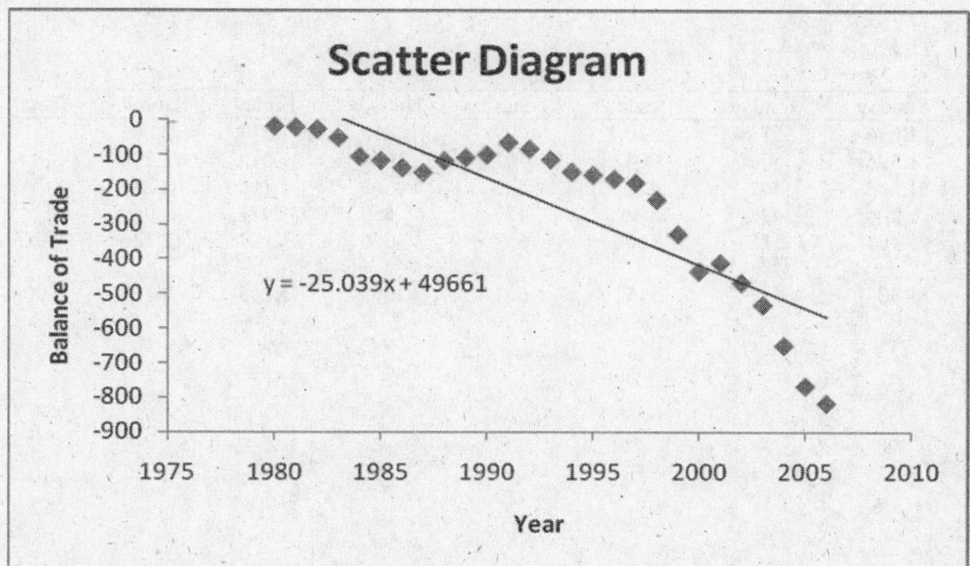

b $\hat{y} = 49{,}661 - 25.039\text{Year}$

© 2012 Cengage Learning. All Rights Reserved. May not be scanned, copied or duplicated, or posted to a publicly accessible website, in whole or in part.

20.28 Regression line: $\hat{y} = 145 + 1.66\ t$

Week	Day	Period t	y	$\hat{y}$ =145+1.66t	$y/\hat{y}$
1	1	1	240	146.66	1.636
	2	2	85	148.32	0.573
	3	3	93	149.98	0.620
	4	4	106	151.64	0.699
	5	5	125	153.3	0.815
	6	6	188	154.96	1.213
	7	7	314	156.62	2.005
2	1	8	221	158.28	1.396
	2	9	80	159.94	0.500
	3	10	75	161.6	0.464
	4	11	121	163.26	0.741
	5	12	110	164.92	0.667
	6	13	202	166.58	1.213
	7	14	386	168.24	2.294
3	1	15	235	169.9	1.383
	2	16	86	171.56	0.501
	3	17	74	173.22	0.427
	4	18	100	174.88	0.572
	5	19	117	176.54	0.663
	6	20	205	178.2	1.150
	7	21	402	179.86	2.235
4	1	22	219	181.52	1.206
	2	23	91	183.18	0.497
	3	24	102	184.84	0.552
	4	25	89	186.5	0.477
	5	26	105	188.16	0.558
	6	27	192	189.82	1.011
	7	28	377	191.48	1.969

	Day							
Week	Sunday	Monday	Tuesday	Wednesday	Thursday	Friday	Saturday	Total
1	1.636	.573	.620	.699	.815	1.213	2.005	
2	1.396	.500	.464	.741	.667	1.213	2.294	
3	1.383	.501	.427	.572	.663	1.150	2.235	
4	1.206	.497	.552	.477	.558	1.011	1.969	
Average	1.405	.518	.516	.657	.676	1.187	2.126	7.085
Seasonal Index	1.404	.517	.515	.621	.675	1.145	2.123	7.000

© 2012 Cengage Learning. All Rights Reserved. May not be scanned, copied or duplicated, or posted to a publicly accessible website, in whole or in part.

20.30

$$\text{MAD} = \frac{|166-173|+|179-186|+|195-192|+|214-211|+|220-223|}{5}$$

$$= \frac{7+7+3+3+3}{5} = \frac{23}{5} = 4.60$$

$$= (166-173)^2 + (179-186)^2 + (195-192)^2 + (214-211)^2 + (220-223)^2$$

$$= 49 + 49 + 9 + 9 + 9 = 125$$

20.32

$$\text{MAD} = \frac{\left|57-63\right|+\left|60-72\right|+\left|70-86\right|+\left|75-71\right|+\left|70-60\right|}{5}$$

$$= \frac{6+12+16+4+10}{5} = \frac{48}{5} = 9.6$$

$$\text{SSE} = (57 - 63)^2 + (60 - 72)^2 + (70 - 86)^2 + (75 - 71)^2 + (70-60)^2$$

$$= 36 + 144 + 256 + 16 + 100 = 552$$

20.34

Quarter	t	$\hat{y} = 150 + 3t$	SI	Forecast
1	41	273	.7	191.1
2	42	276	1.2	331.2
3	43	279	1.5	418.5
4	44	282	.6	169.2

20.36 $\hat{y}_t = 625 - 1.3_{y_{t-1}} = 625 - 1.3(65) = 540.5$

20.38 $F_{17} = F_{18} = F_{19} = F_{20} = S_{16} = 43.08$

20.40

Quarter	t	$\hat{y} = 47.7 - 1.06t$	SI	Forecast
1	21	25.44	1.207	30.71
2	22	24.38	.959	23.38
3	23	23.32	.972	22.67
4	24	22.26	.863	19.21

20.42a $\hat{y}_{2007} = 1{,}775.2 + .9054 y_{2006} = 1{,}775.2 + .9054(17{,}672) = 17{,}775$

b $F_{2007} = S_{2006} = 17{,}146.$

© 2012 Cengage Learning. All Rights Reserved. May not be scanned, copied or duplicated, or posted to a publicly accessible website, in whole or in part.

20.43 a $\hat{y}_{2007} = -4.2245 + 1.1203_{2006} = -4.2245 + 1.1203(-817.3) = -919.8$

$F_{2007} = S_{2006} = -719.5$

20.44

Quarter	t	$\hat{y} = 143 + 7.42t$	SI	Forecast
1	25	328.50	1.063	349.20
2	26	335.92	.962	323.16
3	27	343.34	.927	318.28
4	28	350.76	1.048	367.60

20.46

Day	t	$\hat{y} = 90.4 + 2.02t$	SI	Forecast
1	17	124.74	1.094	136.47
2	18	126.76	0.958	121.44
3	19	128.78	0.688	88.60
4	20	130.80	1.260	164.81

20.48 There is a small upward trend and seasonality.

20.50

	A	B
1	**Seasonal Indexes**	
2		
3	**Season**	**Index**
4	1	0.646
5	2	1.045
6	3	1.405
7	4	0.904

© 2012 Cengage Learning. All Rights Reserved. May not be scanned, copied or duplicated, or posted to a publicly accessible website, in whole or in part.

20.52 a

	A	B
1	**Seasonal Indexes**	
2		
3	**Season**	**Index**
4	1	0.7192
5	2	0.6729
6	3	0.8936
7	4	1.0500
8	5	1.2148
9	6	1.3998
10	7	1.1908
11	8	1.1651
12	9	1.0246
13	10	1.0288
14	11	0.8535
15	12	0.7870

b

Period	Month	$\hat{y} = 16.34 - .1008t$	Seasonal Index	Forecasts	Actual
61	January	10.19	.7192	7.33	2.2
62	February	10.09	.6729	6.79	3.6
63	March	9.99	.8936	8.93	5.3
64	April	9.89	1.0500	10.38	4.5
65	May	9.79	1.2148	11.89	5.7
66	June	9.69	1.3998	13.56	8.1
67	July	9.59	1.1908	11.42	6.1
68	August	9.49	1.1651	11.05	6.5
69	September	9.38	1.0246	9.62	5.8
70	October	9.28	1.0288	9.55	4.9
71	November	9.18	.8535	7.84	4.8
72	December	9.08	.7870	7.15	4.4

c MAD = 4.47

SSE = 254.32

© 2012 Cengage Learning. All Rights Reserved. May not be scanned, copied or duplicated, or posted to a publicly accessible website, in whole or in part.

Chapter 21

21.4 a Chance variation represents the variation in student achievement caused by differences in preparation, motivation, and ability.

b Special variation represents variation due to specific event or factors that can be corrected.

21.6 ARL = $\frac{1}{.0124} = 81$

21.8 ARL = $\frac{1}{.0456} = 22$

21.10 a From Beta-mean spreadsheet, $\beta = .6603$

b Probability = $.6603^{8} = .0361$

21.12 Number of units = Production $\times$ ARL = 50(385) = 19,250

21.14 $P = 1 - \beta = 1 - .8133 = .1867$; ARL = $\frac{1}{P} = \frac{1}{.1867} = 5.36$

21.16 Number of units = Production $\times$ ARL = 2000(385) = 770,000

21.18 $P = 1 - \beta = 1 - .7388 = .2612$; ARL = $\frac{1}{P} = \frac{1}{.2612} = 3.83$

21.20 a From Beta-mean spreadsheet, $\beta = .3659$

b Probability = $.3659^{4} = .0179$

21.22 Sampling 10 units per half hour means that on average we will produce 770,000 units before erroneously concluding that the process is out of control when it isn't. Sampling 20 units per hour doubles this figure. Sampling 10 units per half hour means that when the process goes out of control, the probability of not detecting a shift of .75 standard deviations is .7388 and we will produce on average 3.83 $\times$ 2000 = 7660 units until the chart indicates a problem. Sampling 20 units per hour decreases the probability of not detecting the shift to .3659 and decreases the average number of units produced when the process is out of control to 4000$\times$ 1.58 = 6320.

© 2012 Cengage Learning. All Rights Reserved. May not be scanned, copied or duplicated, or posted to a publicly accessible website, in whole or in part.

21.24 Centerline = $\bar{\bar{x}} = 181.1$

$$\text{Lower control limit} = \bar{x} - \frac{3S}{\sqrt{n}} = 181.1 - 3\left(\frac{11.0}{\sqrt{9}}\right) = 170.1$$

$$\text{Upper control limit} = \bar{x} + \frac{3S}{\sqrt{n}} = 181.1 + 3\left(\frac{11.0}{\sqrt{9}}\right) = 192.1$$

Zone boundaries: 170.10, 173.77, 177.44, 181.10, 184.77, 188.43, 192.10

21.26 a S Chart

	A	B	C	D
1	**Statistical Process Control**			
2				
3			*Data*	
4	Upper control limit		10.0885	
5	Centerline		4.452	
6	Lower control limit		0	

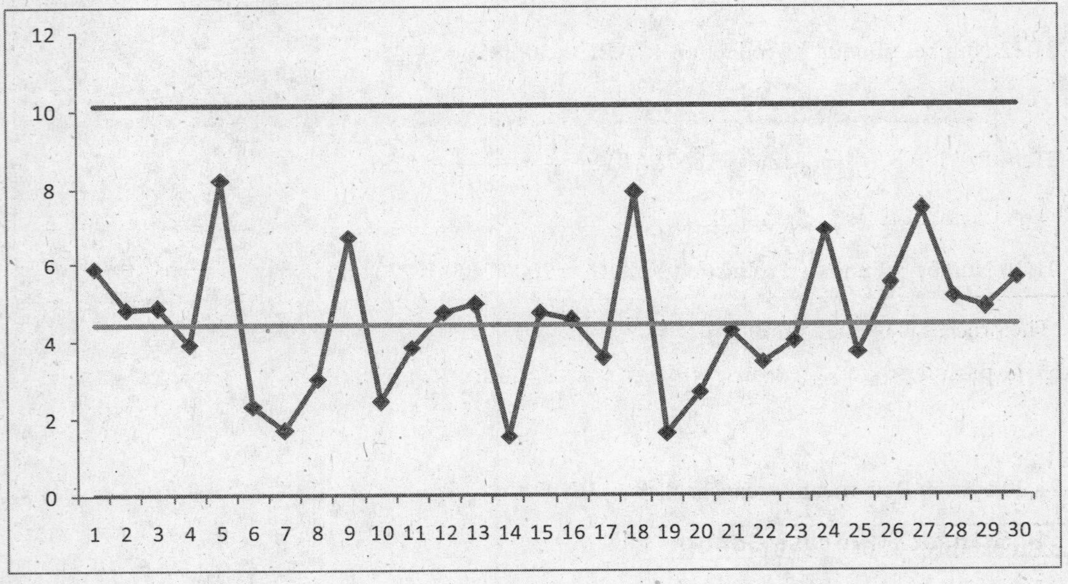

© 2012 Cengage Learning. All Rights Reserved. May not be scanned, copied or duplicated, or posted to a publicly accessible website, in whole or in part.

$\bar{x}$ Chart

	A	B	C	D
1	**Statistical Process Control**			
2				
3			*Data*	
4	Upper control limit		19.9668	
5	Centerline		12.7386	
6	Lower control limit		5.5103	
7	Pattern Test #2 Failed at Points:			29
8	Pattern Test #6 Failed at Points:			29, 30

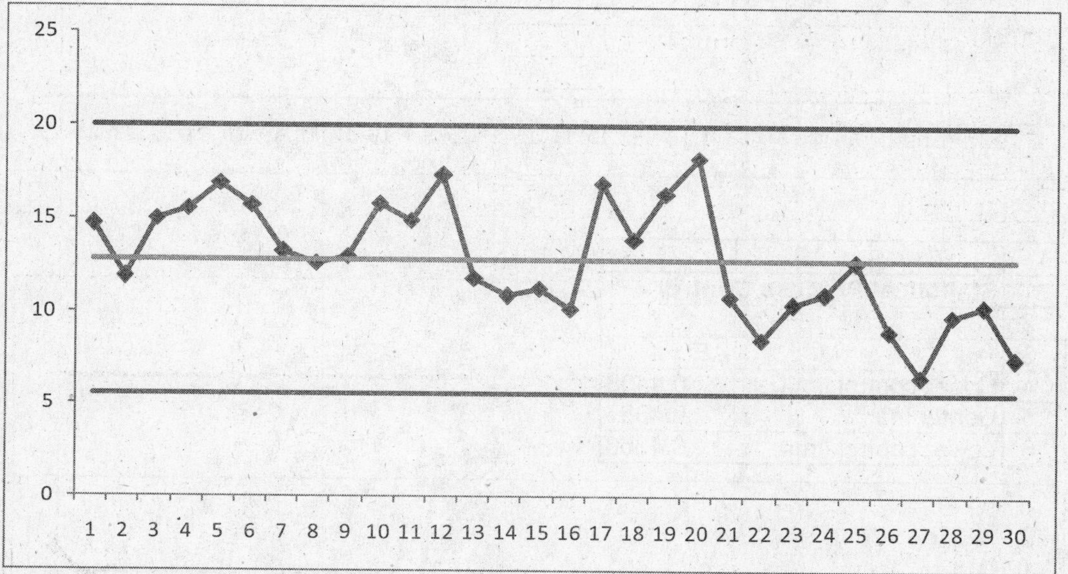

c The process is out of control at samples 29 and 30.

d A level shift occurred.

21.28

	A	B	C
1	**Statistical Process Control**		
2			
3			*AEU*
4	Upper control limit		0.0031
5	Centerline		0.0015
6	Lower control limit		0

© 2012 Cengage Learning. All Rights Reserved. May not be scanned, copied or duplicated, or posted to a publicly accessible website, in whole or in part.

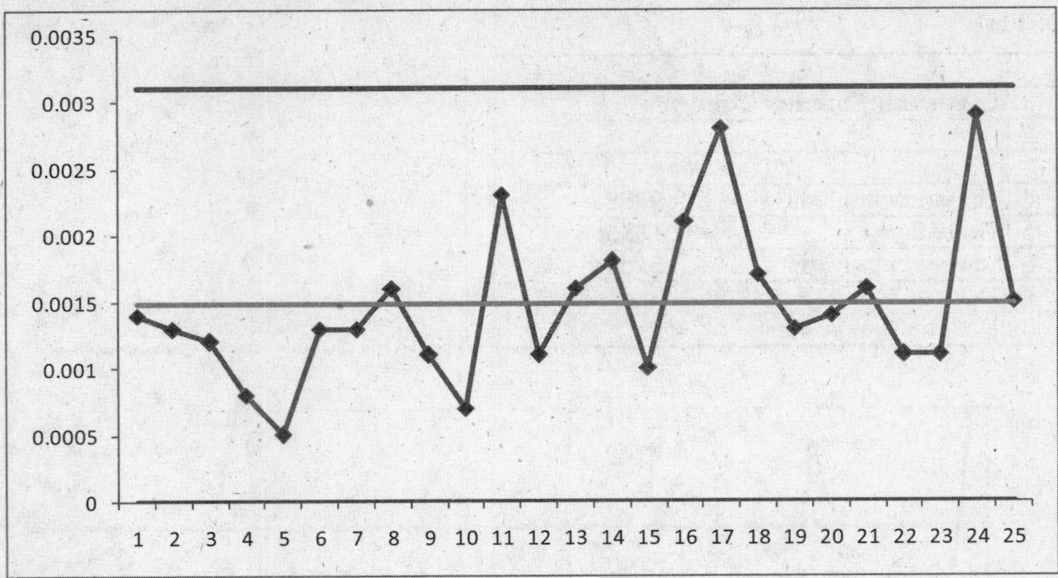

	A	B	C
1	**Statistical Process Control**		
2			
3			*AEU*
4	Upper control limit		0.4408
5	Centerline		0.4387
6	Lower control limit		0.4366

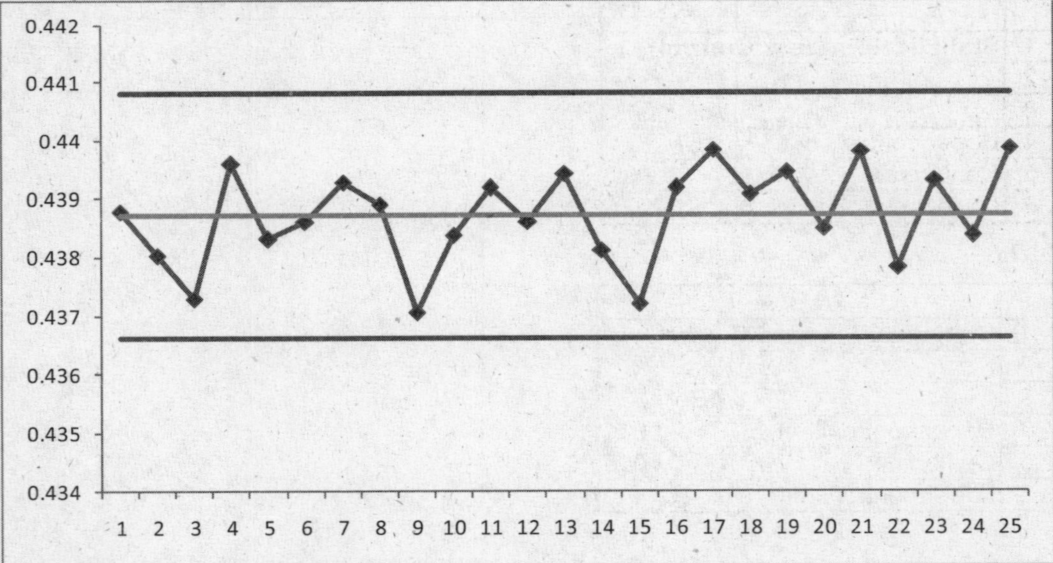

The process is under control.

© 2012 Cengage Learning. All Rights Reserved. May not be scanned, copied or duplicated, or posted to a publicly accessible website, in whole or in part.

21.30

	A	B	C
1	**Statistical Process Control**		
2			
3			*Volume*
4	Upper control limit		1.8995
5	Centerline		0.9093
6	Lower control limit		0

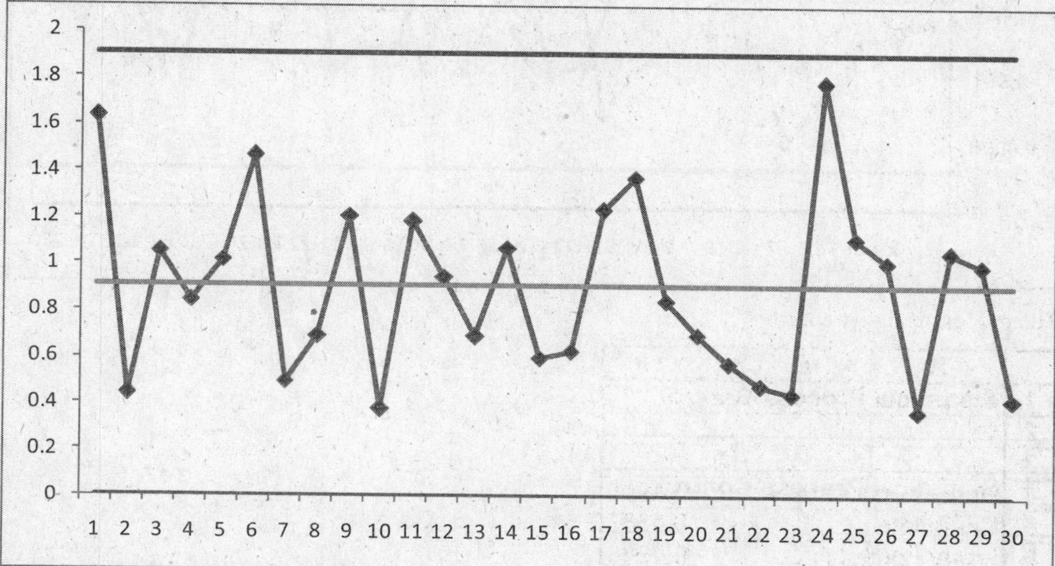

	A	B	C
1	**Statistical Process Control**		
2			
3			*Volume*
4	Upper control limit		1.3871
5	Centerline		0.092
6	Lower control limit		-1.2031

© 2012 Cengage Learning. All Rights Reserved. May not be scanned, copied or duplicated, or posted to a publicly accessible website, in whole or in part.

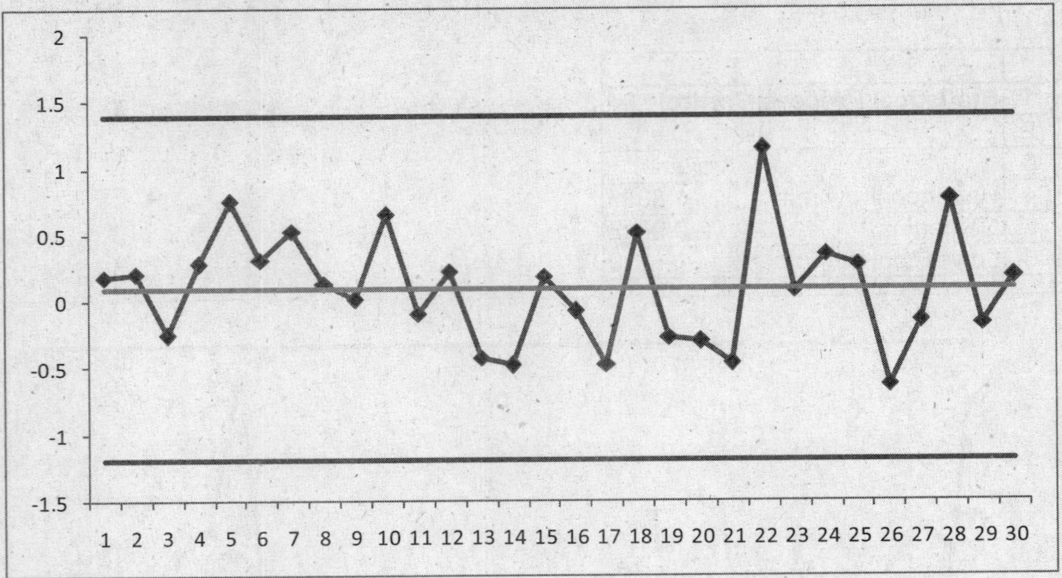

The process is under control.

21.32

	A	B	C
1	**Statistical Process Control**		
2			
3			*Headrest*
4	Upper control limit		2.3313
5	Centerline		0.9078
6	Lower control limit		0

© 2012 Cengage Learning. All Rights Reserved. May not be scanned, copied or duplicated, or posted to a publicly accessible website, in whole or in part.

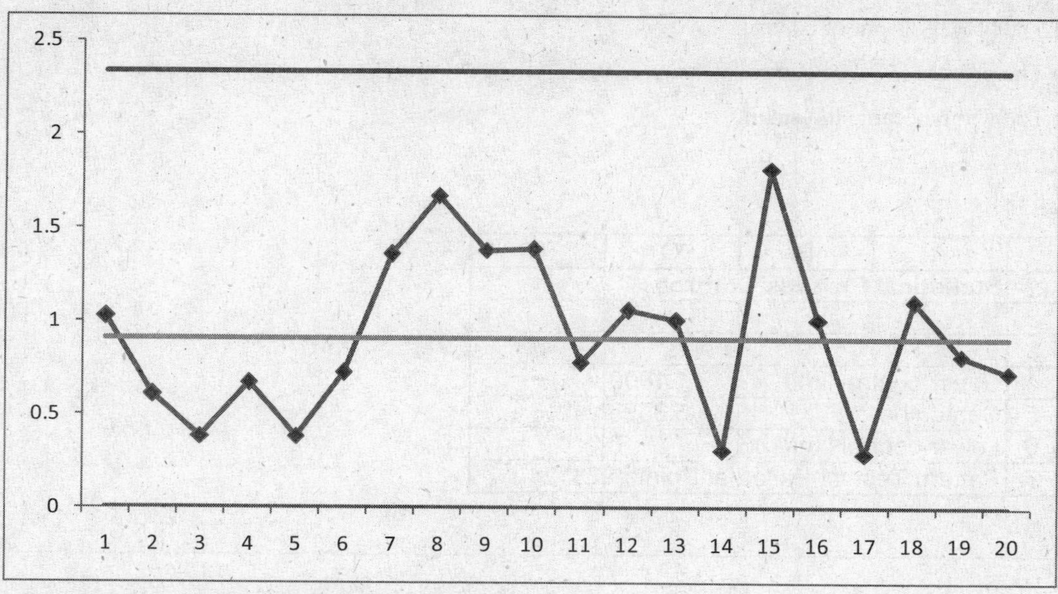

	A	B	C	D
1	**Statistical Process Control**			
2				
3			*Headrest*	
4	Upper control limit		241.3248	
5	Centerline		239.5617	
6	Lower control limit		237.7986	
7	Pattern Test #1 Failed at Points:			19, 20
8	Pattern Test #5 Failed at Points:			20

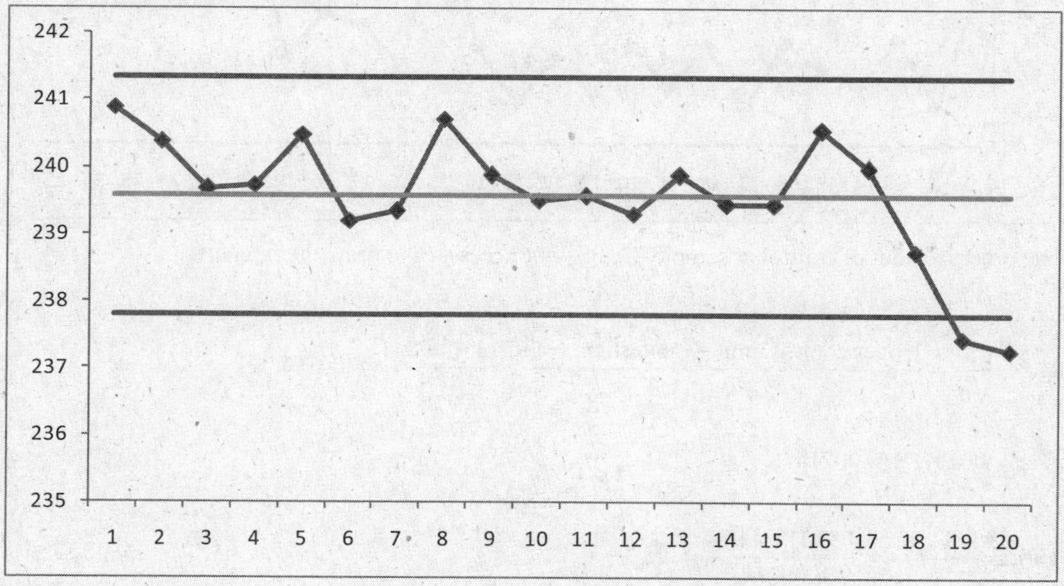

© 2012 Cengage Learning. All Rights Reserved. May not be scanned, copied or duplicated, or posted to a publicly accessible website, in whole or in part.

a The process is out of control.

b The process is out of control at sample 19.

c The width became too small.

21.34

	A	B	C	D
1	**Statistical Process Control**			
2				
3			*Seats*	
4	Upper control limit		11.1809	
5	Centerline		5.3523	
6	Lower control limit		0	
7	Pattern Test #1 Failed at Points: 23, 24			

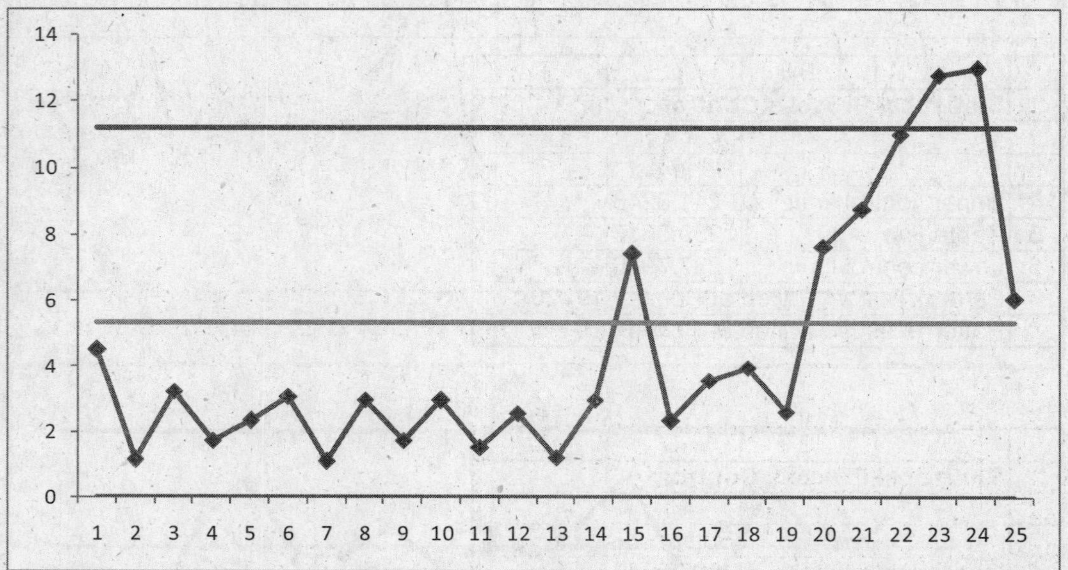

The process is out of control at sample 23. It is not necessary to draw the $\overline{x}$ chart.

21.36 $\frac{S}{\sqrt{n}} = \frac{\text{Upper control limit} - \text{Centerline}}{3} = \frac{4.9873 - 4.9841}{3} = .00107$

$\frac{S}{\sqrt{4}} = .00107; S = .00214$

$CPL = \frac{\overline{\overline{x}} - LSL}{3S} = \frac{4.9841 - 4.978}{3(.00214)} = .95$

$CPU = \frac{USL - \overline{\overline{x}}}{3S} = \frac{4.990 - 4.9841}{3(.00214)} = .92$

$C_{pk} = \text{Min}(CPL, CPU) = .92$

© 2012 Cengage Learning. All Rights Reserved. May not be scanned, copied or duplicated, or posted to a publicly accessible website, in whole or in part.

21.38

	A	B	C
1	**Statistical Process Control**		
2			
3			*Bottles*
4	Upper control limit		69.6821
5	Centerline		33.3567
6	Lower control limit		0

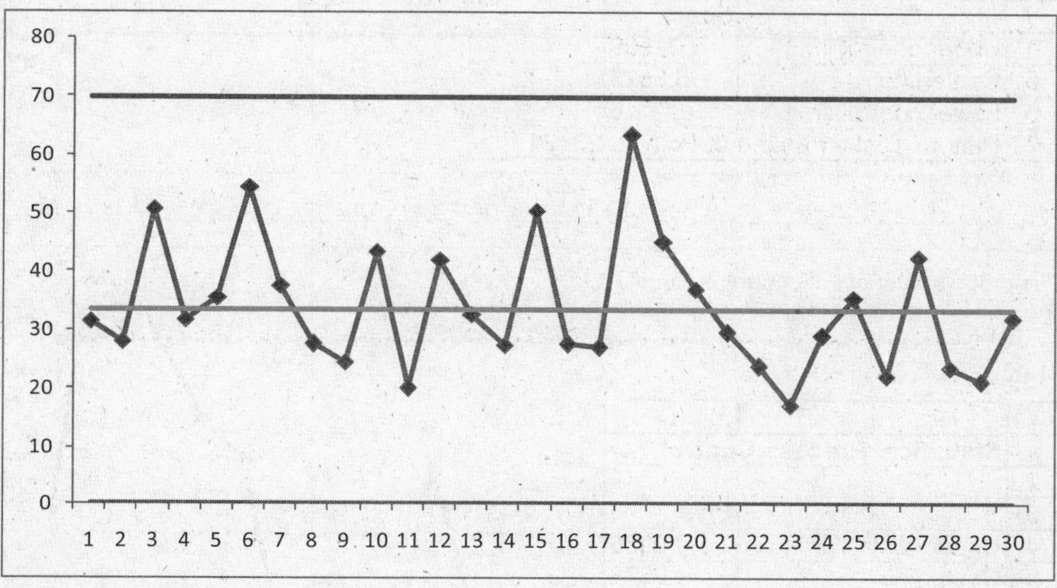

	A	B	C	D
1	**Statistical Process Control**			
2				
3			*Bottles*	
4	Upper control limit		803.9376	
5	Centerline		756.4267	
6	Lower control limit		708.9157	
7	Pattern Test #1 Failed at Points:			30
8	Pattern Test #5 Failed at Points:			29, 30
9	Pattern Test #6 Failed at Points:			30

© 2012 Cengage Learning. All Rights Reserved. May not be scanned, copied or duplicated, or posted to a publicly accessible website, in whole or in part.

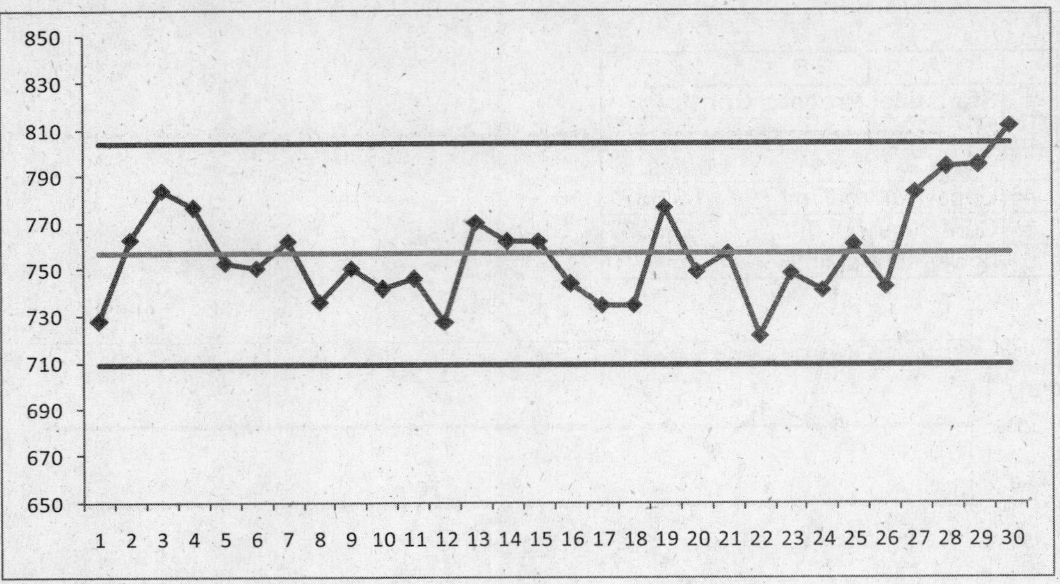

The process went out of control at sample 29.

21.40

	A	B	C
1	**Statistical Process Control**		
2			
3			*Pipes*
4	Upper control limit		0.0956
5	Centerline		0.0372
6	Lower control limit		0

© 2012 Cengage Learning. All Rights Reserved. May not be scanned, copied or duplicated, or posted to a publicly accessible website, in whole or in part.

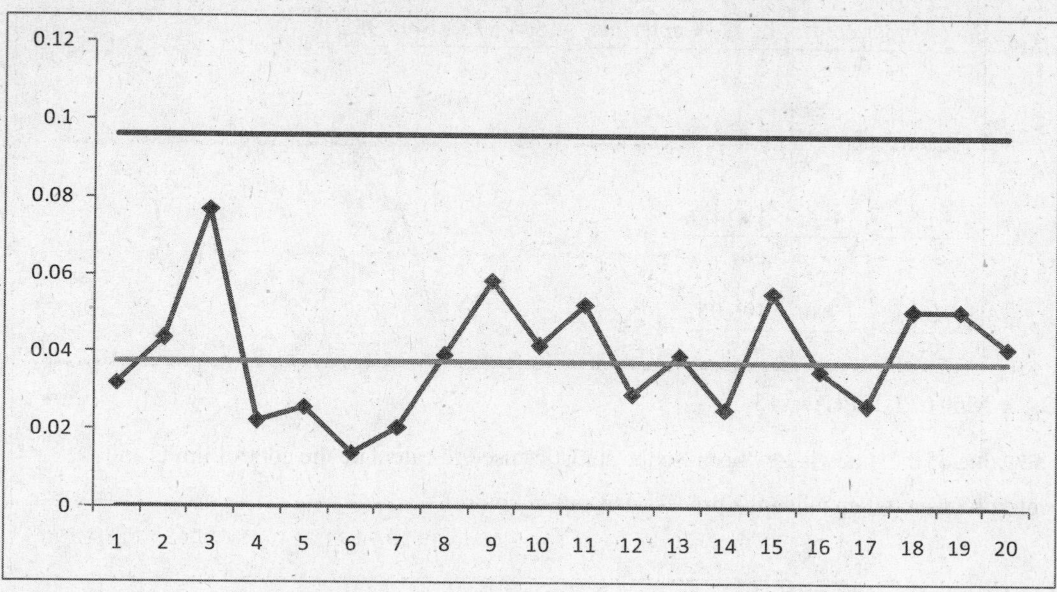

	A	B	C
1	**Statistical Process Control**		
2			
3			*Pipes*
4	Upper control limit		3.0615
5	Centerline		2.9892
6	Lower control limit		2.9168

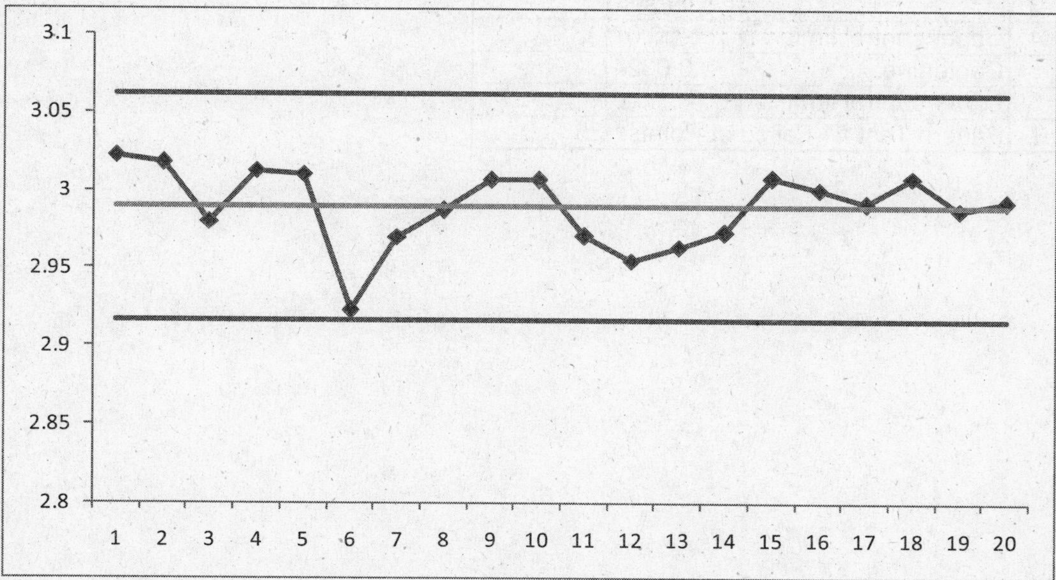

The process is under control.

© 2012 Cengage Learning. All Rights Reserved. May not be scanned, copied or duplicated, or posted to a publicly accessible website, in whole or in part.

21.42 $\frac{S}{\sqrt{n}} = \frac{\text{Upper control limit} - \text{Centerline}}{3} = \frac{1504.572 - 1496.952}{3} = 2.54$

$$\frac{S}{\sqrt{5}} = 2.54; S = 5.68$$

$$CPL = \frac{\bar{\bar{x}} - LSL}{3S} = \frac{1496.952 - 1486}{3(5.68)} = .64$$

$$CPU = \frac{USL - \bar{\bar{x}}}{3S} = \frac{1506 - 1496.952}{3(5.68)} = .53$$

$$C_{pk} = \text{Min}(CPL, CPU) = .53$$

The value of the index is low because the statistics used to calculate the control limits and centerline were taken when the process was out of control.

21.44 Centerline = $\bar{p} = .0324$

Lower control limit = $\bar{p} - 3\sqrt{\frac{\bar{p}(1-\bar{p})}{n}} = .0324 - 3\sqrt{\frac{(.0324)(1-.0324)}{200}} = -.00516\ (= 0)$

Upper control limit = $\bar{p} + 3\sqrt{\frac{\bar{p}(1-\bar{p})}{n}} = .0324 + 3\sqrt{\frac{(.0324)(1-.0324)}{200}} = .06996$

	A	B	C	D
1	**Statistical Process Control**			
2				
3			*Copiers*	
4	Upper control limit		0.07	
5	Centerline		0.0324	
6	Lower control limit		0	
7	Pattern Test #1 Failed at Points:		25	

© 2012 Cengage Learning. All Rights Reserved. May not be scanned, copied or duplicated, or posted to a publicly accessible website, in whole or in part.

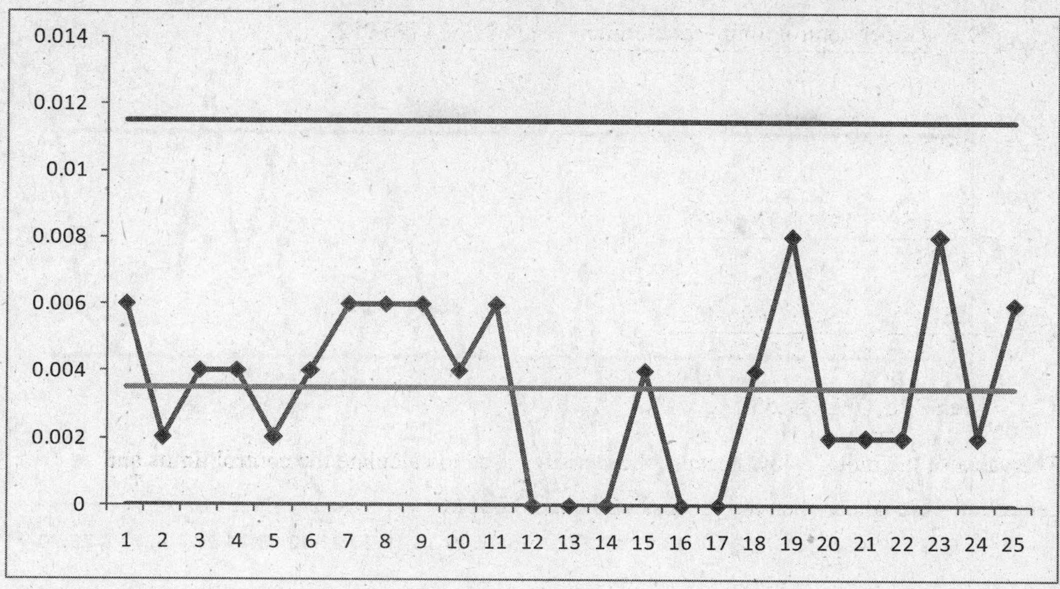

The process is out of control at sample 25.

21.46 Centerline = $\overline{p}$ = . 0383

Lower control limit = $\overline{p} - 3\sqrt{\frac{\overline{p}(1-\overline{p})}{n}} = .0383 - 3\sqrt{\frac{(.0383)(1-.0383)}{100}} = -.0193\ (= 0)$

Upper control limit = $\overline{p} + 3\sqrt{\frac{\overline{p}(1-\overline{p})}{n}} = .0383 + 3\sqrt{\frac{(.0383)(1-.0383)}{100}} = .0959$

	A	B	C	D
1	**Statistical Process Control**			
2				
3			*Telephones*	
4	Upper control limit		0.0959	
5	Centerline		0.0383	
6	Lower control limit		0	
7	Pattern Test #1 Failed at Points: 25, 30			
8				

© 2012 Cengage Learning. All Rights Reserved. May not be scanned, copied or duplicated, or posted to a publicly accessible website, in whole or in part.

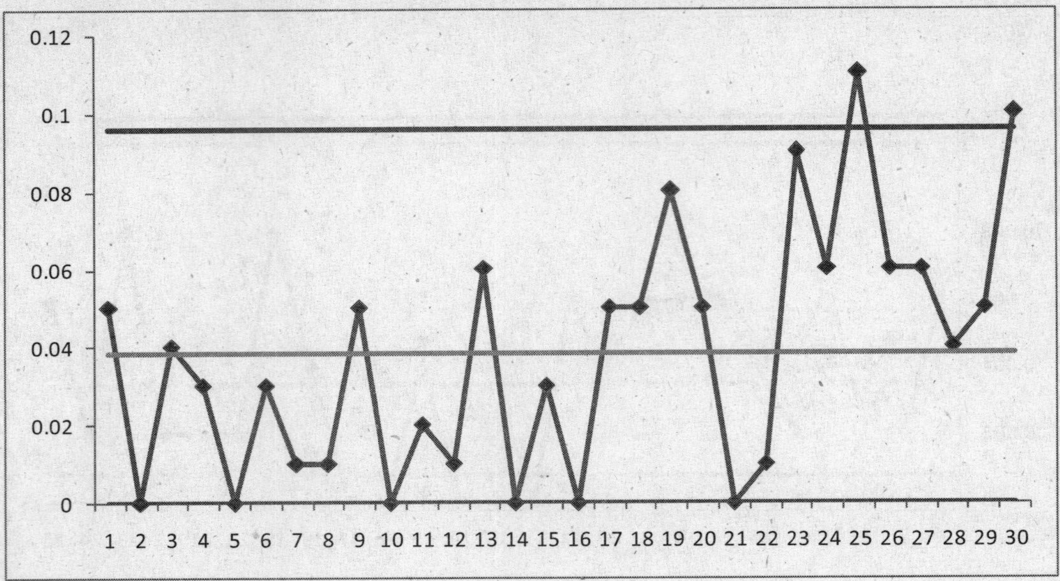

The process is out of control at samples 25 and 30.

21.48

	A	B	C	D	E
1	**Statistical Process Control**				
2					
3			*Batteries*		
4	Upper control limit		0.047		
5	Centerline		0.0257		
6	Lower control limit		0.0045		
7	Pattern Test #1 Failed at Points:			28, 29, 30	

© 2012 Cengage Learning. All Rights Reserved. May not be scanned, copied or duplicated, or posted to a publicly accessible website, in whole or in part.

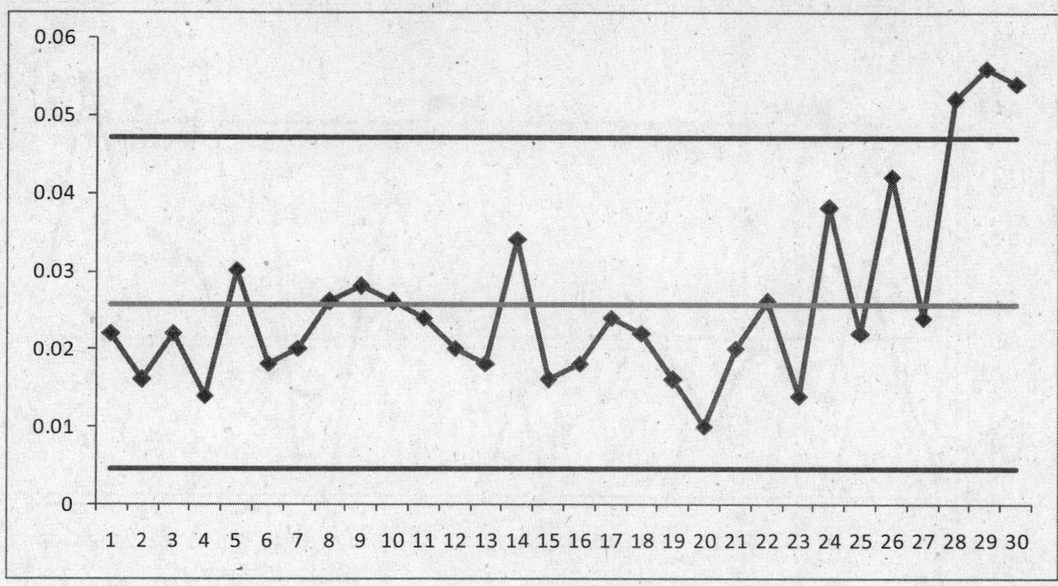

The process is out of control at sample 28.

21.50

	A	B	C	D
1	**Statistical Process Control**			
2				
3			*Scanners*	
4	Upper control limit		0.0275	
5	Centerline		0.0126	
6	Lower control limit		0	
7	Pattern Test #1 Failed at Points: 24			

© 2012 Cengage Learning. All Rights Reserved. May not be scanned, copied or duplicated, or posted to a publicly accessible website, in whole or in part.

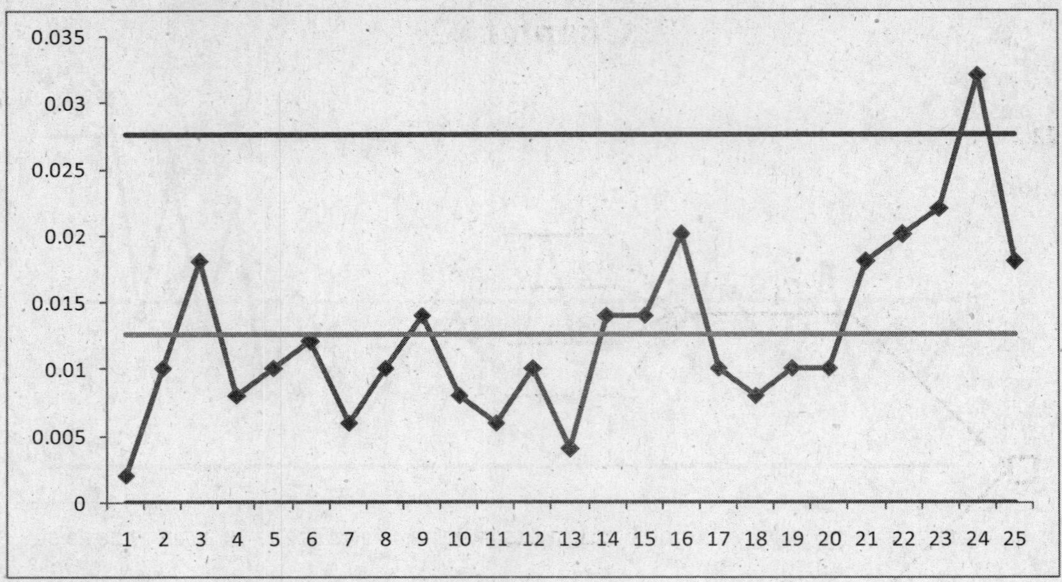

The process is out of control at sample 24.

© 2012 Cengage Learning. All Rights Reserved. May not be scanned, copied or duplicated, or posted to a publicly accessible website, in whole or in part.

Chapter 22

22.2

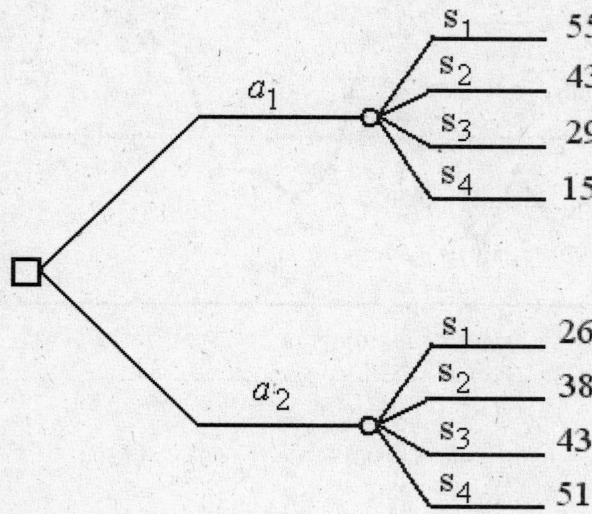

22.4

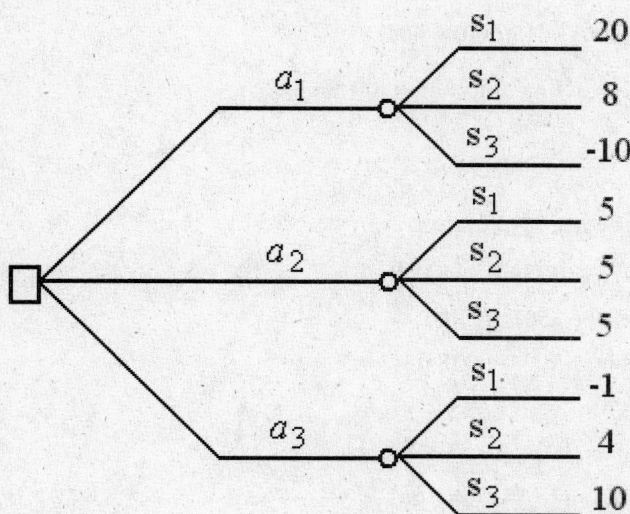

22.6 $EOL(a_1) = .2(0) + .6(0) + .2(20) = 4.0$

$EOL(a_2) = .2(15) + .6(3) + .2(5) = 5.8$

$EOL(a_3) = .2(21) + .6(4) + .2(0) = 6.6$

The EOL decision is a_1.

© 2012 Cengage Learning. All Rights Reserved. May not be scanned, copied or duplicated, or posted to a publicly accessible website, in whole or in part.

22.8 a $EMV(a_0) = 0$

$EMV(a_1) = .25(-3.00) + .25(5.00) + .25(5.00) + .25(5.00) = 3.00$

$EMV(a_2) = .25(-6.00) + .25(2.00) + .25(10.00) + .25(10.00) = 4.00$

$EMV(a_3) = .25(-9.00) + .25(-1.00) + .25(7.00) + .25(15.00) = 3.00$

EMV decision is a_2 (bake 2 cakes)

b $EOL(a_0) = .25(0) + .25(5.00) + .25(10.00) + .25(15.00) = 7.50$

$EOL(a_1) = .25(3.00) + .25(0) + .25(5.00) + .25(10.00) = 4.50$

$EOL(a_2) = .25(6.00) + .25(3.00) + .25(0) + .25(5.00) = 3.50$

$EOL(a_2) = .25(9.00) + .25(6.00) + .25(3.00) + .25(0) = 4.50$

EOL decision is a_2 (bake 2 cakes)

22.10 $EMV(a_1) = -40{,}000$

$EMV(a_2) = .05(0) + .15(-18{,}000) + .30(-36{,}000) + .40(-54{,}000) + .10(-72{,}000) = -42{,}300$

EMV decision is a_1

22.12

$EMV(a_{100}) = 200$

$EMV(a_{200}) = .20(0) + .25(300) + .40(600) + .15(600) = 405$

$EMV(a_{300}) = .20(-150) + .25(150) + .40(450) + .15(750) = 300$

EMV decision is order 200 shirts.

22.14 a EMV(Small) = .15(-220) + .55(-330) + .30(-440) = -346.5

EMV(Medium) = .15(-300) + .55(-320) + .30(-390) = -338.0

EMV(Large) = .15(-350) + .55(-350) + .30(-350) =-350.0

EMV decision: build a medium size plant; EMV*= -338.0

b

Opportunity Loss Table

	Small	Medium	Large
Low	0	80	130
Moderate	10	0	30
High	90	40	0

c EOL(Small) = .15(0) + .55(10) + .30(90) = 32.5

EOL(Medium) = .15(80) + .55(0) + .30(40) = 24.0

© 2012 Cengage Learning. All Rights Reserved. May not be scanned, copied or duplicated, or posted to a publicly accessible website, in whole or in part.

EOL(Large) = .15(130) + .55(30) + .30(0) = 36.0

EOL decision: build a medium size plant

22.16

Payoff Table

	Decision	
Market share	Produce	Don't produce
5%	-28 millio[illegible]	0
10%	2 mil[illegible]	0
15%	8[illegible]	0

EMV(produce) = .1[illegible] + .45(2 million) + .40 (8 million) = -.1 million

EMV (don't pr[illegible]

EMV decis[illegible]

22.[illegible]

[illegible]nity Loss Table

	a_2	a_3
	0	35
	40	0
	100	135
	130	120

[illegible] = .10(50) + .25(110) + .50(0) + .15(0) = 32.5

EOL(a_2) = .10(0) + .25(40) + .50(100) + .15(130) = 79.5

EOL(a_3) = .10(35) + .25(0) + .50(135) + .15(120) = 89

EOL* = 32.5

22.20 a EPPI = .75(65) + .25(110) = 76.25

EMV(a_1) = .75(65) + .25(70) = 66.25

EMV(a_2) = .75(20) + .25(110) = 42.5

EMV(a_3) = .75(45) + .25(80) = 53.75

EMV(a_4) = .75(30) + .25(95) = 46.25

EVPI = EPPI – EMV* = 76.25 – 66.25 = 10

b EPPI = .95(65) + .05(110) = 67.25

EMV(a_1) = .95(65) + .05(70) = 65.25

EMV(a_2) = .95(20) + .05(110) = 24.5

© 2012 Cengage Learning. All Rights Reserved. May not be scanned, copied or duplicated, or posted to a publicly website, in whole or in part.

$EMV(a_3) = .95(45) + .05(80) = 46.75$

$EMV(a_4) = .95(30) + .05(95) = 33.25$

$EVPI = EPPI - EMV^* = 67.25 - 65.25 = 2$

22.22 Posterior Probabilities for I_1

s_j	$P(s_j)$	$P(I_1 \| s_j)$	$P(s_j$ and $I_1)$	$P(s_j \| I_1)$
s_1	.25	.40	(.25)(.40) = .10	20 = .500
s_2	.40	.25	(.40)(.25) = .10	500
s_3	.35	0	(.35)(0) = .0	
			$P(I_1) = .20$	

Posterior Probabilities for I_2

s_j	$P(s_j)$	$P(I_2 \| s_j)$	$P(s_j$ and $I_2)$	$P(s_j \|$
s_1	.25	.30	(.25)(.30) = .075	.075/.28 = .2
s_2	.40	.25	(.40)(.25) = .10	.10/.28 = .357
s_3	.35	30	(.35)(.30) = .105	.105/.28 = .375
			$P(I_2) = .28$	

Posterior Probabilities for I_3

s_j	$P(s_j)$	$P(I_3 \| s_j)$	$P(s_j$ and $I_3)$	$P(s_j \| I_3)$
s_1	.25	.20	(.25)(.20) = .05	.05/.29 = .172
s_2	.40	.25	(.40)(.25) = .10	.10/.29 = .345
	.35	.40	(.35)(.40) = .14	.14/.29 = .483
			$P(I_3) = .29$	

r Probabilities for I_4

	$s_j)$	$P(I_4 \| s_j)$	$P(s_j$ and $I_4)$	$P(s_j \| I_4)$
		.10	(.25)(.10) = .025	.025/.23 = .109
		.25	(.40)(.25) = .10	.10/.23 = .435
		.30	(.35)(.30) = .105	.105/.23 = .456
			$P(I_4) = .23$	

$a_1) = .5(10) + .5(22) = 16$

accessible

ghts Reserved. May not be scanned, copied or duplicated, or posted to a publicly accessible website, in whole or in part.

I_1: $EMV(a_1) = .951(10) + .049(22) = 10.588$

$EMV(a_2) = .951(18) + .049(19) = 18.049$

$EMV(a_3) = .951(23) + .049(15) = 22.608$

Optimal act: a_3

1.748

I_2: $EMV(a_1) = .021(10) + .9$7.979

$EMV(a_2) = .021(18) +$ 5.168

$EMV(a_3) = .021(2$ 21.748) = 22.191

Optimal act: a .91 − 19 = 3.191

b EMV =

EVSI

$EMV(a_1) = .5(60) + .4(90) + .1(150) = 81$

ties for I_1

s_j	$P(s_j)$	$P(I_1 \mid s_j)$	$P(s_j \text{ and } I_1)$	$P(s_j \mid I_1)$
	.5	.7	(.5)(.7) = .35	.35/.57 = .614
s_2	.4	.5	(.4)(.5) = .20	.20/.57 = .351
s_3	.1	.2	(.1)(.2) = .02	.02/.57 = .035
			$P(I_1) = .57$	

Posterior Probabilities for I_2

s_j	$P(s_j)$	$P(I_2 \mid s_j)$	$P(s_j \text{ and } I_2)$	$P(s_j \mid I_2)$
s_1	.5	.3	(.5)(.3) = .15	.15/.43 = .349
s_2	.4	.5	(.4)(.5) = .20	.20/.43 = .465
s_3	.1	.8	(.1)(.8) = .08	.08/.43 = .186
			$P(I_1) = .43$	

I_1: $EMV(a_1) = .614(60) + .351(90) + .035(150) = 73.68$

$EMV(a_2) = 90$

I_2: $EMV(a_1) = .349(60) + .465(90) + .186(150) = 90.69$

$EMV(a_2) = 90$

© 2012 Cengage Learning. All Rights Reserved. May not be scanned, copied or duplicated, or posted to a publicly accessible website, in whole or in part.

EMV` = .57(90) + .43(90.69) = 90.30

EVSI = EMV` - EMV* = 90.30 – 90 = .30

22.28 As the prior probabilities become more diverse [illegible] decreases.

22.30 EMV* = 0

EPPI = .15(0) + .45(2 million) + .40(8 million) = 4.1 million

EVPI = EPPI – EMV* = 4.1 million – 0 = 4.1 million

22.32a

Payoff Table

Market share	Switch	Don't
5%	5(100,000) – 700,000 = -200,000	285,[illegible]
10%	10(100,000) – 700,000 = 300,000	285,000
20%	20(100,000) – 700,000 = 1,300,000	285,000

b EMV(switch) = .4(-200,000) + .4(300,000) + .2(1,300,000) = 300,000

EMV(don't switch) = 285,000

Optimal act: switch (EMV* = 300,000)

c EPPI = .4(285,000) + .4(300,000) + .2(1,300,000) = 494,000

EVPI = EPPI – EMV* = 494,000 – 300,000= 194,000

22.34 Likelihood probabilities (binomial probabilities)

$P(I \mid s_1) = P(x = 12, n= 100 \mid p = .05) = .0028$

$P(I \mid s_2) = P(x = 12, n= 100 \mid p = .10) = .0988$

$P(I \mid s_3) = P(x = 12, n= 100 \mid p = .20) = .0128$

$P(I \mid s_4) = P(x = 12, n= 100 \mid p = .30) = .000013$

Posterior Probabilities

s_j	$P(s_j)$	$P(I \mid s_j)$	$P(s_j \text{ and } I)$	$P(s_j \mid I)$
s_1	.5	.0028	(.5)(.0028) = .0014	.0014/.0323 = .0433
s_2	.3	.0988	(.3)(.0988) = .0296	.0296/.0323 = .9164
s_3	.1	.0128	(.1)(.0128) = .0013	.0013/.0323 = .0402
s_4	.1	.000013	(.1)(.000013) = .000001	.000001/.0323 = .000031
			P(I) = .0323	

[illegible]MV(proceed) = .0433(-30,000) + .9164(-5,000) + .0402(45,000) + .000031(95,000) = -4,069

[illegible]V (don't proceed = 0

[illegible]ecision: don't proceed

[illegible]gage Learning. All Rights Reserved. May not be scanned, copied or duplicated, or posted to a publicly accessible website, in whole or in part.

EOL(Large) = .15(130) + .55(30) + .30(0) = 36.0

EOL decision: build a medium size plant

22.16 Payoff Table

	Decision	
Market share	Produce	Don't produce
5%	-28 million	0
10%	2 million	0
15%	8 million	0

EMV(produce) = .15(-28 million) + .45(2 million) + .40 (8 million) = -.1 million

EMV (don't produce) = 0

EMV decision: don't produce

22.18 Opportunity Loss Table

	a_1	a_2	a_3
s_1	50	0	35
s_2	110	40	0
s_3	0	100	135
s_4	0	130	120

$EOL(a_1) = .10(50) + .25(110) + .50(0) + .15(0) = 32.5$

$EOL(a_2) = .10(0) + .25(40) + .50(100) + .15(130) = 79.5$

$EOL(a_3) = .10(35) + .25(0) + .50(135) + .15(120) = 89$

$EOL^* = 32.5$

22.20 a EPPI = .75(65) + .25(110) = 76.25

$EMV(a_1) = .75(65) + .25(70) = 66.25$

$EMV(a_2) = .75(20) + .25(110) = 42.5$

$EMV(a_3) = .75(45) + .25(80) = 53.75$

$EMV(a_4) = .75(30) + .25(95) = 46.25$

$EVPI = EPPI - EMV^* = 76.25 - 66.25 = 10$

b EPPI = .95(65) + .05(110) = 67.25

$EMV(a_1) = .95(65) + .05(70) = 65.25$

$EMV(a_2) = .95(20) + .05(110) = 24.5$

© 2012 Cengage Learning. All Rights Reserved. May not be scanned, copied or duplicated, or posted to a publicly accessible website, in whole or in part.

$EMV(a_3) = .95(45) + .05(80) = 46.75$

$EMV(a_4) = .95(30) + .05(95) = 33.25$

$EVPI = EPPI - EMV^* = 67.25 - 65.25 = 2$

22.22 Posterior Probabilities for I_1

s_j	$P(s_j)$	$P(I_1 \mid s_j)$	$P(s_j \text{ and } I_1)$	$P(s_j \mid I_1)$
s_1	.25	.40	(.25)(.40) = .10	.12/.20 = .500
s_2	.40	.25	(.40)(.25) = .10	.10/.20 = .500
s_3	.35	0	(.35)(0) = .0	0/.20 = 0
			$P(I_1) = .20$	

Posterior Probabilities for I_2

s_j	$P(s_j)$	$P(I_2 \mid s_j)$	$P(s_j \text{ and } I_2)$	$P(s_j \mid I_2)$
s_1	.25	.30	(.25)(.30) = .075	.075/.28 = .268
s_2	.40	.25	(.40)(.25) = .10	.10/.28 = .357
s_3	.35	30	(.35)(.30) = .105	.105/.28 = .375
			$P(I_2) = .28$	

Posterior Probabilities for I_3

s_j	$P(s_j)$	$P(I_3 \mid s_j)$	$P(s_j \text{ and } I_3)$	$P(s_j \mid I_3)$
s_1	.25	.20	(.25)(.20) = .05	.05/.29 = .172
s_2	.40	.25	(.40)(.25) = .10	.10/.29 = .345
s_3	.35	.40	(.35)(.40) = .14	.14/.29 = .483
			$P(I_3) = .29$	

Posterior Probabilities for I_4

s_j	$P(s_j)$	$P(I_4 \mid s_j)$	$P(s_j \text{ and } I_4)$	$P(s_j \mid I_4)$
s_1	.25	.10	(.25)(.10) = .025	.025/.23 = .109
s_2	.40	.25	(.40)(.25) = .10	.10/.23 = .435
s_3	.35	.30	(.35)(.30) = .105	.105/.23 = .456
			$P(I_4) = .23$	

22.24 a Prior probabilities: $EMV(a_1) = .5(10) + .5(22) = 16$

$EMV(a_2) = .5(18) + .5(19) = 18.5$

$EMV(a_3) = .5(23) + .5(15) = 19$

$EMV^* = 19$

© 2012 Cengage Learning. All Rights Reserved. May not be scanned, copied or duplicated, or posted to a publicly accessible website, in whole or in part.

I_1: $EMV(a_1) = .951(10) + .049(22) = 10.588$

$EMV(a_2) = .951(18) + .049(19) = 18.049$

$EMV(a_3) = .951(23) + .049(15) = 22.608$

Optimal act: a_3

I_2: $EMV(a_1) = .021(10) + .979(22) = 21.748$

$EMV(a_2) = .021(18) + .979(19) = 18.979$

$EMV(a_3) = .021(23) + .979(15) = 15.168$

Optimal act: a_1

b EMV\` = .515(22.608) + .485(21.748) = 22.191

EVSI = EMV\` - EMV* = 22.191 – 19 = 3.191

22.26 Prior probabilities: $EMV(a_1) = .5(60) + .4(90) + .1(150) = 81$

$EMV(a_2) = 90$

$EMV^* = 90$

Posterior Probabilities for I_1

s_j	$P(s_j)$	$P(I_1 \mid s_j)$	$P(s_j \text{ and } I_1)$	$P(s_j \mid I_1)$
s_1	.5	.7	(.5)(.7) = .35	.35/.57 = .614
s_2	.4	.5	(.4)(.5) = .20	.20/.57 = .351
s_3	.1	.2	(.1)(.2) = .02	.02/.57 = .035
			$P(I_1) = .57$	

Posterior Probabilities for I_2

s_j	$P(s_j)$	$P(I_2 \mid s_j)$	$P(s_j \text{ and } I_2)$	$P(s_j \mid I_2)$
s_1	.5	.3	(.5)(.3) = .15	.15/.43 = .349
s_2	.4	.5	(.4)(.5) = .20	.20/.43 = .465
s_3	.1	.8	(.1)(.8) = .08	.08/.43 = .186
			$P(I_1) = .43$	

I_1: $EMV(a_1) = .614(60) + .351(90) + .035(150) = 73.68$

$EMV(a_2) = 90$

I_2: $EMV(a_1) = .349(60) + .465(90) + .186(150) = 90.69$

$EMV(a_2) = 90$

© 2012 Cengage Learning. All Rights Reserved. May not be scanned, copied or duplicated, or posted to a publicly accessible website, in whole or in part.

EMV` = .57(90) + .43(90.69) = 90.30

EVSI = EMV` - EMV* = 90.30 – 90 = .30

22.28 As the prior probabilities become more diverse EVSI decreases.

22.30 EMV* = 0

EPPI = .15(0) + .45(2 million) + .40(8 million) = 4.1 million

EVPI = EPPI – EMV* = 4.1 million – 0 = 4.1 million

22.32a

Payoff Table

Market share	Switch	Don't switch
5%	5(100,000) – 700,000 = -200,000	285,000
10%	10(100,000) – 700,000 = 300,000	285,000
20%	20(100,000) – 700,000 = 1,300,000	285,000

b EMV(switch) = .4(-200,000) + .4(300,000) + .2(1,300,000) = 300,000

EMV(don't switch) = 285,000

Optimal act: switch (EMV* = 300,000)

c EPPI = .4(285,000) + .4(300,000) + .2(1,300,000) = 494,000

EVPI = EPPI – EMV* = 494,000 – 300,000= 194,000

22.34 Likelihood probabilities (binomial probabilities)

$P(I \mid s_1) = P(x = 12, n= 100 \mid p = .05) = .0028$

$P(I \mid s_2) = P(x = 12, n= 100 \mid p = .10) = .0988$

$P(I \mid s_3) = P(x = 12, n= 100 \mid p = .20) = .0128$

$P(I \mid s_4) = P(x = 12, n= 100 \mid p = .30) = .000013$

Posterior Probabilities

s_j	$P(s_j)$	$P(I \mid s_j)$	$P(s_j \text{ and } I)$	$P(s_j \mid I)$
s_1	.5	.0028	(.5)(.0028) = .0014	.0014/.0323 = .0433
s_2	.3	.0988	(.3)(.0988) = .0296	.0296/.0323 = .9164
s_3	.1	.0128	(.1)(.0128) = .0013	.0013/.0323 = .0402
s_4	.1	.000013	(.1)(.000013) = .000001	.000001/.0323 = .000031
			P(I) = .0323	

EMV(proceed) = .0433(-30,000) + .9164(-5,000) + .0402(45,000) + .000031(95,000) = -4,069

EMV (don't proceed = 0

EMV decision: don't proceed

© 2012 Cengage Learning. All Rights Reserved. May not be scanned, copied or duplicated, or posted to a publicly accessible website, in whole or in part.

22.36

I_0 = neither person supports format change

I_1 = one person supports format change

I_2 = both people support format change

Likelihood probabilities $P(I_i \mid s_j)$

	I_0	I_1	I_2
5%	.9025	.0950	.0025
10%	.81	.18	.01
20%	.64	.32	.04

osterior Probabilities for I_0

s_j	$P(s_j)$	$P(I_0 \mid s_j)$	$P(s_j \text{ and } I_0)$	$P(s_j \mid I_0)$
s_1	.4	.9025	(.4)(.9025) = .361	.361/.813 = .444
s_2	.4	.81	(.4)(.81) = .324	.324/.813 = .399
s_3	.2	.64	(.2)(.64) = .128	.128/.813 = .157
			$P(I_0)$ = .813	

Posterior Probabilities for I_1

s_j	$P(s_j)$	$P(I_1 \mid s_j)$	$P(s_j \text{ and } I_1)$	$P(s_j \mid I_1)$
s_1	.4	.0950	(.4)(.0950) = .038	.038/.174 = .218
s_2	.4	.18	(.4)(.18) = .072	.072/.174 = .414
s_3	.2	.32	(.2)(.32) = .064	.064/.174 = .368
			$P(I_1)$ = .174	

Posterior Probabilities for I_3

s_j	$P(s_j)$	$P(I_2 \mid s_j)$	$P(s_j \text{ and } I_2)$	$P(s_j \mid I_2)$
s_1	.4	.0025	(.4)(.0025) = .001	.001/.013 = .077
s_2	.4	.01	(.4)(.01) = .004	.004/.013 = .308
s_3	.2	.04	(.2)(.04) = .008	.008/.013 = .615
			$P(I_2)$ = .013	

I_1: EMV(switch) = .444(-200,000) + .399(300,000) + .157(1,300,000) = 235,000

EMV(don't switch) = 285,000

Optimal act: don't switch

I_2: EMV(switch) = .218(-200,000) + .414(300,000) + .368(1,300,000) = 559,000

EMV(don't switch) = 285,000

Optimal act: switch

I_3: EMV(switch) = .077(-200,000) + .308(300,000) + .615(1,300,000) = 876,500

EMV(don't switch) = 285,000

© 2012 Cengage Learning. All Rights Reserved. May not be scanned, copied or duplicated, or posted to a publicly accessible website, in whole or in part.

Optimal act: switch

EMV` = .813(285,000) + .174(546,000) + .013(876,500) = 338,104

EVSI = EMV` - EMV* = 338,104 – 300,000 = 38,104

22.38 a

Payoff Table

Demand	Battery 1	Battery 2	Battery 3
50,000	20(50,000)-900,000	23(50,000)-1,150,000	25(50,000)-1,400,000
	= 100,000	0	-150,000
100,000	20(100,000)-900,000	23(100,000)-1,150,000	25(100,000)-1,400,000
	=1,100,000	1,150,000	1,100,000
150,000	20(150,000)-900,000	23(150,000)-1,150,000	25(150,000)-1,400,000
	=2,100,000	2,300,000	2,350,000

b

Opportunity Loss table

Demand	Battery 1	Battery 2	Batter3
50,000	0	100,000	250,000
100,000	50,000	0	50,000
150,000	250,000	50,000	9

c EMV(Battery 1) = .3(100,000) + .3(1,100,000) + .4(2,100,000) = 1,200,000

EMV(Battery 2) = .3(0) + .3(1,150,000) + .4(2,300,000) = 1,265,000

EMV(Battery 3) = .3(-150,000) + .3(1,100,000) + .4(2,350,000) = 1,225,000

EMV decision: Battery 2

d EOL(Battery 2) = .3(100,000) + .3(0) + .4(50,000) = 50,000

EVPI = EOL* = 50,000

22.40

I_0 = person does not believe the ad

I_1 = person believes the ad

Likelihood probabilities $P(I_i \mid s_j)$

	I_0	I_1
30%	.70	.30
31%	.69	.31
32%	.68	.32
33%	.67	.33
34%	.66	.34

© 2012 Cengage Learning. All Rights Reserved. May not be scanned, copied or duplicated, or posted to a publicly accessible website, in whole or in part.

Posterior Probabilities for I_0

s_j	$P(s_j)$	$P(I_0 \mid s_j)$	$P(s_j \text{ and } I_0)$	$P(s_j \mid I_0)$
s_1	.1	.70	(.1)(.70) = .070	.070/.674 = .104
s_2	.1	.69	(.1)(.69) = .069	.069/.674 = .102
s_3	.2	.68	(.2)(.68) = .136	.136/.674 = .202
s_4	.3	.67	(.3)(.67) = .201	.201/.674 = .298
s_5	.3	.66	(.3)(.66) = .198	.198/.674 = .294
			$P(I_0)$ = .674	

Posterior Probabilities for I_1

s_j	$P(s_j)$	$P(I_1 \mid s_j)$	$P(s_j \text{ and } I_1)$	$P(s_j \mid I_1)$
s_1	.1	.30	(.1)(.30) = .030	.030/.326 = .092
s_2	.1	.31	(.1)(.31) = .031	.031/.326 = .095
s_3	.2	.32	(.2)(.32) = .064	.064/.326 = .196
s_4	.3	.33	(.3)(.33) = .099	.099/.326 = .304
s_5	.3	.34	(.3)(.34) = .102	.102/.326 = .313
			$P(I_1)$ = .326	

I_0: EMV(Change ad) = .104(-258,000) + .102(-158,000) + .202(-58,000) + .298(42,000) + .294(142,000)

= -400

EMV (don't change) = 0.

Optimal decision: don't change ad

I_1: EMV(Change ad) = .092(-258,000) + .095(-158,000) + .196(-58,000) + .304(42,000) + .313(142,000)

= 7,100

EMV (don't change) = 0.

Optimal decision: change ad

EMV\` = .674(0) + .326(7,100) = 2,315

EVSI = EMV\` - EMV* = 2,315 – 2,000 = 315

22.42

EMV(25 telephones) = 50,000

EMV(50 telephones) = .50(30,000) + .25(60,000) + .25(60,000) = 45,000

EMV(100 telephones) = .50(20,000) + .25(40,000) + .25(80,000) = 40,000

© 2012 Cengage Learning. All Rights Reserved. May not be scanned, copied or duplicated, or posted to a publicly accessible website, in whole or in part.

Optimal decision: 25 telephones (EMV* = 50,000)

I_1 = small number of calls

I_2 = medium number of calls

I_3 = large number of calls

Likelihood probabilities (Poisson distribution)

	I_1	I_2	I_3
$\mu = 5$	$P(X < 8 \mid \mu = 5)$ = .8667	$P(8 \le X < 17 \mid \mu = 5)$ = .1334	$P(X \ge 17 \mid \mu = 5)$ = 0
$\mu = 10$	$P(X < 8 \mid \mu = 10)$ = .2202	$P(8 \le X < 17 \mid \mu = 10)$ = .7527	$P(X \ge 17 \mid \mu = 10)$ = .0270
$\mu = 15$	$P(X < 8 \mid \mu = 15)$ = .0180	$P(8 \le X < 17 \mid \mu = 15)$ = .6461	$P(X \ge 17 \mid \mu = 15)$ = .3359

Posterior Probabilities for I_1

s_j	$P(s_j)$	$P(I_1 \mid s_j)$	$P(s_j \text{ and } I_1)$	$P(s_j \mid I_1)$
s_1	.50	.8667	(.50)(.8667) = .4333	.4333/.4929 = .8792
s_2	.25	.2202	(.25)(.2202) = .0551	.0551/.4929 = .1117
s_3	.25	.0180	(.25)(.0180) = .0045	.0045/.4929 = .0091
			$P(I_1)$ = .4929	

Posterior Probabilities for I_2

s_j	$P(s_j)$	$P(I_2 \mid s_j)$	$P(s_j \text{ and } I_2)$	$P(s_j \mid I_2)$
s_1	.50	.1334	(.50)(.1334) = .0667	.0667/.4164 = .1601
s_2	.25	.7527	(.25)(.7527) = .1882	.1882/.4164 = .4519
s_3	.25	.6461	(.25)(.6461) = .1615	.1615/.4164 = .3879
			$P(I_2)$ = .4164	

Posterior Probabilities for I_3

s_j	$P(s_j)$	$P(I_3 \mid s_j)$	$P(s_j \text{ and } I_3)$	$P(s_j \mid I_3)$
s_1	.50	.0	(.50)(0) = 0	0/.0907 = 0
s_2	.25	.0270	(.25)(.0270) = .0068	.0068/.0907 = .0745
s_3	.25	.3359	(.25)(.3359) = .0840	.0840/.0907 = .9254
			$P(I_3)$ = .0907	

© 2012 Cengage Learning. All Rights Reserved. May not be scanned, copied or duplicated, or posted to a publicly accessible website, in whole or in part.

I_1: EMV(25 telephones) = 50,000

EMV(50 telephones) = .8792(30,000) + .1117(60,000) + .0091(60,000) = 33,624

EMV(100 telephones) = .8792(20,000) + .1117(40,000) + .0091(80,000) = 22,780

Optimal act: 25 telephones

I_2: EMV(25 telephones) = 50,000

EMV(50 telephones) = .1601(30,000) + .4519(60,000) + .3879(60,000) = 55,191

EMV(100 telephones) = .1601(20,000) + .4519(40,000) + .38791(80,000) = 52,310

Optimal act: 50 telephones

I_3: EMV(25 telephones) = 50,000

EMV(50 telephones) = 0(30,000) + .0745(60,000) + .9254(60,000) = 60,000

EMV(100 telephones) = 0(20,000) + .0745(40,000) + .9254(80,000) = 77,012

Optimal act: 100 telephones

EMV` = .4929(50,000) + .4164(55,191) + .0907(77,012) = 54,612

EVSI = EMV` - EMV* = 54,612 – 50,000 = 4,612

Because the value is greater than the cost ($4,000) Max should not sample. If he sees a small number of calls install 25 telephones. If there is a medium number install 50 telephones. If there is a large number of calls, install 100 telephones.

22.44 EMV(Release in North America) = .5(33 million) + .3(12 million) + .2(-15 million) = 17.1 million

EMV(European distributor) = 12 million

Optimal decision: Release in North America

Posterior Probabilities for I_1 (Rave review)

s_j	$P(s_j)$	$P(I_1 \mid s_j)$	$P(s_j \text{ and } I_1)$	$P(s_j \mid I_1)$
s_1	.5	.8	(.5)(.8) = .40	.40/.63 = .635
s_2	.3	.5	(.3)(.5) = .15	.15/.63 = .238
s_3	.2	.4	(.2)(.4) = .08	.08/.63 = .127
			$P(I_1)$ = .63	

EMV(Release in North America) = .635(33 million) + .238(12 million) + .127(-15 million) =21.9 million

EMV(European distributor) = 12 million

Optimal decision: Release in North America

© 2012 Cengage Learning. All Rights Reserved. May not be scanned, copied or duplicated, or posted to a publicly accessible website, in whole or in part.

Posterior Probabilities for I_2 (lukewarm response)

s_j	$P(s_j)$	$P(I_2 \mid s_j)$	$P(s_j \text{ and } I_2)$	$P(s_j \mid I_2)$
s_1	.5	.1	(.5)(.1) = .05	.05/.20 = .25
s_2	.3	.3	(.3)(.3) = .09	.09/.20 = .45
s_3	.2	.3	(.2)(.3) = .06	.06/.20 = .30
			$P(I_2)$ = .20	

EMV(Release in North America) = .25(33 million) + .45(12 million) + .30(-15 million) = 9.2 million

EMV(European distributor) = 12 million

Optimal decision: Sell to European distributor

Posterior Probabilities for I_3 (poor response)

s_j	$P(s_j)$	$P(I_3 \mid s_j)$	$P(s_j \text{ and } I_3)$	$P(s_j \mid I_3)$
s_1	.5	.1	(.5)(.1) = .05	.05/.17 = .294
s_2	.3	.2	(.3)(.2) = .06	.06/.17 = .353
s_3	.2	.3	(.2)(.3) = .06	.06/.17 = .353
			(I_3) = .17	

EMV(Release in North America) = .294(33 million) + .353(12 million) + .353(-15 million) = 8.6 million

EMV(European distributor) = 12 million

Optimal decision: Sell to European distributor.

EMV` = .63(21.9 million) + .20(12 million) + .17(12 million) = 18.2 million

EVSI = EMV` - EMV* = 18.2 million – 17.1 million = 1.1 million

Because EVSI is greater than the sampling cost (100,000) the studio executives should show the movie to a random sample of North Americans. If the response is a rave review release the movie in North America. If not sell it to Europe.

© 2012 Cengage Learning. All Rights Reserved. May not be scanned, copied or duplicated, or posted to a publicly accessible website, in whole or in part.